These safety symbols are used in laboratory and field investigations in this book to indicate possible hazards. Learn the meaning of each symbol and refer to this page often. *Remember to wash your hands thoroughly after completing lab procedures.*

PROTECTIVE EQUIPMENT Do not begin any lab without the proper protection equipment.

 GOGGLES Proper eye protection must be worn when performing or observing science activities that involve items or conditions as listed below.

 APRON Wear an approved apron when using substances that could stain, wet, or destroy cloth.

 SOAP Wash hands with soap and water before removing goggles and after all lab activities.

GLOVES Wear gloves when working with biological materials, chemicals, animals, or materials that can stain or irritate hands.

LABORATORY HAZARDS

Symbols	Potential Hazards	Precaution	Response
DISPOSAL	contamination of classroom or environment due to improper disposal of materials such as chemicals and live specimens	• DO NOT dispose of hazardous materials in the sink or trash can. • Dispose of wastes as directed by your teacher.	• If hazardous materials are disposed of improperly, notify your teacher immediately.
EXTREME TEMPERATURE	skin burns due to extremely hot or cold materials such as hot glass, liquids, or metals; liquid nitrogen; dry ice	• Use proper protective equipment, such as hot mitts and/or tongs, when handling objects with extreme temperatures.	• If injury occurs, notify your teacher immediately.
SHARP OBJECTS	punctures or cuts from sharp objects such as razor blades, pins, scalpels, and broken glass	• Handle glassware carefully to avoid breakage. • Walk with sharp objects pointed downward, away from you and others.	• If broken glass or injury occurs, notify your teacher immediately.
ELECTRICAL	electric shock or skin burn due to improper grounding, short circuits, liquid spills, or exposed wires	• Check condition of wires and apparatus for fraying or uninsulated wires, and broken or cracked equipment. • Use only GFCI-protected outlets	• DO NOT attempt to fix electrical problems. Notify your teacher immediately.
CHEMICAL	skin irritation or burns, breathing difficulty, and/or poisoning due to touching, swallowing, or inhalation of chemicals such as acids, bases, bleach, metal compounds, iodine, poinsettias, pollen, ammonia, acetone, nail polish remover, heated chemicals, mothballs, and any other chemicals labeled or known to be dangerous	• Wear proper protective equipment such as goggles, apron, and gloves when using chemicals. • Ensure proper room ventilation or use a fume hood when using materials that produce fumes. • NEVER smell fumes directly. • NEVER taste or eat any material in the laboratory.	• If contact occurs, immediately flush affected area with water and notify your teacher. • If a spill occurs, leave the area immediately and notify your teacher.
FLAMMABLE	unexpected fire due to liquids or gases that ignite easily such as rubbing alcohol	• Avoid open flames, sparks, or heat when flammable liquids are present.	• If a fire occurs, leave the area immediately and notify your teacher.
OPEN FLAME	burns or fire due to open flame from matches, Bunsen burners, or burning materials	• Tie back loose hair and clothing. • Keep flame away from all materials. • Follow teacher instructions when lighting and extinguishing flames. • Use proper protection, such as hot mitts or tongs, when handling hot objects.	• If a fire occurs, leave the area immediately and notify your teacher.
ANIMAL SAFETY	injury to or from laboratory animals	• Wear proper protective equipment such as gloves, apron, and goggles when working with animals. • Wash hands after handling animals.	• If injury occurs, notify your teacher immediately.
BIOLOGICAL	infection or adverse reaction due to contact with organisms such as bacteria, fungi, and biological materials such as blood, animal or plant materials	• Wear proper protective equipment such as gloves, goggles, and apron when working with biological materials. • Avoid skin contact with an organism or any part of the organism. • Wash hands after handling organisms.	• If contact occurs, wash the affected area and notify your teacher immediately.
FUME	breathing difficulties from inhalation of fumes from substances such as ammonia, acetone, nail polish remover, heated chemicals, and mothballs	• Wear goggles, apron, and gloves. • Ensure proper room ventilation or use a fume hood when using substances that produce fumes. • NEVER smell fumes directly.	• If a spill occurs, leave area and notify your teacher immediately.
IRRITANT	irritation of skin, mucous membranes, or respiratory tract due to materials such as acids, bases, bleach, pollen, mothballs, steel wool, and potassium permanganate	• Wear goggles, apron, and gloves. • Wear a dust mask to protect against fine particles.	• If skin contact occurs, immediately flush the affected area with water and notify your teacher.
RADIOACTIVE	excessive exposure from alpha, beta, and gamma particles	• Remove gloves and wash hands with soap and water before removing remainder of protective equipment.	• If cracks or holes are found in the container, notify your teacher immediately.

NEW YORK

SCIENCE

GRADE 6

McGraw Hill Education

COVER: McGraw-Hill Education

MHEonline.com

Copyright © 2015 McGraw-Hill Education

Send all inquiries to:
McGraw-Hill Education
8787 Orion Place
Columbus, OH 43240

ISBN: 978-0-07-666332-3
MHID: 0-07-666332-9

Printed in the United States of America.

2 3 4 5 6 7 8 9 10 QVS 21 20 19 18 17 16 15

Contents in Brief

Authors

American Museum of Natural History
New York, NY

Michelle Anderson, MS
Lecturer
The Ohio State University
Columbus, OH

Juli Berwald, PhD
Science Writer
Austin, TX

John F. Bolzan, PhD
Science Writer
Columbus, OH

Rachel Clark, MS
Science Writer
Moscow, ID

Patricia Craig, MS
Science Writer
Bozeman, MT

Randall Frost, PhD
Science Writer
Pleasanton, CA

Lisa S. Gardiner, PhD
Science Writer
Denver, CO

Jennifer Gonya, PhD
The Ohio State University
Columbus, OH

Mary Ann Grobbel, MD
Science Writer
Grand Rapids, MI

Whitney Crispen Hagins, MA, MAT
Biology Teacher
Lexington High School
Lexington, MA

Carole Holmberg, BS
Planetarium Director
Calusa Nature Center and
Planetarium, Inc.
Fort Myers, FL

Tina C. Hopper
Science Writer
Rockwall, TX

Jonathan D. W. Kahl, PhD
Professor of Atmospheric Science
University of Wisconsin-
Milwaukee
Milwaukee, WI

Nanette Kalis
Science Writer
Athens, OH

S. Page Keeley, MEd
Maine Mathematics and Science
Alliance
Augusta, ME

Cindy Klevickis, PhD
Professor of Integrated Science
and Technology
James Madison University
Harrisonburg, VA

Kimberly Fekany Lee, PhD
Science Writer
La Grange, IL

Michael Manga, PhD
Professor
University of California, Berkeley
Berkeley, CA

Devi Ried Mathieu
Science Writer
Sebastopol, CA

Elizabeth A. Nagy-Shadman, PhD
Geology Professor
Pasadena City College
Pasadena, CA

William D. Rogers, DA
Professor of Biology
Ball State University
Muncie, IN

Donna L. Ross, PhD
Associate Professor
San Diego State University
San Diego, CA

Marion B. Sewer, PhD
Assistant Professor
School of Biology
Georgia Institute of Technology
Atlanta, GA

Julia Meyer Sheets, PhD
Lecturer
School of Earth Sciences
The Ohio State University
Columbus, OH

Michael J. Singer, PhD
Professor of Soil Science
Department of Land, Air and
Water Resources
University of California
Davis, CA

Karen S. Sottosanti, MA
Science Writer
Pickerington, Ohio

Paul K. Strode, PhD
I.B. Biology Teacher
Fairview High School
Boulder, CO

Jan M. Vermilye, PhD
Research Geologist
Seismo-Tectonic Reservoir
Monitoring (STRM)
Boulder, CO

Judith A. Yero, MA
Director
Teacher's Mind Resources
Hamilton, MT

Dinah Zike, MEd
Author, Consultant, Inventor
of Foldables
Dinah Zike Academy; Dinah-
Might Adventures, LP
San Antonio, TX

Margaret Zorn, MS
Science Writer
Yorktown, VA

Consulting Authors

Alton L. Biggs
Biggs Educational Consulting
Commerce, TX

Ralph M. Feather, Jr., PhD
Assistant Professor
Department of Educational
Studies and Secondary Education
Bloomsburg University
Bloomsburg, PA

Douglas Fisher, PhD
Professor of Teacher Education
San Diego State University
San Diego, CA

Edward P. Ortleb
Science/Safety Consultant
St. Louis, MO

Series Consultants

Science

Solomon Bililign, PhD
Professor
Department of Physics
North Carolina Agricultural and
Technical State University
Greensboro, NC

John Choinski
Professor
Department of Biology
University of Central Arkansas
Conway, AR

Anastasia Chopelas, PhD
Research Professor
Department of Earth and Space
Sciences
UCLA
Los Angeles, CA

David T. Crowther, PhD
Professor of Science Education
University of Nevada, Reno
Reno, NV

A. John Gatz
Professor of Zoology
Ohio Wesleyan University
Delaware, OH

Sarah Gille, PhD
Professor
University of California San
Diego
La Jolla, CA

David G. Haase, PhD
Professor of Physics
North Carolina State University
Raleigh, NC

Janet S. Herman, PhD
Professor
Department of Environmental
Sciences
University of Virginia
Charlottesville, VA

David T. Ho, PhD
Associate Professor
Department of Oceanography
University of Hawaii
Honolulu, HI

Ruth Howes, PhD
Professor of Physics
Marquette University
Milwaukee, WI

**Jose Miguel Hurtado, Jr.,
PhD**
Associate Professor
Department of Geological
Sciences
University of Texas at El Paso
El Paso, TX

Monika Kress, PhD
Assistant Professor
San Jose State University
San Jose, CA

Mark E. Lee, PhD
Associate Chair & Assistant
Professor
Department of Biology
Spelman College
Atlanta, GA

Linda Lundgren
Science writer
Lakewood, CO

Keith O. Mann, PhD
Ohio Wesleyan University
Delaware, OH

Charles W. McLaughlin, PhD
Adjunct Professor of Chemistry
Montana State University
Bozeman, MT

Katharina Pahnke, PhD
Research Professor
Department of Geology and
Geophysics
University of Hawaii
Honolulu, HI

Jesús Pando, PhD
Associate Professor
DePaul University
Chicago, IL

Hay-Oak Park, PhD
Associate Professor
Department of Molecular
Genetics
Ohio State University
Columbus, OH

David A. Rubin, PhD
Associate Professor of Physiology
School of Biological Sciences
Illinois State University
Normal, IL

Toni D. Sauncy
Assistant Professor of Physics
Department of Physics
Angelo State University
San Angelo, TX

Ransom Studios

Online Guide

Video

ConnectED

▷ **Your Digital Science Portal**

 **Video**	 **Audio**	**Review**	**?** **Inquiry**	 **WebQuest**
See the science in real life through these exciting videos.	Click the link and you can listen to the text while you follow along.	Try these interactive tools to help you review the lesson	Explore concepts through hands–on and virtual labs.	These web-based challenges relate the concepts you're learning about to the latest news

The icons in your online student edition link you to interactive learning opportunities. Browse your online student book to find more.

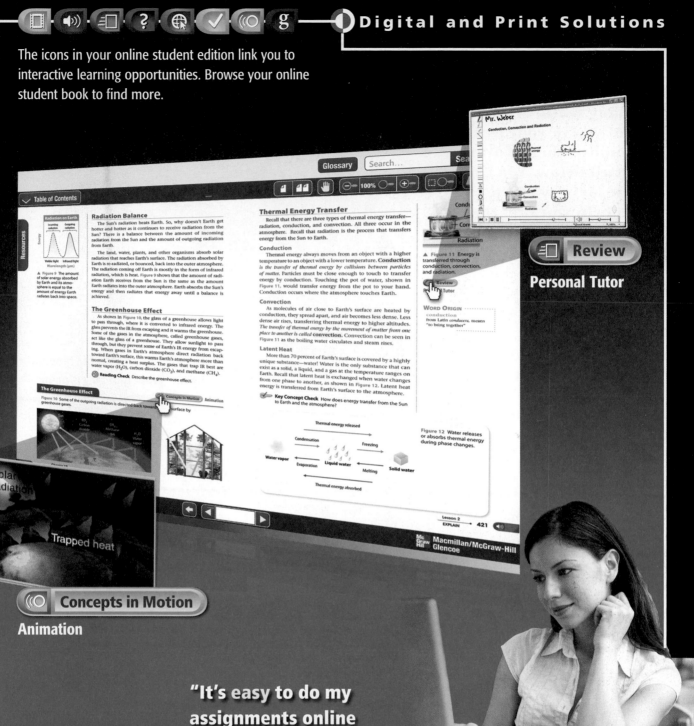

Review

Personal Tutor

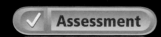 **Concepts in Motion**

Animation

"It's easy to do my assignments online and quick to find everything I need."

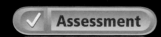 **Assessment**

Check how well you understand the concepts with online quizzes and practice questions.

 **Concepts in Motion**

The textbook comes alive with animated explanations of important concepts.

 **Multilingual eGlossary**

Read key vocabulary in 13 languages.

©Fancy Photography/Veer

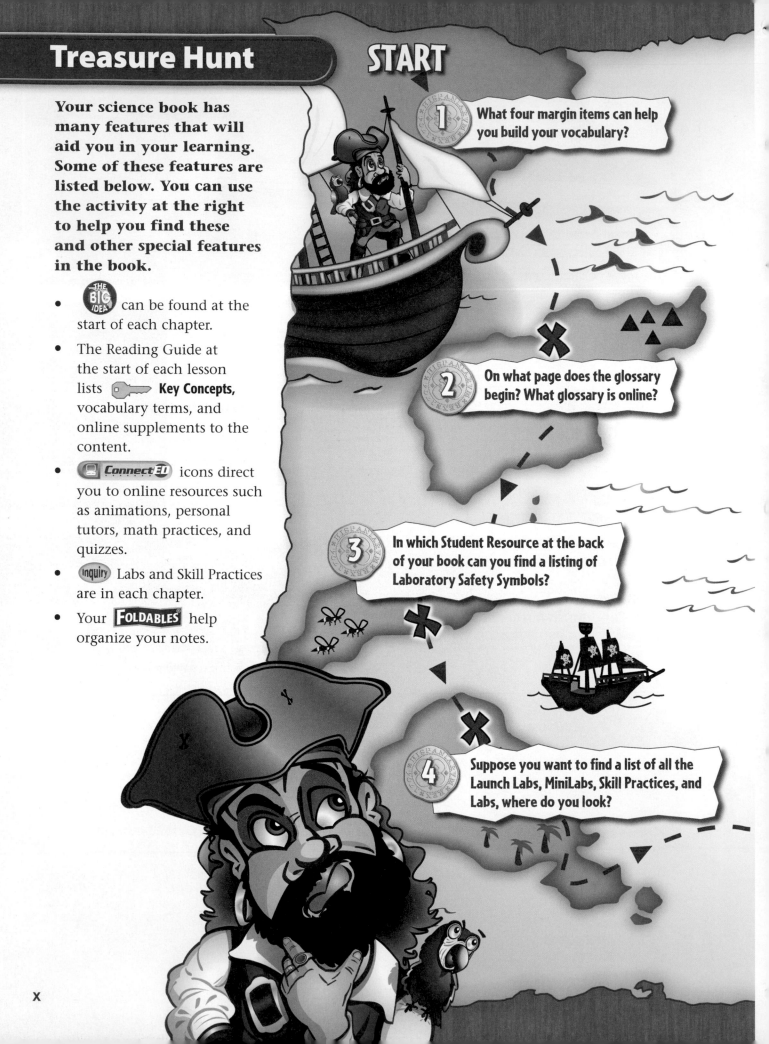

Treasure Hunt

START

Your science book has many features that will aid you in your learning. Some of these features are listed below. You can use the activity at the right to help you find these and other special features in the book.

- **THE BIG IDEA** can be found at the start of each chapter.

- The Reading Guide at the start of each lesson lists **Key Concepts**, vocabulary terms, and online supplements to the content.

- **Connect ED** icons direct you to online resources such as animations, personal tutors, math practices, and quizzes.

- **Inquiry** Labs and Skill Practices are in each chapter.

- Your **FOLDABLES** help organize your notes.

1 What four margin items can help you build your vocabulary?

2 On what page does the glossary begin? What glossary is online?

3 In which Student Resource at the back of your book can you find a listing of Laboratory Safety Symbols?

4 Suppose you want to find a list of all the Launch Labs, MiniLabs, Skill Practices, and Labs, where do you look?

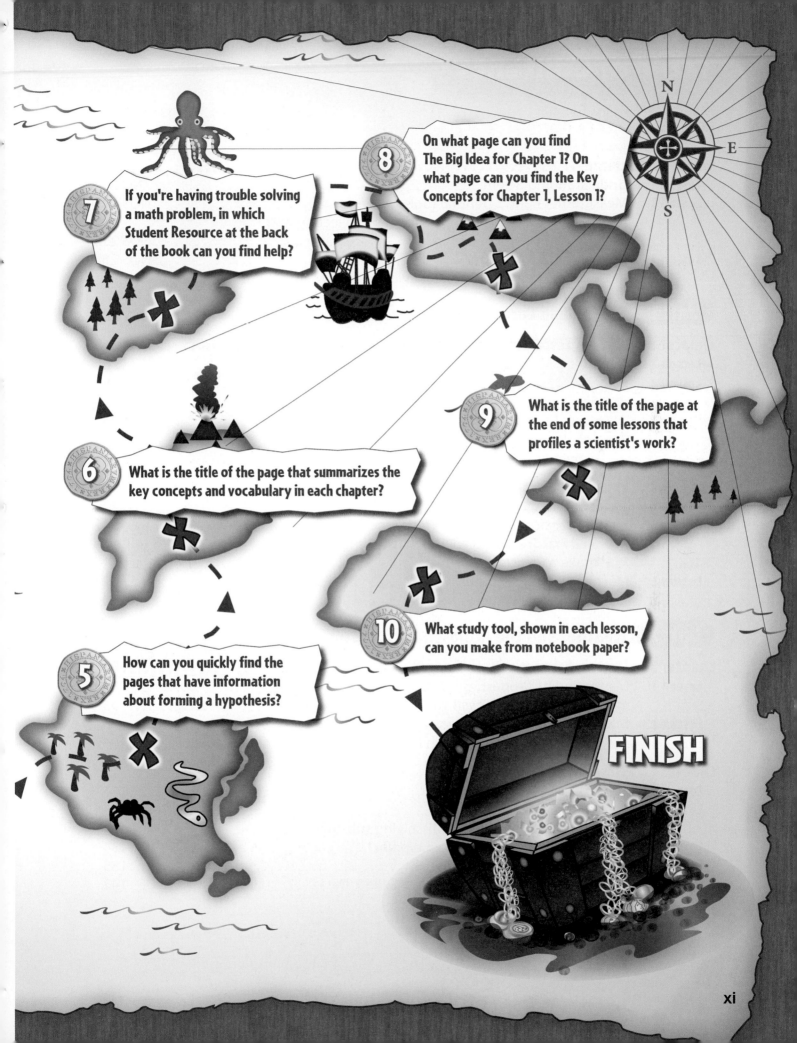

Table of Contents

TABLE OF CONTENTS

Table of Contents

Table of Contents

Table of Contents

TABLE OF CONTENTS

Inquiry Launch Labs

Inquiry

Inquiry MiniLabs

Inquiry Skill Practice

Inquiry

 **Labs**

Features

Nature of Science

AID M1.1a, M1.1c, M3.1a, S1.1a, S1.1b, S1.2a, S1.2b, S1.2c, S1.3, S1.4, S2.1a, S2.1b, S2.1c, S2.1d, S2.2a, S2.2b, S2.2c, S2.2d, S2.2e, S2.3a, S2.3b, S3.1a, S3.2a, S3.2h, T1.1a, T1.2a, T1.3a, T1.3b, T1.4a, T1.5a, T1.5b; IS 1.4a, 1.5, 2.1b, 2.3, 3.3; ICT 2.1, 2.2; IPS 1.3, 1.4

Methods of Science

THE BIG IDEA

What processes do scientists use when they perform scientific investigations?

Inquiry Pink Water?

This scientist is using pink dye to measure the speed of glacier water in the country of Greenland. Scientists are testing the hypothesis that the speed of the glacier water is increasing because amounts of meltwater, caused by climate change, are increasing.

- What is a hypothesis?

- What other ways do scientists test hypotheses?

- What processes do scientists use when they perform scientific investigations?

Ashley Cooper/Woodfall Wild Images/Photoshot

Unit

Nature of SCIENCE

This chapter begins your study of the nature of science, but there is even more information about the nature of science in this book. Each unit begins by exploring an important topic that is fundamental to scientific study. As you read these topics, you will learn even more about the nature of science.

ConnectED Your one-stop online resource

MHEonline.com

- Video
- WebQuest
- Audio
- Assessment
- Review
- Concepts in Motion
- Inquiry
- Multilingual eGlossary

Reading Guide

Key Concepts
ESSENTIAL QUESTIONS

- What is scientific inquiry?
- How do scientific laws and scientific theories differ?
- What is the difference between a fact and an opinion?

Vocabulary

science

observation

inference

hypothesis

prediction

technology

scientific theory

scientific law

critical thinking

 Multilingual eGlossary

🎞 **Video**

- BrainPOP®
- Science Video

 AID S1.1a, S1.1b, S1.2a, S1.2b, S1.2c, S1.3, S1.4, S2.1a, S2.1d, S2.2a, S2.2b, S2.3a, S3.1a, S3.2a, T1.1a, T1.2a, T1.3a, T1.3b, T1.4a, T1.5a, T1.5b; IS 1.5, 2.3, 3.3; ICT 2.1, 2.2; IPS 1.3

Understanding Science

What is science?

Did you ever hear a bird sing and then look in nearby trees to find the singing bird? Have you ever noticed how the Moon changes from a thin crescent to a full moon each month? When you do these things, you are doing science. **Science** *is the investigation and exploration of natural events and of the new information that results from those investigations.*

For thousands of years, men and women of all countries and cultures have studied the natural world and recorded their observations. They have shared their knowledge and findings and have created a vast amount of scientific information. Scientific knowledge has been the result of a great deal of debate and confirmation within the science community.

People use science in their everyday lives and careers. For example, firefighters, as shown in **Figure 1,** wear clothing that has been developed and tested to withstand extreme temperatures and not catch fire. Parents use science when they set up an aquarium for their children's pet fish. Athletes use science when they use high-performance gear or wear high-performance clothing. Without thinking about it, you use science or the results of science in almost everything you do. Your clothing, food, hair products, electronic devices, athletic equipment, and almost everything else you use are results of science.

Figure 1 Firefighters' clothing, oxygen tanks, and equipment are all results of science.

Thomas Del Brase/Getty Images

Branches of Science

There are many different parts of the natural world. Because there is so much to study, scientists often focus their work in one branch of science or on one topic within that branch of science. There are three main branches of science—Earth science, life science, and **physical** science.

WORD ORIGIN · · · · · · · · · · ·

physical
from Latin *physica*, means "study of nature"

Earth Science

The study of Earth, including rocks, soils, oceans, and the atmosphere is Earth science. The Earth scientist to the right is collecting lava samples for research. Earth scientists might ask other questions such as

- How do different shorelines react to tsunamis?
- Why do planets orbit the Sun?
- What is the rate of climate change?

Life Science

The study of living things is life science, or biology. These biologists are attaching a radio collar to a tiger to help track its movements and learn more about its behavior. They are also weighing and measuring the tiger to gain information about this species. Biologists also ask questions such as

- Why do some trees lose their leaves in winter?
- How do birds know which direction they are going?
- How do mammals control their body temperature?

Physical Science

The study of matter and energy is physical science. It includes both physics and chemistry. This research chemist is preparing chemical solutions for analysis. Physicists and chemists ask other questions such as

- What chemical reactions must take place to launch a spaceship into space?
- Is it possible to travel faster than the speed of light?
- What makes up matter?

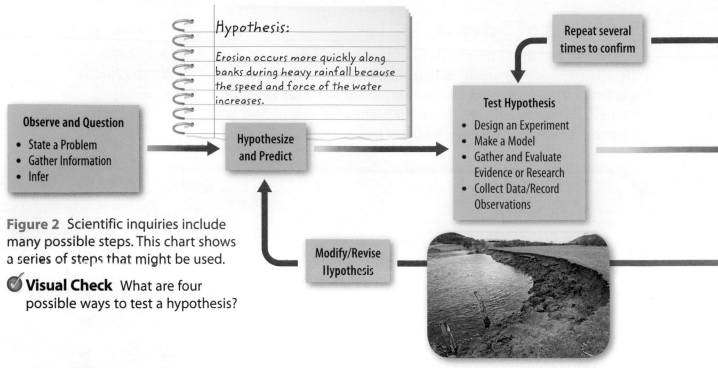

Hypothesis:

Erosion occurs more quickly along banks during heavy rainfall because the speed and force of the water increases.

Observe and Question
- State a Problem
- Gather Information
- Infer

Hypothesize and Predict

Repeat several times to confirm

Test Hypothesis
- Design an Experiment
- Make a Model
- Gather and Evaluate Evidence or Research
- Collect Data/Record Observations

Modify/Revise Hypothesis

Figure 2 Scientific inquiries include many possible steps. This chart shows a series of steps that might be used.

Visual Check What are four possible ways to test a hypothesis?

Scientific Inquiry

When scientists conduct scientific investigations, they use scientific inquiry. Scientific inquiry is a process that uses a set of skills to answer questions or to test ideas about the natural world. There are many kinds of scientific investigations, and there are many ways to conduct them. The series of steps used in each investigation often varies. The flow chart in **Figure 2** shows an example of the skills used in scientific inquiry.

Key Concept Check What is scientific inquiry?

Ask Questions

One way to begin a scientific inquiry is to observe the natural world and ask questions. **Observation** *is the act of using one or more of your senses to gather information and taking note of what occurs.* Suppose you observe that the banks of a river have eroded more this year than in the previous year, and you want to know why. You also note that there was an increase in rainfall this year. After these observations, you make an inference based on these observations. *An* **inference** *is a logical explanation of an observation that is drawn from prior knowledge or experience.*

You infer that the increase in rainfall caused the increase in erosion. You decide to investigate further. You develop a hypothesis and a method to test it.

Hypothesize and Predict

A **hypothesis** *is a possible explanation for an observation that can be tested by scientific investigations.* A hypothesis states an observation and provides an explanation. For example, you might make the following hypothesis: More of the riverbank eroded this year because the amount, the speed, and the force of the river water increased.

When scientists state a hypothesis, they often use it to make predictions to help test their hypothesis. *A* **prediction** *is a statement of what will happen next in a sequence of events.* Scientists make predictions based on what information they think they will find when testing their hypothesis. For example, predictions for the hypothesis above could be: If rainfall increases, then the amount, the speed, and the force of river water will increase. If the amount, the speed, and the force of river water increase, then there will be more erosion.

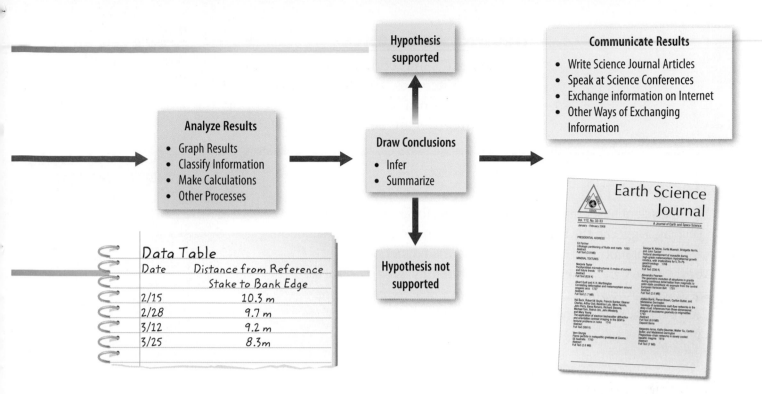

Test Hypothesis

When you test a hypothesis, you often test whether your predictions are true. If a prediction is confirmed, then it supports your hypothesis. If your prediction is not confirmed, you might need to modify your hypothesis and retest it.

There are several ways to test a hypothesis when performing a scientific investigation. Four possible ways are shown in **Figure 2.** For example, you might make a model of a riverbank in which you change the speed and the amount of water and record results and observations.

Analyze Results

After testing your hypothesis, you analyze your results using various methods, as shown in **Figure 2.** Often, it is hard to see trends or relationships in data while collecting it. Data should be sorted, graphed, or classified in some way. After analyzing the data, additional inferences can be made.

Draw Conclusions

Once you find the relationships among data and make several inferences, you can draw conclusions.

A conclusion is a summary of the information gained from testing a hypothesis. Scientists study the available information and draw conclusions based on that information.

Communicate Results

An important part of the scientific inquiry process is communicating results. Several ways to communicate results are listed in **Figure 2.** Scientists might share their information in other ways, too. Scientists communicate results of investigations to inform other scientists about their research and their conclusions. When a scientist uses that information to repeat another scientist's experiment, he or she is replicating the experiment to confirm results.

Further Scientific Inquiry

After finishing an experiment, a scientist must verify his or her results. If the hypothesis is supported, the scientist will repeat the experiment several times to make sure the conclusions are the same—this is called experimental repetition. If the hypothesis is not supported, any new information gained can be used to revise the hypothesis. Hypotheses can be revised and tested many times.

Results of Science

The results and conclusions from an investigation can lead to many outcomes, such as the answers to a question, more information on a specific topic, or support for a hypothesis. Other outcomes are described below.

Technology

During scientific inquiry, scientists often look for answers to questions such as, "How can the hearing impaired hear better?" After investigation, experimentation, and research, the conclusion might be the development of a new technology. **Technology** *is the practical use of scientific knowledge, especially for industrial or commercial use.* Technology, such as the cochlear implant, can help some deaf people hear.

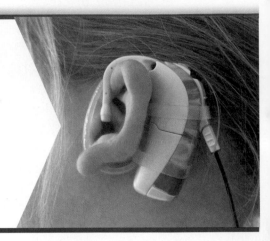

New Materials

Space travel has unique challenges. Astronauts must carry oxygen to breathe. They also must be protected against temperature and pressure extremes, as well as small, high-speed flying objects. Today's spacesuit, a result of research, testing, and design changes, consists of 14 layers of material. The outer layer is made of a blend of three materials. One material is waterproof and another material is heat and fire-resistant.

Possible Explanations

Scientists often perform investigations to find explanations as to why or how something happens. NASA's *Spitzer Space Telescope,* which has aided in our understanding of star formation, shows a cloud of gas and dust with newly formed stars.

 Reading Check What are some results of science?

Scientific Theory and Scientific Law

Another outcome of science is the development of scientific theories and laws. Recall that a hypothesis is a possible explanation about an observation that can be tested by scientific investigations. What happens when a hypothesis or a group of hypotheses has been tested many times and has been supported by the repeated scientific investigations? The hypothesis can become a scientific theory.

Scientific Theory

Often, the word *theory* is used in casual conversations to mean an untested idea or an opinion. However, scientists use *theory* differently. *A* **scientific theory** *is an explanation of observations or events that is based on knowledge gained from many observations and investigations.*

Scientists regularly question scientific theories and test them for validity. A scientific theory generally is accepted as true until it is disproved. An example of a scientific theory is the theory of plate tectonics. The theory of plate tectonics explains how Earth's crust moves and why earthquakes and volcanoes occur. Another example of a scientific theory is discussed in **Figure 3.**

▲ **Figure 3** Scientists once believed Earth was the center of the solar system. In the 16th century, Nicolaus Copernicus hypothesized that Earth and the other planets actually revolve around the Sun.

Scientific Law

A scientific law is different from a social law, which is an agreement among people concerning a behavior. *A* **scientific law** *is a rule that describes a pattern in nature.* Unlike a scientific theory that explains why an event occurs, a scientific law only states that an event will occur under certain circumstances. For example, Newton's law of gravitational force implies that if you drop an object, it will fall toward Earth. Newton's law does not explain why the object moves toward Earth when dropped, only that it will.

 Key Concept Check How do scientific laws and theories differ?

New Information

Scientific information constantly changes as new information is discovered or as previous hypotheses are retested. New information can lead to changes in scientific theories, as explained in **Figure 4.** When new facts are revealed, a current scientific theory might be revised to include the new facts, or it might be disproved and rejected.

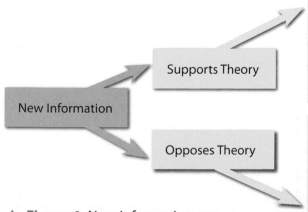

If new information supports a current scientific theory, then the theory is not changed. The information might be published in a scientific journal to show further support of the theory. The new information might also lead to advancements in technology or spark new questions that lead to new scientific investigations.

If new information opposes, or does not support a current scientific theory, the theory might be modified or rejected altogether. Often, new information will lead scientists to look at the original observations in a new way. This can lead to new investigations with new hypotheses. These investigations can lead to new theories.

▲ **Figure 4** New information can lead to changes in scientific theories.

Evaluating Scientific Evidence

Did you ever read an advertisement, such as the one below, that made extraordinary claims? If so, you probably practice **critical thinking**—*comparing what you already know with the information you are given in order to decide whether you agree with it.* To determine whether information is true and scientific or pseudoscience (information incorrectly represented as scientific), you should be skeptical and identify facts and opinions. This helps you evaluate the strengths and weaknesses of information and make informed decisions. Critical thinking is important in all decision making—from everyday decisions to community, national, and international decisions.

Key Concept Check How do a fact and an opinion differ?

Learn Algebra
While You Sleep!

Have you struggled to learn algebra? Struggle no more.

Math-er-ific's new algebra pillow is scientifically proven to transfer math skills from the pillow to your brain while you sleep. This revolutionary scientific design improved the algebra test scores of laboratory mice by 150 percent.

Dr. Tom Equation says, "I have never seen students or mice learn algebra so easily. This pillow is truly amazing."

For only $19.95, those boring hours spent studying are a thing of the past. So act fast! If you order today, you can get the algebra pillow and the equally amazing geometry pillow for only $29.95. That is a $10 savings!

Skepticism

To be skeptical is to doubt the truthfulness or accuracy of something. Because of skepticism, science can be self-correcting. If someone publishes results or if an investigation gives results that don't seem accurate, a skeptical scientist usually will challenge the information and test the results for accuracy.

Identifying Facts

The prices of the pillows and the savings are facts. A fact is a measurement, observation, or statement that can be strictly defined. Many scientific facts can be evaluated for their validity through investigations.

Identifying Opinions

An opinion is a personal view, feeling, or claim about a topic. Opinions are neither true nor false.

Mixing Facts and Opinions

Sometimes people mix facts and opinions. You must read carefully to determine which information is fact and which is opinion.

©Sigrid Olsson/PhotoAlto/Corbis

Science cannot answer all questions.

Scientists recognize that some questions cannot be studied using scientific inquiry. Questions that deal with opinions, beliefs, values, and feelings cannot be answered through scientific investigation. For example, questions that cannot be answered through scientific investigation might include

• Are comedies the best kinds of movies?

• Is it ever okay to lie?

• Which food tastes best?

The answers to all of these questions are based on opinions, not facts.

Safety in Science

It is very important for anyone performing scientific investigations to use safe practices, such as the student shown in **Figure 5.** You should always follow your teacher's instructions. If you have questions about potential hazards, use of equipment, or the meaning of safety symbols, ask your teacher. Always wear protective clothing and equipment while performing scientific investigations. If you are using live animals in your investigations, provide appropriate care and ethical treatment to them. For more information on practicing safe and ethical science, consult the Science Safety Skill Handbook in the back of this book.

Figure 5 Always use safe lab practices when doing scientific investigations.

ACADEMIC VOCABULARY

potential
(adjective) possible, likely, or probable

Lesson 1 Review

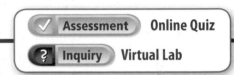

✓ **Assessment** Online Quiz

? **Inquiry** Virtual Lab

Use Vocabulary

1 The practical use of science, especially for industrial or commercial use, is _____.

2 **Distinguish** between a hypothesis and a prediction.

3 **Define** *observation* in your own words.

Understand Key Concepts 🔑

4 Which is NOT part of scientific inquiry?
   A. analyze results   **C.** make a hypothesis
   B. falsify results   **D.** make observations

5 **Explain** the difference between a scientific theory and a scientific law. Give an example of each.

6 **Write** an example of a fact and an example of an opinion.

Interpret Graphics

7 **Organize** Draw a graphic organizer similar to the one below. List four ways a scientist can communicate results.

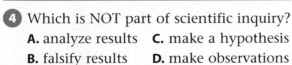

Communicate Results

Critical Thinking

8 **Identify** a real-world problem related to your home, your community, or your school that could be investigated scientifically.

9 **Design** a scientific investigation to test one possible solution to the problem you identified in the previous question.

Hutchings Photography/Digital Light Source

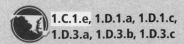

Science & Engineering

The Design Process

1.C.1.e, 1.D.1.a, 1.D.1.c,
1.D.3.a, 1.D.3.b, 1.D.3.c

Scientists & Engineers

Scientists investigate and explore natural events. Then they interpret data and share information learned from those investigations. How do engineers differ from scientists?

Engineers design, construct, and maintain the human-made world. Look around you and notice things that do not occur in nature. Schools, roads, airplanes, toys, microscopes, amusement parks, computer programs, and video games all result from engineering. Science involves the practice of scientific inquiry, but engineering involves the design process—a set of methods used to create a solution to a problem or need.

PureStock/Superstock

The Steps

Identify a Problem or Need

- Determine a problem or a need.
- Document all questions, research, and procedures throughout the process.

↓

Research the Problem & Brainstorm Solutions

- Research any existing solutions that address the problem or need.
- Brainstorm all possible solutions.

↓

Design Solutions

- Suggest limitations of the solutions.
- Look at all solutions and select the best one.
- Create a design of the solution.

Redesign the Solution

- Redesign and modify solution, as needed.
- Construct final solution.

Construct a Prototype

- Estimate materials, costs, resources, and time to develop the solution.
- Construct a prototype.

Test & Evaluate the Solution

- Use models to test the solutions.
- Use graphs, charts, and tables to evaluate results.
- Analyze and evaluate strengths and weaknesses of the solution.

↓

Communicate the Results

- Communicate your designed solution and results to others.

Identify a Problem

Transporting goods by air has become an expensive way to move materials due to the high cost of fuel. A team of engineers has been assigned to come up with a way to reduce the costs of shipping cargo by air. The problem has been identified. What is the next step that these engineers will take in creating a solution to this problem?

Research the Problem & Brainstorm Solutions

After identifying the problem, the engineers' next step in the design process is to research what other people have done to solve this problem. Researching solutions that have been tried before is critical in determining if the problem statement is still accurate. If the original problem statement has a solution, the statement will need to be redefined. After the research is completed the team will brainstorm multiple solutions to the problem. Creativity is extremely important in the brainstorming phase of the design process.

Flow chart:

- Identify Problem
- Research the Problem & Brainstorm Solutions
- Design Solutions
- Redesign ↔ Construct Prototype ↔ Test & Evaluate (cycle)
- Communicate Results

Design Solutions

Once engineers have brainstormed a list of solutions, the best design solution should be selected. The design process can then progress. Before designing the solution, engineers must consider its constraints. Constraints are limitations put on the product from outside factors. These factors can include cost, ethical issues such as animal testing, environmental impacts, or attractiveness. Other constraints such as political and social issues or product safety can limit choices for product design. The materials required for the solution may also present some constraints.

How do engineers decide which materials to use? They are chosen based on chemical, physical, and mechanical properties as well as their interactions with other materials. It also might not make sense to use materials that are expensive, rare, or difficult to work with.

Construct a Prototype

A product prototype is the first example of the design. Prototypes are developed to test the design under real conditions. A prototype also can be called a model.

Models are used to think about processes that happen too slowly, too quickly, or on too small a scale to observe directly, as well as ones that are potentially dangerous or too large to otherwise study. Models that can be seen and touched are called physical models. Engineers also develop mathematical models and graphical models. In many instances multiple types of models are produced during the development of a product.

Limitations of Models

When scientists create models, they are using the best information they have at the time. However, models can be misleading because they might not always work the way a real product works. This can cause dissatisfaction in the final product.

Graphical Models

Some models are ideas or concepts that describe how someone thinks about something in the natural world. Graphical models are sketches or drawings. For example, Leonardo da Vinci, the inventor, was trained as an artist and made many graphical models of his designs.

One of his famous sketches was of the Helical Air Screw, drawn in 1480. This sketch, or graphical model, depicts an early form of what would become the helicopter. Modern helicopters look very different from da Vinci's, but the scientific principles behind helicopter flight remain the same since the time of da Vinci.

Mathematical Models

A mathematical model uses numerical data and equations to model an event or idea. They allow engineers to determine how changing one variable affects the product's design.

The image on the right is a computer simulation of the test conditions for one of NASA's experimental vehicles.

Mathematical variables can be adjusted in the simulation to change conditions and see the effects. The wing model was produced with a computer-aided design program (CAD). CAD programs can produce 2D and 3D models.

Physical Models

Physical models are those that you can see and touch. Models, such as NASA's experimental vehicle, show how parts relate to one another. Physical models are much easier to evaluate because their properties can be tested.

Test & Evaluate

At all stages of the design process, the design must be tested and reviewed. Testing and evaluating the solution allows the engineer to find and correct problems. Sometimes the design is changed. Ideas are always being changed. After evaluation and testing, one solution will be chosen as the best.

Identify Problem

↓

Research the Problem & Brainstorm Solutions

↓

Design Solutions

↓

Redesign ⟲ Construct Prototype

Test & Evaluate

↓

Communicate Results

Redesign

After testing and evaluating is completed, the engineers could determine that the model needs to be redesigned. This can be due to information gained in the testing process, or finding out that the model did not behave in the expected manner. The model might be redesigned to better solve the current problem or to avoid developing a new one. After the model is redesigned, it is tested and evaluated again.

Communicate Results

After testing the aircraft model, engineers share the data with other engineers and scientists. The team might need to conduct more research, modify the prototype, and test again. Engineers may go through this process many times before they develop a model that meets their needs. The final design and prototype are then sent to manufacturing for production.

(bkgd)Design Pics/David Chapman, (inset)Steve Cole/Getty Images

Design a Zipline Ride

The engineers you just read about used the design process to solve a problem in airplane development. Using this same process, you can be an engineer and solve a very different kind of problem.

You are a guide for an adventure tour company that specializes in physically challenging activities in natural environments. You have been hired to design an exciting zipline ride near your town.

☐ Identify the Problem

You know nothing about zipline rides or the requirements to construct a fast and safe zipline course. Consider the best location, platform design and construction, maximum angle of descent, length of ride, and materials required. Is it possible to zip too quickly or too slowly? Record your problem and questions with possible solutions in your Science Journal.

☐ Research Existing Solutions

Begin answering your questions by researching existing ziplines, roller coasters, and other similar thrill rides. Note possible limitations to your solutions, such as cost, size, materials, location, time, or other restraints.

☐ Design Solutions

Continue recording ideas for your zipline ride. Include possible locations for it in your environment, sites for launching and safe-landing platforms, length of zipline, materials and equipment needed for the zipline and rider, estimated costs, and time of development and construction.

☐ Construct a Prototype

Draw several plans to answer your problems. Use simple materials to construct a scale model of your zipline. Check for accurate scale of dimensions and weight for each element to guarantee a fun, fast, and safe ride.

☐ Test and Evaluate Solutions

Test your model many times to guarantee weight, speed, distance, and safe solutions. Use graphs, charts, and tables to evaluate the process and identify strengths and weaknesses in your solutions.

☐ Redesign your Zipline and ☐ Communicate Your Results

Communicate your design process and solution to peers using your visual displays and model. Discuss and critique your working solution. Do further research and testing, if necessary. Redesign and modify your solution to meet design objectives. Finally, construct a model of your solution.

Reading Guide

Key Concepts
ESSENTIAL QUESTIONS

- Why is it important for scientists to use the International System of Units?

- What causes measurement uncertainty?

- What are mean, median, mode, and range?

Vocabulary

description

explanation

International System of Units (SI)

significant digits

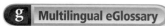 **Multilingual eGlossary**

AID M1.1c, M3.1a, S1.2c, S2.1d; IS 1.4a, 2.1b, 3.3; IPS 1.4

Measurement and Scientific Tools

Description and Explanation

The scientist in **Figure 6** is observing a volcano. He describes in his journal that the flowing lava is bright red with a black crust, and it has a temperature of about 630°C. A **description** *is a spoken or written summary of observations.* There are two types of descriptions. When making a qualitative description, such as *bright red,* you use your senses (sight, sound, smell, touch, taste) to describe an observation. When making a quantitative description, such as *630°C,* you use numbers and measurements to describe an observation. Later, the scientist might explain his observations. An **explanation** *is an interpretation of observations.* Because the lava was bright red and about 630°C, the scientist might explain that these conditions indicate the lava is cooling and the volcano did not recently erupt.

The International System of Units

At one time, scientists in different parts of the world used different units of measurement. Imagine the confusion when a British scientist measured weight in pounds-force, a French scientist measured weight in Newtons, and a Japanese scientist measured weight in momme (MOM ee). Sharing scientific information was difficult, if not impossible.

In 1960, scientists adopted a new system of measurement to eliminate this confusion. The **International System of Units (SI)** *is the internationally accepted system for measurement.* SI uses standards of measurement, called base units, which are shown in **Table 1** on the next page. A base unit is the most common unit used in the SI system for a given measurement.

Figure 6 Scientists use descriptions and explanations when observing natural events.

Table 1 SI Base Units		
Quantity Measured	**Unit**	**Symbol**
Length	meter	m
Mass	kilogram	kg
Time	second	s
Electric current	ampere	A
Temperature	Kelvin	K
Amount of substance	mole	mol
Intensity of light	candela	cd

◀ **Table 1** You can use SI units to measure the physical properties of objects.

((O)) **Concepts in Motion**
Interactive Table

SI Unit Prefixes

In addition to base units, SI uses prefixes to identify the size of the unit, as shown in **Table 2.** Prefixes are used to indicate a fraction of ten or a multiple of ten. In other words, each unit is either ten times smaller than the next larger unit or ten times larger than the next smaller unit. For example, the prefix *deci–* means 10^{-1}, or 1/10. A decimeter is 1/10 of a meter. The prefix *kilo–* means 10^{3}, or 1,000. A kilometer is 1,000 m.

Converting Between SI Units

Because SI is based on ten, it is easy to convert from one SI unit to another. To convert SI units, you must multiply or divide by a factor of ten. You also can use proportions as shown below in the Math Skills activity.

Table 2 Prefixes are used in SI to indicate the size of the unit. ▼

Table 2 Prefixes	
Prefix	**Meaning**
Mega- (M)	1,000,000 (10^{6})
Kilo- (k)	1,000 (10^{3})
Hecto- (h)	100 (10^{2})
Deka- (da)	10 (10^{1})
Deci- (d)	0.1 (10^{-1})
Centi- (c)	0.01 (10^{-2})
Milli- (m)	0.001 (10^{-3})
Micro- (µ)	0.000 001 (10^{-6})

 Key Concept Check Why is it important for scientists to use the International System of Units (SI)?

Math Skills $\times \div +$ **Use Proportions**

A book has a mass of **1.1 kg**. Using a proportion, find the mass of the book in grams.

① Use the table to determine the correct relationship between the units. One kg is 1,000 times greater than 1 g. So, there are 1,000 g in 1 kg.

② Then set up a proportion.

$$\left(\frac{x}{1.1 \text{ kg}}\right) = \left(\frac{1{,}000 \text{ g}}{1 \text{ kg}}\right)$$

$$x = \left(\frac{(1{,}000 \text{ g})(1.1 \text{ kg})}{1 \text{ kg}}\right) = 1{,}100 \text{ g}$$

③ Check your units. The answer is 1,100 g.

Review

• **Math Practice**
• **Personal Tutor**

Practice

1. Two towns are separated by 15,328 m. What is the distance in kilometers?

2. A dosage of medicine is 325 mg. What is the dosage in grams?

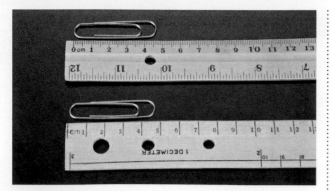

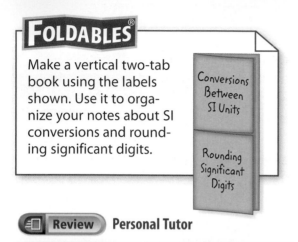

Figure 7 All measurements have some uncertainty.

FOLDABLES®

Make a vertical two-tab book using the labels shown. Use it to organize your notes about SI conversions and rounding significant digits.

Conversions Between SI Units

Rounding Significant Digits

Review Personal Tutor

Table 3 Significant Digits Rules

1. All nonzero numbers are significant.
2. Zeros between significant digits are significant.
3. All final zeros to the right of the decimal point are significant.
4. Zeros used solely for spacing the decimal point are NOT significant. The zeros only indicate the position of the decimal point.

* The blue numbers in the examples are the significant digits.

Number	Significant Digits	Applied Rules
1.234	4	1
1.02	3	1, 2
0.023	2	1, 4
0.200	3	1, 3
1,002	4	1, 2
3.07	3	1, 2
0.001	1	1, 4
0.012	2	1, 4
50,600	3	1, 2, 4

Measurement and Uncertainty

Have you ever measured an object, such as a paper clip? The tools used to take measurements can limit the accuracy of the measurements. Look at the bottom ruler in **Figure 7.** Its measurements are divided into centimeters. The paper clip is between 4 cm and 5 cm. You might guess that it is 4.7 cm long. Now, look at the top ruler. Its measurements are divided into millimeters. You can say with more precision that the paper clip is about 4.75 cm long. This measurement is more precise than the first measurement.

 Key Concept Check What causes measurement uncertainty?

Significant Digits and Rounding

Because scientists duplicate each other's work, they must record numbers with the same degree of precision as the original data. Significant digits allow scientists to do this. **Significant digits** *are the number of digits in a measurement that you know with a certain degree of reliability.* **Table 3** lists the rules for expressing and determining significant digits.

In order to achieve the same degree of precision as a previous measurement, it often is necessary to round a measurement to a certain number of significant digits. Suppose you have the number below, and you need to round it to four significant digits.

1,348.527 g

To round to four significant digits, you need to round the 8. If the digit to the right of the 8 is 0, 1, 2, 3, or 4, the digit being rounded (8) remains the same. If the digit to the right of the 8 is 5, 6, 7, 8, or 9, the digit being rounded (8) increases by one. The rounded number is 1,349 g.

What if you need to round 1,348.527 g to two significant digits? You would look at the number to the right of the 3 to determine how to round. 1,348.527 rounded to two significant digits would be 1,300 g. The 4 and 8 become zeros.

Mean, Median, Mode, and Range

A rain gauge measures the amount of rain that falls on a location over a period of time. A rain gauge can be used to collect data in scientific investigations, such as the data shown in **Table 4a.** Scientists often need to analyze their data to obtain information. Four values often used when analyzing numbers are median, mean, mode, and range.

 Key Concept Check What are mean, median, and mode?

Median

The median is the middle number in a data set when the data are arranged in numerical order. The rainfall data are listed in numerical order in Table 4b. If you have an even number of data items, add the two middle numbers together and divide by two to find the median.

$$\text{median} = \frac{8.18 \text{ cm} + 8.84 \text{ cm}}{2}$$

$$= 8.51 \text{ cm}$$

Table 4a
Rainfall Data

January	7.11 cm
February	11.89 cm
March	9.58 cm
April	8.18 cm
May	7.11 cm
June	1.47 cm
July	18.21 cm
August	8.84 cm

Mean

The mean, or average, of a data set is the sum of the numbers in a data set divided by the number of entries in the set. To find the mean, add the numbers in your data set and then divide the total by the number of items in your data set.

$$\text{mean} = \frac{(\text{sum of numbers})}{(\text{number of items})}$$

$$= \frac{72.39 \text{ cm}}{8 \text{ months}}$$

$$= \frac{9.05 \text{ cm}}{\text{month}}$$

Mode

The mode of a data set is the number or item that appears most often. The number in blue in Table 4b appears twice. All other numbers appear only once.

$$\text{mode} = 7.11 \text{ cm}$$

Table 4b
Rainfall Data
(numerical order)

1.47 cm
7.11 cm
7.11 cm
8.18 cm
8.84 cm
9.58 cm
11.89 cm
18.21 cm

Range

The range is the difference between the greatest number and the least number in the data set.

$$\text{range} = 18.21 \text{ cm} - 1.47 \text{ cm}$$

$$= 16.74 \text{ cm}$$

Scientific Tools

As you engage in scientific inquiry, you will need tools to help you take quantitative measurements. Always follow appropriate safety procedures when using scientific tools. For more information about the proper use of these tools, see the Science Skill Handbook at the back of this book.

◀ Science Journal

Use a science journal to record observations, questions, hypotheses, data, and conclusions from your scientific investigations. A science journal is any notebook that you use to take notes or record information and data while you conduct a scientific investigation. Keep it organized so you can find information easily. Write down the date whenever you record new information in the journal. Make sure you are recording your data honestly and accurately.

Rulers and Metersticks ▶

Use rulers and metersticks to measure lengths and distances. The SI unit of measurement for length is the meter (m). For small objects, such as pebbles or seeds, use a metric ruler with centimeter and millimeter markings. To measure larger objects, such as the length of your bedroom, use a meterstick. To measure long distances, such as the distance between cities, use an instrument that measures in kilometers. Be careful when carrying rulers and metersticks, and never point them at anyone.

◀ Glassware

Use beakers to hold and pour liquids. The lines on a beaker do not provide accurate measurements. Use a graduated cylinder to measure the volume of a liquid. Volume is typically measured in liters (L) or milliliters (mL).

Triple-Beam Balance ▶

Use a triple-beam balance to measure the mass of an object. The mass of a small object is measured in grams. The mass of large object is usually measured in kilograms. Triple-beam balances are instruments that require some care when using. Follow your teacher's instructions so that you do not damage the instrument. Digital balances also might be used.

◀ Thermometer

Use a thermometer to measure the temperature of a substance. Although Kelvin is the SI unit for temperature, you will use a thermometer to measure temperature in degrees Celsius (°C). To use a thermometer, place a room-temperature thermometer into the substance for which you want to measure temperature. Do not let the thermometer touch the bottom of the container that holds the substance or you will get an inaccurate reading. When you finish, remember to place your thermometer in a secure place. Do not lay it on a table, because it can roll off the table. Never use a thermometer as a stirring rod.

Computers and the Internet ▶

Use a computer to collect, organize, and store information about a research topic or scientific investigation. Computers are useful tools to scientists for several reasons. Scientists use computers to record and analyze data, to research new information, and to quickly share their results with others worldwide over the Internet.

(t)Hutchings Photography/Digital Light Source; (c)McGraw-Hill Education; (b)Steve Cole/Getty Images

Tools Used by Earth Scientists

Binoculars

Binoculars are instruments that enable people to view faraway objects more clearly. Earth scientists use them to view distant landforms, animals, or even incoming weather.

Compass

A compass is an instrument that shows magnetic north. Earth scientists use compasses to navigate when they are in the field and to determine the direction of distant landforms or other natural objects.

Wind Vane and Anemometer

A wind vane is a device, often attached to the roofs of buildings, that rotates to show the direction of the wind. An anemometer, or wind-speed gauge, is used to measure the speed and the force of wind.

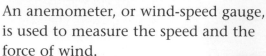

Streak Plate

A streak plate is a piece of hard, unglazed porcelain that helps you identify minerals. When you scrape a mineral along a streak plate, the mineral leaves behind powdery marks. The color of the mark is the mineral's streak.

Lesson 2 Review

✔ **Assessment**   **Online Quiz**

Use Vocabulary

1 **Distinguish** between description and explanation.

2 **Define** *significant digits* in your own words.

Understand Key Concepts 🔑

3 Which base unit is NOT part of the International System of Units?

A. ampere   **C.** pound

B. meter   **D.** second

4 **Give an example** of how scientific tools cause measurement uncertainty.

5 **Differentiate** among mean, median, mode, and range.

Interpret Graphics

6 **Change** Copy the graphic organizer below, and change the number shown to have the correct number of significant digits indicated.

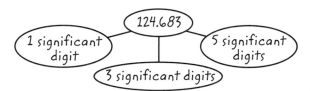

124.683

1 significant digit

5 significant digits

3 significant digits

Critical Thinking

7 **Write** a short essay explaining why the United States should consider adopting SI as the measurement system used by supermarkets and other businesses.

Math Skills   📱 **Review**

— Math Practice —

8 **Convert** 52 m to kilometers. Explain how you got your answer.

Materials

250-mL beaker

large piece of newsprint

1-L containers

forceps

strainer

probe

Also needed:
soil mixture, balance, plastic containers

Safety

What can you learn by collecting and analyzing data?

People who study ancient cultures often collect and analyze data from soil samples. Soil samples contain bits of pottery, bones, seeds, and other clues to how ancient people lived and what they ate. In this activity, you will separate and analyze a simulated soil sample from an ancient civilization.

Learn It

Data includes observations you can make with your senses and observations based on measurements of some kind. **Collecting and analyzing data** includes collecting, classifying, comparing and contrasting, and interpreting (looking for meaning in the data).

Try It

1 Read and complete a lab safety form.

2 Obtain a 200-mL sample of "soil."

3 Spread the newsprint over your workspace. Slowly pour the soil through a strainer over a plastic container. Shake the strainer gently so that all of the soil enters the container.

4 Pour the remaining portion of the soil sample onto the newsprint. Use a probe and forceps to separate objects. Classify different types of objects, and place them into the other plastic containers.

5 Copy the data tables from the board into your Science Journal.

6 Use the balance to measure and record the masses of each group of objects found in your soil sample. Write your group's data in the data table on the board.

7 When all teams have finished, use the class data from the board to find the mean, the median, the mode, and the range for each type of object.

Apply It

8 **Make Inferences** Assuming that the plastic objects represented animal bones, how many different types of animals were indicated by your analysis? Explain.

9 **Evaluate** Archaeologists often include information about the depth at which soil samples are taken. If you received a soil sample that kept the soil and other objects in their original layers, what more might you discover?

10  **Key Concept** Why didn't everyone in the class get the same data? What were some possible sources of uncertainty in your measurements?

3

Reading Guide

Key Concepts
ESSENTIAL QUESTIONS

- How are independent variables and dependent variables related?

- How is scientific inquiry used in a real-life scientific investigation?

Vocabulary

variable

independent variable

dependent variable

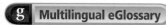 **g** Multilingual eGlossary

AID M1.1a, S1.1a, S1.2c, S2.1a, S2.1b, S2.1c, S2.1d, S2.2a, S2.2b, S2.2c, S2.2d, S2.2e, S2.3a, S2.3b, S3.1a, S3.2h; IPS 1.4

Case Study

The Iceman's Last Journey

The Tyrolean Alps border western Austria, northern Italy, and eastern Switzerland, as shown in **Figure 8.** They are popular with tourists, hikers, mountain climbers, and skiers. In 1991, two hikers discovered the remains of a man, also shown in **Figure 8,** in a melting glacier on the border between Austria and Italy. They thought the man had died in a hiking accident. They reported their discovery to the authorities.

Initially authorities thought the man was a music professor who disappeared in 1938. However, they soon learned that the music professor was buried in a nearby town. Artifacts near the frozen corpse indicated that the man died long before 1938. The artifacts, as shown in **Figure 9,** were unusual. The man, nicknamed the Iceman, was dressed in leggings, a loincloth, and a goatskin jacket. A bearskin cap lay nearby. He wore shoes made of red deerskin with thick bearskin soles. The shoes were stuffed with grass for insulation. In addition, investigators found a copper ax, a partially constructed longbow, a quiver containing 14 arrows, a wooden backpack frame, and a dagger at the site.

Figure 8 Excavators used jackhammers to free the man's body from the ice, which caused serious damage to his hip. Part of a longbow also was found nearby.

A Controlled Experiment

The identity of the corpse was a mystery. Several people hypothesized about his identity, but controlled experiments were needed to unravel the mystery of who the Iceman was. Scientists and the public wanted to know the identity of the man, why he had died, and when he had died.

Identifying Variables and Constants

When scientists design a controlled experiment, they have to identify factors that might affect the outcome of an experiment. A **variable** *is any factor that can have more than one value.* In controlled experiments, there are two kinds of variables. The **independent variable** *is the factor that you want to test. It is changed by the investigator to observe how it affects a dependent variable.* The **dependent variable** *is the factor you observe or measure during an experiment.* When the independent variable is changed, it causes the dependent variable to change.

A controlled experiment has two groups—an experimental group and a control group. The experimental group is used to study how a change in the independent variable changes the dependent variable. The control group contains the same factors as the experimental group, but the independent variable is not changed. Without a control, it is difficult to know if your experimental observations result from the variable you are testing or from another factor.

Scientists used inquiry to investigate the mystery of the Iceman. As you read the rest of the story, notice how scientific inquiry was used throughout the investigation. The blue boxes in the margins point out examples of the scientific inquiry process. The notebooks in the margin identify what a scientist might have written in a journal.

Figure 9 These models show what the Iceman and the artifacts found with him might have looked like.

Scientific investigations often begin when someone asks a question about something observed in nature.

Observation: A corpse was found buried in ice in the Tyrolean Alps.

Hypothesis: The corpse found in the Tyrolean Alps is the body of a missing music professor because he disappeared in 1938, and had not been found.

Observation: Artifacts near the body suggested that the body was much older than the music professor would have been.

Revised Hypothesis: The corpse found was dead long before 1938 because the artifacts found near him appear to date before the 1930s.

Prediction: If the artifacts belong to the corpse, and date back before 1930, then the corpse is not the music professor.

Inference: Based on its construction, the ax is at least 4,000 years old.
Prediction: If the ax is at least 4,000 years old, then the body found near it is also at least 4,000 years old.
Test Results: Radiocarbon dating showed the man to be 5,300 years old.

After many observations, revised hypotheses, and tests, conclusions often can be made.

Conclusion: The Iceman is about 5,300 years old. He was a seasonal visitor to the high mountains. He died in autumn. When winter came the Iceman's body became buried and frozen in the snow, which preserved his body.

Figure 10 This ax, bow and quiver, and dagger and sheath were found with the Iceman's body.

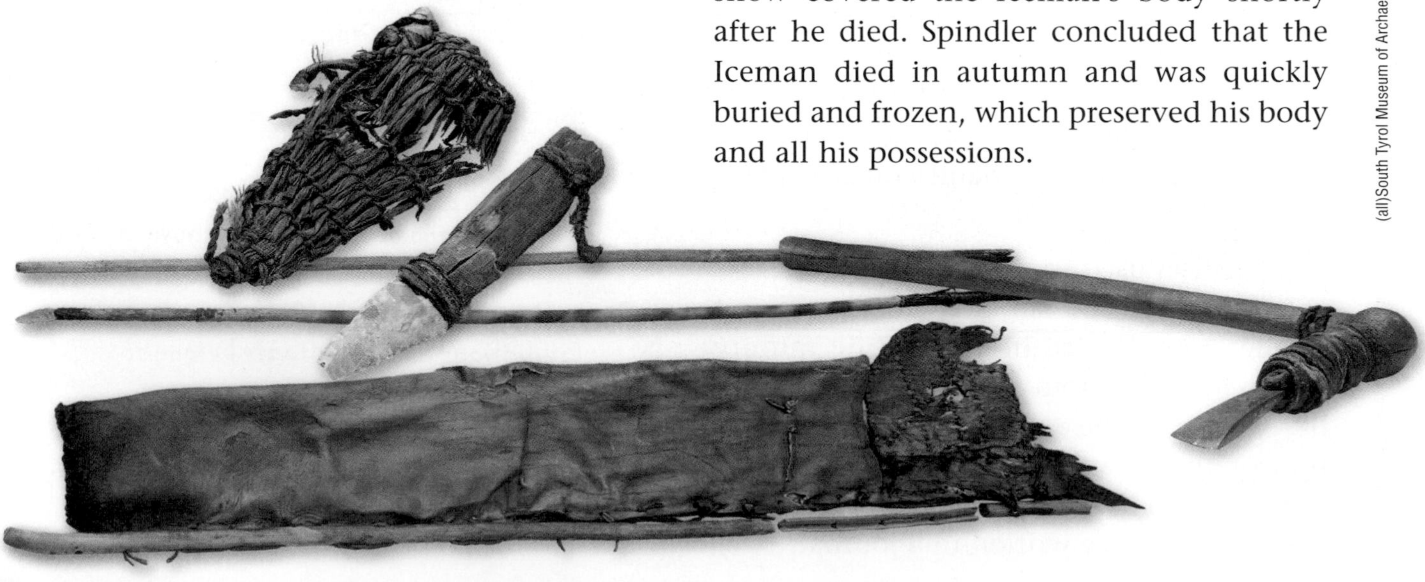

An Early Conclusion

Konrad Spindler was a professor of archeology at the University of Innsbruck in Austria when the Iceman was discovered. Spindler estimated that the ax, shown in **Figure 10,** was at least 4,000 years old based on its construction. If the ax was that old, then the Iceman was also at least 4,000 years old. Later, radiocarbon dating showed that the Iceman actually lived about 5,300 years ago.

The Iceman's body was in a mountain glacier 3,210 m above sea level. What was this man doing so high in the snow- and ice-covered mountains? Was he hunting for food, shepherding his animals, or looking for metal ore?

Spindler noted that some of the wood used in the artifacts was from trees that grew at lower elevations. He concluded that the Iceman was probably a seasonal visitor to the high mountains.

Spindler also hypothesized that shortly before the Iceman's death, the Iceman had driven his herds from their summer high mountain pastures to the lowland valleys. However, the Iceman soon returned to the mountains where he died of exposure to the cold, wintry weather.

The Iceman's body was extremely well preserved. Spindler inferred that ice and snow covered the Iceman's body shortly after he died. Spindler concluded that the Iceman died in autumn and was quickly buried and frozen, which preserved his body and all his possessions.

(all)South Tyrol Museum of Archaeology, Italy (www.iceman.it)

More Observations and Revised Hypotheses

When the Iceman's body was discovered, Klaus Oeggl was an assistant professor of botany at the University of Innsbruck. His area of study was plant life during prehistoric times in the Alps. He was invited to join the research team studying the Iceman.

Upon close examination of the Iceman and his belongings, Professor Oeggl found three plant materials—grass from the Iceman's shoe, as shown in **Figure 11,** a splinter of wood from his longbow, and a tiny fruit called a sloe berry.

Over the next year, Professor Oeggl examined bits of charcoal wrapped in maple leaves that had been found at the discovery site. Examination of the samples revealed the charcoal was from the wood of eight different types of trees. All but one of the trees grew only at lower elevations than where the Iceman's body was found. Like Spindler, Professor Oeggl suspected that the Iceman had been at a lower elevation shortly before he died. From Oeggl's observations, he formed a hypothesis and made some predictions.

Oeggl realized that he would need more data to support his hypothesis. He requested that he be allowed to examine the contents of the Iceman's digestive tract. If all went well, the study would show what the Iceman had swallowed just hours before his death.

Observations: Plant matter near body to study—grass on shoe, splinter from longbow, sloe berry fruit, charcoal wrapped in maple leaves, wood in charcoal from 8 different trees— 7 of 8 types of wood in charcoal grow at lower elevations
Hypothesis: The Iceman had recently been at lower elevations before he died because the plants identified near him grow only at lower elevations.
Prediction: If the identified plants are found in the digestive tract of the corpse, then the man actually was at lower elevations just before he died.
Question: What did the Iceman eat the day before he died?

Figure 11 Professor Oeggl examined the Iceman's belongings along with the leaves and grass that were stuck to his shoe.

(all)South Tyrol Museum of Archaeology, Italy (www.iceman.it)

Experiment to Test Hypothesis

The research teams provided Professor Oeggl with a tiny sample from the Iceman's digestive tract. He was determined to study it carefully to obtain as much information as possible. Oeggl carefully planned his scientific inquiry. He knew that he had to work quickly to avoid the decomposition of the sample and to reduce the chances of contaminating the samples.

His plan was to divide the material from the digestive tract into four samples. Each sample would undergo several chemical tests. Then, the samples would be examined under an electron microscope to see as many details as possible.

Professor Oeggl began by adding a saline solution to the first sample. This caused it to swell slightly, making it easier to identify particles using the microscope at a relatively low magnification. He saw particles of a wheat grain known as einkorn, which was a common type of wheat grown in the region during prehistoric times. He also found other edible plant material in the sample.

Oeggl noticed that the sample also contained pollen grains in the digestive tract of the Iceman, who is shown in **Figure 12**. To see the pollen grains more clearly, he used a chemical that separated unwanted substances from the pollen grains. He washed the sample a few times with alcohol. After each wash, he examined the sample under a microscope at a high magnification. The pollen grains became more visible. Many more microscopic pollen grains could now be seen. Professor Oeggl identified these pollen grains as those from a hop hornbeam tree.

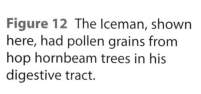

There is more than one way to test a hypothesis. Scientists might gather and evaluate evidence, collect data and record their observations, create a model, or design and perform an experiment. They also might perform a combination of these skills.

Test Plan:
- Divide a sample of the Iceman's digestive tract into four sections.
- Examine the pieces under microscopes.
- Gather data from observations of the pieces and record observations.

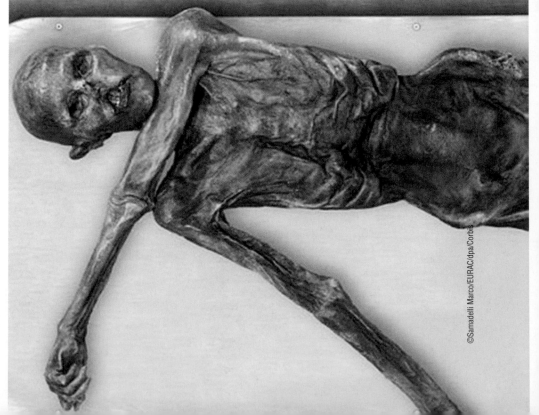

Figure 12 The Iceman, shown here, had pollen grains from hop hornbeam trees in his digestive tract.

©Samadelli Marco/EURAC/dpa/Corbis

Analyzing Results

Professor Oeggl observed that the hop-hornbeam pollen grains had not been digested. Therefore, the Iceman must have swallowed them within hours before his death. But, hop hornbeam trees only grow in lower valleys. Oeggl was confused. How could pollen grains from trees at low elevations be ingested within a few hours of this man dying in high, snow-covered mountains? Perhaps the samples from the Iceman's digestive tract had been contaminated. Oeggl knew he needed to investigate further.

Further Experimentation

Oeggl realized that the most likely source of contamination would be Oeggl's own laboratory. He decided to test whether his lab equipment or saline solution contained hop-hornbeam pollen grains. To do this, he prepared two identical, sterile slides with saline solution. Then, on one slide, he placed a sample from the Iceman's digestive tract. The slide with the sample was the experimental group. The slide without the sample was the control group.

The independent variable, or the variable that Oeggl changed, was the presence of the sample on the slide. The dependent variable, or the variable Oeggl tested, was whether hop-hornbeam pollen grains showed up on the slides. Oeggl examined the slides carefully.

Analyzing Additional Results

The experiment showed that the control group (the slide without the digestive tract sample) contained no hop-hornbeam pollen grains. Therefore, the pollen grains had not come from his lab equipment or solutions. Each sample from the Iceman's digestive tract was closely re-examined. All of the samples contained the same hop-hornbeam pollen grains. The Iceman had indeed swallowed the hop-hornbeam pollen grains.

Error is unavoidable in scientific research. Scientists are careful to document procedures and any unanticipated factors or accidents. They also are careful to document possible sources of error in their measurements.

Procedure:
- Sterilize laboratory equipment.
- Prepare saline slides.
- View saline slides under electron microscope. Results: no hop-hornbeam pollen grains
- Add digestive tract sample to one slide.
- View this slide under electron microscope. Result: hop hornbeam pollen grains present.

Controlled experiments contain two types of variables.

Dependent Variables: amount of hop-hornbeam pollen grains found on slide
Independent Variable: digestive tract sample on slide

Without a control group, it is difficult to determine the origin of some observations.

Control Group: sterilized slide
Experimental Group: sterilized slide with digestive tract sample

Observation: The Iceman's digestive tract contains pollen grains from the hop hornbeam tree and other plants that bloom in spring.

Inference: Knowing the rate at which food and pollen decompose after swallowed, it can be inferred that the Iceman ate three times on the day that he died.

Prediction: The Iceman died in the spring within hours of digesting the hop-hornbeam pollen grains.

Mapping the Iceman's Journey

The hop-hornbeam pollen grains were helpful in determining the season the Iceman died. Because the pollen grains were whole, Professor Oeggl inferred that the Iceman swallowed the pollen grains during their blooming season. Therefore, the Iceman must have died between March and June.

After additional investigation, Professor Oeggl was ready to map the Iceman's final trek up the mountain. Because Oeggl knew the rate at which food travels through the digestive system, he inferred that the Iceman had eaten three times in the final day and a half of his life. From the digestive tract samples, Oeggl estimated where the Iceman was located when he ate.

First, the Iceman ingested pollen grains native to higher mountain regions. Then he swallowed hop-hornbeam pollen grains from the lower mountain regions several hours later. Last, the Iceman swallowed other pollen grains from trees of higher mountain areas again. Oeggl proposed the Iceman traveled from the southern region of the Italian Alps to the higher, northern region as shown in **Figure 13**, where he died suddenly. He did this all in a period of about 33 hours.

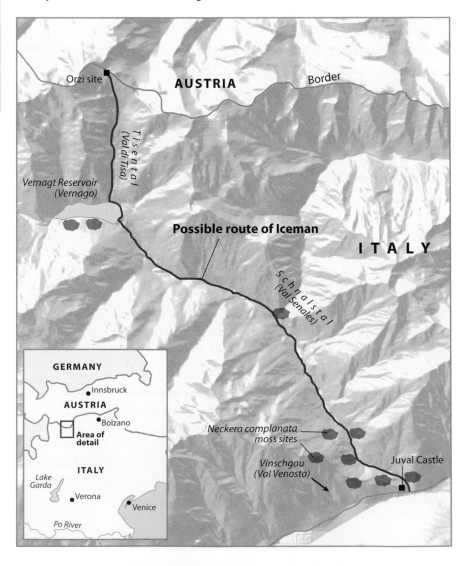

Figure 13 By examining the contents of the Iceman's digestive tract, Professor Oeggl was able to reconstruct the Iceman's last journey.

Conclusion

Researchers from around the world worked on different parts of the Iceman mystery and shared their results. Analysis of the Iceman's hair revealed his diet usually contained vegetables and meat. Examining the Iceman's one remaining fingernail, scientists determined that he had been sick three times within the last six months of his life. X-rays revealed an arrowhead under the Iceman's left shoulder. This suggested that he died from that serious injury rather than from exposure.

Finally, scientists concluded that the Iceman traveled from the high alpine region in spring to his native village in the lowland valleys. There, during a conflict, the Iceman sustained a fatal injury. He retreated back to the higher elevations, where he died. Scientists recognize their hypotheses can never be proved, only supported or not supported. However, with advances in technology, scientists are able to more thoroughly investigate mysteries of nature.

> Scientific investigations may disprove early hypotheses or conclusions. However, new information can cause a hypothesis or conclusion to be revised many times.

> **Revised Conclusion:**
> In spring, the Iceman traveled from the high country to the valleys. After he was involved in a violent confrontation, he climbed the mountain into a region of permanent ice where he died of his wounds.

Lesson 3 Review

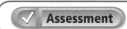 **Assessment** **Online Quiz**

Use Vocabulary

1. A factor that can have more than one value is a(n) _____.

2. **Differentiate** between independent and dependent variables.

Understand Key Concepts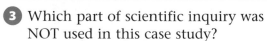

3. Which part of scientific inquiry was NOT used in this case study?
   A. Draw conclusions.
   B. Make observations.
   C. Hypothesize and predict.
   D. Make a computer model.

4. **Determine** which is the control group and which is the experimental group in the following scenario: Scientists are testing a new kind of aspirin to see whether it will relieve headaches. They give one group of volunteers the aspirin. They give another group of volunteers pills that look like aspirin but are actually sugar pills.

Interpret Graphics

5. **Summarize** Copy and fill in the flow chart below summarizing the sequence of scientific inquiry steps that was used in one part of the case study. Draw the number of boxes needed for your sequence.

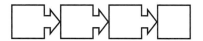

6. **Explain** What is the significance of the hop-hornbeam pollen found in the Iceman's digestive tract?

Critical Thinking

7. **Formulate** more questions about the Iceman. What would you want to know next?

8. **Evaluate** the hypotheses and conclusions made during the study of the Iceman. Do you see anything that might be an assumption? Are there holes in the research?

Materials

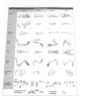

owl pellet

bone identification chart

dissecting needle

forceps

magnifying lens

Also needed:
toothpicks, small brush, paper plate, ruler

Safety

Inferring from Indirect Evidence

In the case study about the Iceman, you learned how scientists used evidence found in or near the body to learn how the Iceman might have lived and what he ate. In this investigation, you will use similar indirect evidence to learn more about an owl.

An owl pellet is a ball of fur and feathers that contains bones, teeth, and other undigested parts of animals eaten by the owl. Owls and other birds, such as hawks and eagles, swallow their prey whole. Stomach acids digest the soft parts of the food. Skeletons and body coverings are not digested and form a ball. When the owl coughs up the ball, it might fall to the ground. Feathers, straw, or leaves often stick to the moist ball when it strikes the ground.

Ask a Question

What kinds of information can I learn about an owl by analyzing an owl pellet?

Make Observations

1 Read and complete a lab safety form.

2 Carefully measure the length, the width, and the mass of your pellet. Write the data in your Science Journal.

3 Gently examine the outside of the pellet using a magnifying lens. Do you see any sign of fur or feathers? What other substances can you identify? Record your observations.

4 Use a dissecting needle, toothpicks, and forceps to gently pull apart the pellet. Try to avoid breaking any of the tiny bones. Spread out the parts on a paper plate.

5 Copy the table into your Science Journal. Use the bone identification chart to identify each of the bones and other materials found in your pellet. Make a mark in the table for each part you identify.

Bone Identification Chart		
Bone	**Animal**	**Number**
Skull		
Jaw		
Shoulder blade		
Forelimb		
Hind limb		
Hip/pelvis		
Rib		
Vertebrae		
Insect parts		

Analyze and Conclude

6 **Assemble** the bones you find into a skeleton. You may need to locate pictures of rodents, shrews, moles, and birds.

7 **Discuss** with your teammates why parts of an animal skeleton might be missing.

8 **Write** a report that includes your data and conclusions about the owl's diet.

9 **Identify Cause and Effect** Is every bone you found in the pellet necessarily from the owl's prey? Why or why not?

10 **Analyze** What conclusions can you reach about the diet of the particular owl from which your pellet came? Can you extend this conclusion to the diets of all owls? Why or why not?

11 **The Big Idea** How did the scientific inquiry you used in the investigation compare to those used by the scientists studying the Iceman? In what ways were they the same? In what ways were they different?

Communicate Your Results

Compare your results with those of several other teams. Discuss any evidence to support that the owl pellets did or did not come from the same area.

 **Extension**

Put your data on the board. Use the class data to determine a mean, median, mode, and range for each type of bone.

Lab Tips

☑ When using your forceps, squeeze the sides very lightly so that you don't crush fragile bones.

☑ Use the brush to clean each bone. Try rotating the bones as you match them to the chart.

☑ Lay the bones on the matching box on the chart as you separate them. Then count them when you are finished.

4

Remember to use scientific methods.

Make Observations

↓

Ask a Question

↓

Form a Hypothesis

↓

Test your Hypothesis

↓

Analyze and Conclude

↓

Communicate Results

 THE BIG IDEA

Scientists use the process of scientific inquiry to perform scientific investigations.

Key Concepts Summary 🗝	Vocabulary
Lesson 1: Understanding Science • Scientific inquiry is a process that uses a set of skills to answer questions or to test ideas about the natural world. • A **scientific law** is a rule that describes a pattern in nature. A **scientific theory** is an explanation of things or events that is based on knowledge gained from many **observations** and investigations. • Facts are measurements, observations, and theories that can be evaluated for their validity through objective investigation. Opinions are personal views, feelings, or claims about a topic that cannot be proven true or false.	**science** **observation** **inference** **hypothesis** **prediction** **technology** **scientific theory** **scientific law** **critical** thinking
Lesson 2: Measurement and Scientific Tools • Scientists worldwide use the **International System of Units** because their work is easier to confirm and repeat by their peers. • Measurement uncertainty occurs because no scientific tool can provide a perfect measurement. • Mean, median, mode, and range are statistical calculations that are used to evaluate sets of data.	**description** **explanation** **International System of Units (SI)** **significant digits**
Lesson 3: Case Study: The Iceman's Last Journey • The **independent variable** is the factor a scientist changes to observe how it affects a **dependent variable.** A dependent variable is the factor a scientist measures or observes during an experiment. • Scientific inquiry was used throughout the investigation of the Iceman when hypotheses, predictions, tests, analysis, and conclusions were developed.	**variable** **independent variable** **dependent variable**

Use Vocabulary

Replace each underlined term with the correct vocabulary word.

1 A <u>description</u> is an interpretation of observations.

2 The <u>means</u> are the numbers of digits in a measurement that you know with a certain degree of reliability.

3 The act of watching something and taking note of what occurs is a(n) <u>inference</u>.

4 A <u>scientific theory</u> is a rule that describes a pattern in nature.

Understand Key Concepts 🔑

5 In the diagram of the process of scientific inquiry, which skill is missing from the Test Hypothesis box?

> **Test Hypothesis**
> - Design an Experiment
> - Gather and Evaluate Evidence
> - Collect Data/Record Observations

A. Analyze results.

B. Communicate results.

C. Make a model.

D. Make observations.

6 You have the following data set: 2, 3, 4, 4, 5, 7, and 8. Is 6 the mean, the median, the mode, or the range of the data set?

A. mean

B. median

C. mode

D. range

7 Which best describes an independent variable?

A. It is a factor that is not in every test.

B. It is a factor the investigator changes.

C. It is a factor you measure during a test.

D. It is a factor that stays the same in every test.

Critical Thinking

8 **Predict** what would happen if every scientist tried to use all the skills of scientific inquiry in the same order in every investigation.

9 **Assess** the role of measurement uncertainty in scientific investigations.

10 **Evaluate** the importance of having a control group in a scientific investigation.

Writing in Science

11 **Write** a five-sentence paragraph explaining why the International System of Units (SI) is an easier system to use than the English system of measurement. Be sure to include a topic sentence and a concluding sentence in your paragraph.

REVIEW THE **BIG IDEA**

12 What process do scientists use to perform scientific investigations? List and explain three of the skills involved.

13 Infer the purpose of the pink dye in the scientific investigation shown in the photo.

Math Skills ✕✗
➗➕

 Review

── Math Practice ──

Use Numbers

14 Convert 162.5 hg to grams.

15 Convert 89.7 cm to millimeters.

Unit 1

Simple and Complex Machines

3500 B.C.
The oldest wheeled vehicle is depicted in Mesopotamia, near the Black Sea.

400 B.C.
The Greeks invent the stone-hurling catapult.

1698
English military engineer Thomas Savery invents the first crude steam engine while trying to solve the problem of pumping water out of coal mines.

1760–1850
The Industrial Revolution results in massive advances in technology and social structure in England.

1769
The first vehicle to move under its own power is designed by Nicholas Joseph Cugnot and constructed by M. Breszin. A second replica is built that weighs 3,629 kg and has a top speed of 3.2 km per hour.

1794
Eli Whitney receives a patent for the mechanical cotton gin.

1000 B.C.   1600   1700

1800

1817
Baron von Drais invents a machine to help him quickly wander the grounds of his estate. The machine is made of two wheels on a frame with a seat and a pair of pedals. This machine is the beginning design of the modern bicycle.

1900

1903
Wilbur and Orville Wright build their airplane, called the Flyer, and take the first successful, powered, piloted flight.

1976
The first computer for home use is invented by college dropouts Steve Wozniak and Steve Jobs, who go on to found Apple Computer, Inc.

 Inquiry

Visit ConnectED for this unit's STEM activity.

Models

ICT 2.2

Have you ridden on an amusement park roller coaster such as the one in **Figure 1?** As you were going down the steepest hill or hanging upside down in a loop, did you think to yourself, "I hope I don't fly off this thing"? Before construction begins on a roller coaster, engineers build different models of the thrill ride to ensure proper construction and safety. A **model** is a representation of an object, an idea, or a system that is similar to the physical object or idea being studied.

Using Models in Physical Science

Models are used to study things that are too big or too small, happen too quickly or too slowly, or are too dangerous or too expensive to study directly. Different types of models serve different purposes. Roller-coaster engineers might build a physical model of their idea for a new, daring coaster. Using mathematical and computer models, the engineers can calculate the measurements of hills, angles, and loops to ensure a safe ride. Finally, the engineers might create another model called a blueprint, or drawing, that details the construction of the ride. Studying the various models allows engineers to predict how the actual roller coaster will behave when it travels through a loop or down a giant hill.

Figure 1 Engineers use various models to design roller coasters.

Types of Models

Physical Model

A physical model is a model that you can see and touch. It shows how parts relate to one another, how something is built, or how complex objects work. Physical models often are built to scale. A limitation of a physical model is that it might not reflect the physical behavior of the full-size object. For example, this model will not accurately show how wind will affect the ride.

Mathematical Model

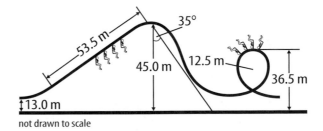

35°

53.5 m

45.0 m   12.5 m

36.5 m

13.0 m

not drawn to scale

A mathematical model uses numerical data and equations to model an event or idea. Mathematical models often include input data, constants, and output data. When designing a thrill ride, engineers use mathematical models to calculate the heights, the angles of loops and turns, and the forces that affect the ride. One limitation of a mathematical model is that you cannot use it to model how different parts are assembled.

Making Models

An important factor in making a model is determining its purpose. You might need a model that physically represents an object. Or, you might need a model that includes only important elements of an object or a process. When you build a model, first determine the function of the model. What variables need to change? What materials should you use? What do you need to communicate to others? **Figure 2** shows two models of a glucose molecule, each with a different purpose.

Limitations of Models

It is impossible to include all the details about an object or an idea into one model. All models have limitations. When using models to design a structure, an engineer must be aware of the information each model does and does not provide. For example, a blueprint of a roller coaster does not show the maximum weight that a car can support. However, a mathematical model would include this information. Scientists and engineers consider the purpose and the limitations of the model they use to ensure they draw accurate conclusions from models.

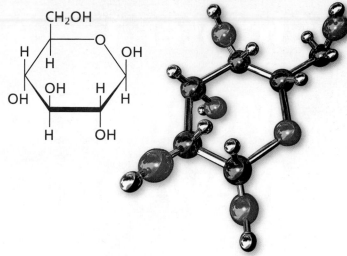

Figure 2 The model on the left is used to represent how the atoms in a glucose molecule bond together. The model on the right is a 3-D representation of the molecule, which shows how atoms might interact.

Computer Simulation

A computer simulation is a model that combines large amounts of data and mathematical models with computer graphic and animation programs. Simulations can contain thousands of complex mathematical models. When roller coaster engineers change variables in mathematical models, they use computer simulation to view the effects of the change.

inquiry MiniLab
30 minutes

Can you model a roller coaster?

You are an engineer with an awesome idea for a new roller coaster—the car on your roller coaster makes a jump and then lands back on the track. You model your idea to show it to managers at a theme park in hopes that you can build it.

1. Read and complete a lab safety form.
2. Create a blueprint of your roller coaster. Include a scale and measurements.
3. Follow your blueprint to build a scaled physical model of your roller coaster. Use **foam hose insulation, tape,** and other **craft supplies.**
4. Use a **marble** as a model for a roller-coaster car. Test your model. Record your observations in your Science Journal.

Analyze and Conclude

1. **Compare** your blueprint and physical model.

2. **Evaluate** After you test your physical model, list the design changes you would make to your blueprint.

3. **Identify** What are the limitations of each of your models?

AID M1.1a, M1.1c, S1.2b, S1.4, S2.1a, S2.1b,
S2.1c, S2.1d, S2.2a, S2.2b, S2.2c, S2.2d, S2.2e,
S2.3a, S2.3b, S3.1a, S3.1b, S3.2c, S3.2d, S3.2f,
S3.2h; ICT 5.1; IPS 1.4, 2.1; PS 5.2d

Motion, Forces, and Newton's Laws

THE BIG IDEA

In what ways do forces affect an object's motion?

Inquiry **How did they get up there?**

When you stop a video of moving acrobats, they sometimes look as if they are frozen in the air. A still photo of an acrobat in midair can help you analyze exactly what is happening.

- What are some ways you could describe the motion of the acrobats in the air?

- What caused the acrobats to fly high into the air?

- In what ways do forces affect the motion of the acrobats?

Get Ready to Read

What do you think?

Before you read, decide if you agree or disagree with each of these statements. As you read this chapter, see if you change your mind about any of the statements.

1 You must use a reference point to describe an object's motion.

2 An object that is accelerating must be speeding up.

3 Objects must be in contact with one another to exert a force.

4 Gravity is a force that depends on the masses of two objects and the distance between them.

5 All forces change the motion of objects.

6 The net force on an object is equal to the mass of the object times the acceleration of the object.

ConnectED Your one-stop online resource

MHEonline.com

- Video
- WebQuest
- Audio
- Assessment
- Review
- Concepts in Motion
- Inquiry
- Multilingual eGlossary

Reading Guide

Key Concepts 🗝
ESSENTIAL QUESTIONS

- What information do you need to describe the motion of an object?

- How are speed, velocity, and acceleration related?

- How can a graph help you understand the motion of an object?

Vocabulary

motion

reference point

distance

displacement

speed

velocity

acceleration

 Multilingual eGlossary

 Video BrainPOP®

 AID M1.1c, S1.4; ICT 5.1

Describing Motion

WINNER EVERY GAME

SMALL
MEDIUM   ONE
LARGE   BALL 2^{00}
JUMBO   THREE
CHOICE   BALLS 5^{00}

EVERY BALL A WINNER!

ᴵⁿᑫᵘᴵʳʸ Where is the white ball?

In an arcade, many games involve something moving. Objects speed up, slow down, and change direction. How would you describe the position of the white ball in this game at any moment in time? How is its motion different from the motion of the other balls? What words could you use to describe the motion of the ball?

Blend Images/Getty Images

How can you describe motion?

You see things move in many ways each day. You might see a train moving along a track or raindrops falling to the ground. What information do you need to describe an object's motion?

1. Read and complete a lab safety form.

2. Choose a **small object,** such as a ball or a pencil. Move the object in some way.

3. Have a partner write a short description of the movement in the Science Journal.

4. Exchange objects and descriptions with several other pairs of students. Each time, use the description to try to duplicate the original motion.

Think About This

1. **Contrast** Why were some descriptions more useful than others when you tried to duplicate the motion?

2. 🔑 **Key Concept** What information do you think you need to accurately describe an object's motion?

Motion

Suppose you have been playing a shuffleboard game in an arcade. You decide to try something new, so you walk to a racing game. As you walk to the new game, your position in the room changes. **Motion** *is the process of changing position.* If the games are 5 m apart, you could say that your position changed by 5 m.

Motion and Reference Points

How would you describe your motion to a friend? You could say that you walked 5 m away from the shuffleboard game. Or you could say that you moved 5 m toward the racing game. *The starting point you use to describe the motion or the position of an object is called the* **reference point.** Motion is described differently depending on the reference point you choose. You can choose any point as a reference point. Both the racing game and the shuffleboard game can be reference points.

In addition to using a reference point to describe motion, you also need a direction. For example, the puck is moving away from the girl in **Figure 1.** Other descriptions of direction might include east or west, or up or down.

✔ **Reading Check** Describe your motion as you walk from your desk to the door. Use a reference point and a direction.

Figure 1 🔑 A description of the motion of the puck depends on the reference point you choose.

✔ **Visual Check** Name three different reference points you could choose in order to describe the motion of the puck.

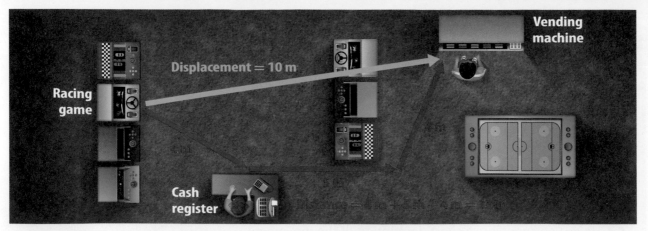

▲ **Figure 2** The distance traveled and the displacement from the game to the vending machine differ.

Distance and Displacement

Suppose you finish playing the racing game, and you go to the cash register to get more tokens. Then, you go to the vending machine for a snack. Your path is shown by the red arrows in **Figure 2.** How far did you travel? **Distance** *is the total length of your path*. The total distance you traveled is 4 m + 5 m + 4 m = 13 m.

Your **displacement** *is the distance between your initial, or starting, position and your final position*. Displacement is represented with a straight arrow extending from the starting point to the ending point. The displacement between the racing game where you started and the vending machine where you stopped is shown by the blue arrow in **Figure 2.** Your displacement is 10 m. To give a complete description of your motion, you must include a reference point, your displacement, and your direction from the reference point.

 Key Concept Check What information do you need to describe an object's motion?

Speed

Suppose you run out of tokens and leave the arcade. Walking slowly, it takes a long time to get to the end of the block. When you realize that you need to meet a friend at the library in 15 minutes, you start to run. When running, you travel the distance of the next block in a shorter time. How does your motion differ in the two blocks? Since you traveled the second block in less time than the first, your speed was different. **Speed** *is the distance an object moves divided by the time it took to move that distance*.

Constant and Changing Speed

Speed can be constant or changing. Look at **Figure 3.** The stopwatches above the girl show her motion every second for 6 seconds. In the first 4 seconds, the girl moves with constant, or unchanging, speed because she travels the same distance during each second. When the girl starts running, the distance she travels each second gets larger and larger. The girl's speed changes.

▼ **Figure 3** The girl's speed begins to change between seconds 4 and 5.

Average Speed

Suppose you want to figure out how fast you ran from the arcade to the library. As you ran, your speed probably changed from second to second. Therefore, in order to describe the speed you traveled, you describe the average speed of the entire trip. Average speed is the ratio of the distance an object moves to the time it takes for the object to move that distance. If it takes you 15 minutes, or 0.25 h, to run the 1 km to the library, your average speed was 1 km/0.25 h, or 4 km/h.

Velocity

If you tell your friend that you traveled about 4 km/h, you are describing your speed. You could give your friend a better description of your motion if you also told him or her the direction in which you are moving. **Velocity** *is the speed and direction of an object's motion.*

Often, velocity is shown by using an arrow, as shown in **Figure 4.** The length of the arrow represents the speed of an object, while the direction in which the arrow points represents the direction in which the object is moving.

Constant Velocity

Velocity is constant, or does not change, when an object's speed and direction of movement do not change. If you use an arrow to describe velocity, you can divide the arrow into segments to show whether velocity is constant. Look at the skateboarding arrow in **Figure 4.** Each segment of the arrow shows the distance and the direction you move in a given unit of time. Because each segment is the same length, you are moving the same distance and in the same direction during each interval of time. Because both your speed and direction of movement are constant, you are moving at a constant velocity.

WORD ORIGIN

velocity
from Latin *velocitatem*, means "swiftness or speed"

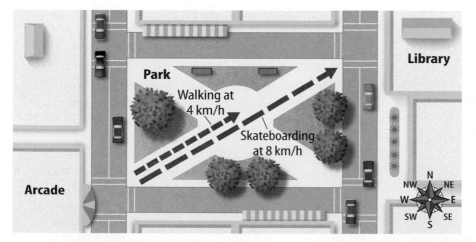

Figure 4 🔑 Your skateboarding velocity is greater than your walking velocity. Both velocities are constant because they represent a constant speed in a constant direction.

Library

Park

Walking at 4 km/h

Skateboarding at 8 km/h

Arcade

N
NW   NE
W   E
SW   SE
S

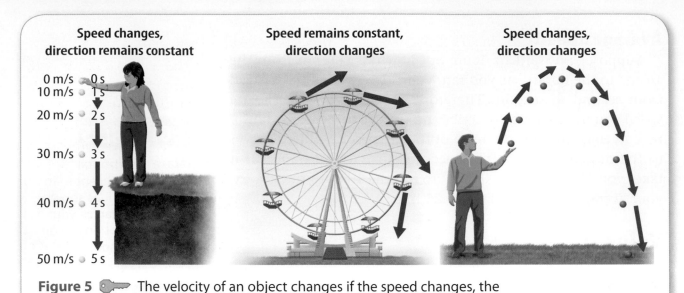

Speed changes, direction remains constant

0 m/s — 0 s
10 m/s — 1 s
20 m/s — 2 s
30 m/s — 3 s
40 m/s — 4 s
50 m/s — 5 s

Speed remains constant, direction changes

Speed changes, direction changes

Figure 5 🔑 The velocity of an object changes if the speed changes, the direction changes, or both the speed and the direction change.

Changing Velocity

Velocity can change even if the speed of an object remains constant. Recall that velocity includes both an object's speed and its direction of travel. **Figure 5** shows several examples of changing velocity.

In the first panel, the ball drops toward the ground in a straight line, or constant direction. The increased length of each arrow shows that the speed of the ball increases as it falls. As speed changes, velocity changes.

In the second panel, each arrow is the same length. This tells you that the Ferris-wheel cars travel around a circle at a constant speed. However, each arrow points in a different direction. This tells you that the cars are changing direction. As direction changes, velocity changes.

The third panel of **Figure 5** shows the path of a ball thrown into the air. The arrows show that both the ball's speed and direction change, so its velocity changes.

When either an object's speed or velocity changes, the object is accelerating. **Acceleration** *is the measure of the change in velocity during a period of time.*

🔑 **Key Concept Check** Can an object traveling at a constant speed have a changing velocity? Why or why not?

Hutchings Photography/Digital Light Source

Calculating Acceleration

When a ball is dropped, as in the first panel of **Figure 5,** its speed increases as it falls toward the ground. The velocity of the ball is changing. Therefore, the ball is accelerating. You can calculate acceleration using the following equation:

$$\bar{a} = \frac{v_f - v_i}{t}$$

The symbol for acceleration is *a*. In this lesson, *v* represents only the speed of an object. You do not need to consider the object's direction. The symbol v_f represents the final speed, and the symbol v_i represents the initial, or starting, speed. The symbol *t* stands for the time it takes to make that change in speed.

 Key Concept Check How does acceleration differ from velocity?

Positive Acceleration

When an object, such as a falling ball, speeds up, its final speed is greater than its initial speed. If you calculate the ball's acceleration, the numerator (final speed minus initial speed) is positive, so the acceleration is positive. In other words, when an object speeds up, it has positive acceleration.

Negative Acceleration

If a ball is thrown straight up into the air, it slows down as it travels upward. The initial speed of the ball is greater than its final speed. The numerator in the equation is negative, so the acceleration is negative. In other words, as an object slows down, it has negative acceleration. Some people refer to this as deceleration.

Math Skills ×÷ **Solve One-Step Equation**

Solve for Acceleration A skateboarder moving at 2 m/s starts skating down a ramp. As the skateboarder heads down the ramp, she accelerates to a speed of 6 m/s in 4 seconds. What is the skateboarder's acceleration?

1 **This is what you know:**

final speed:	$v_f = 6$ m/s
initial speed:	$v_i = 2$ m/s
time:	$t = 4$ s

2 **This is what you need to find out:** acceleration: *a*

3 **Use this formula:** $a = \dfrac{v_f - v_i}{t}$

4 **Substitute:**

the values for v_f, v_i, and t $\dfrac{6 \text{ m/s} - 2 \text{ m/s}}{4 \text{ s}}$

subtract $\dfrac{4 \text{ m/s}}{4 \text{ s}}$

and divide $= 1 \text{ m/s}^2$

Answer: The acceleration is 1 m/s².

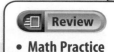
Review
- Math Practice
- Personal Tutor

Practice

As the skateboarder starts moving up the other side of the ramp, her velocity changes from 6 m/s to 0 m/s in 3 seconds. What was her acceleration?

Using Graphs to Represent Motion

How can you track the motion of an animal that can move hundreds of miles without being seen by humans? In order to understand the movements of animals, such as the polar bear in **Figure 6,** biologists put tracking devices on them. These devices constantly send information about the position of the animal to **satellites.** Biologists download the data from the satellites and create graphs of motion such as those shown in **Figures 7** and **8.**

Displacement-Time Graphs

Figure 7 is a displacement-time graph of a polar bear's motion. The x-axis shows the time, and the y-axis shows the displacement of the polar bear from a reference point.

The line on a displacement-time graph represents the average speed the bear at that particular moment in time. It does not show the actual path of motion. As the average speed of the bear changes, the slope of the line on the graph changes. Because of this, you can use a displacement-time graph to describe the motion of an object.

▲ **Figure 6** Tracking devices help scientists record the movement of animals, such as polar bears.

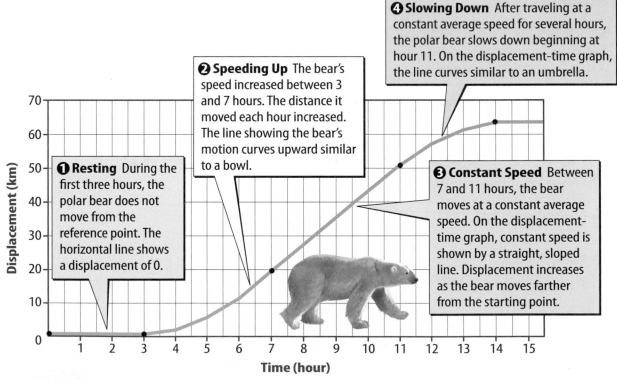

❹ **Slowing Down** After traveling at a constant average speed for several hours, the polar bear slows down beginning at hour 11. On the displacement-time graph, the line curves similar to an umbrella.

❷ **Speeding Up** The bear's speed increased between 3 and 7 hours. The distance it moved each hour increased. The line showing the bear's motion curves upward similar to a bowl.

❶ **Resting** During the first three hours, the polar bear does not move from the reference point. The horizontal line shows a displacement of 0.

❸ **Constant Speed** Between 7 and 11 hours, the bear moves at a constant average speed. On the displacement-time graph, constant speed is shown by a straight, sloped line. Displacement increases as the bear moves farther from the starting point.

▲ **Figure 7** 🔑 The displacement-time graph shows the bear's speed and distance from the reference point at any point in time.

✓ **Visual Check** What was the average speed of the bear between hours 7 and 11?

 **Review** **Personal Tutor**

Figure 8 The speed-time graph shows the speed of the bear at any given time during its journey. A horizontal line on a speed-time graph shows an object with a constant speed.

✔ **Visual Check** What happened to the bear's speed between hours 5 and 6?

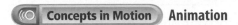 **Concepts in Motion** Animation

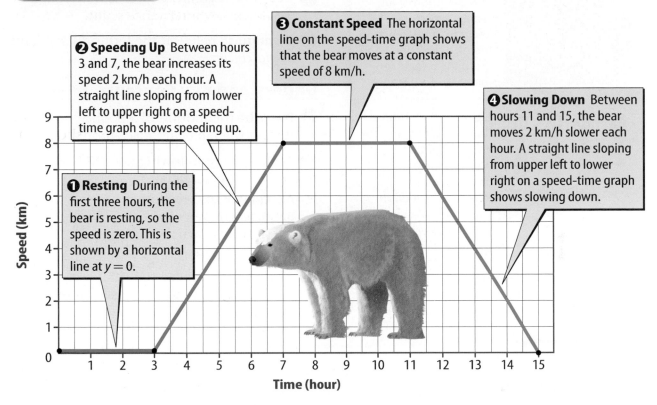

❷ **Speeding Up** Between hours 3 and 7, the bear increases its speed 2 km/h each hour. A straight line sloping from lower left to upper right on a speed-time graph shows speeding up.

❸ **Constant Speed** The horizontal line on the speed-time graph shows that the bear moves at a constant speed of 8 km/h.

❹ **Slowing Down** Between hours 11 and 15, the bear moves 2 km/h slower each hour. A straight line sloping from upper left to lower right on a speed-time graph shows slowing down.

❶ **Resting** During the first three hours, the bear is resting, so the speed is zero. This is shown by a horizontal line at $y = 0$.

Speed-Time Graphs

Figure 8 is a speed-time graph of the polar bear's motion. The *x*-axis shows the time, and the *y*-axis shows the speed of the bear. Notice that, in this case, the line shows how the speed, rather than the displacement, changes as the bear moves. A horizontal line at $y = 0$ means the bear is at rest because its speed is 0 km/hr. Notice that a horizontal line at $y = 0$ on either a displacement-time graph or a speed-time graph represents the bear at rest.

Keep in mind that *constant speed* is describing average speed. The bear might have sped up or slowed down slightly each second. But, during hours 7–11, you could describe that the bear's average speed remained constant since it covered the same distance each hour.

Interpreting the lines on graphs can provide you with a lot of information about the motion of an object.

✔ **Key Concept Check** How can a graph help you understand an object's motion?

ACADEMIC VOCABULARY

satellite
(*noun*) an object in orbit around another object

✓ **Assessment** Online Quiz
? **Inquiry** Virtual Lab

Visual Summary

A description of an object's motion includes a reference point, a direction from the reference point, and a distance.

Speed is the distance traveled by an object in a unit of time. Velocity includes both speed and direction of motion.

Acceleration is a change in velocity. Velocity changes when either the speed, the direction, or both the speed and the direction change.

FOLDABLES

Use your lesson Foldable to review the lesson. Save your Foldable for the project at the end of the chapter.

What do you think NOW?

You first read the statements below at the beginning of the chapter.

1. You must use a reference point to describe an object's motion.

2. An object that is accelerating must be speeding up.

Did you change your mind about whether you agree or disagree with the statements? Rewrite any false statements to make them true.

Use Vocabulary

1 **Describe** in your own words how you would choose a reference point.

2 **Distinguish** between the terms *distance* and *displacement*.

Understand Key Concepts

3 **Describe** the motion of a book as you lift it from the table and place it on a shelf.

4 Which of the following does NOT cause an object to accelerate?
   A. change in direction
   B. constant velocity
   C. slowing down
   D. speeding up

5 **Apply** Draw a speed-time graph of a parade float that accelerates from rest to 0.5 km/hr in 1 min and then moves at a constant speed for 10 min.

Interpret Graphics

6 **Draw** The table below includes information about the motion of an elevator. Draw a displacement-time graph using the data, and explain the elevator's motion.

Displacement	Time
0 m	0 s
1 m	1 s
4 m	2 s
10 m	3 s
10 m	4 s

Critical Thinking

7 **Analyze** whether you could have a vertical line on a displacement-time graph. Why or why not?

Math Skills $\frac{\times}{\div}$

 Review
──── Math Practice ────

8 What is the acceleration of a track star who goes from a speed of 0 m/s to a speed of 9 m/s to the east in 3 s?

It's Moving!

Fooling the Eye

You know that you describe an object's motion by explaining how its position changes. Did you know that you can use this concept to make a movie that shows nonmoving objects in motion! It's called stop-motion photography. How does it work?

1 First, set an object in a scene and take a picture of it. Keep changing the position of the object in the scene, taking a picture after each change.

2 Now use software to link all the pictures into a video. When you view the video, it will appear as if the object moved on its own. Of course, it's just an illusion. The illusion works because of the way your eye works. Motion is a change of position, and that's exactly what your eyes are seeing with stop-motion photography.

It's Your Turn

EXPERIMENT Set up your own stop-motion photography studio. If you don't have a camera, make sketches of each change. When you are finished, make a flip book of your sketches or photographs.

Forces

Reading Guide

Key Concepts
ESSENTIAL QUESTIONS

- How do different types of forces affect objects?
- What factors affect the way gravity acts on objects?
- How do balanced and unbalanced forces differ?

Vocabulary

force

contact force

noncontact force

friction

gravity

balanced forces

unbalanced forces

 g **Multilingual eGlossary**

Video

What's Science Got to do With It?

AID M1.1a, S2.1a, S2.1b, S2.1c, S2.1d, S2.2a, S2.2b, S2.2c, S2.2d, S2.2e, S2.3a, S2.3b, S3.1a, S3.1b, S3.2a, S3.2c, S3.2d, S3.2f, S3.2h; IPS 1.4, 2.1; PS 5.2d

Inquiry **Why is one side of the ball flat?**

A ball, such as this tennis ball, is usually round. Its shape lets it roll farther and travel farther in the air. What could cause part of a ball to become flat like this one? Does the same thing happen when a baseball hits a bat? Or when a golf club hits a golf ball?

Ted Kinsman/Science Source

How can you change an object's shape and motion?

You probably can think of many ways that things change. For example, paper can change from a flat sheet to a crumpled ball. A sailboat changes its location as it moves across a lake. How can you change an object's shape and motion?

1 Read and complete a lab safety form.

2 Observe and record in your Science Journal how you make the following changes. Change the shape of a handful of **clay** several times.

3 Mold the clay into a log. Cause the log to roll, and then cause it to stop rolling.

4 Cause the log to roll so that its speed changes. Then change the log's direction of motion. Observe and record in your Science Journal how you make these changes.

Think About This

1. **Describe** what you did to change the shape of the clay.

2. **Explain** how you changed the motion of the clay.

3. 🔑 **Key Concept** How was your interaction with the clay similar when you changed its shape and when you changed its motion?

What are forces?

What do typing on a computer, lifting a bike, and putting on a sweater have in common? They all involve an interaction between you and another object. You push on the keys. You push or pull on the bike. You pull on the sweater. *A push or pull on an object is a* **force.**

A force has both size and direction. In **Figure 9,** the length of the arrow represents the size of the force. The direction in which the arrow points represents the direction of the force. The unit of force is the newton (N). It takes about 4 N of force to lift a can of soda.

There are two ways a force can affect an object. A force can change an object's speed. It also can change the direction in which the object is moving. In other words, a force can cause acceleration. Recall that acceleration is a change in an object's velocity—its speed and/or its direction in a given time. When you apply a force to a tennis ball, such as the one shown in the picture on the previous page, the force first stops the motion of the ball. The force then causes the ball to accelerate in the opposite direction, changing both its speed and direction.

✓ **Reading Check** In what ways can forces affect objects?

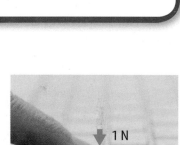

Figure 9 The arrows show forces with very different sizes acting in opposite directions.

Types of Forces

Some forces are easy to recognize. You can see a hammer applies a force as it hits a nail. Other forces seem to act on objects without touching them. For example, what force causes your ice cream to fall toward the ground if it slips out of the cone?

Contact Forces

The top left image of **Figure 10** shows a baker pushing his hand into dough, causing the top of the dough to accelerate downward. You can see the baker's hand and the dough come into contact with each other. *A* **contact force** *is a push or a pull applied by one object to another object that is touching it.* Contact forces also are called mechanical forces. The top half of **Figure 10** also shows other types of contact forces.

Noncontact Forces

The bottom left image of **Figure 10** shows a girl's hair being pulled toward the slide even though it isn't touching the slide. *A force that pushes or pulls an object without touching it is a* **noncontact force.** The force that pulls the girl's hair is an electric force. The bottom half of **Figure 10** shows other noncontact forces, such as magnetism and gravity.

 Key Concept Check What is the difference between the way contact and noncontact forces affect objects?

Figure 10 The pictures in the top row show examples of various types of contact forces. The ones in the bottom row show examples of several types of noncontact forces.

A **contact**, or mechanical, force is a force exerted by a physical object that touches another object.

An **applied force** is a force in which one object directly pushes or pulls on another object.

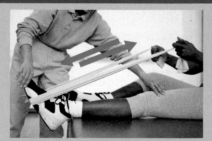

An **elastic** or spring force is the force exerted by a compressed or stretched object.

A **normal force** is the support force exerted on an object that touches another stable object.

A **noncontact**, or field, force is a force exerted when there is no visible object exerting the force.

Electric forces cause the girl's hair to stick out.

Magnetic forces hold these magnets apart.

Gravity is the force that pulls these divers toward the water.

How does friction affect an object's motion?

Air resistance is a force that opposes the motion of an object moving through air.

1 Read and complete a lab safety form.

2 Make a model parachute from **tissue paper, string, tape,** and a **metal washer.**

3 Use a **meterstick** to measure heights of 1, 2, 3, and 4 m on a nearby wall. Mark them with **tape.**

4 Drop the parachute from the 4-m mark. Your partner should start a **stopwatch** as soon as you drop the parachute and should stop the stopwatch when the washer passes the 3-m mark. Repeat this step three more times stopping the stopwatch at the 2-m mark, the 1-m mark, and the ground. Record the times in your Science Journal.

5 Remove the washer from the parachute. Measure and record the time for the washer to fall from the 4-m mark to the floor without the parachute.

Think About This

1. **Graph** the motion of the parachute on a distance-time graph.

2. **Calculate** the average speed of the washer with and without the parachute.

3. **Key Concept** How did friction affect the speed of the parachute and the washer?

Friction

Why does the baseball player in **Figure 11** slow down as he slides toward the base? **Friction** *is a contact force that resists the sliding motion between two objects that are touching.* The force of friction acts in the opposite direction of the motion, as shown by the blue arrow. Rougher surfaces produce greater friction than smooth surfaces. Other factors, such as the weight of an object, also affect the force of friction.

Gravity

Is there anywhere on Earth where you could drop a pencil and not have it fall? No! **Gravity** *is a noncontact attractive force that exists between all objects that have mass.*

Mass is the amount of matter in an object. Both your pencil and Earth have mass. They exert a gravitational pull on each other. In fact, they exert the same gravitational force on each other. Why doesn't your pencil pull Earth toward it? It actually does! The pencil has very little mass, so the force of gravity causes it to rapidly accelerate downward toward Earth's surface. Earth "falls" upward toward the pencil at the same time, but because of its mass, Earth's motion is too small to see.

Figure 11 The player must overcome friction or he won't reach the base.

WORD ORIGIN

gravity
from Latin *gravitare*, means to unite, join together

(t)Hutchings Photography/Digital Light Source, (b)David Madison/Getty Images

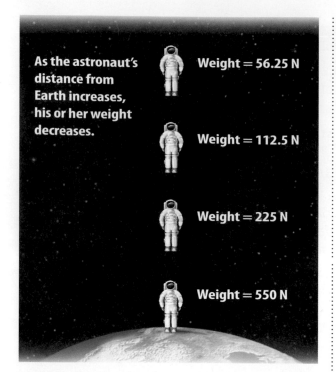

As the astronaut's distance from Earth increases, his or her weight decreases.

Weight = 56.25 N

Weight = 112.5 N

Weight = 225 N

Weight = 550 N

▲ **Figure 12** 🔑 Gravitational force (weight) decreases as the distance between the centers of the objects increases.

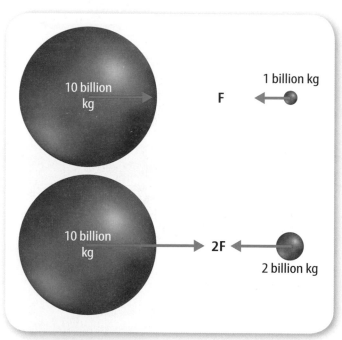

10 billion kg

1 billion kg

F

10 billion kg

2F

2 billion kg

▲ **Figure 13** The force of attraction between the bottom two objects is twice as much as between the top two objects.

✔ **Visual Check** Describe the acceleration of the bottom spheres due to the gravitational force between them.

 **Personal Tutor**

Distance and Gravity

You may have heard that astronauts become weightless in space. This is not true. Astronauts do have some weight in space, but it is much less in space than their weight on Earth. Weight is a measure of the force of gravity acting on an object. As two objects get farther apart, the gravitational force between the objects decreases. **Figure 12** shows how the weight of an astronaut changes as he or she moves farther from Earth.

You know that all objects exert a force of gravity on all other objects. If the astronaut drops a hammer on the Moon, will it fall toward Earth? No, the attraction between the Moon and the hammer is stronger than the attraction between Earth and the hammer because the hammer is very close to the Moon and very far from Earth. The hammer will fall down toward the Moon.

Mass and Gravity

Another factor that affects the force of gravity between two objects is the mass of the objects. As the mass of one or both objects increases, the gravitational force between them increases. For example, in **Figure 13**, *F* stands for the gravitational force. As the figure shows, doubling the mass of one of the objects doubles the force of attraction.

The effect of mass on the force of gravity is most noticeable when one object is very massive, such as a planet, and the other object has much less mass, such as a person. Even though the force of gravity acts equally on both objects, the less massive object accelerates more quickly due to its smaller mass. Because the planet accelerates so slowly, all you observe is the object with less mass "falling" toward the object with greater mass.

🔑 **Key Concept Check** What factors affect the way gravity acts on objects?

Combining Forces

Have you ever played tug-of-war? If you alone pull against a team, you will probably be pulled over the line. However, if you are on a team, your team might pull the rope hard enough to cause the other team to move in your direction. When several forces act on an object, the forces combine to act as a single force. The sum of the forces acting on an object is called the net force.

Forces in the Same Direction

When different forces act on an object in the same direction, you can find the net force by adding the forces together. In **Figure 14,** each team member pulls in the same direction. The net force on the rope is 110 N + 90 N + 100 N = 300 N.

Forces in Opposite Directions

When forces act in opposite directions, you must include the direction of the force when you add them. Like numbers on a number line, forces in the direction to the right are normally considered to be positive values. Forces to the left are negative values. In the first panel of **Figure 15,** the team on the right pulls with a force of 300 N. The team on the left pulls with a force of −300 N. The net force is 300 N + (−300 N) = 0.

Balanced and Unbalanced Forces

The net force on the rope in the top of **Figure 15** is 0. *When the net force on an object is 0 N, the forces acting on it are* **balanced forces.** If the forces acting on an object are balanced, the object's motion does not change. *When the net force acting on an object is not 0, the forces acting on the object are* **unbalanced forces.** The forces acting on the rope in the bottom of **Figure 15** are unbalanced. Unbalanced forces cause objects to change their motion, or accelerate.

Key Concept Check How do balanced and unbalanced forces differ?

▲ **Figure 14** Forces in the same direction act as a single force.

Visual Check What would the total force be if the person on the right stopped pulling?

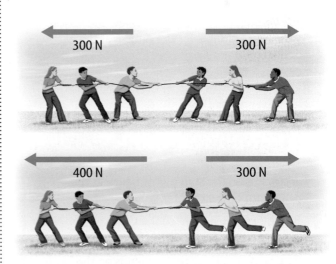

▲ **Figure 15** No change in motion takes place when forces on an object are balanced. Unbalanced forces cause the team on the right to accelerate to the left.

 Review **Personal Tutor**

Lesson 2 Review

✓ Assessment   Online Quiz

Visual Summary

Forces are pushes and pulls exerted by objects on each other. Contact forces occur when objects are touching. Noncontact forces act from a distance.

Gravity is a force of attraction between two objects. The amount of gravitational force depends on the mass of the objects and the distance between them.

Balanced forces do not affect motion. Unbalanced forces change motion.

FOLDABLES®

Use your lesson Foldable to review the lesson. Save your Foldable for the project at the end of the chapter.

What do you think NOW?

You first read the statements below at the beginning of the chapter.

3. Objects must be in contact with one another to exert a force.

4. Gravity is a force that depends on the masses of two objects and the distance between them.

Did you change your mind about whether you agree or disagree with the statements? Rewrite any false statements to make them true.

Use Vocabulary

1 **Describe** friction in your own words.

2 Two examples of _____ are gravity and magnetism.

Understand Key Concepts

3 As the distance between two objects increases, the gravitational force between the objects

   A. increases.   **C.** creates friction.

   B. decreases.   **D.** stays the same.

4 **Describe** the forces acting on a cyclist who is slowing down as he or she climbs a hill.

5 **Identify** any balanced and unbalanced forces acting on a book resting on a table.

Interpret Graphics

6 **Copy and complete** the graphic organizer to explain how distance and mass affect the force of gravity.

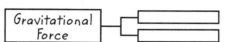

7 **Analyze** the four forces acting on the airplane flying at an altitude of 3,000 m, as shown below. How do the forces affect the plane's motion?

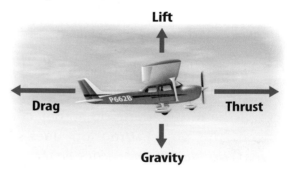

Critical Thinking

8 **Construct** a diagram that shows three forces acting on an object in the same direction and two forces acting in the opposite direction. Give the forces values that would cause no change in motion.

sciencephotos/Alamy

What factors affect friction?

Materials

balance

masking tape

sandpaper
(fine, medium,
coarse)

5-N spring
scale, 10-N
spring scale

string

Also needed:
wooden block,
250-g weight,
thumbtack

Safety

When you push or pull an object across a surface, the force of friction resists the object's motion. If the friction is strong, you need a greater force to move the object. How does manipulating variables, such as mass and surface texture, affect friction?.

Learn It

In any experiment, it is important to **identify and manipulate variables.** The independent variable is the factor that you change during the experiment. The variable that might change as a result of the independent variable is called the dependent variable. Changing only one variable at a time helps you focus clearly on what is causing the dependent variable to change.

Try It

1. Read and complete a lab safety form.

2. You will test the effect that mass, surface area, and surface texture have on the force needed to pull a block across a surface. Discuss the investigation with your partner. Predict whether each of the three variables will affect friction between a block and the surface.

3. Think about how you can test your prediction. Consider the following questions:

- What tests will you perform? For each test, identify the independent variable and the dependent variable.

- What materials will you use?

- What type of data table will you construct to record your data?

4. Test several methods for moving your object that you think might work. Based on your results, write a plan for your teacher to approve.

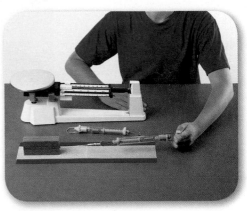

Apply It

5. Work with your partner to carry out your experiment. Record your results in your Science Journal.

6. Describe the independent variable and the dependent variables you used for each test you performed.

7. 🔑 **Key Concept** Did your tests support your prediction about the effects of mass, surface area, and surface texture on friction? Explain.

Lesson 3

Reading Guide

Key Concepts 🔑
ESSENTIAL QUESTIONS

- How do unbalanced forces affect an object's motion?
- How are the acceleration, the net force, and the mass of an object related?
- What happens to an object when another object exerts a force on it?

Vocabulary

inertia

Newton's first law of motion

Newton's second law of motion

Newton's third law of motion

force pair

 Multilingual eGlossary

 Video **BrainPOP®**

 AID M1.1c, S1.2b; IPS 2.1

Newton's Laws of Motion

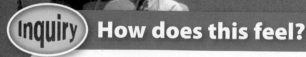 **How does this feel?**

Rides like this are called thrill rides because the riders feel as if they are going to crash, fall, or take off into space. How do forces cause these sensations? Why are the bars that hold the riders in place so important?

Inac/Alamy

How are forces and motion related?

In the last lesson, you read about different forces acting on objects. Sometimes forces can produce unexpected results. In this lab, you will observe the effect of forces on an object's motion.

1 Read and complete a lab safety form.

2 Place an **index card** on a **plastic jar.** Center a **nickel** on top of the card.

3 Flick the card away horizontally. Observe the motion of the nickel. Record your observations about the motion in your Science Journal.

4 Spread a sheet of **newspaper** on the table with about 10 cm hanging over the edge.

5 Place a **book,** a **pen,** and a **paper clip** on top of the paper. Then quickly pull the edge of the paper straight down. Record your observations in your Science Journal.

Think About This

1. **Identify** the forces acting on the objects in steps 3 and 5.

2. 🔑 **Key Concept** How do you think forces are related to the motion of the objects?

Newton's Laws

Recall that forces are measured in a unit called a newton (N), named after English scientist Isaac Newton, who studied the motion of objects. Newton summarized his findings in three laws of motion. You demonstrate Newton's laws when you run to catch a baseball or ride your bike. How could you use Newton's laws to explain how the rides and the games at an amusement park work?

Newton's First Law

What causes the motion of amusement park rides to give riders a thrill? Without protective devices to hold you in your seat, you could fly off the ride! *The tendency of an object to resist a change in motion is called* **inertia.** Inertia acts to keep you at rest when the ride starts moving. It also keeps you moving in a straight line when the ride stops or changes direction. Your safety belt keeps you in the seat and moving with the ride.

Newton's first law of motion *states that if the net force acting on an object is zero, the motion of the object does not change.* In other words, an object remains at rest or in constant motion unless an outside, unbalanced force acts on it. Newton's first law of motion is sometimes called the law of inertia.

FOLDABLES

Use two sheets of paper to make a layered book. Label it as shown. Use it to organize your notes on Newton's laws.

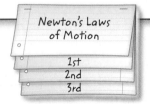

Newton's Laws of Motion
1st
2nd
3rd

SCIENCE USE v. COMMON USE

inertia

Science Use the tendency to resist a change in motion

Common Use lack of action

Hutchings Photography/Digital Light Source

Force of cables

Force of gravity

At Rest

Force of cables

Force of gravity

Constant Speed

Figure 16 The free-fall car's velocity is constant in both images because the forces are balanced.

Effects of Balanced Forces

Suppose you are at an amusement park and you want to ride a free-fall car, such as the one shown in **Figure 16.** How does the ride illustrate Newton's first law of motion? Recall that when the forces acting on an object are balanced, the object is either at rest or moving with a constant velocity.

Objects at Rest At the top of the ride, the force of the cable pulling upward on the car is equal to the force of gravity pulling downward on the car. Gravity and the cables pull on the car equally, but in opposite directions, so the forces are balanced. The car is at rest, as shown in the first panel of **Figure 16.** As long as the forces remain balanced, the car remains at rest.

Objects in Motion To lift the car to the top of the ride, the cable pulls upward. After a short acceleration, the car moves upward at a constant speed. The force of the cable pulling upward is the same size as the force of gravity pulling downward. With the forces once again balanced, the car rises to the top of the ride at a constant velocity. This is shown in the second panel of **Figure 16.** Newton's first law describes the car's motion when the forces applied to it are balanced.

Balanced forces act on the car only when it is at rest or moving with a constant velocity. When the car reaches the top of the ride, it doesn't remain at rest for long. When the operator releases the upward pull on the cable, the forces become unbalanced. Gravity causes the car to accelerate toward the ground. Because inertia tends to keep you at rest, the car feels as if it falls out from under you. Your safety belt acts as an outside force to keep you attached to the car.

✓ **Reading Check** What happens to the velocity of the car when the upward pull of the cable is greater than the downward pull of gravity as the car rises toward the top?

---

inquiry MiniLab
20 minutes

How does inertia affect an object? 🥽 🧴 ✂️ ✋

1. Read and complete a lab safety form.

2. Attach one end of a 20-cm long **string** to the **eye hook** that is attached to one end of a **wooden block.**

3. Half fill a **large test tube** with **colored water. Stopper** the tube tightly. Use **transparent tape** to attach the test tube to the block.

4. Use the string to pull the block. Observe the water when the block is at rest, as its velocity changes, and when its velocity is constant. Record your observations in your Science Journal.

Analyze and Conclude

1. **Describe** the motion of the water in the tube when the tube is at rest, accelerating, and moving at a constant velocity.

2. 🔑 **Key Concept** How does Newton's first law explain your observations?

Speeding Up

Key
→ Force
→ Acceleration

Slowing Down

◀ **Figure 17** 🔑➤
Unbalanced forces cause the
bungee jumper to speed up
or slow down.

Effects of Unbalanced Forces

You continue your visit to the amusement park with a ride on the reverse bungee jump. According to Newton's first law of motion, the motion of an object changes only when a net force acts on it. This ride gives you two chances to experience what a net force can do.

Speeding Up After the ride attendant releases you, the upward force of the bungee cord is greater than the downward force of gravity. The forces are unbalanced as shown by the blue arrows in the left image in **Figure 17.** The net force acting on you is upward, and you **accelerate** upward as shown by the green arrow.

Slowing Down As you approach the top of your bungee jump, the cords become slack, as shown on the right in **Figure 17.** The blue arrows show that the upward force becomes less than the downward force of gravity. Even though you are still are moving upward because of inertia, the net force is now due to the downward force of gravity. You slow down, or decelerate.

 Key Concept Check If one force on an object is 5 N upward and the other is 10 N downward, what is the object's motion?

Changing Direction Your next stop is a swing ride such as the one shown in **Figure 18.** When the ride starts to turn, the force of the cables pulls your chair toward the center of the ride. The force of gravity acts downward. Because these forces don't act in opposite directions, the unbalanced force constantly changes your direction. You accelerate as you move in a circle.

The designers of amusement-park rides use inertia to create excitement. Much of what makes a swing ride fun is the feeling that you might fly off the ride with constant velocity if your safety belt didn't hold you in place.

WORD ORIGIN · · · · · · · · · · ·
accelerate
from Latin *celer*, means "swift"

▲ **Figure 18** 🔑➤ The unbalanced force of the cable pulling toward the center causes acceleration in a circle.

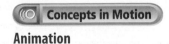 **Concepts in Motion**
Animation

(tl)(tr)camera lucida lifestyle/Alamy, (b)Richard Green/Alamy

Figure 19 Using a large force to throw the ball gives you the best chance of knocking over the bottles.

Newton's Second Law of Motion

Suppose you play a carnival game in which you throw a ball to knock over wooden bottles, as shown in **Figure 19.** You throw the ball, but not all the bottles fall over. On your second throw, you use all your strength to throw the ball as fast as you can. The ball hits the bottles and they all fall over.

When you threw the ball the second time, the ball left your hand with a greater final velocity than when you threw it the first time. This means the acceleration of the second ball was greater than the acceleration of the first ball. Why is this? **Newton's second law of motion** *states that the acceleration of an object is equal to the net force applied to the object divided by the object's mass.* When you threw the ball the second time, you used your muscles and arm to push harder, or increase the force, on the ball. When you increased the force, the ball's acceleration increased. The increased acceleration resulted in a greater final velocity of the ball as it left your hand.

$$\text{acceleration} = \frac{\text{force}}{\text{mass}} \qquad a = \frac{F}{m}$$

Calculating Acceleration

You can use the equation to calculate the acceleration of the ball. If you apply a force of **1.5 N** to a ball with a mass of **0.3 kg**, what is the ball's acceleration?

$$\text{acceleration} = \frac{\text{force}}{\text{mass}} \qquad \text{acceleration} = \frac{1.5\text{ N}}{0.3\text{ kg}} = \frac{5\text{ m}}{s^2}$$

What do you think would happen to the acceleration if you double the force on the ball? The equation tells you!

$$\text{acceleration} = \frac{\text{force}}{\text{mass}} \qquad \text{acceleration} = \frac{3.0\text{ N}}{0.3\text{ kg}} = \frac{10\text{ m}}{s^2}$$

When you double the force, the acceleration also doubles.

Changing the Mass

What would happen to the acceleration if the force you apply stays the same, but the mass of the ball changes? Instead of 0.3 kg, the ball has a mass of **0.6 kg**.

$$\text{acceleration} = \frac{\text{force}}{\text{mass}} \qquad \text{acceleration} = \frac{1.5\text{ N}}{0.6\text{ kg}} = \frac{2.5\text{ m}}{s^2}$$

A ball with twice the mass has half the acceleration. Newton's second law lets you predict what combination of force and mass you need to get the acceleration you need.

 Key Concept Check How are the acceleration, the net force, and the mass of an object related?

Figure 20 Each car exerts a force of the same size on the other car. The amount that each car accelerates depends on its mass.

Newton's Third Law

Suppose you are driving bumper cars with a friend, like in Figure 20. What happens when you crash into each other? **Newton's third law of motion** *says that when one object exerts a force on a second object, the second object exerts a force of the same size, but in the opposite direction, on the first object.* According to Newton's third law, the bumper cars apply forces to each other that are equal but are in opposite directions.

Action and Reaction Forces

When two objects apply forces on each other, one of the forces is called the action force, and the other is called the reaction force. For example, if the left car hits the right car in Figure 20, then the force exerted by the left car is the action force. The force exerted by the right car is the reaction force.

 Key Concept Check What happens when one object exerts a force on a second object?

Force Pairs

As you walk, your shoes push against the ground. If the ground did not push back with equal force, gravity would pull you down into the ground! *When two objects exert forces on each other, the two forces are a* **force pair.** The opposite forces of the bumper cars hitting each other in Figure 20 are a force pair. Force pairs are not the same as balanced forces. Balanced forces combine or cancel each other out because they act on the same object. Each force in a force pair acts on a different object.

In Figure 21, the girl exerts a force on the ball. The ball exerts an equal but opposite force on the girl. Why does the ball's motion change more than the girl's motion? Newton's laws work together. Newton's first law explains that a force is needed to change an object's motion. His third law describes the action-reaction forces. Newton's second law explains why the effect of the force is greater on the ball. The mass of the ball is much less than the mass of the girl. A force of the same size produces a greater acceleration in an object with less mass—the ball.

Figure 21 The opposite forces of the girl's head and the ball are a force pair. ▼

Visual Check If the force of the girl's head on the ball is 1.5 N upward, what is the force of the ball on the girl's head?

Newton's Laws in Action

Newton's laws do not apply to all motion in the universe. For example, they don't correctly predict the motion of very tiny objects, such as atoms or electrons. They do not work for objects that approach the speed of light.

However, because Newton's laws apply to the moving objects you observe each day, from amusement park rides to the movement of stars and planets, they are extremely useful. Using Newton's laws, humans have traveled to other planets and invented many useful tools and machines. You can often see the effects of all three laws at the same time. **Table 1** gives you some everyday examples of Newton's laws in action. Think about Newton's laws as you move through your day.

Table 1 🔑 Newton's laws explain the motions you experience every day.

☑ **Visual Check** How do you know that the table is exerting a force on the bowl of fruit?

Table 1 Newton's Laws in Action

Example	Newton's First Law	Newton's Second Law	Newton's Third Law
Resting Mass = 2 kg	The upward and downward forces on the bowl are balanced. The motion of the bowl is not changing. It is at rest.	Because the bowl is at rest, its acceleration is 0 m/s^2. You can use Newton's second law to calculate the net force on the bowl: $F = m \times a$ $F = 2$ kg $\times 0$ m/s^2 $F = 0$ N	The force of gravity pulls the bowl down so it exerts a force on the table. The table pushes up on the bowl with a force that is the same size, but in the opposite direction.
Walking	The forces acting on the man and the woman are balanced. Their inertia keeps them moving at a constant speed in a straight line.	When an object moves at a constant velocity, there is no acceleration. A net force would have to act on the people before they would speed up or slow down.	The woman's feet push against the sand as she walks. The sand pushes on the woman's feet with equal force, moving her forward. The same is true of the man.
Skateboarding	Inertia keeps the dog and the skateboard at rest until the dog produces a net force by pushing its paw on the road.	When net forces act on the dog and the road, or Earth, the dog will accelerate at a much greater rate because its mass is much less than that of Earth.	The dog's paw exerts a backward force on the road. The road exerts an equal but opposite force on the dog's paw, pushing it forward.

Visual Summary

Newton's first law of motion states that the motion of an object remains constant unless acted on by an outside force. This also is called the law of inertia.

Newton's second law of motion relates an object's acceleration to its mass and the net force applied to the object.

Newton's third law of motion states that for every action force, there is an equal but opposite reaction force. The two forces are called a force pair.

FOLDABLES

Use your lesson Foldable to review the lesson. Save your Foldable for the project at the end of the chapter.

What do you think NOW?

You first read the statements below at the beginning of the chapter.

5. All forces change the motion of objects.

6. The net force on an object is equal to the mass of the object times the acceleration of the object.

Did you change your mind about whether you agree or disagree with the statements? Rewrite any false statements to make them true.

Use Vocabulary

1 **Describe** an example of Newton's third law of motion.

2 **Distinguish** between Newton's first and second laws of motion.

Understand Key Concepts

3 In order to accelerate, an object must be acted on by
- **A.** a force pair.
- **B.** a large mass.
- **C.** balanced forces.
- **D.** unbalanced forces.

4 **Interpret** A bicyclist rides with a constant velocity of 8 m/s. What would you need to know to calculate the net force on the rider?

Interpret Graphics

5 **Analyze** The diagram below shows the forces acting on a box. Describe the motion of the box.

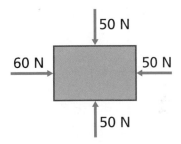

6 **Copy and complete** the graphic organizer by describing each of Newton's laws.

Critical Thinking

7 **Apply** Why does a box on the seat of a car slide around on the seat when the car speeds up, slows down, or turns a corner?

8 **Predict** what would happen if two people with equal mass standing on skateboards pushed against each other.

9 **Solve** A hockey player hits a 0.2-kg puck that accelerates at a rate of 20 m/s². What force did the player exert on the puck?

(t)Per Breiehagen/Getty Images; (c)skip caplan/Alamy; (b)Jill Braaten/McGraw-Hill Education

Materials

wood board
(1-m x 20-cm)

masking tape

string

tennis ball

large rubber
band

foam tubing

Also needed:
marble

Safety

Design an amusement park attraction using Newton's laws

What is your favorite ride or game at an amusement park? You may think that amusement parks are just for fun, but Newton's laws are important in the design of every ride and game. Work with a group to design and build a ride or game that applies Newton's laws.

Ask a Question

How do Newton's laws describe an amusement-park ride or game?

Make Observations

1. Read and complete a lab safety form.

2. Discuss different rides and games with your group. Think about how Newton's laws explain each attraction.

3. Your model ride or game must be a working model. You will not use motors, but your ride must use several different forces to make it work. If you design a game, it must demonstrate one or more of Newton's laws. Test several ideas with your group. If one idea does not work, adjust the design or try a different idea.

4. Based on your tests, choose one model ride or game to build.

5. Decide on the materials you will use. You may use some from the list or others approved by your teacher.

6. Write a design, along with a sketch, for your ride or game. List the materials, and describe how the ride or game will work. Ask your teacher to approve your design.

Form a Hypothesis

7 Based on your observations, formulate a hypothesis that explains why your ride or game will work according to one or more of Newton's laws.

Test Your Hypothesis

8 Build your ride or game according to your approved design.

9 Use your ride or game to test your design. In your Science Journal, identify which of Newton's laws are demonstrated by each part of your model. Also record details about your tests and your results.

Analyze and Conclude

10 **Evaluate** Did your ride or game clearly model Newton's laws? Explain.

11 **Analyze** Which of Newton's laws of motion most describes the way your ride or game works? Why?

12 **Compare** your ride or game to those built by other groups. Which do you think is the best example of each of Newton's laws? Explain your opinion.

13 **The Big Idea** Describe the relationship between the forces and the motion for the ride or the game you built.

Communicate Your Results

Demonstrate your ride or game for the class. Explain how one or more of Newton's laws influence the way the ride or game works.

Work with others in your group to write a brochure titled *Newton's Amusement Park*. The brochure should include descriptions and illustrations of the various rides and games, along with a brief explanation of how Newton's laws affect each ride or game.

Lab Tips

☑ Test different parts of your design idea to be sure each part works before you settle on one design to build.

☑ Avoid making your ride or game too complicated. A simple ride or game might be better.

Remember to use scientific methods.

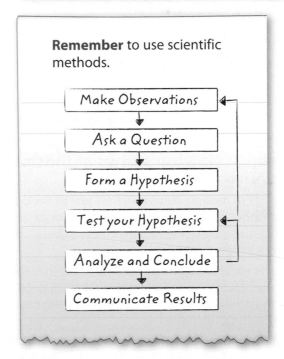

Make Observations

Ask a Question

Form a Hypothesis

Test your Hypothesis

Analyze and Conclude

Communicate Results

WebQuest

THE BIG IDEA Forces are pushes and pulls that may change the motion of an object. Balanced forces result in an object remaining at rest or moving at a constant speed. Unbalanced forces result in the acceleration of an object.

Key Concepts Summary

Vocabulary

Lesson 1: Describing Motion

- An object's **motion** depends on how it changes position. Motion can be described using **speed, velocity,** or **acceleration.**

- Speed is how fast an object moves. Velocity describes an object's speed and the direction it moves. Acceleration describes the rate at which an object's velocity changes.

- A graph can show you how either the displacement or the speed of an object changes over time.

motion
reference point
distance
displacement
speed
velocity
acceleration

Lesson 2: Forces

- A **force** is a push or pull on an object. **Contact forces** include **friction** and applied forces. **Noncontact forces** include **gravity,** electricity, and magnetism.

- Gravity is a force of attraction between any two objects. Gravitational force increases as the masses of the objects increase and decreases as the distance between the objects increases.

- **Balanced forces** acting on an object cause no change in the motion of the object. When **unbalanced forces** act on an object, the sum of the forces is not equal to zero. Unbalanced forces cause acceleration.

force
contact force
noncontact force
friction
gravity
balanced forces
unbalanced forces

Lesson 3: Newton's Laws of Motion

- **Inertia** is the tendency of an object to resist a change of motion. **Newton's first law of motion** states that an object will remain at rest or in constant straight-line motion unless unbalanced forces act on the object.

- **Newton's second law of motion** states that the acceleration of an object increases as the force acting on it increases and decreases as the mass of the object increases.

- **Newton's third law of motion** states that for every action force, there is an equal but opposite reaction force. The action-reaction forces are called a **force pair.**

inertia
Newton's first law of motion
Newton's second law of motion
Newton's third law of motion
force pair

(t)sciencephotos/Alamy, (b)skip caplan/Alamy

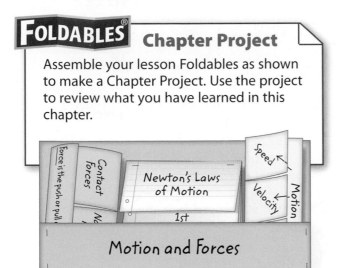

FOLDABLES® Chapter Project

Assemble your lesson Foldables as shown to make a Chapter Project. Use the project to review what you have learned in this chapter.

Use Vocabulary

1 An object's _____ is the difference between a object's final position and its starting position.

2 Give a specific example of motion.

3 Name two forces that may act on objects at a distance.

4 Explain what must happen to an object in order for it to accelerate.

5 What kinds of things can you predict using Newton's second law of motion?

6 The law of inertia is another name for _____.

7 You can explain the forces that act when you push against a wall using _____.

8 A _____ describes two forces that act on different objects.

Link Vocabulary and Key Concepts

Concepts in Motion Interactive Concept Map

Copy this concept map, and then use vocabulary terms and other terms from the chapter to complete the concept map.

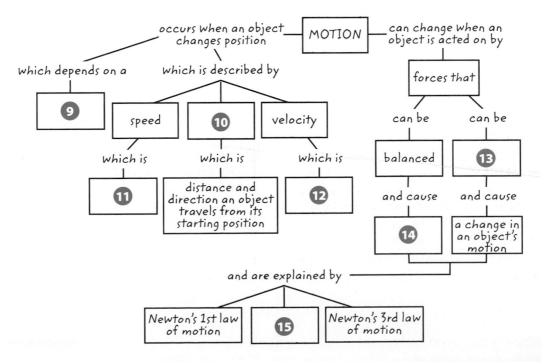

Chapter 1 Review

Understand Key Concepts

1. In which motions are the distance and the displacement the same?
   A. A bird flies from its nest to the ground and back to its nest.
   B. A dog chases its tail in a circle four times.
   C. A fish swims all the way across a pond and then halfway back.
   D. A worm moves 5 cm along a straight crack in a sidewalk.

2. The graph below represents the motion of a swimmer. Which statement best describes the swimmer's motion?

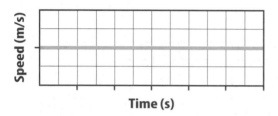

   A. The swimmer is at rest.
   B. The swimmer is in constant motion.
   C. The swimmer's speed is changing.
   D. The swimmer is accelerating.

3. An airplane travels 290 km between Austin and Dallas in 1 h 15 min. What is its average speed?
   A. 160 km/h
   B. 200 km/h
   C. 232 km/h
   D. 250 km/h

4. Which represents a force pair?
   A. A book pushes down on a table, and gravity pulls the book toward the floor.
   B. A boy's foot pushes down on a bicycle pedal. The pedal pushes up on his foot.
   C. A golf club hits a golf ball. Gravity pulls the ball back down to Earth.
   D. A person's foot pushes on the floor, and the person's weight pushes on the floor.

Use the figure below to answer questions 5–7.

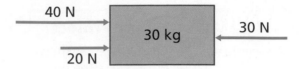

5. What is the net force on the object?
   A. 30 N to the right
   B. 30 N to the left
   C. 60 N to the right
   D. 90 N to the left

6. Which statement best describes the motion of the object?
   A. It accelerates to the right.
   B. It remains at rest.
   C. It doesn't change speed but changes its direction of motion.
   D. It moves at constant speed to the right.

7. What is the acceleration of the object?
   A. 0 m/s^2
   B. 1.0 m/s^2 to the right
   C. 1.6 m/s^2 to the right
   D. 3 m/s^2 to the left

8. Which is a contact force?
   A. A girl pulls the plug of an electric hair dryer from the socket.
   B. A leaf falls to the ground because of Earth's gravitational force.
   C. A magnet pulls on a nail 2 cm away.
   D. A small bit of paper is pulled toward an electrically charged comb.

9. Which best describes the relationship between the force acting on an object, the object's mass, and the acceleration of the object?
   A. Newton's first law of motion
   B. Newton's law of inertia
   C. Newton's second law of motion
   D. Newton's third law of motion

Critical Thinking

10 **Contrast** the force of gravity between these pairs of objects: a 1-kg mass and a 2-kg mass that are 1 m apart; a 1-kg mass and a 2-kg mass that are 2 m apart; and two 2-kg masses that are 1 m apart.

11 **Construct** Ed rides an escalator moving at a constant speed to the second floor, which is 12 m above the first floor. The ride takes 15 s. Draw a displacement-time graph and a speed-time graph of his ride.

12 **Calculate** A marathon runner covers 42.0 km in 3 h 45 min. What was the runner's average speed?

13 **Justify** An astronomer measures the velocity of an object in space and decides that there is no net force acting on the object. Which of Newton's laws helped the astronomer make this decision?

14 **Analyze** The photo shows an astronaut tethered to a spacecraft. Use Newton's laws to describe what will happen when the astronaut pushes against the spacecraft.

Writing in Science

15 **Write** A driver followed a van with a surfboard strapped on top. The driver claims that the van stopped so quickly that the surfboard flew backward, hitting his car and causing damage. He wants the driver of the van to pay for damage to his vehicle and medical costs. You are the judge in the case. Use Newton's laws of motion to write a judgment in the case.

REVIEW **THE BIG IDEA**

16 While carrying a heavy box up the stairs, you set the box on a step and rest. Then you pick up the box and carry it to the top of the stairs. Describe these actions in terms of balanced and unbalanced forces acting on the box.

17 In what ways did balanced and unbalanced forces affect the motion of the acrobats in the air. What forces caused them to rise into the air? What forces are acting on them in the picture?

Math Skills ✕ ÷

📑 Review
— Math Practice —

Solve One-Step Equations

18 A runner covers a distance of 1,500 m in 4 min. What is the runner's average speed?

19 Leaving the starting block, the runner accelerates from a speed of 0 m/s to a speed of 2 m/s in 3 s. What is the runner's acceleration?

20 What acceleration is produced when a 3,000-N force acts on a 1,200-kg car? Ignore any friction.

21 What force would a bowler have to exert on a 6-kg bowling ball to cause it to accelerate at the rate of 4 m/s²?

Standardized Test Practice

Record your answers on the answer sheet provided by your teacher or on a sheet of paper.

Multiple Choice

1 Which is the result of an object's motion?

  A a change in mass

  B a change in position

  C a change in reference point

  D a change in volume

2 Which would be used to calculate an object's acceleration?

  A change in its time divided by speed

  B change in its velocity divided by time

  C change in its speed divided by velocity

  D change in its velocity divided by speed

Use the table below to answer questions 3 and 4.

Car	Initial Speed (m/s)	Final Speed (m/s)	Time (s)
A	0	25	10
B	25	15	10
C	15	25	20
D	10	10	25

3 Which car had a negative acceleration?

  A car A

  B car B

  C car C

  D car D

4 Which car or cars had an acceleration greater than 2 m/s²?

  A car A only

  B car B only

  C cars A and C

  D cars A, C, and D

Use the graph to answer questions 5 and 6.

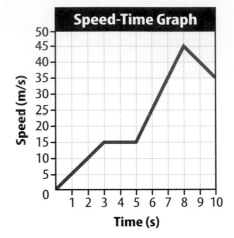

5 During which time period did the object slow down?

  A 0–3 seconds

  B 3–5 seconds

  C 5–8 seconds

  D 8–10 seconds

6 Which term describes the motion in the time period from 3 to 5 seconds?

  A at rest

  B constant speed

  C slowing down

  D speeding up

7 Which is a contact force?

  A gravity

  B friction

  C magnetic force

  D electrical force

8 Which can cause the force of gravity between two objects to increase?

    A if both objects start to spin

    B if one object increases in mass

    C if both objects decrease in mass

    D if the objects move farther apart

9 Which could be the net force acting on an object when the forces are balanced?

    A −10 N

    B 0 N

    C 2 N

    D 10 N

Use the diagram to answer question 10.

10 A skateboarder is traveling at a constant speed to the left. Suddenly the two forces shown act on him. Which describes the motion of the skateboarder when the two forces shown suddenly act on him?

    A His motion stops.

    B His speed increases.

    C His speed decreases.

    D His motion stays the same.

Constructed Response

Use the blank graph to answer questions 11 and 12.

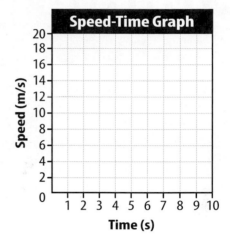

11 Describe how a period of constant acceleration would appear on a speed-time graph.

12 Describe how a period of nonconstant, positive acceleration would appear on a speed-time graph.

13 How does increasing the mass of an object affect the acceleration of an object if the forces acting on the object remain the same.? Explain.

14 According to Newton's third law of motion, what happens when you push on a sturdy wall with a force of 10 N?

NEED EXTRA HELP?														
If You Missed Question...	1	2	3	4	5	6	7	8	9	10	11	12	13	14
Go to Lesson...	1	1	1	1	1	1	2	2	2	3	1	1	3	3

Chapter 2

AID S1.3, S1.4, S2.1a, S2.1b, S2.1d, T1.2a, T1.3a, T1.3b, T1.4a, T1.5a, T1.5b; IS 3.1, 3.2; ICT 5.2, 6.1; IPS 1.3, 2.1; PS 4.1a, 4.1c, 4.1d, 4.1e, 4.2a, 4.5a, 4.5b, 5.2c, 5.2d, 5.2e, 5.2f, 5.2g

Energy, Work, and Simple Machines

THE BIG IDEA

How does energy cause change?

Inquiry **Simple Machines?**

Sailing is one activity in which simple machines are used. The pulleys on this deck help raise and lower the heavy sails on the boat. Without simple machines, transferring energy can be a much harder task.

- What are simple machines?
- How do simple machines transfer energy?
- How does energy cause change?

Get Ready to Read

What do you think?

Before you read, decide if you agree or disagree with each of these statements. As you read this chapter, see if you change your mind about any of the statements.

1 Energy is the ability to produce motion.

2 Waves transfer energy from place to place.

3 Energy cannot be created or destroyed, but it can be transformed.

4 Work describes how much energy it takes for a force to push or to pull an object.

5 All machines are 100 percent efficient.

6 Simple machines do work using one motion.

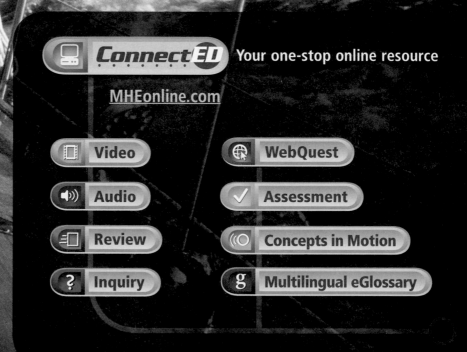

Connect[ED] Your one-stop online resource

MHEonline.com

- Video
- WebQuest
- Audio
- Assessment
- Review
- Concepts in Motion
- Inquiry
- Multilingual eGlossary

Reading Guide

Key Concepts
ESSENTIAL QUESTIONS

- What is energy?
- What are the different forms of energy?
- How is energy used?

Vocabulary

energy
kinetic energy
electric energy
potential energy
chemical energy
nuclear energy
mechanical energy
thermal energy
sound energy
seismic energy
radiant energy

 Multilingual eGlossary

 Video **BrainPOP®**

AID S2.1a, S2.1b, S2.1d;
IS 3.1, 3.2; ICT 5.2; PS 4.1a, 4.1c,
4.1d, 4.1e

Types of Energy

Inquiry Robots?

What do energy and this production line have in common? The car bodies use energy when they move. The robots transform electric energy to thermal energy when they weld parts together. Can you identify other energy transformations in the photo?

Andy Sacks/Getty Images

Where does energy come from?

How can you heat your hands when they are cold? You could rub them together, put them in your pockets, or hold them near a heater. What makes your hands get warmer?

1 Read and complete a lab safety form.

2 As you complete each of the following steps, observe and record any changes in your Science Journal. Discuss the changes with your lab group. In each case, ask: What caused this change to occur? Record your ideas.

3 Rub your hands together. What do you feel?

4 Use a **match** to light a **candle.** Holding your hands near the flame, what do you see and feel?

⚠ *Use caution around an open flame.*

5 Turn on a **flashlight.** Where did the light come from?

6 Observe the overhead lights in your classroom. What is the source of the light?

Think About This

1. Where did the light and the heat come from in steps 3, 4, 5, and 6?

2. 🔑 **Key Concept** How many different sources of energy can you recall? Briefly explain each one and tell how they differ from one another.

What is energy?

You probably have heard the word *energy* used on the television, the radio, or the Internet. Commercials claim that the newest models of cars are energy efficient. What is energy? Scientists define **energy** as *the ability to cause a change.*

Using this definition, what does energy have to do with the cars in production on the previous page? Most cars use some type of fuel such as gasoline or diesel as their energy source. The car's engine transforms the energy stored in the fuel to a form of energy that moves the car. Compared to other cars, an energy-efficient car uses less fuel to move the car a certain distance.

Gasoline and diesel fuel are not the only sources of energy. Food is an energy source for your body. The solar panels shown in **Figure 1** provide energy for the *International Space Station*. As you will read, wind, coal, nuclear fuel, Earth's interior, and the Sun also are sources of energy. Energy from each of these sources can be transformed into other forms of energy, such as electric energy. Every time you turn on a light, you use energy that was transformed from one form to another.

🔑 **Key Concept Check** What is energy?

Figure 1 🔑 Satellites need a source of energy to run their systems and to stay in orbit. The *International Space Station* uses solar panels to generate energy.

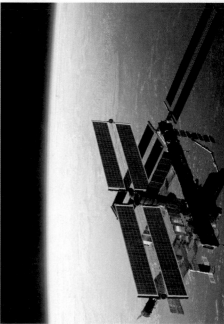

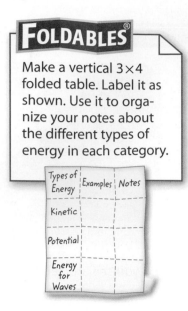

FOLDABLES®

Make a vertical 3×4 folded table. Label it as shown. Use it to organize your notes about the different types of energy in each category.

WORD ORIGIN ············

electric
from Greek *electrum*, means "amber"; because electricity was first generated by rubbing pieces of amber together

Kinetic Energy

You just turned the page of this book. As the page was moving it had **kinetic energy**—*the energy an object has because it is in motion.* Anything that is in motion has kinetic energy, including large objects that you can see as well as small particles, such as molecules, ions, atoms, and electrons.

Kinetic Energy of Objects

When the wind blows, the blades of the wind turbines in **Figure 2** turn. Because they are moving, they have kinetic energy. Kinetic energy depends on mass. If the turbine blades were smaller and had less mass, they would have less kinetic energy. Kinetic energy also depends on speed. When the wind blows harder, the blades move faster and have more kinetic energy. When the wind stops, the blades stop. When the blades are not moving, the kinetic energy of the blades is zero. One of the drawbacks of using wind-generated energy is that wind does not always blow, making the supply of energy inconsistent.

 Reading Check What is one drawback of wind energy?

Electric Energy

When you turn on a lamp or use a cell phone, you are using a type of kinetic energy—electric energy. Recall that all objects are composed of atoms. Electrons move around the nucleus of an atom, and they move from one atom to another. When electrons move, they have kinetic energy and create an electric current. *The energy that an electric current carries is a form of kinetic energy called* **electric energy.**

Electric energy can be produced by moving objects. When the blades of wind turbines rotate, they turn a generator that changes the kinetic energy of the moving blades into electric energy. Electric energy generated from the kinetic energy of wind creates no waste products.

Figure 2 🔑 Wind turbines convert kinetic energy in the wind to electric energy.

✓ **Visual Check** Why does the kinetic energy of the blades change?

Glen Allison/Getty Images

Figure 3 🔑 Hydroelectric energy plants use the gravitational potential energy stored in water to produce electricity.

Potential Energy

Suppose you hold up a piece of paper. When the paper is held above the ground, it has potential energy. **Potential energy** *is stored energy that depends on the interaction of objects, particles, or atoms.*

Gravitational Potential Energy

Gravitational potential energy is a type of potential energy stored in an object due to its height above Earth's surface. The water at the top of the dam in **Figure 3** has gravitational potential energy. Gravitational potential energy depends on the mass of an object and its distance from Earth's surface. The more mass an object has and the greater its distance from Earth, the greater its gravitational potential energy.

In a hydroelectric energy plant, water above a dam flows through turbines as it falls. Generators connected to the spinning turbines convert the gravitational potential energy of the water into electric energy.

Hydroelectric power plants are a very clean source of energy. About 7 percent of all electric power in the United States is produced from hydroelectric energy. However, hydroelectric plants can interrupt the movement of animals in streams and rivers.

©Bettmann/Corbis

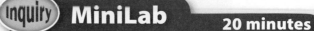

inquiry MiniLab   **20 minutes**

What affects an object's potential energy? 🥽 🧪

Have you ever accidentally dropped a dish? Did it break? Why is the dish more likely to break if it falls all the way to the floor than if it falls just a short distance to a table?

1. Read and complete a lab safety form.
2. Copy the table into your Science Journal.
3. Use a **balance** to find the mass of a **ball bearing** and a **marble.** Record the masses.
4. Stand a **meterstick** on the table next to a flat pad of **clay.** Drop the ball bearing onto the clay from heights of 20 cm, 60 cm, and 100 cm. Drop the ball so that it forms three separate craters.
5. Observe the differences in the craters. Use a **dropper** to measure the number of drops of water it takes to fill each crater.
6. Flatten the clay again. Repeat steps 4 and 5 with the marble.

Object	Mass (g)	Drop Height (20 cm) Crater Volume (drops)	Drop Height (60 cm) Crater Volume (drops)	Drop Height (100 cm) Crater Volume (drops)
Ball bearing				
Marble				

Analyze and Conclude

1. **Recognize Relationships** What is the relationship between the mass of the object and the volume of the crater and between the drop height and the volume of the crater?

2. 🔑 **Key Concept** What caused the differences in the sizes of the craters? Explain in terms of gravitational potential energy and kinetic energy.

Coal contains potential energy stored in the chemical bonds between atoms.

Nuclear fuel pellets contain potential energy stored in the nuclei of atoms.

Figure 4 Chemical energy and nuclear energy are two forms of potential energy.

Chemical Energy

Most electric energy in the United States comes from fossil fuels such as petroleum, natural gas, and coal. The atoms that make up these fossil fuels are joined by chemical bonds. Chemical bonds have the potential to break apart. Therefore, chemical bonds have a form of potential energy called chemical energy. **Chemical energy** *is energy that is stored in and released from the bonds between atoms.*

When fossil fuels burn, the chemical bonds between the atoms that make up the fossil fuel break apart. When this happens, chemical energy transforms to thermal energy. This energy is used to heat water and form steam. The steam is used to turn a turbine, which is connected to a generator that generates electric energy.

A drawback of fossil fuels is that they introduce harmful waste products, such as sulfur dioxide and carbon dioxide, into the environment. Sulfur dioxide in the air creates acid rain. Most scientists suspect that increased levels of carbon dioxide in the atmosphere contribute to climate change. Scientists are searching for replacement fuels that do not harm the environment.

Fossil fuels are not the only source of chemical energy. Chemical energy also is stored in the foods you eat. Your body converts the energy stored in chemical bonds in food into the kinetic energy of your moving muscles and into the electric energy that sends signals through your nerves to your brain.

✓ **Reading Check** What is chemical energy?

Nuclear Energy

The majority of energy on Earth comes from the Sun. A process, called nuclear fusion, in the Sun joins the nuclei of atoms and, in the process, releases large amounts of energy. On Earth, nuclear energy plants, such as the one shown in **Figure 4,** break apart the nuclei of certain atoms using a process called nuclear fission. Both nuclear fusion and nuclear fission release **nuclear energy**—*energy stored in and released from the nucleus of an atom.*

Nuclear fission produces a large amount of energy from just a small amount of fuel. However, the process produces radioactive waste that is hazardous and difficult to dispose of safely.

Kinetic and Potential Energies Combined

Recall that a moving object has kinetic energy. Objects such as wind turbine blades and particles, such as molecules, ions, atoms, and electrons, often have kinetic and potential energies.

Mechanical Energy

The sum of potential energy and kinetic energy in a system of objects is **mechanical energy.** Mechanical energy is the energy a system has because of the movement of its parts (kinetic energy) and because of the position of its parts (potential energy). An object, such as the wind turbine shown in **Figure 5,** has mechanical energy because the parts that make up the system have both potential energy and kinetic energy. A rotating blade has kinetic energy because of its motion, and it has gravitational potential energy because of its distance from Earth's surface.

Thermal Energy

The particles that make the wind turbine also have thermal energy. **Thermal energy** *is the sum of the kinetic energy and potential energy of the particles that make up an object.* Although you cannot see the individual particles move, they vibrate back and forth in place. This movement gives the particles kinetic energy. The particles also have potential energy because of the distance between particles and the charge of the particles.

Geothermal Energy

The particles in Earth's interior contain great amounts of thermal energy. This energy is called geothermal energy. In geothermal energy plants, such as the one shown in **Figure 6,** thermal energy is used to heat water and turn it to steam. The steam turns turbines in electric generators, converting the geothermal energy to electric energy. Geothermal energy produces almost no pollution. However, geothermal plants must be built in places where molten rock is close to Earth's surface.

▲ **Figure 5** 🔑 The entire wind turbine has mechanical energy. The particles that make up the wind turbine have thermal energy.

◀ **Figure 6** 🔑 Geothermal energy plants convert thermal energy of the particles deep inside Earth to electric energy. The states with the most geothermal plants are Alaska, Hawaii, and California.

(t)Jim West/Alamy, (b)ARCTIC IMAGES/Alamy

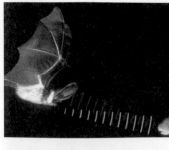

▲ **Figure 7** 🗝 Bats use sound energy to detect the location of their prey.

✔️ **Visual Check** If the bat was farther away from the prey, how would the time it takes for the bat to receive the bounced wave change?

Energy from Waves

Have you ever seen waves crash on a beach? When a big wave crashes, you hear the sound of the impact. The movement and the sound result from the energy carried by the wave. Waves are disturbances that carry energy from one place to another. Waves move only energy, not matter.

Sound Energy

If you clap your hands together, you create a sound wave in the air. Sound waves move through matter. **Sound energy** *is energy carried by sound waves.* Some animals, such as the bat shown in **Figure 7,** emit sound waves to find their prey. The length of time it takes sound waves to travel to their prey and echo back tells the bat the location of the prey it is hunting.

Seismic Energy

You probably have seen news reports showing photographs of damage caused by earthquakes, similar to that in **Figure 8.** Earthquakes occur when Earth's tectonic plates, or large portions of Earth's crust, suddenly shift position. The kinetic energy of the plate movement is carried through the ground by seismic waves. **Seismic energy** *is the energy transferred by waves moving through the ground.* Seismic energy can destroy buildings and roads.

🗝 **Key Concept Check** What are the different forms of energy?

▲ **Figure 8** 🗝 The seismic energy of a large earthquake caused severe damage to this building in San Francisco, California. In some locations, newly constructed homes and buildings are built to withstand many earthquakes.

(t)E Menz/age fotostock; (b)©Roger Ressmeyer/Corbis

Radiant Energy

When you listen to the radio, use a lamp to read, or call someone on your cell phone, do you think of waves? Electromagnetic waves are electric and magnetic waves that move perpendicular to each other, as shown in **Figure 9.** Radio waves, light waves, and microwaves are all electromagnetic waves, as shown in **Figure 10.** Some electromagnetic waves can travel through solids, liquids, gases, and **vacuums.** *The energy carried by electromagnetic waves is* **radiant energy.**

The Sun's energy is transmitted to Earth by electromagnetic waves. Photovoltaic (foh toh vohl TAY ihk) cells, also called solar cells, are made of special material that transforms the radiant energy of light into electric energy. You might have used a solar calculator. It does not need batteries because it has a photovoltaic cell. Photovoltaic cells also are used to provide energy to satellites, offices, and homes. Because so much sunlight hits the surface of Earth, the supply of solar energy is plentiful. Also, using solar energy as a source for electric energy produces almost no waste or pollution. However, only about 0.1 percent of the electric energy used in the United States comes directly from the Sun.

 Key Concept Check How is radiant energy used?

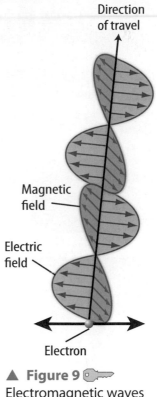

Direction of travel

Magnetic field

Electric field

Electron

▲ **Figure 9** Electromagnetic waves carry radiant energy.

Review
Personal Tutor

Figure 10 Radiant energy is carried by different forms of electromagnetic waves. ▼

Visible light waves

Radio waves

Microwaves

Solar cell (transforms radiant energy to electric energy)

Infrared waves (used by computer to read compact disc)

Infrared waves (thermal energy emitted from body as waves)

Microwaves

Lesson 1 Review

Visual Summary

There are different forms of energy, including solar energy.

Wind turbines have different kinds of energy including kinetic, mechanical, potential, and thermal.

Nuclear fuel pellets contain potential energy that is stored in the nuclei of atoms.

FOLDABLES

Use your lesson Foldable to review the lesson. Save your Foldable for the project at the end of the chapter.

What do you think NOW?

You first read the statements below at the beginning of the chapter.

1. Energy is the ability to produce motion.

2. Waves transfer energy from place to place.

Did you change your mind about whether you agree or disagree with the statements? Rewrite any false statements to make them true.

Use Vocabulary

1 **Define** *energy* in your own words.

2 **Distinguish** between kinetic energy and potential energy.

3 Energy carried by electromagnetic waves is _____.

Understand Key Concepts

4 **Compare** seismic and sound energies.

5 Which of the following is NOT a form of stored energy?
  A. chemical energy
  B. electric energy
  C. gravitational potential energy
  D. nuclear energy

6 **Explain** how hydroelectric energy plants convert potential energy into kinetic energy.

Interpret Graphics

7 **Summarize** Fill in the following graphic organizer to show forms of potential energy.

Critical Thinking

8 **Apply** At graduation a student throws a cap into the air. During which part of the cap's journey does it have the most kinetic energy? When does it have the most potential energy? Explain your answer.

9 **Assess** Which forms of energy are involved when you turn on a desk lamp and the bulb becomes hot?

10 **Summarize** List the different types of energy plants mentioned in this lesson and identify which type of energy (kinetic energy, potential energy, or radiant energy) is converted into electric energy in each.

Using Solar Panels

Energy from Sunlight

A home's roof does more than keep the rain out! It's equipped with solar panels that supply some of the home's energy needs. Solar panels make electricity without using fossil fuels.

Large solar panels, such as those on this house, are made up of many individual photovoltaic cells. The term *photovoltaic* refers to an energy transformation from light to electricity.

Solar panels have a variety of components. Each has an important function. Most solar panels have a top layer of glass that protects the parts inside the panel. Under the glass is an anti-reflective layer that helps the panel absorb sunlight rather than reflect it. On the back, is a layer made to keep the solar panel from getting too hot.

▲ These solar panels contain materials that can transform energy from one form to another.

Sunlight

Antireflection coating

Doped semiconductor

Electric current

Cover glass

Back layer

The middle of the solar panel contains a large number of individual photovoltaic cells. That's where the energy happens! In a photovoltaic cell, sunlight strikes a doped semiconductor, or a semiconductor with atoms of other elements that increase conductivity. The energy in the sunlight knocks electrons in the doped semiconductor out of their positions and gives them energy to move. Recall that when electrons move, they create an electric current. Wires attached to the doped semiconductor allow the flowing electrons, or electric current, to travel to the electric circuits within the home and back again.

▲ Electric current flows from the solar panel to objects in the home that use electricity, such as lightbulbs, and back to the solar panel in a complete circuit.

It's Your Turn

RESEARCH AND REPORT How might solar panels affect your life? How is new technology making solar panels less expensive to make and more efficient to use? Research to find out, and then share what you learn with in the rest of your class.

Reading Guide

Key Concepts
ESSENTIAL QUESTIONS

- What is the law of conservation of energy?
- In what ways can energy be transformed?
- How are energy and work related?

Vocabulary

energy transformation

law of conservation of energy

work

 Multilingual eGlossary

 Video

- **Science Video**
- **What's Science Got to do With It?**

AID T1.3a, T1.3b, T1.4a, T1.5a, T1.5b; ICT 6.1; PS 4.1c, 4.1d, 4.2a, 4.5a, 4.5b

Energy Transformations and Work

Inquiry Space Aliens?

It might look like an invasion from space, but these solar-powered cars are in a race. Large solar panels across the width of the cars transform radiant energy from the Sun into electric energy that moves the cars.

©Idealink Photography/Alamy

How far will it go?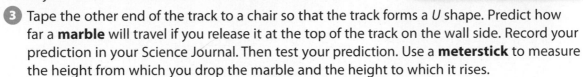

Suppose you are hired to design a roller coaster. Could you make it any shape you wanted? Could a hill in the middle of the ride be higher than the starting point?

1. Read and complete a lab safety form.

2. **Tape** one end of a **foam track** to the wall or other vertical object so that the end is 70–100 cm above the floor.

3. Tape the other end of the track to a chair so that the track forms a *U* shape. Predict how far a **marble** will travel if you release it at the top of the track on the wall side. Record your prediction in your Science Journal. Then test your prediction. Use a **meterstick** to measure the height from which you drop the marble and the height to which it rises.

4. Repeat step 3 several times using different heights above and below the starting point.

Think About This

1. How does the height to which the marble rises relate to the height at which it started?

2. 🔑 **Key Concept** Do you think a hill at the end of the roller coaster ride could be higher than the starting point of the coaster car? Why or why not? Explain in terms of potential and kinetic energy.

Energy Transformations

As you read in Lesson 1, different types of electric energy plants supply the energy you use in your home and school. **Energy transformation** *is the conversion of one form of energy to another,* as shown in **Figure 11.** The electric energy in the wiring of the heat lamp is transformed into thermal energy.

Energy also is transferred when it moves from one object to another. When energy is transferred, the form of energy does not have to change. For example, the thermal energy in the heat lamp is transferred to the air and then to the piglets.

Energy Conservation

Suppose you turn on a light switch. The radiant energy coming from the bulb had many other forms before it shined in your eyes. It was electric energy in the lamp's wiring, chemical energy in the fuel at the electric energy plant. The **law of conservation of energy** *says that energy can be transformed from one form to another, but it cannot be created or destroyed.* Even though energy can change forms, the total amount of energy in the universe does not change. It just changes form.

🔑 **Key Concept Check** What is the law of conservation of energy?

(t)Hutchings Photography/Digital Light Source; (b)FinnanOHare/Getty Images

ACADEMIC VOCABULARY

transform
(verb) to change form or structure

Figure 11 🔑 Electric energy is transformed into thermal energy in the heat lamp. Thermal energy from the lamp is transferred to the piglets.

 Review
Personal Tutor

1 GPE high
KE low

2 KE high
GPE low

GPE = gravitational potential energy
KE = kinetic energy

▲ **Figure 12** 🔑 When you ride a roller coaster, your gravitational potential energy is transformed to kinetic energy and back to gravitational potential energy.

Figure 13 🔑 To carry out life processes, humans and other animals transform the chemical energy of plants into other forms of energy.
▼

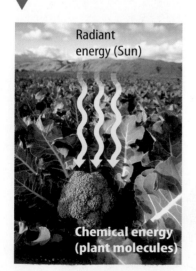

Radiant energy (Sun)

Chemical energy (plant molecules)

Roller Coasters

Have you ever thought about the energy transformations that occur on a roller coaster? Most roller coasters start off by pulling you to the top of a big hill. When you go up a hill, the distance between you and Earth increases and so does your potential energy. Next, you race down the hill. You move faster and faster. The gravitational potential energy is transformed to kinetic energy. At the bottom of the hill, your gravitational potential energy is small, but you have a lot of kinetic energy. This kinetic energy is transformed back to gravitational potential energy as you move up the next hill.

Plants and the Body

When a plant carries on photosynthesis, as shown in **Figure 13,** it transforms radiant energy from the Sun into chemical energy. The chemical energy is stored in the bonds of the plant's molecules. When you eat the broccoli, your body breaks apart the chemical bonds in the molecules that make up the broccoli. This releases chemical energy that your body transforms to energy your body needs, such as energy for movement, temperature control, and other life processes.

Electric Energy Plants

About 300 million years ago, plants carried out photosynthesis, just like plants do today. These ancient plants stored radiant energy from the Sun as chemical energy in their molecular bonds. After they died, the plants became buried under sediment. After much time and pressure from the sediments above them, these plants turned into fossil fuels. When electric energy plants burn fossil fuels, they transform the chemical energy from the molecules that were made by plants that lived millions of years ago. That chemical energy is transformed to the electric energy that you use in your home and school.

As you read in Lesson 1, other forms of energy, such as solar, wind, geothermal, and hydroelectric energy, also are transformed to electric energy by electric energy plants.

 Key Concept Check Identify three energy transformations that occur to make electric energy.

Energy and Work

When you study for a test, do you do work? It might seem like it, but it would not be work as defined by science. **Work** *is the transfer of energy that occurs when a force makes an object move in the direction of the force while the force acts on the object.* Recall that forces are pushes or pulls. When you lift an object, you transfer energy from your body to the object. As the boy lifts the drums in **Figure 14**, they move and have kinetic energy. As the drums get higher off the ground, they gain gravitational potential energy. The boy has done work on the drums.

On the right in **Figure 14,** the boy is standing still with his drums lifted in place. Because he is not moving the drums, he is not doing work. To do work on an object, an object must move in the direction of the force. Work is done only while the force is moving the object.

 Key Concept Check If you do work on an object, how will its energy change?

Figure 14 🗝 The boy does work on the drums when he lifts them. Once the drums are in place, no work is being done.

✔ **Visual Check** What energy transformations occur as the drums are lifted?

Upward force

Drums' weight

The drummer does work on the drums as he lifts them. The drums' kinetic energy and gravitational potential energy increase.

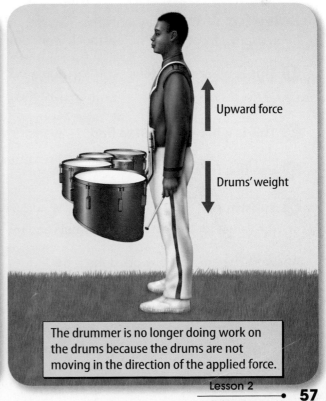

Upward force

Drums' weight

The drummer is no longer doing work on the drums because the drums are not moving in the direction of the applied force.

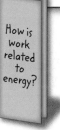

WORD ORIGIN

work

from Greek *ergon*, means "activity"

FOLDABLES

Create a vertical half-book. Label it as shown. Use It to summarize, in your own words, the relationship between work and energy.

How is work related to energy?

Doing Work

How much **work** do you do when you lift your backpack off the ground? If you lift a backpack with a force of 20 N, you do less work than if you lift a backpack with a force of 40 N. Work depends on the amount of force applied to the object.

Work also depends on the distance the object moves during the time the force is applied. If you lift a backpack 1 m you do less work than if you lift it 2 m. Suppose you toss a backpack in the air. When you release it, it continues moving upward. Even though the backpack is still moving when you let go, no work is being done. This is because you are no longer applying a force to the backpack while it is in the air.

Calculating Work

The equation for work is shown below. *Force* is the force applied to the object. *Distance* is the distance the object moves in the direction of the force while the force is acting on it.

Work Equation

work (in joules) = **force** (in newtons) × **distance** (in meters)

$$W = Fd$$

The force in the equation is in newtons (N), and distance is in meters (m). The product of newtons and meters is newton-meter (N·m). A newton-meter is also called a joule (J).

Math Skills   Work Equation

Solve for Work A student lifts a bag from the floor to his or her shoulder 1.2 m above the floor, using a force of 50 N. How much work does the student do on the bag?

1 This is what you know:

force: $F = 50\ N$

distance: $d = 1.2\ m$

2 This is what you need to find:

work: W

3 Use this formula:

$W = Fd$

4 Substitute:

$W = (50\ N) \times (1.2\ m) = 60\ N{\cdot}m = 60\ J$

the values for *F* and *d* into the formula and multiply

Answer: The amount of work done is **60 J**.

 Review

- **Math Practice**
- **Personal Tutor**

Practice

A student pulls out his or her chair in order to sit down. The student pulls the chair 0.75 m with a force of 20 N. How much work does he or she do on the chair?

Energy and Heat

Have you ever heard the phrase *burning rubber?* The tires of race cars are made of rubber. The tires and the road are in contact, and they move past each other very fast. Recall that friction is a force between two surfaces in contact with each other. The direction of friction is in the opposite direction of the motion.

Friction between a car's tires and the road causes some of the kinetic energy of the tires to transform into thermal energy. If race cars are going really fast, thermal energy in the tires causes the rubber to give off a burnt odor.

 Reading Check What is friction?

In every energy transformation and every energy transfer, some energy is transformed into thermal energy, as shown in **Figure 15.** This thermal energy is transferred to the surroundings. Thermal energy moving from a region of higher temperature to a region of lower temperature is called heat. Scientists sometimes call this heat *waste energy* because it is not easily used to do useful work.

Figure 15 🔑 Thermal energy is released to the surroundings during energy transformations and energy transfers in the engines of race cars.

Waste energy from energy transformations in engine

Waste energy from friction between air and car

Waste energy from transfer of energy from engine to wheel axle

Waste energy from friction between tires and road

Glowimages/Getty Images

Inquiry **MiniLab**   20 minutes

How do energy transformations work for you?

Every time you turn on a light, comb your hair, or ride your bike, you are transforming energy. What forms of energy are involved?

1 Copy the table into your Science Journal.

2 On the table, record an energy chain for each object, similar to the example. Include all types of energy used to make the object function, as well as the types of energy produced. Use the following abbreviations:

R = radiant; T = thermal; C = chemical; N = nuclear; E = electric; S = sound; Mp = potential mechanical; Mk = kinetic mechanical

Object	Energy Chain	Object	Energy Chain
Flashlight	C-E-T & R	Nuclear power plant	
Sun		Automobile	
Microwave oven		Television	

Analyze and Conclude

1. **Apply** Give three different examples in which the following energy transformations would take place: electric to thermal, chemical to thermal, and mechanical to electric.

2. **Generalize** Which type of energy that is no longer useful is produced in all transformations? Explain.

3. 🔑 **Key Concept** Select three of the energy changes, and explain how each one does work.

Lesson 2 Review

Visual Summary

Energy is always conserved.

Energy can be transformed into different kinds of energy.

Work and energy are related.

FOLDABLES

Use your lesson Foldable to review the lesson. Save your Foldable for the project at the end of the chapter.

What do you think NOW?

You first read the statements below at the beginning of the chapter.

3. Energy cannot be created or destroyed, but it can be transformed.

4. Work describes how much energy it takes for a force to push or to pull an object.

Did you change your mind about whether you agree or disagree with the statements? Rewrite any false statements to make them true.

Use Vocabulary

1 A(n) _____ occurs when energy is converted from one form to another.

Understand Key Concepts

2 Distinguish between work and energy.

3 Define the law of conservation of energy in your own words.

4 Which is NOT an example of work?
- A. holding books in your arms
- B. lifting a box from a table
- C. placing a bowl on a high shelf
- D. pushing a cart across the room

5 Describe the energy transformations that occur when a piece of wood is burned.

Interpret Graphics

6 Explain the gravitational potential energy transformations that occur when the object at right is in motion.

7 Summarize Copy and fill in the graphic organizer below to show what work is the product of.

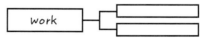

Critical Thinking

8 Consider Which energy transformations and energy transfers occur in a flashlight?

9 Model Draw a picture showing how energy is transferred to a sidewalk on a hot summer day. Label the different forms of energy in your drawing.

Math Skills

Review
— Math Practice —

10 Calculate the work done by a bird pulling a worm from the dirt with a force of 0.05 N a distance 0.07 m.

How can you transfer energy to make a vehicle move?

Materials

corrugated cardboard

bamboo skewer

meterstick

rubber bands of different lengths and widths

masking tape

Also needed:
string, scissors, compact disks, 1.5 cm faucet washers, adhesive putty

Safety

You have learned how energy can transform from one type to another. How can you and your classmates use this information to build a vehicle that uses an unusual source of energy?

Learn It

It is helpful to **follow a procedure** when you are doing something for the first time. A procedure tells you how to use the materials and what steps to take.

Try It

1. Read and complete a lab safety form.

2. Obtain instructions for building a vehicle. Gather the materials for your vehicle.

3. Build your vehicle according to the directions on your instruction sheet. When you are finished, have your teacher check your vehicle before testing it.

4. Test your vehicle several times. Try to begin with the same amount of potential energy for each trial.

5. Discuss with your teammates how you could make your vehicle go faster or farther. If the vehicle doesn't travel in a straight line, modify the design.

6. Modify your vehicle so that it uses only gravitational potential energy as its energy source. You may not use the original energy source and the vehicle must run on a straight, level course. You may not provide any external energy to get your vehicle started.

Apply It

7. Which energy transformations moved your vehicle? Be sure to describe both potential and kinetic types of energy.

8. Compare the energy sources that you used to power your vehicle. What are the advantages and the disadvantages of each energy source?

9. What variables affect the amount of gravitational potential energy you can use to move your vehicle?

10. 🔑 **Key Concept** Was energy conserved as it moved your vehicle? Explain your answer. Why did your vehicle stop?

Reading Guide

Key Concepts
ESSENTIAL QUESTIONS

- What are simple machines?
- In what ways can machines make work easier?

Vocabulary

simple machine

inclined plane

screw

64ley

complex machine

 Multilingual eGlossary

Video **BrainPOP®**

AID S1.3, S1.4, T1.2a, T1.3a, T1.3b, T1.4a, T1.5a, T1.5b; ICT 1.2; IPS 1.3, 2.1; PS 5.2c, 5.2d, 5.2e, 5.2f, 5.2g

Machines

 **A Machine?**

When you look at a unicycle, you probably don't see a collection of simple machines. However just like the bicycle that you will read about in this lesson, a unicycle contains simple machines.

Joe McBride/Getty Images

Can you make work easier?

Have you ever tried to pull a nail from a board without a claw hammer? The claw hammer makes an impossible task quite easy. What are some other ways to make work easier?

1. Read and complete a lab safety form.

2. Try to press the tip of a piece of **wire** into a **pine block** with your fingers. Then press a **thumbtack** with the same diameter into the block. Describe in your Science Journal how the amount of force you used differed in each case.

3. Screw an **eyehook** into the block as far as it will go. Start a **second eyehook** and then run your **pencil** through the hole in the eyehook. Use the pencil to screw in the eyehook. Compare the force you used in each case.

4. Tie a length of **string** around a **book.** Hook a **spring scale** through the string and lift the book to a height of 30 cm. Record the reading on the scale. Then use the spring scale to slide the book along a **ramp** to a height of 30 cm. Record the reading on the scale as you pull the book.

Think About This

1. How did the force needed in the first attempt of each task differ from the second attempt? What caused this difference?

2. 🔑 **Key Concept** How did the amount of work you did using the two methods in each step compare? What was the same? What was different? Explain.

Machines Transfer Mechanical Energy

Suppose you want to open a bottle like the one in **Figure 16.** If you use a bottle opener, you can easily pry off the top. A bottle opener is a machine. Many machines transfer mechanical energy from one object to another. The bottle opener transfers mechanical energy from your hand to the bottle cap. In this lesson, you will read about the ways in which machines transfer mechanical energy to other objects.

Simple Machines

Did you walk up a ramp this morning? Did you cut food with a knife? If so, you used a simple machine. **Simple machines** *are machines that do work using one movement.* As shown in **Figure 17** on the next page, a simple machine can be an inclined plane, a screw, a wedge, a lever, a pulley, or a wheel and axle. Simple machines do not change the amount of work required to do a task; they only change the way work is done.

✓ **Reading Check** What is a simple machine?

Figure 16 The bottle opener is a machine that transfers energy from your hand to the bottle cap.

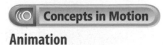 **Concepts in Motion**

Animation

(t)Hutchings Photography/Digital Light Source, (b)Lew Robertson/Getty Images

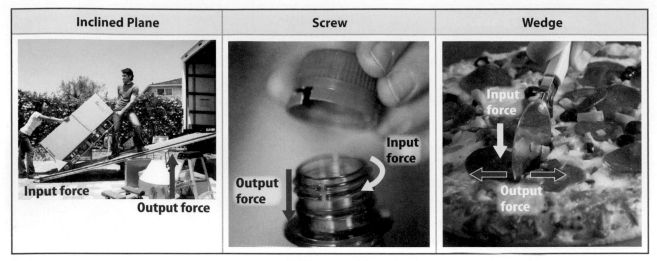

Inclined Plane	Screw	Wedge
Input force / Output force	Output force / Input force	Input force / Output force

Figure 17 🔑 Simple machines do work using one movement. They can change the direction of a force or the amount of force required to perform a task.

✓ **Visual Check** Identify another example for each simple machine.

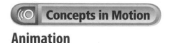
Concepts in Motion
Animation

REVIEW VOCABULARY
plane
a flat, level surface

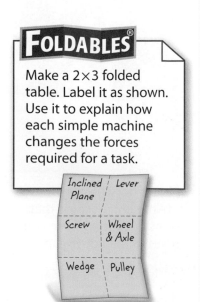

Make a 2×3 folded table. Label it as shown. Use it to explain how each simple machine changes the forces required for a task.

Inclined Plane	Lever
Screw	Wheel & Axle
Wedge	Pulley

Inclined Plane Furniture movers often use ramps to move furniture into a truck. It is easier to slide a sofa up a ramp than to lift it straight up into the truck. An **inclined plane**, such as the ramp shown in **Figure 17**, *is a flat, sloped surface.* Ramps with gentle slopes require less force to move an object than steeper ramps, but you have to move the object a greater distance.

Screw A screw, such as screw-top bottle, is a special type of inclined plane. A **screw** *is an inclined plane wrapped around a cylinder.* A screw changes the direction of the force from one that acts in a straight line to one that rotates.

Wedge Like all knives, pizza cutters are a special type of inclined plane. A **wedge** *is an inclined plane that moves.* Notice how the wedge changes the direction of the input force.

Lever The tab in **Figure 17** on the next page, is a **lever**, *which is a simple machine that pivots around a fixed point.* The fixed point on a beverage can is where the finger tab attaches to the can. Bottle openers, scissors, seesaws, tennis racquets, and wheel barrows are other examples of levers. Levers decrease the amount of force required to complete a task, but the force must be applied over a longer distance.

Wheel and Axle A doorknob, a car's steering wheel, and a screwdriver are a type of simple machine called a **wheel and axle**—*a shaft attached to a wheel of a larger diameter so that both rotate together.* The wheel and the axle are usually both circular objects. The object with the larger diameter is the wheel, and the object with the smaller diameter is the axle. When you use a wheel and axle, such as a screwdriver, you apply a small input force over a large distance to the wheel (screwdriver handle). This causes the axle (screwdriver shaft) to rotate a smaller distance with a greater output force.

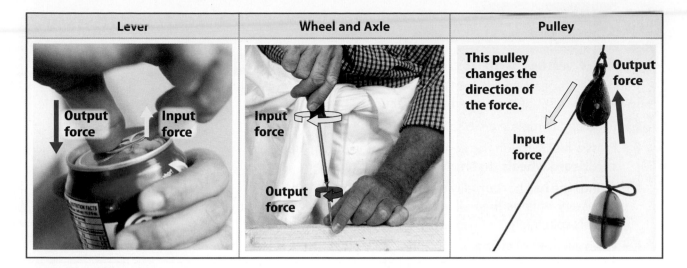

Lever	Wheel and Axle	Pulley
Output force / Input force	Input force / Output force	This pulley changes the direction of the force. / Output force / Input force

Pulley

Have you ever raised a flag on a flagpole or watched someone raise a flag? The rope that you pull goes through a **pulley,** *which is a grooved wheel with a rope or cable wrapped around it.* A single pulley, such as the kind on a flagpole, changes the direction of a force. A series of pulleys decreases the force you need to lift an object because the number of ropes or cables supporting the object increases.

 Key Concept Check What are examples of simple machines?

Complex Machines

Bicycles, such as the one in **Figure 18,** are made up of many different simple machines. The pedal stem is a lever. The pedal and gears together act as a wheel and axle. The chain around the gear acts as a pulley system. *Two or more simple machines working together are a* **complex machine.** Complex machines, such as bicycles, use more than one motion to accomplish tasks.

 Reading Check How is a complex machine different from a simple machine?

Figure 18 A bicycle is a complex machine that is made of many simple machines.

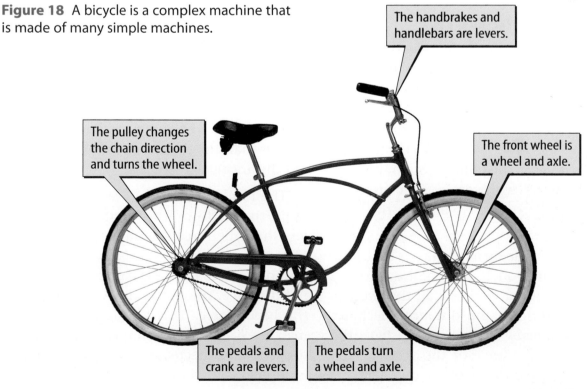

The handbrakes and handlebars are levers.

The pulley changes the chain direction and turns the wheel.

The front wheel is a wheel and axle.

The pedals and crank are levers.

The pedals turn a wheel and axle.

Does a wheel and axle make work easier?

Can you shift gears on a bike? Why is it easier to push the pedals in one gear than in another? How do the sizes of the two wheels affect one another?

1. Read and complete a lab safety form.

2. Press a **nail** through the center of 5-cm and 10-cm diameter **cardboard wheels** that have been **glued** together.

3. **Clamp** the nail horizontally at the top of a **ring stand.** If necessary, enlarge the nail hole in the wheels slightly so that the wheels spin freely.

4. Wrap a length of **string** around the groove in each wheel. Attach one end of each string to the wheel groove with a **pin.** The strings should hang down on opposite sides of the two wheels. Attach four **clothespins** to the free end of the string on the smaller wheel. Add clothespins to the free end of the string on the larger wheel until the four clothespins are lifted. Record the number of clothespins on each string in your Science Journal.

5. Repeat step 4, using other combinations of clothespins on the larger and smaller wheels. Record the combinations.

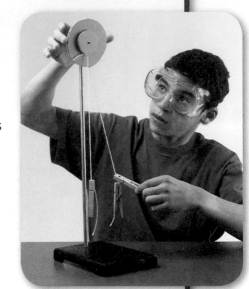

Analyze and Conclude

1. **Infer** In terms of work, what do the clothespins represent?

2. **Apply** What simple machines are used in this investigation?

3. 🔑 **Key Concept** Explain why a smaller force on the large wheel was able to lift a larger force on the small wheel.

Machines and Work

Think of a window washer like the one in **Figure 19** on the next page. It takes a great amount of work to lift the washer's own weight plus the weight of buckets of water, window-washing tools, and the platform up in the air. The window washer is able to do this work because the pulley system that lifts him makes the work easier. Because two ropes are supporting the platform, the force required is half.

The work you do on a machine is called the input work. The work the machine does on an object is the output work. Recall that work is the product of force and distance. Machines make work easier by changing the distance the object moves, the force or the speed of the force required to do work on an object.

Changing Distance and Force

To pull himself toward the top of the building, the window washer pulls down on a rope. The rope runs through a pulley system. The distance the window washer must pull the rope (the input distance) is much greater than the distance he moves (the output distance).

The force the window washer has to use to lift the platform (the input force) is much less than the force the pulley exerts on the platform (the output force). When the input distance of a machine is larger than the output distance, the output force is larger than the input force. This is true for all simple machines. Like other simple machines, the input force is decreased, but the distance it is applied is increased.

Hutchings Photography/Digital Light Source

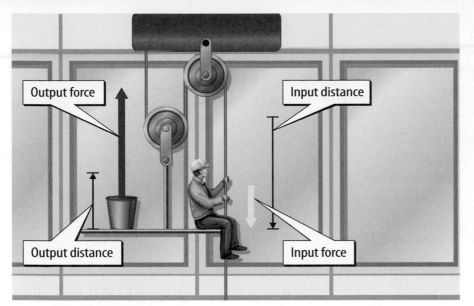

Figure 19 The window washer lifts his platform using a pulley system that increases the distance over which the force is exerted, decreases the input force needed, and changes the direction of the force.

✔ **Visual Check** How does the pulley make raising the platform easier for the window washer?

Changing Direction

Machines also can change the direction of a force. A window washer pulls down on the rope. The pulley system changes the direction of the force, which pulls the platform up.

 Key Concept Check How can machines make work easier?

Efficiency

Suppose the window washer wants to buy a new pulley system. One way to compare machines is to calculate each machine's efficiency. **Efficiency** *is the ratio of output work to input work.* In other words, it is a measure of how much work put into the machine is changed into useful output work. Input and output work are measured in joules (J). Efficiency is expressed as a percentage by multiplying the ratio by 100%.

WORD ORIGIN · · · · · · · · · · ·

efficiency
from Latin *efficere*, means "work out, accomplish"

> ### Efficiency Equation
>
> $$\text{efficiency (in \%)} = \frac{\text{output work (in J)}}{\text{input work (in J)}} \times 100\% = \frac{W_{out}}{W_{in}} \times 100\%$$

The window washer considers two systems that require 100 J of input work. The first one does 90 J of output work on his platform. The other pulley system does 95 J of output work. The efficiency of the first pulley system is (90 J/100 J) × 100% = 90%. The efficiency of the second one is (95 J/100 J) × 100% = 95%. The window washer decides to buy the second pulley system.

The efficiency of a machine is never 100%. Some work is always transformed into wasted thermal energy because of friction. One way to improve the efficiency of a machine is to lubricate the moving parts by applying a substance, such as oil, to them. This reduces the friction between the moving parts so that less input work is transformed to waste energy.

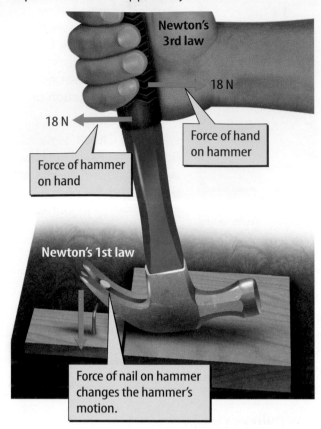

Figure 20 🗝️ Newton's laws of motion help explain the forces applied by machines.

Newton's 3rd law

18 N

Force of hand on hammer

18 N

Force of hammer on hand

Newton's 1st law

Force of nail on hammer changes the hammer's motion.

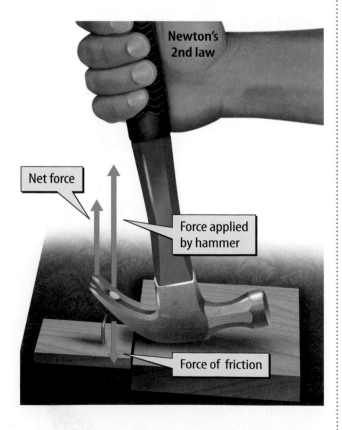

Newton's 2nd law

Net force

Force applied by hammer

Force of friction

Newton's Laws and Simple Machines

Recall that Newton's laws of motion tell you how forces change the motion of objects. As you have read, machines apply forces on objects. For example, Newton's third law says that if one object applies a force on a second object, the second object applies an equal and opposite force on the first object.

As shown in the top part of **Figure 20,** when you use a hammer as a lever to pull out a nail, you apply a force on the hammer. The hammer applies an equal force in the opposite direction on your hand.

✓ **Reading Check** What is Newton's third law?

According to Newton's first law, the motion of an object changes when the forces that act on the object are unbalanced. When you pull on the hammer handle, the claws of the hammer apply a force on the nail. However, unless you pull hard enough, the nail does not move.

The nail does not move because there is another force acting on the nail—the force due to friction between the nail and the wood. Unless you pull hard enough, the force of friction balances the force the hammer exerts on the nail. As a result, the motion of the nail does not change—the nail does not move.

If you pull hard enough, then the upward force the hammer applies on the nail is greater than the force of friction on the nail, as shown in the bottom part of **Figure 20.** Then the forces on the nail are unbalanced and the motion of the nail changes—the nail moves upward.

According to Newton's second law of motion, the change in motion of an object is in the same direction as the total, or net, force on the object. The nail moves upward because the net force on the nail is upward.

Visual Summary

A bottle opener is a simple machine.

There are six types of simple machines, and a ramp is one example.

A bicycle is an example of a complex machine that is made up of different simple machines.

FOLDABLES

Use your lesson Foldable to review the lesson. Save your Foldable for the project at the end of the chapter.

What do you think NOW?

You first read the statements below at the beginning of the chapter.

5. All machines are 100 percent efficient.

6. Simple machines do work using one motion.

Did you change your mind about whether you agree or disagree with the statements? Rewrite any false statements to make them true.

Use Vocabulary

❶ **Contrast** simple and complex machines.

❷ **Define** *efficiency* in your own words.

❸ **Explain** the six simple machines discussed in this lesson.

Understand Key Concepts

❹ **Identify** What kind of simple machine is a thumbtack?

❺ How does an inclined plane affect the work that is done on an object?
- **A.** It decreases the input distance.
- **B.** It increases the input distance.
- **C.** It changes the direction of the input force.
- **D.** It changes the direction of the output force.

Interpret Graphics

❻ **Explain** which simple machine the object shown below represents.

❼ **Summarize** Copy and complete the following graphic organizer showing the ways that simple machines can change the work done on an object.

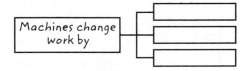

Critical Thinking

❽ **Design** a machine that you could use to lift a bag of groceries from the floor to the counter using less force than if you lifted the bag with just your hands. Which simple machine would you use?

Build a Powered Vehicle

Materials

antacid tablets

plastic bottle

vinegar

baking soda

office supplies

Also needed:
craft supplies, creative building materials, creative construction tools

Safety

In this chapter, you read about various forms of energy, how energy is transferred to do work, and how simple machines change how work is done. Now you can put it all together to design your own powered vehicle. Your teacher will give you the rules for this challenge.

Ask a Question

How can you design and construct a powered vehicle that will meet the criteria for the challenge? Consider the possible sources of energy you might use. How will you transfer energy to power the vehicle? Will you design a vehicle for speed, distance, or both? Consider the materials you have available. What materials could you bring from home?

Make Observations

1. Read and complete a lab safety form.

2. Brainstorm ideas with your teammates. Generate ideas by asking questions such as a) What are some possible energy sources? Consider possibilities such as wind, solar, chemical, electric, elastic, or magnetic. b) How will you convert potential energy to kinetic energy? c) What energy transformations will you use? d) How will you reduce the loss of energy due to friction? e) What will you use for the body of the vehicle? f) Will the vehicle have wheels? If so, how large will they be? What will they be made of? Record all of your ideas in your Science Journal.

3. Outline the steps in constructing your vehicle. Draw a diagram of the vehicle. Decide who will obtain which materials before the next lab period. Make sure each person on the team has a task in the design and building of the vehicle. You must be able to explain how your vehicle works and how it applies the ideas found in this chapter.

4. On the second lab day, follow the steps you outlined and build your vehicle. Be sure you have followed all the rules.

5. Test your vehicle and make any needed modifications. Make sure that your vehicle is sturdy enough to make a number of runs.

(t to b, 5)McGraw-Hill Education; (2)Janette Beckman/McGraw-Hill Education; (3–4)Jacques Cornell/McGraw-Hill Education; (r)Hutchings Photography/Digital Light Source

Form a Hypothesis

6 Formulate a hypothesis that explains why your vehicle will move due to energy transformations.

Test Your Hypothesis

7 On day 3, place your vehicle in competition with vehicles from other teams. Points will be awarded for distance, speed, and creativity in the application and transformation of energy sources. Be prepared to explain and answer questions about your design.

8 Write a report describing the design and scientific principles that went into making your vehicle.

Analyze and Conclude

9 **Identify Cause and Effect** What caused your vehicle to begin moving? What caused it to stop?

10 **Analyze** How could you increase the distance traveled by your vehicle without changing the source of energy?

11 **The Big Idea** Describe the relationship between the energy from your source and the work done on the vehicle.

Communicate Your Results

Work with your team to describe the design process and explain how you arrived at your choices for powering and building your team's vehicle. Compare and contrast the processes used by each team and discuss why some might have been more effective than others.

Inquiry Extension

If you could hold the challenge outdoors, how might you use wind energy, solar energy, or water to power your vehicle? Draw a design showing the parts of your vehicle and how it would work.

7

Lab Tips

☑ Don't ignore less-obvious sources of energy in your discussions. Could you use a chemical reaction to power your vehicle? Could you produce portable electricity without a battery?

☑ Think outside the box. For example, instead of pushing the car, how could a power source pull the car?

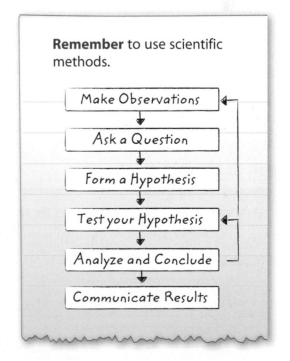

Remember to use scientific methods.

Make Observations →
Ask a Question →
Form a Hypothesis →
Test your Hypothesis →
Analyze and Conclude →
Communicate Results

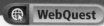

THE BIG IDEA

Energy causes change by affecting the movement and position of objects. Energy can be transformed from one form to another and transferred from object to object.

Key Concepts Summary

| Vocabulary |

Lesson 1: Types of Energy

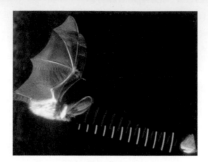

- **Energy** is the ability to cause change.
- **Kinetic energy** is the energy of objects in motion, including **electric energy.** The forms of **potential energy** include gravitational potential energy, **chemical energy,** and **nuclear energy. Thermal energy** and **mechanical energy** are forms of energy involving both kinetic and potential energies. **Sound energy, seismic energy,** and **radiant energy** are all transferred by waves.
- Energy is used to move cars, heat homes, produce light, move muscles, catch prey, and cook food among many other examples.

Vocabulary:
- energy
- kinetic energy
- electric energy
- potential energy
- chemical energy
- nuclear energy
- mechanical energy
- thermal energy
- sound energy
- seismic energy
- radiant energy

Lesson 2: Energy Transformations and Work

- The **law of conservation of energy** states that energy can be transformed from one form to another, but it can never be created or destroyed.
- Energy can be transformed from one form to another in a variety of ways.
- Doing **work** on an object transfers energy to the object.

Vocabulary:
- energy transformation
- law of conservation of energy
- work

Lesson 3: Machines

- **Simple machines** do work using one movement.
- Machines make work easier by changing the size of the force required, the distance over which the object moves, or the direction of the input and output forces.

Vocabulary:
- simple machine
- inclined plane
- screw
- wedge
- lever
- weel and axle
- pulley
- complex machine
- efficiency

⊟ **Review**

• **Personal Tutor**
• **Vocabulary eGames**
• **Vocabulary eFlashcards**

FOLDABLES® **Chapter Project**

Assemble your lesson Foldables as shown to make a Chapter Project. Use the project to review what you have learned in this chapter.

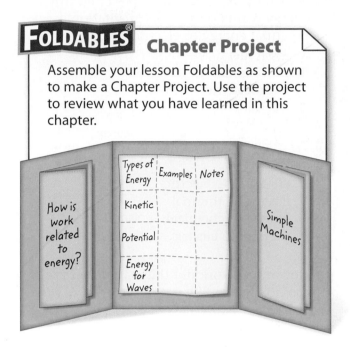

Use Vocabulary

1 Use the term *thermal energy* in a sentence.

2 The _____ of an object increases as it moves faster.

3 Define the term *energy transformation* in your own words.

4 The product of force and distance is _____.

5 Define the term *radiant energy* in your own words.

6 A(n) _____ is made of more than one simple machine.

Link Vocabulary and Key Concepts

 **Concepts in Motion** **Interactive Concept Map**

Copy this concept map, and then use vocabulary terms from the previous page to complete the concept map.

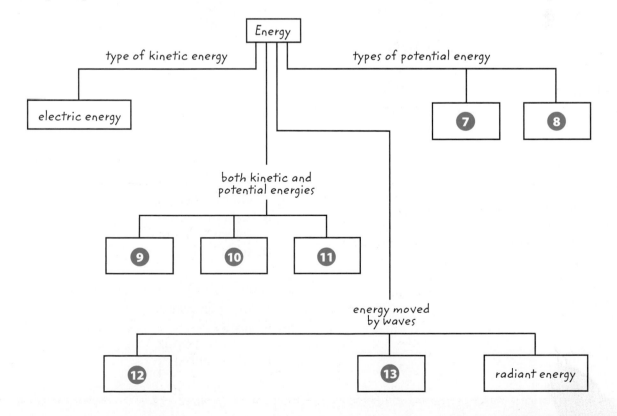

Chapter 2 Review

Understand Key Concepts

1 Which of the following is gravitational potential energy?
A. the energy stored in an object that is 10 m above the ground
B. the energy of an electron moving through a copper wire
C. the energy stored in the bonds of a carbohydrate molecule
D. the energy stored in the nucleus of a uranium atom

2 Which of the following increases the kinetic energy of an object?
A. decreasing the mass of the object
B. decreasing the volume of the object
C. increasing the object's height
D. increasing the object's speed

3 At which point in the photo below is the gravitational potential energy the greatest?
A. I
B. II
C. III
D. IV

4 The input work Shelly does on a rake is 80 J. The output work the rake does on the leaves is 70 J. What is the efficiency of the rake?
A. 70 percent
B. 80 percent
C. 87.5 percent
D. 95.4 percent

5 Which of the following types of electric energy plants transforms gravitational potential energy to electric energy?
A. fossil fuel
B. geothermal
C. hydroelectric
D. nuclear

6 What energy transformation occurs in a clothes iron?
A. chemical to electric
B. electric to thermal
C. kinetic to chemical
D. thermal to electric

7 How much work did the man do on the toolbox in the illustration below?

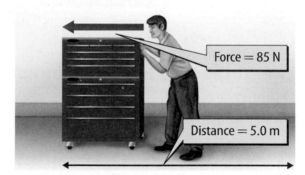

A. 0.06 m/N
B. 17 N/m
C. 425 J
D. 2,125 J

8 Which form of energy is NOT carried by waves?
A. chemical energy
B. radiant energy
C. seismic energy
D. sound energy

9 Which is NOT a simple machine?
A. inclined plane
B. lever
C. loop and hook
D. wheel and axle

Critical Thinking

10 Infer How does an airplane's kinetic energy and potential energy change as it takes off and lands?

11 Critique You overhear someone say, "I'm going to nuke it" when referring to cooking food in a microwave. Explain why this terminology is incorrect.

12 Consider You are going to turn a screw using a wrench. Will the work you do on the wrench be more or less than the work done by the wrench on the screw? Explain.

13 Compare Describe the energy transformations that are similar in the human body and in fossil fuel electric energy plants.

14 Explain A coach sets up a tug-of-war between two evenly matched teams. Both teams pull against the rope as hard as they can, but the rope does not move. Is any work being done? Why or why not?

15 Consider You pull a nail out of a piece of wood using the back of a hammer. When you feel the nail, it is warm. Why?

16 Explain at least two reasons why the spatula pictured below is considered a simple machine.

Writing in Science

17 Write Find a complex machine around your house or your school, and write a paragraph describing the different simple machines that it contains.

REVIEW **THE BIG IDEA**

18 How is energy transformed in electric energy plants, in roller coasters, and by machines?

19 The photo below shows the deck of a sailboat. How do the pulleys make rasing the sails easier?

  Review

Math Skills ✕−÷+

— Math Practice —

Calculate Work

20 Humpty Dumpty weighs 400 N. He falls off a wall 3 m high. How much work was done by gravity on Humpty Dumpty?

21 A mover lifts a 12-kg box straight up 1.5 m. How much work is done on the box?

Standardized Test Practice

Record your answers on the answer sheet provided by your teacher or on a sheet of paper.

Multiple Choice

1 What does all energy have?

   A size and shape

   B mass and volume

   C the ability to cause change

   D the ability to transport matter

Use the figure below to answer question 2.

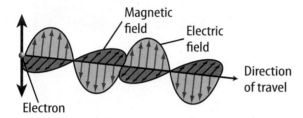

2 Which form of energy is being transmitted in the picture?

   A chemical energy

   B electric energy

   C radiant energy

   D sound energy

3 How do people use the nuclear energy produced from nuclear fission?

   A to produce electric energy

   B to power handheld machines

   C to grow and maintain body cells

   D to cook food in a microwave oven

4 Which is true of energy?

   A It cannot be destroyed.

   B It cannot be transmitted.

   C It cannot change matter.

   D It cannot be transformed.

Use the figure below to answer questions 5 and 6.

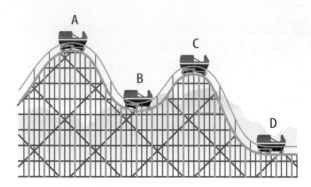

5 The figure shows four cars on a roller coaster track. At which point is gravitational potential energy the greatest?

   A point A

   B point B

   C point C

   D point D

6 What happens to the roller-coaster car's energy as it moves from point A to point B?

   A New energy is created.

   B The energy is destroyed.

   C New energy transforms from the car's mass.

   D The energy transforms from one kind to another.

7 Which equation shows how work and force are related?

   A work = force + distance

   B work = force − distance

   C work = force × distance

   D work = force ÷ distance

Use the figure below to answer question 8.

8 The figure shows a person using a hammer to remove a nail from a board. Which simple machine describes how the hammer is being used in this picture?

  A inclined plane

  B lever

  C pulley

  D wedge

9 How can simple machines make work easier?

  A by increasing the amount of work done

  B by decreasing the amount of work done

  C by changing the distance or the force needed to do work

  D by getting rid of the work needed to move an object

Constructed Response

10 A softball has more mass than a baseball. Compare the kinetic energy of a softball with that of a baseball moving at the same speed.

11 What is an energy transformation? Give an example of an energy transformation used to cook food.

Use the figure to answer questions 13 and 14.

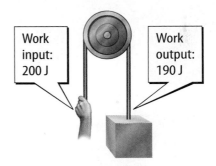

Work input: 200 J

Work output: 190 J

12 What simple machine is shown? What is the efficiency of this machine?

13 How could the efficiency of this machine be improved? Could it ever by 100%? Explain.

NEED EXTRA HELP?													
If You Missed Question...	1	2	3	4	5	6	7	8	9	10	11	12	13
Go to Lesson...	1	1	1	2	2	2	2	3	3	1	2	3	3

Unit 2

Weather and the Atmosphere

Glad you could tune in, folks! There's a hurricane rollin' in and we thought we'd get a few shots of it!

Look at those waves!

Woo!

Rain's coming in! Definitely a defining characteristic of hurricanes!

1441
Prince Munjong of Korea invents the first rain gauge to gather and measure the amount of liquid precipitation over a period of time.

1450
The first anemometer, a tool to measure wind speed, is developed by Leone Battista Alberti.

1643
Italian physicist Evangelista Torricelli invents the barometer to measure pressure in the air. This tool improves meteorology, which relied on simple sky observations.

1714
German physicist Daniel Fahrenheit develops the mercury thermometer, making it possible to measure temperature.

1752
Swedish astronomer Andres Celsius proposes a centigrade temperature scale where 0° is the freezing point of water and 100° is the boiling point of water.

1806
Francis Beaufort creates a system for naming wind speeds and aptly names it the Beaufort Wind Force Scale. This scale is used mainly to classify sea conditions.

1960
TIROS 1, the world's first weather satellite, is sent into space equipped with a TV camera.

1964
The U.S. National Severe Storms Laboratory begins experimenting with the use of Doppler radar for weather-monitoring purposes.

2006
Meteorologists hold 8,800 jobs in the United States alone. These scientists work in government and private agencies, in research services, on radio and television stations, and in education.

? Inquiry
Visit ConnectED for this unit's **STEM** activity.

Systems

 ICT 1.2, 1.4

You have probably heard about a computer's operating system, a weather system, and the system of government in the United States. What exactly is a system? A **system** is a collection of parts that influence or interact with one another. Systems often are used to achieve a goal or are developed with a specific purpose in mind. Like most systems, a milk-bottling manufacturing system is described in terms of the system's input, processing, output, and feedback, as shown in **Figure 1.**

Some systems, such as ecosystems and solar systems, are natural systems. Political, educational, and health-care systems are social systems that involve interactions among people. Transportation, communication, and manufacturing systems are designed systems that provide services or products.

Subsystems and Their Interactions

Large systems often are made of groups of smaller subsystems. Subsystems within a large system interact. **Figure 2** shows specialized transportation subsystems that are a part of an overall transportation system. These subsystems interact with one another, moving people and goods from place to place.

Input—things, such as milk, lids, labels, energy, and information, that enter a system to achieve a goal

Processing—the changes that the system makes to the inputs, such as fastening lids to milk jugs

Output—material, information, or energy that leaves the system, such as sealed and labeled milk jugs

Feedback—information a system uses to regulate the input, process, and output.

▲ **Figure 1** Many systems are designed to achieve a goal.

Figure 2 The subsystems within a transportation system interact with one another. ▼

Waterways transport ships and boats on rivers, lakes, and oceans.

Roadways conveniently transport cars, buses, and trucks on highways, streets, and roads.

Airways quickly transport people and materials long distances.

Pipelines transport large amounts of fluids, such as oil, through a network of pipes.

Railways transport trains and subways on rail lines between stations, at relatively low cost.

Bike paths and sidewalks transport people and packages over short distances at low cost.

The Earth and the Moon are a subsystem of our solar system.

Our solar system is a subsystem of the Milky Way galaxy.

▲ **Figure 3** Natural systems, such as the Milky Way galaxy, consist of subsystems.

Natural Systems

Like a designed system, natural systems have interacting subsystems. As shown in **Figure 3,** Earth and the Moon are a subsystem of our solar system. Our solar system is a subsystem of the Milky Way galaxy. The interactions among these subsystems depend on the gravitational forces that affect the motions of planets, stars, moons, and other objects in space.

Most natural systems constantly change. For example, gravity between Earth and the Moon causes tides. The movements of water against seafloors is altered by friction. This friction affects the tilt of Earth on its axis, if only just a little. The tilt of the Earth is important because it causes the seasons and influences weather patterns. As shown in **Figure 4,** the northern hemisphere is warmer during summer because of the tilt of Earth.

Thinking in Terms of Systems

If you think of the world as one system made up of interacting subsystems, you will better understand the effects of your choices. For example, when people choose to disrupt an ecosystem in one part of the world by clearing huge areas of forests, the resulting climate change affects the weather system in another part of the world. This in turn affects the agricultural system and, therefore, the cost of food. Actions you take locally affect everyone globally.

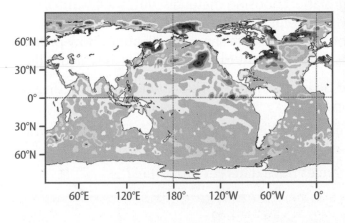

Figure 4 The darker reds show that the temperatures are warmer in the northern hemisphere in summer. ▶

Inquiry MiniLab
25 minutes

How can you get a package to Mars?

Suppose humans colonize Mars. How could materials be transported from Earth to Martian space colonies?

1. Plan a transportation system that could deliver a product made in Montana to colonies on Mars.

2. Draw a diagram of your system, labeling subsystems and explaining how the parts of the system interact.

Analyze and Conclude

1. **Analyze** Identify the input, processing, output, and feedback in your system.

2. **Explain** How does your system include or interact with designed systems, social systems, and natural systems?

Chapter 3

AID M1.1b, M1.1c, M3.1a, S1.3, S2.1a,
S2.1b, S3.1a, S3.2b, S3.2d, S3.2f, S3.2g,
S3.2h, S3.3; ICT 5.1; PS 3.1a, 3.1c, 3.1d,
3.1e, 3.1f, 3.1h, 3.2a, 4.2c

Matter: Properties and Changes

THE BIG IDEA

What gives a substance its unique identity?

Inquiry **What properties does it have?**

When designing a safe airplane, choosing materials with specific properties is important. Notice how the metal used in the outer shell of this airplane is curved, yet it is strong enough to hold its shape. Think about how properties of the airplane's materials are important to the conditions in which it flies.

• What properties would be important to consider when constructing the outer shell of an airplane?

• Why is metal used for electrical wiring and plastic used for interior walls of an airplane?

• Why do different substances have different properties?

age fotostock/SuperStock

Get Ready to Read

What do you think?

Before you read, decide if you agree or disagree with each of these statements. As you read this chapter, see if you change your mind about any of the statements.

1. The particles in a solid object do not move.

2. Your weight depends on your location.

3. The particles in ice are the same as the particles in liquid water.

4. Mixing powdered drink mix with water causes a new substance to form.

5. If you combine two substances, bubbling is a sign that a new type of substance might be forming.

6. If you stir salt into water, the total amount of matter decreases.

ConnectED Your one-stop online resource

MHEonline.com

- Video
- WebQuest
- Audio
- Assessment
- Review
- Concepts in Motion
- Inquiry
- Multilingual eGlossary

Matter and Its Properties

Reading Guide

Key Concepts 🔑
ESSENTIAL QUESTIONS

- How do particles move in solids, liquids, and gases?
- How are physical properties different from chemical properties?
- How are properties used to identify a substance?

Vocabulary
volume
solid
liquid
gas
physical property
mass
density
solubility
chemical property

 Multilingual eGlossary

 Video **BrainPOP®**

 AID M1.1b, M1.1c, M3.1a, S1.3, S2.1a, S2.1b, S3.1a; ICT 5.1; PS 3.1a, 3.1c, 3.1d, 3.1e, 3.1f, 3.1h

Inquiry What makes this possible?

White-water rafting is a lot of fun, but you have to be prepared. The ride down the rapids can be dangerous, and you need good equipment. What properties must the helmets, the raft, the oars, and the life vests have to make a safe white-water ride possible?

How can you describe a substance?

Think about the different ways you can describe a type of matter. Is it hard? Can you pour it? What color is it? Answering questions like these can help you describe the properties of a substance. In this lab, you will observe how the properties of a mixture can be very different from the properties of the substances it is made from.

1. Read and complete a lab safety form.

2. Using a **small plastic spoon,** measure two spoonfuls of **cornstarch** into a **clear plastic cup.** What does the cornstarch look like? What does it feel like?

3. Slowly stir one spoonful of **water** into the cup containing the cornstarch. Gently roll the new substance around in the cup with your finger.

Think About This

1. What were some properties of the cornstarch and water before they were mixed?

2.  **Key Concept** How were the properties of the mixture different from the original properties of the cornstarch and water?

What is matter?

Imagine the excitement of white-water rafting through a mountain pass. As your raft plunges up and down through the rushing water, you grip your oar. You hope that the powerful current will lead you safely past the massive boulders. Only after you reach a quiet pool of water can you finally take a breath and enjoy the beautiful surroundings.

Imagine looking around and asking yourself, "What is matter?" Trees, rocks, water, and all the things you might see on a rafting trip are **matter** because they have mass and take up space. Air, even though you can't see it, is also matter because it has mass and takes up space. Light from the Sun is not matter because it does not have mass and does not take up space. Sounds, forces, and energy also are not matter.

Think about the properties of matter you would see on your white water rafting trip. The helmet you wear is hard and shiny. The rubber raft is soft and flexible. The water is cool and clear. Matter has many different properties. You will learn about some physical properties and chemical properties of matter in this chapter. You will also read about how these properties help to identify many types of matter.

Hutchings Photography/Digital Light Source

REVIEW VOCABULARY

matter
anything that has mass and takes up space

States of Matter

One property that is useful when you are describing different materials is the state of matter. Three familiar states of matter are solids, liquids, and gases. You can determine a material's state of matter by answering the following questions:

- Does it have a definite shape?

- Does it have a definite volume?

Volume *is the amount of space a sample of matter occupies.* As shown in **Table 1,** a material's state of matter determines whether its shape and its volume change when it is moved from one container to another.

Solids, Liquids, and Gases

Notice in **Table 1** that *a* **solid** *is a state of matter with a definite shape and volume.* The shape and volume of a solid do not change regardless of whether it is inside or outside a container. *A* **liquid** *is a state of matter with a definite volume but not a definite shape.* A liquid changes shape if it is moved to another container, but its volume does not change. *A state of matter without a definite shape or a definite volume is a* **gas.** A gas changes both shape and volume depending on the size and shape of its container.

 Reading Check Which state of matter has a definite shape and a definite volume?

Table 1 Solids, Liquids, and Gases

Solid Solids, such as rocks, do not change shape or volume regardless of whether they are inside or outside a container.	
Liquid A liquid, such as fruit juice, changes shape if it is moved from one container to another. Its volume does not change.	
Gas A gas, such as nitrogen dioxide, changes both shape and volume if it is moved from one container to another. If the container is not closed, the gas spreads out of the container.	

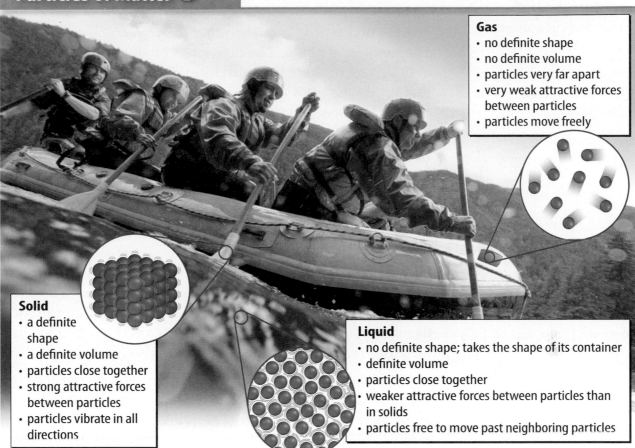

Gas
- no definite shape
- no definite volume
- particles very far apart
- very weak attractive forces between particles
- particles move freely

Solid
- a definite shape
- a definite volume
- particles close together
- strong attractive forces between particles
- particles vibrate in all directions

Liquid
- no definite shape; takes the shape of its container
- definite volume
- particles close together
- weaker attractive forces between particles than in solids
- particles free to move past neighboring particles

Figure 1 The movement and attraction between particles are different in solids, liquids, and gases.

✔️ **Visual Check** How does the force between particles differ in a solid, a liquid, and a gas?

 **Concepts in Motion**

Animation

Moving Particles

All matter is made of tiny particles that are constantly moving. Notice in **Figure 1** how the movement of particles is different in each state of matter. In solids, particles vibrate back and forth in all directions. However, particles in a solid cannot move from place to place. In liquids, the distance between particles is greater. Particles in liquids can slide past one another, similar to the way marbles in a box slide around. In a gas, particles move freely rather than staying close together.

🔑 **Key Concept Check** How do particles move in solids, liquids, and gases?

Attraction Between Particles

Particles of matter that are close together exert an attractive force, or pull, on each other. The strength of the attraction depends on the distance between particles. Think about how this attraction affects the properties of the objects in **Figure 1**. A strong attraction holds particles of a solid close together in the same position. Liquids can flow because forces between the particles are weaker. Particles of a gas are so spread apart that they are not held together by attractive forces.

Fold and cut a sheet of paper to make a two-tab book. Label it as shown. Use it to organize your notes about properties of matter.

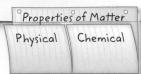

°Properties of Matter°

Physical | Chemical

SCIENCE USE v. COMMON USE

state

Science Use a condition or physical property of matter

Common Use an organized group of people in a defined territory, such as one of the fifty states in the United States

Figure 2 You can measure a material's mass and volume and then calculate its density.

Review   Personal Tutor

What are physical properties?

Think again about the properties of matter you might observe on a rafting trip. The water feels cold. The raft is heavy. The helmets are hard. The properties of all materials, or types of matter, depend on the substances that make them up. Recall that a substance is a type of matter with a composition that is always the same. *Any characteristic of matter that you can observe without changing the identity of the substances that make it up is a* **physical property.** **State** of matter, temperature, and the size of an object are all examples of physical properties.

Mass and Weight

Some physical properties of matter, such as mass and weight, depend on the size of the sample. **Mass** *is the amount of matter in an object.* Weight is the gravitational pull on the mass of an object. To measure the mass of a rock, you can use a balance, as shown in **Figure 2.** If more particles were added to the rock, its mass would increase, and the reading on the balance would increase. The weight of the rock would also increase.

Weight depends on the location of an object, but its mass does not. For example, the mass of an object is the same on Earth as it is on the Moon. The object's weight, however, is greater on Earth because the gravitational pull on the object is greater on Earth than on the Moon.

✓ **Reading Check** How do mass and weight differ?

Mass, Volume, and Density

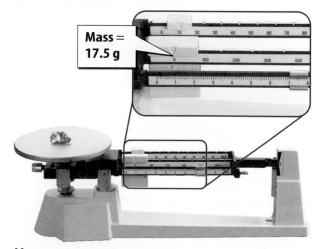

**Mass =
17.5 g**

Mass
A balance measures an object's mass by comparing it to the known mass of the slides on the balance. Common units for measuring mass are the kilogram (kg) and the gram (g).

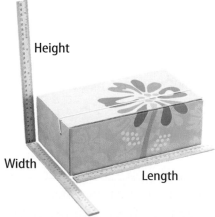

Volume = length × width × height

Height

Width

Length

Volume of a Rectangular-Shaped Solid
If a solid has a rectangular shape, you can find its volume by multiplying its length, its width, and its height together. A common unit of volume for a solid is the cubic centimeter (cm^3).

Hutchings Photography/Digital Light Source

Volume

Another physical property of matter that depends on the amount or size of the sample is volume. You can measure the volume of a liquid by pouring it into a graduated cylinder or a measuring cup and reading the volume mark. Two ways to measure the volume of a solid are shown in **Figure 2.** If a solid has a regular geometric shape, you can calculate its volume by using the correct formula. If a solid has an irregular shape, you can use the displacement method to measure its volume.

Density

Density is a physical property of matter that does not depend on the size or amount of the sample. **Density** is *the mass per unit volume of a substance.* Density is useful when identifying unknown substances because it is constant for a given substance, regardless of the size of the sample. For example, imagine hiking in the mountains and finding a shiny yellow rock. Is it gold? Suppose you calculate that the density of the rock is 5.0 g/cm³. This rock cannot be gold because the density of gold is 19.3 g/cm³. A sample of pure gold, regardless of the size, will always have a density of 19.3 g/cm³.

Inquiry MiniLab
10 minutes

How can you find an object's mass and volume?

1. Read and complete a lab safety form.
2. Obtain a small sample of **modeling clay.**
3. Using a **balance,** find the mass of the sample. Record it in your Science Journal.
4. Add exactly 25 mL of **tap water** to a **50-mL graduated cylinder.**
5. Shape the clay so that it can be placed into the graduated cylinder.
6. Slide the clay into the graduated cylinder. Record the new volume of the water.

Analyze and Conclude

1. **Compare** the volume of the water with the total volume of the water and the clay. What is the volume of the clay?
2. 🗝 **Key Concept** Why are mass and volume considered physical properties?

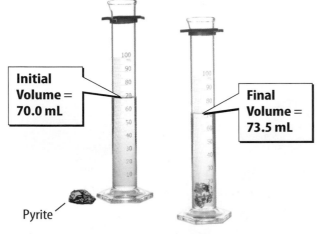

Initial Volume = 70.0 mL

Final Volume = 73.5 mL

Pyrite

Volume of an Irregular-Shaped Solid
The volume of an irregular-shaped object can be measured by displacement. The volume of the object is the difference between the water level before and after placing the object in the water. The common unit for liquid volume is the milliliter (mL).

Density Equation
$$\text{Density (in g/mL)} = \frac{\text{mass (in g)}}{\text{volume (in mL)}}$$

$$D = \frac{m}{V}$$

To find the density of the rock, first determine the mass and the volume of the rock:

mass: $m = \textbf{17.5 g}$
volume: $V = 73.5 \text{ mL} - 70.0 \text{ mL} = \textbf{3.5 mL}$

Then, divide the mass by the volume:

$$D = \frac{\textbf{17.5 g}}{\textbf{3.5 mL}} = 5.0 \text{ g/mL}$$

Density Calculation
Density can be calculated using the density equation. The common units of density are grams per milliliter (g/mL) or grams per cubic centimeter (g/cm³). 1 mL = 1 cm³.

| Drink Mix | Sand |

Figure 3 The drink mix is soluble in water. The sand is not soluble in water.

WORD ORIGIN ············

solubility
from Latin *solubilis*, means "capable of being dissolved"

Solubility

You can observe another physical property of matter if you stir a powdered drink mix into water. The powder dissolves, or mixes evenly, in the water. **Solubility** *is the ability of one material to dissolve in another.* You cannot see the drink mix powder in the left glass in **Figure 3** because the powder is soluble in water. The liquid is red because of the food coloring in the powder. The sand settles in the glass because it is not soluble in water.

Melting and Boiling Point

Melting point and boiling point also are physical properties. The melting point is the temperature at which a solid changes to a liquid. Ice cream, for example, melts when it warms enough to reach its melting point. The boiling point is the temperature at which a liquid changes to a gas. If you heat a pan of water, the water will boil, or change to a gas, at its boiling point. Different materials have different melting and boiling points. These temperatures do not depend on the size or amount of the material.

 Reading Check How does a substance change at its melting point and at its boiling point?

Additional Physical Properties

Several other physical properties—magnetism, malleability, and electrical conductivity—are shown in **Figure 4.** Notice how the physical properties of each material make it useful. Can you think of other examples of materials chosen for certain uses because of their physical properties?

Physical Properties 🔑

Figure 4 Physical properties include magnetism, malleability, and electrical conductivity.

Magnetism is a physical property that allows some materials to attract certain metals.

A malleable material, such as aluminum foil used in cooking, is useful because it can be hammered or rolled into thin sheets.

Some metals, such as copper, are used in electrical wire because of their high electrical conductivity.

Figure 5 Flammability and the ability to rust are examples of chemical properties.

Flammability
In 1937 the airship *Hindenburg* caught fire and crashed. It was filled with hydrogen, a highly flammable gas.

Ability to rust
The metal parts of an old car soon rust because the metal contains iron. The ability to rust is a chemical property of iron.

What are chemical properties?

Have you ever seen an apple turn brown? When you bite into or cut open apples or other fruits, substances that make up the fruit react with oxygen in the air. When substances react with each other, their particles combine to form a new, different substance. The ability of substances in fruit to react with oxygen is a chemical property of the substances. *A* **chemical property** *is the ability or inability of a substance to combine with or change into one or more new substances.* A chemical property is a characteristic of matter that you observe as it reacts with or changes into a different substance. For example, copper on the roof of a building turns green as it reacts with oxygen in the air. The ability to react with oxygen is a chemical property of copper. Two other chemical properties—flammability and the ability to rust—are shown in **Figure 5.**

 Key Concept Check How do chemical properties and physical properties differ?

Flammability

Flammability is the ability of a type of matter to burn easily. Suppose you are on a camping trip and want to light a campfire. You see rocks, sand, and wood. Which would you choose for your fire? Wood is a good choice because it is flammable. Rocks and sand are not flammable.

Materials are often chosen for certain uses based on flammability. For example, gasoline is used in cars because it burns easily in engines. Materials that are used for cooking pans must not be flammable. The tragedy shown in **Figure 5** resulted when hydrogen, a highly flammable gas, was used in the airship *Hindenburg.* Today, airships are filled with helium, a nonflammable gas.

Ability to Rust

You have probably seen old cars that have begun to rust like the one in **Figure 5.** You might also have seen rust on bicycles or tools left outside. Rust is a substance that forms when iron reacts with water and oxygen in the air. The ability to rust is a chemical property of iron or metals that contain iron.

Table 2 Identifying an Unknown Material by its Physical Properties 🔑

Substance	Color	Mass (g)	Melting Point (°C)	Density (g/cm³)
Table salt	white	14.5	801	2.17
Sugar	white	11.5	148	1.53
Baking soda	white	16.0	50	2.16
Unknown	white	16.0	801	2.17

Math Skills ✕÷ ＋

Solve a One-Step Equation

A statement that two expressions are equal is an equation. For example, examine the density equation:

$$D = \frac{m}{V}$$

This equation shows that density, **D**, is equal to mass, **m**, divided by volume, **V**. To solve a one-step equation, place the variables you know into the equation. Then solve for the unknown variable. For example, if an object has a mass of **52 g** and a volume of **4 cm³**, calculate the density as follows:

$$D = \frac{52\ g}{4\ cm^3} = 13\ g/cm^3$$

Practice

A cube of metal measures 3 cm on each side. It has a mass of 216 g. What is the density of the metal?

 Review

- **Math Practice**
- **Personal Tutor**

Identifying Matter Using Physical Properties

Physical properties are useful for describing types of matter, but they are also useful for identifying unknown substances. For example, look at the substances in **Table 2.** Notice how their physical properties are alike and how they are different. How can you use these properties to identify the unknown substance?

You cannot identify the unknown substance by its color. All of the substances are white. You also cannot identify the unknown substance by its mass or volume. Mass and volume are properties of matter that change with the amount of the sample present. However, recall that melting point and density are properties of matter that do not depend on the size or the amount of the sample. They are more reliable for identifying an unknown substance. Notice that both the melting point and the density of the unknown substance match those of table salt. The unknown substance must be table salt.

When you identify matter using physical properties, consider how the properties are alike and how they are different from known types of matter. It is important that the physical properties you use to identify an unknown type of matter are properties that do not change for any sample size. A cup of salt and a spoonful of salt will have the same melting point and density even though the mass and volume for each will be different. Therefore, melting point and density are physical properties that are reliable when identifying an unknown substance.

🔑 **Key Concept Check** How are properties used to identify a substance?

Sorting Materials Using Properties

Both physical properties and chemical properties are useful for sorting materials. The beads in **Figure 6** are sorted by color and shape—two physical properties. When you bring groceries home from the store, you might put crackers in a cupboard, but you probably put milk and yogurt in the refrigerator to keep them from spoiling. The tendency to spoil is a chemical property of the milk and yogurt. You probably often sort other types of matter by physical or chemical properties without realizing it.

Separating Mixtures Using Physical Properties

Physical properties are useful for separating different types of matter that are mixed. For example, suppose you have a frozen juice pop on a stick. How could you separate the frozen juice from the stick? If you set the freezer pop on a counter, the frozen juice will melt and separate from the stick. The melting point of the juice is much lower than the melting point of the stick. Melting point is a physical property you can use to separate mixtures. Other ways that you can use physical properties to separate mixtures are shown in **Figure 7.**

 Reading Check How could you separate a mixture of sand and small pebbles?

▲ **Figure 6** These beads are sorted by color and shape.

Figure 7 Physical properties, such as state of matter, boiling point, and magnetism, can be used to separate mixtures. ▼

Separating Mixtures

Separation by State of Matter	Separation by Boiling Point	Separation by Magnetism

▲ Water can flow through the holes in the strainer because it is a liquid. The pasta cannot flow through because the pieces are solid and too large.

▲ If you boil a mixture of salt and water, the liquid water changes to a gas when it reaches its boiling point. The salt is left behind.

▲ Iron filings, which have the property of magnetism, can be separated from the sand using a magnet. The magnet attracts the iron filings but not the sand.

Visual Check How could you separate a mixture of salt, sand, and iron filings?

Visual Summary

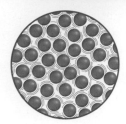

The movement of particles is different in a solid, a liquid, and a gas.

Physical properties and chemical properties are used to describe types of matter.

Physical properties such as magnetism can be used to separate mixtures.

FOLDABLES®

Use your lesson Foldable to review the lesson. Save your Foldable for the project at the end of the chapter.

What do you think NOW?

You first read the statements below at the beginning of the chapter.

1. The particles in a solid object do not move.

2. Your weight depends on your location.

3. The particles in ice are the same as the particles in liquid water.

Did you change your mind about whether you agree or disagree with the statements? Rewrite any false statements to make them true.

Use Vocabulary

1 A state of matter that has a definite volume but not a definite shape is a _____.

2 **Distinguish** between a physical property and a chemical property.

Understand Key Concepts

3 **Analyze** Which can be used to identify an unknown substance: mass, melting point, density, volume, state of matter?

4 **Contrast** the movement of particles in a solid, a liquid, and a gas.

5 Which of these is a chemical property?
- **A.** boiling point
- **C.** flammability
- **B.** density
- **D.** solubility

Interpret Graphics

6 **Explain** Use the drawing to explain why a gas has no definite shape or volume.

7 **Calculate** Copy the table below and calculate the density of each object.

Object	Mass	Volume	Density
1	6.50 g	1.25 cm³	
2	8.65 g	2.50 mL	

Critical Thinking

8 **Design** an investigation you could use to find the density of a penny.

Math Skills

📘 **Review**
— Math Practice —

9 The mass of a mineral is 9.6 g. The mineral is placed in a graduated cylinder containing 8.0 mL of water. The water level rises to 16.0 mL. What is the mineral's density?

(t)John A. Rizzo/Getty Images, (b)Hutchings Photography/Digital Light Source

How can you calculate density?

Materials

metal block

100-mL graduated cylinder

metric ruler

triple-beam balance

Safety

Density is the mass per unit volume of a substance. In this lab, you will measure the mass of a solid block. Next you will measure the volume in two different ways. Then you will calculate the density of the block for each volume measurement.

Learn It

Scientists take measurements when collecting data. In this lab, you will **measure** mass and volume, then use these data to calculate density.

Try It

1. Read and complete a lab safety form.

2. Copy the data table in your Science Journal. Use a triple beam balance to measure the mass of the metal block. Record your measurements.

3. Use a ruler to measure the length, width, and height of the block. Record your measurements.

4. Pour 30 mL of water into a 100-mL graduated cylinder. Record the volume of the water.

5. Carefully slide the metal block into the graduated cylinder. Record the total volume.

6. Using the measurements from step 3, determine the volume of the block using this equation:
   volume = length × width × height

7. Calculate the volume of the block using displacement. Subtract the volume of the water in step 4 from the volume of the water and block in step 5.

Apply It

8. **Calculate** Using the mass and each volume measurement of the block, calculate the density of the block.

9. **Compare** the density of the block calculated by the two different volumes. *Hint:* 1 mL = 1 cm^3. Are they same? Why or why not?

10. 🔑 **Key Concept** Why is density a physical property of the block?

Measurements	
Mass (g)	
Length (cm)	
Width (cm)	
Height (cm)	
Volume of water (mL)	
Volume of water and block (mL)	

Lesson 2

Reading Guide

Key Concepts 🗝
ESSENTIAL QUESTIONS

- How are physical changes different from chemical changes?

- How do physical and chemical changes affect mass?

Vocabulary
physical change

chemical change

law of conservation of mass

 Multilingual eGlossary

 Video BrainPOP®

 AID S1.3, S2.1a, S2.1b, S3.2b, S3.2d, S3.2f, S3.2g, S3.2h, S3.3; PS 3.2a, 4.2c

Matter and Its Changes

Inquiry Why is it orange?

Streams are usually filled with clear freshwater. What happened to this water? Chemicals from a nearby mine seeped through rocks before flowing into the stream. These chemicals combined with metals in the rocks, causing orange rust to form in the water.

BRUCE DALE/National Geographic Image Collection

What does a change in the color of matter show?

Matter has many different properties. Chemical properties can only be observed if the matter changes from one type to another. How can you tell if a chemical property has changed? Sometimes a change in the color of matter shows that its chemical properties have changed.

1 Read and complete a lab safety form.

2 Obtain the **red indicator sponge** and the **red acid solution** from your teacher. Predict what will happen if the red acid solution touches the red sponge.

3 Use a **dropper** to remove a few drops of acid solution from the **beaker.** Place the drops on the sponge. ⚠ *Be careful not to splash the liquid onto yourself or your clothing.*

4 Record your observations in your Science Journal.

Think About This

1. **Compare** the properties of the sponge before and after you placed the acid solution onto the sponge. Was your prediction correct?

2. 🔑 **Key Concept** How do you know that physical properties and chemical properties changed?

Changes of Matter

Imagine going to a park in the spring and then going back to the same spot in the fall. What changes do you think you might see? The changes would depend on where you live. An example of what a park in the fall might look like in many places is shown in **Figure 8.** Leaves that are green in the spring might turn red, yellow, or brown in the fall. The air that was warm in the spring might be cooler in the fall. If you visit the park early on a fall morning, you might notice a thin layer of frost on the leaves. Matter, such as the things you see at a park, can change in many ways. These changes can be either physical or chemical.

✓ **Reading Check** What are some examples of matter changing in winter?

Figure 8 The physical and chemical properties of matter change in a park throughout the year.

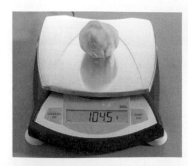

Figure 9 Changing the shape of the modeling clay does not change its mass.

What are physical changes?

A change in the size, shape, form, or state of matter that does not change the matter's identity is a **physical change**. You can see an example of a physical change in **Figure 9.** Recall that mass is an example of a physical property. Notice that the mass of the modeling clay is the same before and after its shape was changed. When a physical change occurs, the chemical properties of the matter stay the same. The substances that make up matter are exactly the same both before and after a physical change.

Dissolving

One of the physical properties you read about in Lesson 1 was solubility—the ability of one material to dissolve, or mix evenly, in another. Dissolving is a physical change because the identities of the substances do not change when they are mixed. As shown in **Figure 10,** the identities of the water molecules and the sugar molecules do not change when sugar crystals dissolve in water.

 Reading Check Explain why dissolving is classified as a physical change.

Dissolving—A Physical Change

Figure 10 The sugar crystals dissolve because they are soluble in water.

Key

Sugar crystal

1 Sugar molecule

$C_{12}H_{22}O_{11}$

1 Water molecule

H_2O

Crystals of sugar are made up of many sugar molecules. The crystals are surrounded by molecules of water.

As the sugar begins to dissolve, the crystals break apart.

Individual sugar and water molecules remain unchanged even after all sugar crystals have dissolved.

Changing State

In Lesson 1 you read about three states of matter—solid, liquid, and gas. Can you think of examples of matter changing from one state to another? A layer of ice might form on a lake in the winter. A glassblower melts glass into a liquid so that it can be formed into shapes. Changes in the state of matter are physical changes.

Melting and Boiling If you heat ice cubes in a pot on the stove, the ice will melt, forming water that soon begins to boil. When a material melts, it changes from a solid to a liquid. When it boils, it changes from a liquid to a gas. The substances that make up the material do not change during a change in the state of matter, as shown in **Figure 11.** The particles that make up ice (solid water) are the same as the particles that make up water as a liquid or as a gas.

Energy and Change in State The energy of the particles and the distances between the particles are different for a solid, a liquid, and a gas. Changes in energy cause changes in the state of matter. For example, energy must be added to a substance to change it from a solid to a liquid or from a liquid to a gas. Adding energy to a substance can increase its temperature. When the temperature reaches the substance's melting point, the solid changes to a liquid. At the boiling point, the liquid changes to a gas.

What would happen if you changed the rate at which you add energy to a substance? For example, what would happen if you heated an ice cube in your hand instead of in a pot on the stove? The ice would reach its melting point more slowly in your hand. The rate at which one state of matter changes to another depends on the rate at which energy is added to or taken away from the substance.

Changing State

Figure 11 The particles that make up ice (solid water), liquid water, and water vapor (water in the gaseous state) are the same. Changing from one state to another changes only the amount of energy of the particles and the distances between the particles.

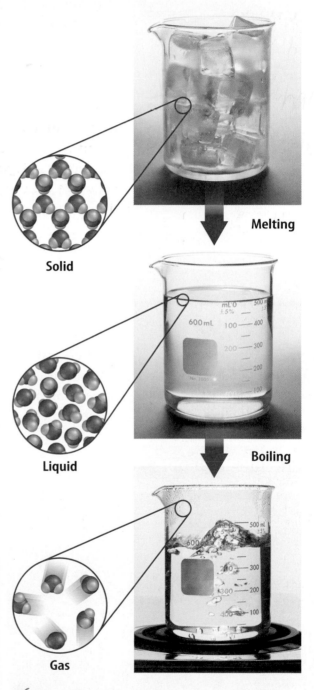

Solid

Melting

Liquid

Boiling

Gas

⊘ Visual Check Describe the change in the energy and motion of particles of a substance if the substance changes from a gas to a liquid.

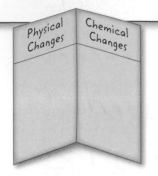

FOLDABLES

Make a half book from a sheet of paper. Use it to record and compare information about physical and chemical changes.

Physical Changes | Chemical Changes

What are chemical changes?

Some changes in matter involve more than just changing physical properties. *A* **chemical change** *is a change in matter in which the substances that make up the matter change into other substances with different chemical and physical properties.* Recall that a chemical property is the ability or inability of a substance to combine with or change into one or more new substances. During a physical change, only the physical properties of matter change. However, the new substance produced during a chemical change has different chemical and physical properties. Another name for a chemical change is a chemical reaction. The particles that make up two or more substances react, or combine, with each other and form a new substance.

🔑 **Key Concept Check** How are chemical changes different from physical changes?

Signs of a Chemical Change

How can you tell that the burning of the trees in **Figure 12** is a chemical change? The reaction produces two gases—carbon dioxide and water vapor—even though you cannot see them. After the fire, you can see that any part of the trees that remains is black, and you can see ash—another new substance. But with some changes, the only new substance formed is a gas you cannot see. As trees burn in a forest fire, light and heat are signs of a chemical change. For many reactions, changes in physical properties, such as color or state of matter, are signs that a chemical change has occurred. However, the only sure sign of a chemical change is the formation of a new substance.

Figure 12 A forest fire causes a chemical change in the trees, producing new substances.

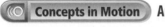  **Concepts in Motion** Animation

Chemical Change

Light and heat during a forest fire are signs that a chemical change is occurring.

After the fire, the formation of new substances shows that a chemical change has taken place.

✓ **Visual Check** Why is the smoke produced during a forest fire a sign of a chemical change?

(l)©Creatas/PunchStock; (r)©Digital Vision/PunchStock

Formation of Gas Bubbles of gas can form during both a physical change and a chemical change. When you heat a substance to its boiling point, the bubbles show that a liquid is changing to a gas—a physical change. When you combine substances, such as the medicine tablet and the water in **Figure 13,** gas bubbles show that a chemical change is occurring. Sometimes you cannot see the gas produced, but you might be able to smell it. The aroma of freshly baked bread, for example, is a sign that baking bread causes a chemical reaction that produces a gas.

 Reading Check How can you determine whether the formation of bubbles is the result of a physical change or a chemical change?

Formation of a Precipitate Some chemical reactions result in the formation of a precipitate (prih SIH puh tut). As shown in the middle photo in **Figure 13,** a precipitate is a solid that sometimes forms when two liquids combine. When a liquid freezes, the solid formed is not a precipitate. A precipitate is not a state change from a liquid to a solid. Instead, the particles that make up two liquids react and form the particles that make up the solid precipitate, a new substance.

Color Change Suppose you want your room to be a different color. You would simply apply paint to the walls. The change in color is a physical change because you have only covered the wall. A new substance does not form. But notice the color of the precipitate in the middle photo of **Figure 13.** In this case, the change in color is a sign of a chemical change. The photo in the bottom of the figure shows that marshmallows change from white to brown when they are toasted. The change in the color of the marshmallows is also a sign of a chemical change.

 Reading Check What are some signs that a chemical change has occurred?

Signs of Chemical Change

Figure 13 Formation of a gas, formation of a precipitate, and color change are all signs of a chemical change.

Formation of gas bubbles

Formation of a precipitate

Color change

 Visual Check What is a sign besides color change that indicates that the marshmallow is undergoing a chemical change?

(t)Milton Heilberg/Photo Researchers, Inc.; (b)dmilovanovic/Getty Images; (br)Paris L. Gray/AP Images

▲ **Figure 14** The flames, the light, and the sound of a fireworks display are signs of a chemical change.

Energy and Chemical Change

Think about a fireworks show. Again and again, you hear loud bangs as the fireworks burst into a display of colors, as in **Figure 14.** The release of thermal energy, light, and sound are signs that the fireworks result from chemical changes. All chemical reactions involve energy changes.

Thermal energy is often needed for a chemical reaction to take place. Suppose you want to bake pretzels, as shown in **Figure 15.** What would happen if you placed one pan of unbaked pretzel dough in the oven and another pan of unbaked pretzel dough on the kitchen counter? Only the dough in the hot oven would become pretzels. Thermal energy is needed for the chemical reactions to occur that bake the pretzels.

Energy in the form of light is needed for other chemical reactions. Photosynthesis is a chemical reaction by which plants and some unicellular organisms produce sugar and oxygen. This process only occurs if the organisms are **exposed** to light. Many medicines also undergo chemical reactions when exposed to light. You might have seen some medicines stored in orange bottles. If the medicines are not stored in these light-resistant bottles, the ingredients can change into other substances.

ACADEMIC VOCABULARY

expose
(verb) to uncover; to make visible

Figure 15 Thermal energy is needed for the chemical reactions that take place when baking pretzels. ▶

Can changes be reversed?

Think again about the way matter changes form during a fireworks display. Once the chemicals combine and cause the explosions, you cannot get back the original chemicals. Like most chemical changes, the fireworks display cannot be reversed.

Grating a carrot and cutting an apple are physical changes, but you cannot reverse these changes either. Making a mixture by dissolving salt in a pan of water is also a physical change. You can reverse this change by boiling the mixture. The water will change to a gas, leaving the salt behind in the pan. Some physical changes can be easily reversed, but others cannot.

 Reading Check Identify one physical change that can be reversed and one that cannot be reversed.

Conservation of Mass

Physical changes do not affect the mass of substances. When ice melts, for example, the mass of the ice equals the mass of the resulting liquid water. If you cut a piece of paper into strips, the total mass of the paper remains the same. Mass is conserved, or unchanged, during a physical change.

Mass is also conserved during a chemical change. Antoine Lavoisier (AN twon · luh VWAH zee ay) (1743–1794), a French chemist, made this discovery. Lavoisier carefully measured the masses of materials before and after chemical reactions. His discovery is now a scientific law. *The **law of conservation of mass** states that the total mass before a chemical reaction is the same as the total mass after the chemical reaction.* Weight also is the same because it depends on mass. For example, the mass of an unburned match plus the mass of the oxygen it reacts with equals the mass of the ashes plus the masses of all the gases given off when the match burns.

Key Concept Check How do physical and chemical changes affect mass?

Is mass conserved during a chemical reaction?

If you have ever seen the glow of a light stick, you have observed a chemical change. How does the chemical reaction affect the mass of the light stick?

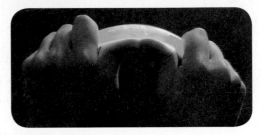

1. Read and complete a lab safety form.
2. Obtain a **light stick** from your teacher. Carefully remove it from the packaging.
3. Observe the structure of the light stick. Record your observations in your Science Journal.
4. Measure and record the mass of the light stick using a **balance.**
5. Grasp the ends of the light stick. Gently bend it to break the inner vial. Shake the stick gently to start the reaction.
6. Use a **stopwatch** to time the reaction for 3 minutes. Record your observations.
7. Repeat step 4.

Analyze and Conclude

1. **Explain** the purpose of the inner vial in the light stick.

2. **Describe** what occurred when the inner vial was broken.

3. **Key Concept** What effect did the chemical reaction have on the mass? Why?

WORD ORIGIN ·

conservation
from Latin *conservare*, means "to keep, preserve"

Comparing Physical and Chemical Changes

Suppose you want to explain to a friend the difference between a physical change and a chemical change. What would you say? You could explain that the identity of matter does not change during a physical change, but the identity of matter does change during a chemical change. However, you might not be able to tell just by looking at a substance whether its identity changed. You cannot tell whether the particles that make up the matter are the same or different.

Sometimes deciding if a change is physical or chemical is easy. Often, however, identifying the type of change is like being a detective. You have to look for clues that will help you figure out whether the identity of the substance has changed. For example, look at the summary of physical changes and chemical changes in **Table 3.** A change in color can occur during a chemical change or when substances are mixed (a physical change). Bubbles might indicate the formation of gas (a chemical change) or boiling (a physical change). You must consider many factors when comparing physical and chemical changes.

Reading Check What are some clues you can use to decide if a change is a physical change or a chemical change?

Table 3 Chemical changes produce a new substance, but physical changes do not.

Concepts in Motion

Interactive Table

Table 3 Comparing Physical and Chemical Changes		
Type of Change	**Examples**	**Characteristics**
Physical change	• melting • boiling • changing shape • mixing • dissolving • increasing or decreasing in temperature	• Substance is the same before and after the change. • Only physical properties change.
Chemical change	• changing color • burning • rusting • formation of gas • formation of a precipitate • spoiling food • tarnishing silver • digesting food	**Physical change** **Chemical change** • Substance is different after the change. • Both physical and chemical properties change.

Visual Summary

The identity of a substance does not change during a physical change such as a change in the state of matter.

A new substance is produced during a chemical change.

The law of conservation of mass states that the mass of a material does not change during a chemical change.

FOLDABLES

Use your lesson Foldable to review the lesson. Save your Foldable for the project at the end of the chapter.

What do you think NOW?

You first read the statements below at the beginning of the chapter.

4. Mixing powdered drink mix with water causes a new substance to form.

5. If you combine two substances, bubbling is a sign that a new type of substance might be forming.

6. If you stir salt into water, the total amount of mass decreases.

Did you change your mind about whether you agree or disagree with the statements? Rewrite any false statements to make them true.

Use Vocabulary

1 The particles that make up matter do not change during a(n) _____.

Understand Key Concepts

2 **Explain** how physical and chemical changes affect the mass of a material.

3 Which is a physical change?
   A. burning wood   **C.** rusting iron
   B. melting ice   **D.** spoiling food

Interpret Graphics

4 **Analyze** Suppose you mix 12.8 g of one substance with 11.4 g of another. The picture shows the mass you measure for the mixture. Is this reasonable? Explain.

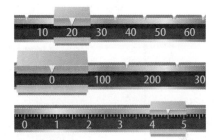

5 **Organize Information** Copy the graphic organizer below, and list an example of each type of change.

Type of Change	Examples
Physical change with formation of bubbles	
Chemical change with formation of bubbles	

Critical Thinking

6 **Consider** Suppose you mix baking soda and white vinegar. What signs might indicate that a chemical change occurs?

7 **Evaluate** You read that a physical change is a change in physical properties, and a chemical change is a change in chemical properties. Do you agree? Explain your answer.

(t)Hutchings Photography/Digital Light Source; (c)Stephen Frisch/McGraw-Hill Education; (b)Dennis Lane Photography/Getty Images

Materials

mineral
samples

nail

100-mL
graduated
cylinder

triple-beam
balance

Safety

Identifying Unknown Minerals

Imagine you are a geologist digging for minerals. You find one that you would like to identify. What properties of the mineral would help you? Geologists consider many physical properties of a mineral when determining its identification.

Question

How can you use physical properties to identify unknown minerals?

Procedure

1. Read and complete the lab safety form.

2. Select a mineral sample to observe. Record its color in your Science Journal.

3. Observe the hardness of your mineral.

   a. Scratch your mineral with your fingernail. If it scratches, then your mineral has a low hardness. Go to step 4. If it does not scratch, go to step 3b.

   b. Scratch your mineral with a nail. If it scratches, it has a moderate hardness. If it does not scratch, it has a high hardness.

4. Compare the properties of your mineral with the properties in the chart.

Physical Properties of Minerals			
Mineral	Color	Typical Density (g/cm³)	Hardness
Fluorite	white or light green	3.1	moderate
Gypsum	white or brown	2.3	fairly soft
Hornblende	black or grayish brown	3.2	moderate
Magnetite (iron ore)	dark gray	5.2	moderate
Quartz	white or colorless	2.6	fairly hard
Sphalerite (zinc ore)	black or reddish brown	4.1	fairly soft

5 Think about the properties you observed so far. Are you able to determine which mineral you have based on your initial observations? Explain why or why not in your Science Journal.

6 Look back through the chapter to review the physical property *density*.

7 Design an experiment using mass and volume to determine the density of your mineral.

8 Share your procedure with your teacher for approval before conducting your experiment.

9 Compare your results with information in the Physical Properties of Minerals table.

Analyze and Conclude

10 **Infer** the identity of your mineral sample.

11 **The Big Idea** Which physical property was most useful in identifying the mineral? Why?

12 **Predict** Suppose you have another sample of the same mineral. What properties would you expect to be the same? What properties would be different?

Lab Tips

☑ To measure the water in a cylinder accurately, first put your eye at the level of the liquid. Then observe the level at the meniscus (the center or bottom of the curve in the surface of the liquid).

☑ $1 \text{ mL} = 1 \text{ cm}^3$

Communicate Your Results

In a small group, share your experiences and your results. How did you collect and record data? What was successful? Did others use different techniques or get different results? Did anything surprise you?

 **Extension**

Choose a different unknown sample to test that looks similar to the one you tested. Which properties might be different? Test your sample in the same way you tested the first one. Were the results the same or different? What can you conclude from this?

Remember to use scientific methods.

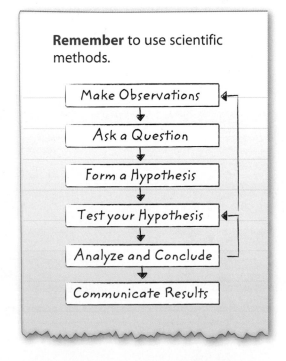

Make Observations
Ask a Question
Form a Hypothesis
Test your Hypothesis
Analyze and Conclude
Communicate Results

THE BIG IDEA

Physical and chemical properties give a substance its unique identity.

Key Concepts Summary 🔑	Vocabulary
Lesson 1: Matter and Its Properties  • Particles of a **solid** vibrate about a definite position. Particles of a **liquid** can slide past one another. Particles of a **gas** move freely within their container. • A **physical property** is a characteristic of matter that you can observe without changing the identity of the substances that make it up. A **chemical property** is the ability or inability of a substance to combine with or change into one or more new substances. • Some properties of matter do not depend on size or amount of the sample. You can identify a substance by comparing these properties to those of other known substances.	volume solid liquid gas physical property mass density solubility chemical property
Lesson 2: Matter and Its Changes • A change in the size, shape, form, or state of matter in which the identity of the matter stays the same is a **physical change.** A change in matter in which the substances that make it up change into other substances with different chemical and physical properties is a **chemical change.** • The **law of conservation of mass** states that the total mass before a chemical reaction is the same as the total mass after the reaction. 	physical change chemical change law of conservation of mass

FOLDABLES® Chapter Project

Assemble your lesson Foldables as shown to make a Chapter Project. Use the project to review what you have learned in this chapter.

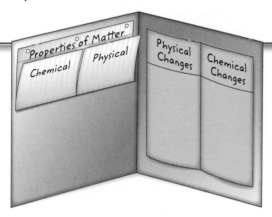

Use Vocabulary

1 A state of matter with a definite volume and a definite shape is a _____.

2 Flammability is an example of a _____ of wood because when wood burns, it changes to different materials.

3 A drink mix dissolves in water because of its _____ in water.

4 The rusting of a metal tool left in the rain is an example of a _____.

5 According to the _____, the mass of an untoasted marshmallow equals its mass after it is toasted plus the mass of any gases produced as it was toasting.

6 Slicing an apple into sections is an example of a _____ that cannot be reversed.

Link Vocabulary and Key Concepts

Concepts in Motion Interactive Concept Map

Copy this concept map, and then use vocabulary terms from the previous page to complete the concept map.

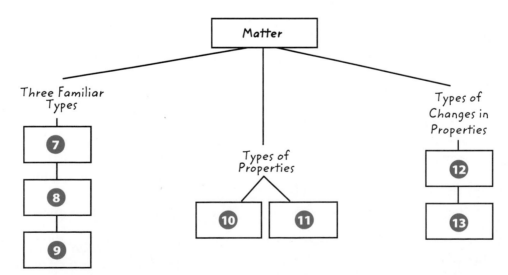

Understand Key Concepts

1. Which is a property of all solids?
   A. Particles are far apart.
   B. Particles vibrate in all directions.
   C. Volume and shape can easily change.
   D. Weak forces exist between particles.

2. Which characteristic is a chemical property?
   A. highly flammable
   B. mass of 15 kg
   C. woolly texture
   D. golden color

3. Which property of an object depends on its location?
   A. density
   B. mass
   C. volume
   D. weight

4. How are the particles of a gas different from the particles of a liquid shown here?

   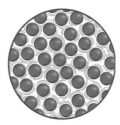

   A. They move more slowly.
   B. They are farther apart.
   C. They have less energy.
   D. They have stronger attractions.

5. Which is a physical change?
   A. burning natural gas
   B. chopping onions
   C. digesting food
   D. exploding dynamite

6. Which stays the same when a substance changes from a liquid to a gas?
   A. density
   B. mass
   C. forces between particles
   D. distance between particles

7. Which is a chemical change?
   A. boiling water
   B. copper turning green in air
   C. freezing fruit juice
   D. slicing a potato

8. Which would be most useful for identifying an unknown liquid?
   A. density
   B. mass
   C. volume
   D. weight

9. What mass is measured on this balance?

   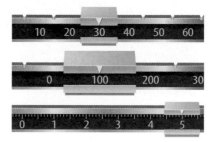

   A. 35 g
   B. 45 g
   C. 135 g
   D. 145 g

10. What causes a chemical reaction when you prepare scrambled eggs?
    A. removing the eggs from the shells
    B. mixing the egg yolks and the egg whites together
    C. heating the eggs in a pan
    D. sprinkling pepper onto the cooked eggs

11. Which describes the formation of a precipitate?
    A. A gas forms when a solid is placed in a liquid.
    B. A liquid forms when a block of metal is heated.
    C. A solid forms when one liquid is poured into another.
    D. Bubbles form when an acid is poured onto a rock.

Critical Thinking

12 **Apply** Suppose you find a gold-colored ring. Explain why you could use some physical properties but not others to determine whether the ring is actually made of gold.

13 **Reason** You make lemonade by mixing lemon juice, sugar, and water. Is this a physical change or a chemical change? Explain.

14 **Give an example** of a physical change you might observe at your school that is reversible and a physical change that is not reversible.

15 **Defend** A classmate defines a liquid as any substance that can be poured. Use the picture below to explain why this is not an acceptable definition.

16 **Suggest** a way that you could use displacement to determine the volume of a rock that is too large to fit into a graduated cylinder.

17 **Hypothesize** A scientist measures the mass of two liquids before and after combining them. The mass after combining the liquids is less than the sum of the masses before. Where is the missing mass?

Writing in Science

18 **Write** a four-sentence description of an object in your home or classroom. Be sure to identify both physical properties and chemical properties of the object.

REVIEW THE B|G IDEA

19 What gives a substance its unique identity?

20 What are some physical and chemical properties that an airplane manufacturer must consider when choosing materials to be used in constructing the shell of the aircraft shown below?

Math Skills ×−÷

▣ Review
──── Math Practice ────

21 Use what you have learned about density to complete the table below. Then, determine the identities of the two unknown metals.

Metal	Mass (g)	Volume (cm^3)	Density (g/cm^3)
Iron	42.5	5.40	
Lead	28.8	2.55	
Tungsten	69.5	3.60	
Zinc	46.4	6.50	
	61.0	5.40	
	46.4	2.40	

Record your answers on the answer sheet provided by your teacher or on a sheet of paper.

Multiple Choice

1 Which describes the particles in a substance with no definite volume or shape?

  A Particles are close but can move freely.

  B Particles are close but can vibrate in all directions.

  C Particles are far apart and cannot move.

  D Particles are far apart and move freely.

2 Which diagram shows a chemical change?

  A

  B

  C

  D

3 Which is NOT true about firewood that burns completely?

  A Ashes and gases form from the substances in the wood.

  B Oxygen from the air combines with substances in the wood.

  C The total mass of substances in this process decreases.

  D The wood gives off thermal energy and light.

Use the diagram below to answer question 4.

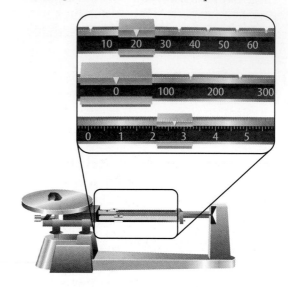

4 What is the mass of the object on the balance scale?

  A 22 g

  B 22.5 g

  C 22.7 g

  D 30 g

5 Which is true when an ice cube melts?

  A Volume and mass increase.

  B Volume and mass do not change.

  C Volume decreases, but mass does not change.

  D Volume increases, but mass decreases.

6 What is the BEST way to separate and save the parts of a sand-and-water mixture?

  A Boil the mixture and collect the steam.

  B Pour the mixture through a filter that only the water can pass through.

  C Lift the sand out of the mix with a spoon.

  D Pour a strong acid into the mixture to dissolve the sand.

Use the table below to answer questions 7 and 8.

Action	Time	Result
Heated	30 minutes	solid
Heated	60 minutes	liquid
Not heated	30 minutes	solid
Not heated	60 minutes	solid

7 Based on the results of this experiment, what can you conclude about heating this unknown substance?

A Heating melted it in 30 minutes.

B Heating melted it in 60 minutes.

C Heating made it solid in 60 minutes.

D Heating caused no changes.

8 What can you conclude about the original state of the substance?

A It is part solid and part liquid.

B It is a liquid.

C It is a solid.

D It is part liquid and part gas.

9 Which is a sign of a physical change?

A Bread gets moldy with age.

B Ice forms on a puddle in winter.

C The metal on a car starts to rust.

D Yeast causes bread dough to rise.

Constructed Response

Use the table below to answer questions 10–13.

Properties	Substance 1	Substance 2	Substance 3
Color	yellow	yellow	yellow
State	solid	solid	solid
Mass	217 g	217 g	75 g
Melting point	505°C	230°C	505°C
Density	3.78 g/cm³	2.76 g/cm³	3.78 g/cm³
Flammable	yes	yes	yes

10 Identify each property of the unknown substances as either chemical or physical. Explain your reasoning.

11 Of the three unknown substances tested, two are the same substance and one is different. Which two substances do you think are the same? Explain your reasoning.

12 Which properties in the table helped you determine your answer in number 11? Which properties were not helpful? Explain your reasoning.

13 What additional physical and chemical properties of substances might the table have included?

NEED EXTRA HELP?													
If You Missed Question...	1	2	3	4	5	6	7	8	9	10	11	12	13
Go to Lesson...	1	2	2	1	1,2	1	2	2	2	1	1	1	1

AID S1.2a, S1.2b, S2.1a, S2.1b, S2.1c, S2.1d, S2.2a, S2.2b, S2.2c, S2.2d, S2.2e, S2.3a, S2.3b, S3.1a, S3.1b, S3.2a, S3.2c, S3.2d, S3.2g, S3.2h, S3.3; IS 1.1, 1.3, 3.1; ICT 2.1, 2.2, 2.3; IPS 1.2; PS 3.1a, 3.1c, 3.1d, 3.1e, 3.1f, 3.1h, 3.2a, 4.1e, 4.2c

States of Matter

THE BIG IDEA

What physical changes and energy changes occur as matter goes from one state to another?

Inquiry Liquid Glass?

When you look at this blob of molten glass, can you envision it as a beautiful vase? The solid glass was heated in a furnace until it formed a molten liquid. Air is blown through a pipe to make the glass hollow and give it form.

- Can you identify a solid, a liquid, and a gas in the photo?

- What physical changes and energy changes do you think occurred when the glass changed state?

Get Ready to Read

What do you think?

Before you read, decide if you agree or disagree with each of these statements. As you read this chapter, see if you change your mind about any of the statements.

1 Particles moving at the same speed make up all matter.

2 The particles in a solid do not move.

3 Particles of matter have both potential energy and kinetic energy.

4 When a solid melts, thermal energy is removed from the solid.

5 Changes in temperature and pressure affect gas behavior.

6 If the pressure on a gas increases, the volume of the gas also increases.

 **Connect** Your one-stop online resource

MHEonline.com

 Video    WebQuest

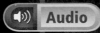 Audio   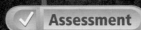 Assessment

 Review   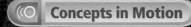 Concepts in Motion

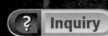 Inquiry   **g** Multilingual eGlossary

Lesson 1

Reading Guide

Key Concepts 🔑
ESSENTIAL QUESTIONS

- How do particles move in solids, liquids, and gases?

- How are the forces between particles different in solids, liquids, and gases?

Vocabulary

solid

liquid

viscosity

surface tension

gas

vapor

 Multilingual eGlossary

 AID S1.2b, S3.2e; IS 1.3; ICT 2.1, 2.2; IPS 1.2; PS 3.1a, 3.1c, 3.1d, 3.1e, 3.1f, 3.1h

Solids, Liquids, and Gases

Inquiry Giant Bubbles?

Giant bubbles can be made from a solution of water, soap, and a syrupy liquid called glycerine. These liquids change the properties of water. Soap changes water's surface tension. Glycerine changes the evaporation rate. How do surface tension and evaporation work?

How can you see particles in matter?

It's sometimes difficult to picture how tiny objects, such as the particles that make up matter, move. However, you can use other objects to model the movement of these particles.

1. Read and complete a lab safety form.

2. Place about 50 **copper pellets** into a **plastic petri dish.** Place the cover on the dish, and secure it with **tape.**

3. Hold the dish by the edges. Gently vibrate the dish from side to side no more than 1–2 mm. Observe the pellets. Record your observations in your Science Journal.

4. Repeat step 3, vibrating the dish less than 1 cm from side to side.

5. Repeat step 3, vibrating the dish 3–4 cm from side to side.

Think About This

1. If the pellets represent particles in matter, what do you think the shaking represents?

2. In which part of the experiment do you think the pellets were like a liquid? Explain.

3. **Key Concept** If the pellets represent molecules of water, what do you think are the main differences among molecules of ice, water, and vapor?

Describing Matter

Take a closer look at the photo on the previous page. Do you see **matter?** The three most common forms, or states, of matter on Earth are solids, liquids, and gases. The giant bubble contains air, which is a mixture of gases. The ocean water and the soap mixture used to make the bubble are liquids. The sand, sign, and walkway are a few of the solids in the photo.

There is a fourth state of matter, plasma, that is not shown in this photo. Plasma is high-energy matter consisting of positively and negatively charged particles. Plasma is the most common state of matter in space. It also is in lightning flashes, fluorescent lighting, and stars, such as the Sun.

There are many ways to describe matter. You can describe the state, the color, the texture, and the odor of matter using your senses. You also can describe matter using measurements, such as mass, volume, and density. Mass is the amount of matter in an object. The units for mass are often grams (g) or kilograms (kg). Volume is the amount of space that a sample of matter occupies. The units for liquid volume are usually liters (L) or milliliters (mL). The units for solid volume are usually cubic centimeters (cm^3) or cubic meters (m^3). Density is the mass per unit volume of a substance. The units are usually g/cm^3 or g/mL. Density of a given substance remains constant, regardless of the size of the sample.

REVIEW VOCABULARY

matter
anything that takes up space and has mass

New York FYI

Density, Mass and Volume If two objects have equal volume, but one has more mass, the one with more mass is denser. If two object have equal mass, but different volumes, the one with the smaller volume is denser.

Particles in Motion

Have you ever wondered what makes something a solid, a liquid, or a gas? Two main factors that determine the state of matter are particle motion and particle forces.

Particles, such as atoms, ions, or molecules, moving in different ways make up all matter. The particles that make up some matter are close together and vibrate back and forth. In other types of matter, the particles are farther apart, move freely, and can spread out. Regardless of how close particles are to each other, they all move in random motion—movement in all directions and at different speeds. However, particles will move in straight lines until they collide with something. Collisions usually change the speed and direction of the particles' movements.

Forces Between Particles

Recall that atoms that make up matter contain positively charged protons and negatively charged electrons. There is a force of attractions between these oppositely charged particles, as shown in **Figure 1.**

You just read that the particles that make up matter move at all speeds and in all directions. If the motion of particles slows, the particles move closer together. This is because the attraction between them pulls them toward each other. Strong attractive forces hold particles close together. As the motion of particles increases, particles move farther apart. The attractive forces between particles get weaker. The spaces between them increase and the particles can slip past one another. As the motion of particles continues to increase, they move even farther apart. Eventually, the distance between particles is so great that there are little or no attractive forces between the particles. The particles move randomly and spread out. As you continue to read, you will learn how particle motion and particle forces determine whether matter is a solid, a liquid, or a gas.

Figure 1 The forces between particles of matter and the movement of particles determine the physical state of matter.

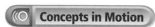

Concepts in Motion

Animation

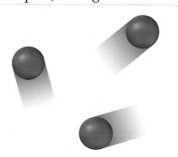

Particles move slowly and can only vibrate in place. Therefore, the attractive forces between particles are strong.

Particles move faster and slip past each other. The distance between particles increases. Therefore, the attractive forces between particles are weaker.

Particles move fast. The distance between the particles is great, and therefore, the attractive forces between particles are very weak.

Solids

If you had to describe a solid, what would you say? You might say, a **solid** *is matter that has a definite shape and a definite volume.* For example, if the skateboard in **Figure 2** moves from one location to another, the shape and volume of it do not change.

Particles in a Solid

Why doesn't a solid change its shape and volume? Notice in **Figure 2** how the particles in a solid are close together. The particles are very close to their neighboring particles. That's because the attractive forces between the particles are strong and hold them close together. The strong attractive forces and slow motion of the particles keep them tightly held in their positions. The particles simply vibrate back and forth in place. This arrangement gives solids a definite shape and volume.

 Key Concept Check Describe the movement of particles in a solid and the forces between them.

Types of Solids

All solids are not the same. For example, a diamond and a piece of charcoal don't look alike. However, they are both solids made of only carbon atoms. A diamond and a lump of charcoal both contain particles that strongly attract each other and vibrate in place. What makes them different is the arrangement of their particles. Notice in **Figure 3** that the arrangement of particles in a diamond is different from that in charcoal. A diamond is a crystalline solid. It has particles arranged in a specific, repeating order. Charcoal is an amorphous solid. It has particles arranged randomly. Different particle arrangements give these materials different properties. For example, a diamond is a hard material, and charcoal is a brittle material.

 Reading Check What is the difference between crystalline and amorphous solids?

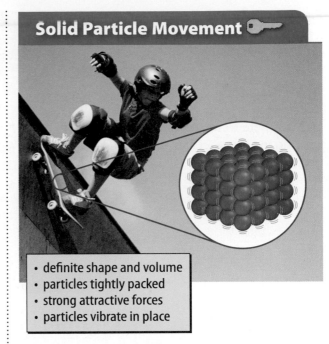

Solid Particle Movement

- definite shape and volume
- particles tightly packed
- strong attractive forces
- particles vibrate in place

▲ **Figure 2** The particles in a solid have strong attractive forces and vibrate in place.

Figure 3 Carbon is a solid that can have different particle arrangements. ▼

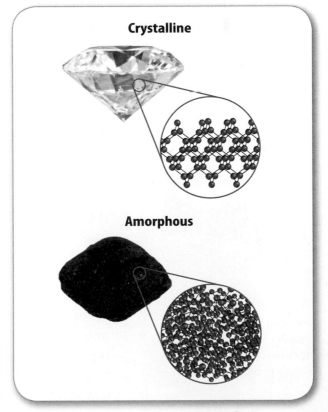

Crystalline

Amorphous

(t)Fuse/Getty Images; (c)©Steve Hamblin/Alamy; (b)McGraw-Hill Education

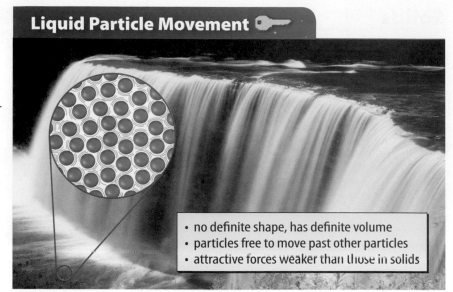

Liquid Particle Movement 🔑

- no definite shape, has definite volume
- particles free to move past other particles
- attractive forces weaker than those in solids

Liquids

You have probably seen a waterfall, such as the one in **Figure 4.** Water is a liquid. *A* **liquid** *is matter with a definite volume but no definite shape.* Liquids flow and can take the shape of their containers. The container for this water is the riverbed.

Particles in a Liquid

How can liquids change their shape? The particle motion in the liquid state of a material is faster than the particle motion in the solid state. This increased particle motion causes the particles to move slightly farther apart. As the particles move farther apart, the attractive forces between the particles decrease. The weaker attractive forces allow particles to slip past one another. The weather forces also enable liquids to flow and take the shape of their containers.

Viscosity

If you have ever poured or dipped honey, as shown in **Figure 5,** you have experienced a liquid with a high viscosity. **Viscosity** (vihs KAW sih tee) *is a measurement of a liquid's resistance to flow.* Honey has high viscosity, while water has low viscosity. Viscosity is due to particle mass, particle shape, and the strength of the attraction between the particles of a liquid. In general, the stronger the attractive forces between particles, the higher the viscosity. For many liquids, viscosity decreases as the liquid becomes warmer. As a liquid becomes warmer, particles begin to move faster and the attractive forces between them get weaker. This allows particles to more easily slip past one another. The mass and shape of particles that make up a liquid also affect viscosity. Large particles or particles with complex shapes tend to move more slowly and have difficulty slipping past one another.

WORD ORIGIN ·············

viscosity
from Latin *viscum,* means "sticky"

Figure 5 Honey has a high viscosity. ▼

Figure 6 The surface tension of water enables this spider to walk on the surface of a lake.

Surface Tension

How can the nursery web spider in **Figure 6** walk on water? Believe it or not, it is because of the interactions between molecules.

The blowout in **Figure 6** shows the attractive forces between water molecules. Water molecules below the surface are surrounded on all sides by other water molecules. Therefore, they have attractive forces, or pulls, in all directions. The attraction between similar molecules, such as water molecules, is called cohesion.

Water molecules at the surface of a liquid do not have liquid water molecules above them. As a result, they experience a greater downward pull, and the surface particles become tightly stretched like the head of a drum. Molecules at the surface of a liquid have **surface tension**, *the uneven forces acting on the particles on the surface of a liquid.* Surface tension allows a spider to walk on water. In general, the stronger the attractive forces between particles, the greater the surface tension of the liquid.

Recall the giant bubbles at the beginning of the chapter. The thin water-soap film surrounding the bubbles forms because of surface tension between the particles.

 Key Concept Check Describe the movement of particles in a liquid and the forces between them.

 **MiniLab** 20 minutes

How can you make bubble films?

Have you ever observed surface tension? Which liquids have greater surface tension?

1. Read and complete a lab safety form.
2. Place about 100 mL of cool water in a **small bowl.** Lower a **wire bubble frame** into the bowl, and gently lift it. Use a **magnifying lens** to observe the edges of the frame. Write your observations in your Science Journal.
3. Add a full **dropper** of **liquid dishwashing soap** to the water. Stir with a **toothpick** until mixed. Lower the frame into the mixture and lift it out. Record your observations.
4. Use a toothpick to break the bubble film on one side of the thread. Observe.

Analyze and Conclude

1. **Recognize Cause and Effect** Explain what caused the thread to form an arc when half the bubble film broke.

2. **Key Concept** Explain why pure water doesn't form bubbles. What happens to the forces between water molecules when you add soap?

- no definite shape or volume
- particles far apart and move freely
- slight or weak attractive forces between particles

Figure 7 The particles in a gas are far apart, and there are little or no attractive forces between particles.

Visual Check What are gas particles likely to hit as they move?

Gases

Look at the photograph in **Figure 7.** Where is the gas? *A* **gas** *is matter that has no definite volume and no definite shape.* It is not easy to identify the gas because you cannot see it. However, gas particles are inside and outside the inflatable balls. Air is a mixture of gases, including nitrogen, oxygen, argon, and carbon dioxide.

Reading Check What is a gas, and what is another object that contains a gas?

Particles in a Gas

Why don't gases have definite volumes or definite shapes like solids and liquids? Compare the particles in **Figures 2, 4,** and **7.** Notice how the distance between particles differs. As the particles move faster, such as when matter goes from the solid state to the liquid state, the particles move farther apart. When the particles in matter move even faster, such as when matter goes from the liquid state to the gas state, the particles move even farther apart. When the distances between particles change, the attractive forces between the particles also change.

Forces Between Particles

As a type of matter goes from the solid state to the liquid state, the distance between the particles increases and the attractive forces between the particles decrease. When the same matter goes from the liquid state to the gas state, the particles are even farther apart and the attractive forces between the particles are weak or absent. As a result, the particles spread out to fill their container. Because gas particles lack attractive forces between particles, they have no definite shape or definite volume.

Vapor

Have you ever heard the term *vapor? The gas state of a substance that is normally a solid or a liquid at room temperature is called* **vapor.** For example, water is normally a liquid at room temperature. When it is in a gas state, such as in air, it is called water vapor. Other substances that can form a vapor are rubbing alcohol, iodine, mercury, and gasoline.

Key Concept Check How do particles move and interact in a gas?

Alberto Coto/Getty Images

Visual Summary

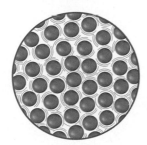

The particles that make up a solid can only vibrate in place. The particles are close together, and there are strong forces among them.

The particles that make up a liquid are far enough apart that particles can flow past other particles. The forces among these particles are weaker than those in a solid.

The particles that make up a gas are far apart. There is little or no attraction between the particles.

Use your lesson Foldable to review the lesson. Save your Foldable for the project at the end of the chapter.

What do you think NOW?

You first read the statements below at the beginning of the chapter.

1. Particles moving at the same speed make up all matter.

2. The particles in a solid do not move.

Did you change your mind about whether you agree or disagree with the statements? Rewrite any false statements to make them true.

Use Vocabulary

1 A measurement of how strongly particles attract one another at the surface of a liquid is _____.

2 **Define** *solid*, *liquid*, and *gas* in your own words.

3 A measurement of a liquid's resistance to flow is known as _____.

Understand Key Concepts 🔑

4 Which state of matter rarely is found on Earth?

  A. gas   **C.** plasma
  B. liquid   **D.** solid

5 **Compare** particle movement in solids, liquids, and gases.

6 **Compare** the forces between particles in a liquid and in a gas.

Interpret Graphics

7 **Explain** why the particles at the surface in the image below have surface tension while the particles below the surface do not.

8 **Summarize** Copy and fill in the graphic organizer to compare two types of solids.

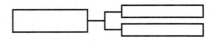

Critical Thinking

9 **Hypothesize** how you could change the viscosity of a cold liquid, and explain why your idea would work.

10 **Summarize** the relationship between the motion of particles and attractive forces between particles.

Freeze-Drying Foods

Have you noticed that the berries you find in some breakfast cereals are lightweight and dry—much different from the berries you get from the market or the garden?

Fresh fruit would spoil quickly if it were packaged in breakfast cereal, so fruits in cereals are often freeze-dried. When liquid is returned to the freeze-dried fruit, its physical properties more closely resemble fresh fruit. Freeze-drying, or lyophilization (lie ah fuh luh ZAY shun), is the process in which a solvent (usually water) is removed from a solid. During this process, a frozen solvent changes to a gas without going through the liquid state. Freeze-dried foods are lightweight and long-lasting. Astronauts have been using freeze-dried food during space travel since the 1960s.

How Freeze-Drying Works

1 Machines called freeze-dryers are used to freeze-dry foods and other products. Fresh or cooked food is flash-frozen, changing moisture in the food to a solid.

2 The frozen food is placed in a large vacuum chamber, where moisture is removed. Heat is applied to accelerate moisture removal. Condenser plates remove vaporized solvent from the chamber and convert the frozen food to a freeze-dried solid.

3 Freeze-dried food is sealed in oxygen- and moisture-proof packages to ensure stability and freshness. When the food is rehydrated, it returns to its near-normal state of weight, color, and texture.

ASTRONAUT
Ice Cream

NET WT .7 OZ (19g)

It's Your Turn

PREDICT/DISCOVER What kinds of products besides food are freeze-dried? Use library or internet resources to learn about other products that undergo the freeze-drying process. Discuss the benefits or drawbacks of freeze-drying.

(t)Carina Lochner/Getty Images; (b)Michael Rosenfeld/Getty Images

Changes in State

Reading Guide

Key Concepts
ESSENTIAL QUESTIONS

- How is temperature related to particle motion?
- How are temperature and thermal energy different?
- What happens to thermal energy when matter changes from one state to another?

Vocabulary

kinetic energy
temperature
thermal energy
vaporization
evaporation
condensation
sublimation
deposition

 Multilingual eGlossary

Video

- BrainPOP®
- What's Science Got to do With It?

 AID S1.2a, S2.1a, S2.1b, S2.1c, S2.1d, S3.1a, S3.1b, S3.2c, S3.2d, S3.2e, S3.2h, S3.3; PS 3.1c, 3.2a, 4.1e, 4.2c

Inquiry Spring Thaw?

When you look at a snowman, you probably don't think about states of matter. However, water is one of the few substances that you frequently observe in three states of matter at Earth's temperatures. What energy changes are involved when matter changes state?

Do liquid particles move?

If you look at a glass of milk sitting on a table, it appears to have no motion. But appearances can be deceiving!

1 Read and complete a lab safety form.

2 Use a **dropper,** and place one drop of **2 percent milk** on a **glass slide.** Add a **cover slip.**

3 Place the slide on a **microscope** stage, and focus on low power. Focus on a single globule of fat in the milk. Observe the motion of the globule for several minutes. Record your observations in your Science Journal.

Think About This

1. Describe the motion of the fat globule.

2. What do you think caused the motion of the globule?

3. 🔑 **Key Concept** What do you think would happen to the motion of the fat globule if you warmed the milk? Explain.

Kinetic and Potential Energy

When snow begins to melt after a snowstorm, all three states of water are present. The snow is a solid, the melted snow is a liquid, and the air above the snow and ice contains water vapor, a gas. What causes particles to change state?

Kinetic Energy

Recall that the particles that make up matter are in constant motion. These particles have **kinetic energy,** *the energy an object has due to its motion.* The faster particles move, the more kinetic energy they have. Within a given substance, such as water, particles in the solid state have the least amount of kinetic energy. This is because they only vibrate in place. Particles in the liquid state move faster than particles in the solid state. Therefore, they have more kinetic energy. Particles in the gaseous state move very quickly and have the most kinetic energy of particles of a given substance.

Temperature *is a measure of the average kinetic energy of all the particles in an object.* Within a given substance, a temperature increase means that the particles, on average, are moving at greater speeds, or have a greater average kinetic energy. For example, water molecules at 25°C are generally moving faster and have more kinetic energy than water molecules at 10°C.

📋 **Key Concept Check** How is temperature related to particle motion?

Hutchings Photography/Digital Light Source

Potential Energy

In addition to kinetic energy, particles have potential energy. Potential energy is stored energy due to the interactions between particles or objects. For example, when you pick up a ball and then let it go, the gravitational force between the ball and Earth causes the ball to fall toward Earth. Before you let the ball go, it has potential energy.

Potential energy typically increases when objects get farther apart and decreases when they get closer together. The basketball in the top part of **Figure 8** is farther off the ground than it is in the bottom part of the figure. The farther an object is from Earth's surface, the greater the gravitational potential energy. As the ball gets closer to the ground, the potential energy decreases.

You can think of the potential energy of particles in a similar way. The chemical potential energy is due to the position of the particles relative to other particles. The chemical potential energy of particles increases and decreases as the distances between particles increase or decrease. The particles in the top part of **Figure 8** are farther apart than the particles in the bottom part. The particles that are farther apart have greater chemical potential energy.

Thermal Energy

Thermal energy *is the total potential and kinetic energies of an object.* You can change an object's state of matter by adding or removing thermal energy. When you add thermal energy to an object, the particles either move faster (increased kinetic energy) or get farther apart (increased potential energy) or both. The opposite is true when you remove thermal energy from an object. If enough thermal energy is added or removed, a change of state can occur.

 Key Concept Check How do thermal energy and temperature differ?

Figure 8 The potential energy of the ball depends on the distance between the ball and Earth. The potential energy of particles in matter depends on the distances between the particles.

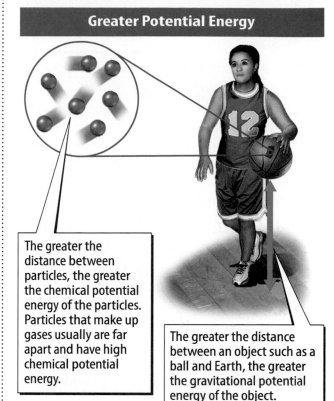

Greater Potential Energy

The greater the distance between particles, the greater the chemical potential energy of the particles. Particles that make up gases usually are far apart and have high chemical potential energy.

The greater the distance between an object such as a ball and Earth, the greater the gravitational potential energy of the object.

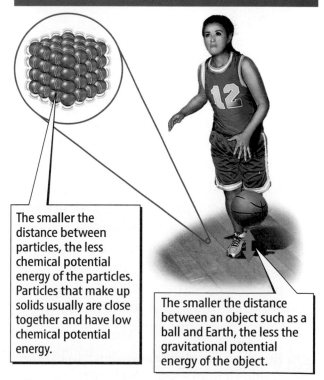

Less Potential Energy

The smaller the distance between particles, the less chemical potential energy of the particles. Particles that make up solids usually are close together and have low chemical potential energy.

The smaller the distance between an object such as a ball and Earth, the less the gravitational potential energy of the object.

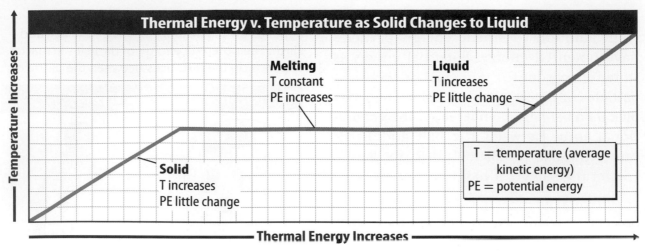

Thermal Energy v. Temperature as Solid Changes to Liquid

Temperature Increases →

Thermal Energy Increases →

Melting
T constant
PE increases

Liquid
T increases
PE little change

Solid
T increases
PE little change

T = temperature (average kinetic energy)
PE = potential energy

Figure 9 Adding thermal energy to matter causes the particles that make up the matter to increase in kinetic energy, potential energy, or both.

Visual Check During melting, which factor remains constant?

Solid to Liquid or Liquid to Solid

When you drink a beverage from an aluminum can, do you recycle the can? Aluminum recycling is one example of a process that involves changing matter from one state to another by adding or removing thermal energy.

Melting

The first part of the recycling process involves melting aluminum cans. To change matter from a solid to a liquid, thermal energy must be added. The graph in **Figure 9** shows the relationship between increasing temperature and increasing thermal energy (potential energy + kinetic energy).

At first, both the thermal energy and the temperature increase. The temperature stops increasing when it reaches the melting point of the matter, the temperature at which the solid state changes to the liquid state. As aluminum changes from solid to liquid, the temperature does not change. However, energy changes still occur.

Reading Check What is added to matter to change it from a solid to a liquid?

Energy Changes

What happens when a solid reaches its melting point? Notice the line on the graph is horizontal. This means that the temperature, or average kinetic energy, stops increasing. However, the amount of thermal energy continues to increase. How is this possible?

Once a solid reaches its melting point, the average speed of particles does not change, but the distance between the particles does change. The particles move farther apart and potential energy increases. Once a solid completely melts, the addition of thermal energy will cause the kinetic energy of the particles to increase again, as shown by a temperature increase.

Freezing

After the aluminum melts, it is poured into molds to cool. As the aluminum cools, thermal energy leaves it. Freezing is a process that is the reverse of melting. The temperature at which matter changes from the liquid state to the solid state is its freezing point. To observe the temperature and thermal energy changes that occur to hot aluminum blocks, move from right to left on the graph in **Figure 9.**

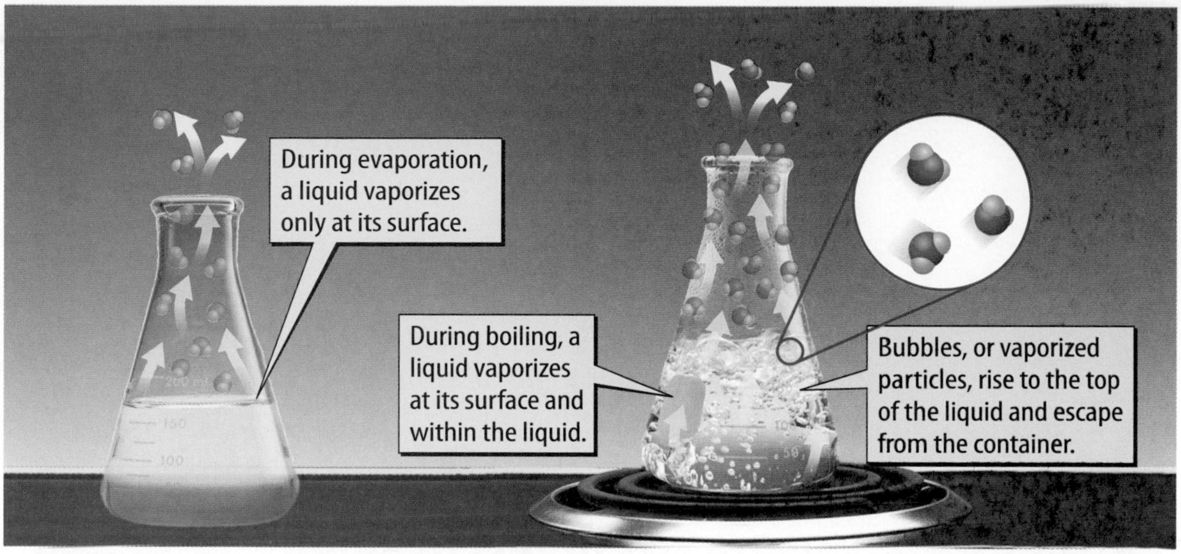

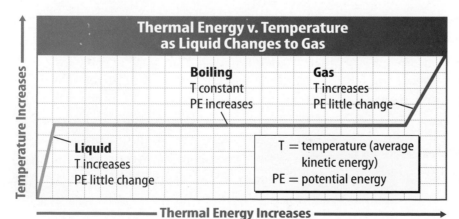

During evaporation, a liquid vaporizes only at its surface.

During boiling, a liquid vaporizes at its surface and within the liquid.

Bubbles, or vaporized particles, rise to the top of the liquid and escape from the container.

Liquid to Gas or Gas to Liquid

When you heat water, do you ever notice how bubbles begin to form at the bottom and rise to the surface? The bubbles contain water vapor, a gas. *The change in state of a liquid into a gas is* **vaporization. Figure 10** shows two types of vaporization—evaporation and boiling.

Boiling

Vaporization that occurs within a liquid is called boiling. The temperature at which boiling occurs in a liquid is called its boiling point. In **Figure 11,** notice the energy changes that occur during this process. The kinetic energy of particles increases until the liquid reaches its boiling point.

At the boiling point, the potential energy of particles begins increasing. The particles move farther apart until the attractive forces no longer hold them together. At this point, the liquid changes to a gas. When boiling ends, if thermal energy continues to be added, the kinetic energy of the gas particles begins to increase again. Therefore, the temperature begins to increase again as shown on the graph.

▲ **Figure 10** Boiling and evaporation are two kinds of vaporization.

☑ **Visual Check** Why doesn't the evaporation flask have bubbles below the surface?

Review

Personal Tutor

◀ **Figure 11** When thermal energy is added to a liquid, kinetic energy and potential energy changes occur.

Thermal Energy v. Temperature as Liquid Changes to Gas

Temperature Increases →

Boiling
T constant
PE increases

Gas
T increases
PE little change

Liquid
T increases
PE little change

T = temperature (average kinetic energy)
PE = potential energy

Thermal Energy Increases →

Hutchings Photography/Digital Light Source

WORD ORIGIN ·············
evaporation
from Latin *evaporare*, means "disperse in steam or vapor"

Evaporation

Unlike boiling, **evaporation** *is vaporization that occurs only at the surface of a liquid.* Liquid in an open container will vaporize, or change to a gas, over time due to evaporation.

Condensation

Boiling and evaporation are processes that change a liquid to a gas. A reverse process also occurs. When a gas loses enough thermal energy, the gas changes to a liquid, or condenses. *The change of state from a gas to a liquid is called* **condensation.** Overnight, water vapor often condenses on blades of grass, forming dew.

Solid to Gas or Gas to Solid

Is it possible for a solid to become a gas without turning to a liquid first? Yes, in fact, dry ice does. Dry ice, as shown in **Figure 12,** is solid carbon dioxide. It turns immediately into a gas when thermal energy is added to it. The process is called sublimation. **Sublimation** *is the change of state from a solid to a gas without going through the liquid state.* As dry ice sublimes, it cools and condenses the water vapor in the surrounding air, creating a thick fog.

SCIENCE USE v. COMMON USE ··
deposition
Science Use the change of state of a gas to a solid without going through the liquid state

Common Use giving a legal testimony under oath

The opposite of sublimation is deposition. **Deposition** *is the change of state of a gas to a solid without going through the liquid state.* For deposition to occur, thermal energy has to be removed from the gas. You might see deposition in autumn when you wake up and there is frost on the grass. As water vapor loses thermal energy, it changes into a solid known as frost.

 Reading Check Why are sublimation and deposition unusual changes of state?

Figure 12 Dry ice sublimes—goes directly from the solid state to the gas state—when thermal energy is added. Frost is an example of the opposite process—deposition.

(l)Charles D. Winters/Photo Researchers, Inc., (r)Jean du Boisberranger/Getty Images

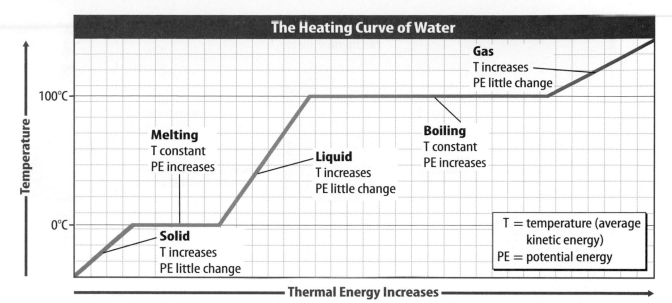

The Heating Curve of Water

Melting
T constant
PE increases

Liquid
T increases
PE little change

Boiling
T constant
PE increases

Gas
T increases
PE little change

Solid
T increases
PE little change

T = temperature (average kinetic energy)
PE = potential energy

Temperature

100°C

0°C

Thermal Energy Increases

States of Water

Water is the only substance that exists naturally as a solid, a liquid, and a gas within Earth's temperature range. To better understand the energy changes during a change in state, it is helpful to study the heating curve of water, as shown in **Figure 13.**

Adding Thermal Energy

Suppose you place a beaker of ice on a hot plate. The hot plate transfers thermal energy to the beaker and then to the ice. The temperature of the ice increases. Recall that this means the average kinetic energy of the water molecules increases.

At 0°C, the melting point of water, the water molecules vibrate so rapidly that they begin to move out of their places. At this point, added thermal energy only increases the distance between particles and decreases attractive forces—melting occurs. Once melting is complete, the average kinetic energy of the particles (temperature) begins to increase again as more thermal energy is added.

When water reaches 100°C, the boiling point, liquid water begins to change to water vapor. Again, kinetic energy is constant as vaporization occurs. When the change of state is complete, the kinetic energy of molecules increases once more, and so does the temperature.

 Key Concept Check Describe the changes in thermal energy as water goes from a solid to a liquid.

Removing Thermal Energy

The removal of thermal energy is the reverse of the process shown in **Figure 13.** Cooling water vapor changes the gas to a liquid. Cooling the water further changes it to ice.

Figure 13 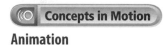 Water undergoes energy changes and state changes as thermal energy is added and removed.

Concepts in Motion
Animation

FOLDABLES

Fold a sheet of notebook paper to make a four-tab Foldable as shown. Label the tabs, define the terms, and record what you learn about each term under the tabs.

Vaporization
Boiling Evaporation
Condensation
Sublimation
Deposition

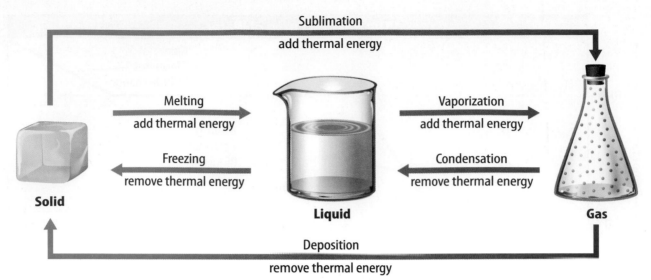

Sublimation
add thermal energy

Melting
add thermal energy

Freezing
remove thermal energy

Solid

Liquid

Vaporization
add thermal energy

Condensation
remove thermal energy

Gas

Deposition
remove thermal energy

Figure 14 For a change of state to occur, thermal energy must move into or out of matter.

Conservation of Mass and Energy

The diagram in **Figure 14** illustrates the energy changes that occur as thermal energy is added or removed from matter. Notice that opposite processes, melting and freezing and vaporization and condensation, are shown. When matter changes state, matter and energy are always conserved.

When water vaporizes, it appears to disappear. If the invisible gas is captured and its mass added to the remaining mass of the liquid, you would see that matter is conserved. This is also true for energy. Surrounding matter, such as air, often absorbs thermal energy. If you measured all the thermal energy, you would find that energy is conserved.

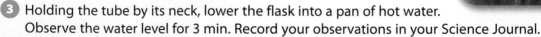

Inquiry MiniLab   **20 minutes**

How can you make a water thermometer?

What causes liquid in a thermometer to rise and fall?

1 Read and complete a lab safety form.

2 Place one drop of **food coloring** in a **flask.** Fill the flask to the top with room temperature tap water. Over a **sink or pan,** insert a **one-holed stopper fitted with a glass tube** into the flask. Press down gently. The liquid should rise partway into the tube. Mark the level of the water with a **grease pencil.**

3 Holding the tube by its neck, lower the flask into a pan of hot water. Observe the water level for 3 min. Record your observations in your Science Journal.

4 Remove the flask from the hot water, and lower it into a pan of **ice water.** Observe the water level for 3 min, and record your observations.

Analyze and Conclude

Key Concept Explain what happens to the column of water and the water particles as they are heated and cooled.

Visual Summary

All matter has thermal energy. Thermal energy is the sum of potential and kinetic energy.

When thermal energy is added to a liquid, vaporization can occur.

When enough thermal energy is removed from matter, a change of state can occur.

FOLDABLES®

Use your lesson Foldable to review the lesson. Save your Foldable for the project at the end of the chapter.

What do you think

You first read the statements below at the beginning of the chapter.

3. Particles of matter have both potential energy and kinetic energy.

4. When a solid melts, thermal energy is removed from the solid.

Did you change your mind about whether you agree or disagree with the statements? Rewrite any false statements to make them true.

Use Vocabulary

1 The measure of average kinetic energy of the particles in a material is _____.

2 **Define** *kinetic energy* and *thermal energy* in your own words.

3 The change of a liquid into a gas is known as _____.

Understand Key Concepts

4 The process that is opposite of condensation is known as
- **A.** deposition.
- **B.** freezing.
- **C.** melting.
- **D.** vaporization.

5 **Explain** how temperature and particle motion are related.

6 **Describe** the relationship between temperature and thermal energy.

7 **Generalize** the changes in thermal energy when matter increases in temperature and then changes state.

Interpret Graphics

8 **Describe** what is occurring below.

9 **Summarize** Copy and fill in the graphic organizer below to identify the two types of vaporization that can occur in matter.

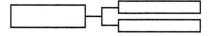

Critical Thinking

10 **Summarize** the energy and state changes that occur when freezing rain falls and solidifies on a wire fence.

11 **Compare** the amount of thermal energy needed to melt a solid and the amount of thermal energy needed to freeze the same liquid.

(tl)©DP RM/Alamy; Hutchings Photography/Digital Light Source; (b)Jean du Boisberranger/Getty Images; (br)Charles D. Winters/Photo Researchers, Inc.

How does dissolving substances in water change its freezing point?

Materials

triple-beam balance

beaker

foam cup

50-mL graduated cylinder

distilled water

Also needed:
ice-salt slush, test tubes, thermometers

Safety

You know that when thermal energy is removed from a liquid, the particles move more slowly. At the freezing point, the particles move so slowly that the attractive forces pull them together to form a solid. What happens if the water contains particles of another substance, such as salt? You will form a hypothesis and test the hypothesis to find out.

Learn It

To **form a hypothesis** is to propose a possible explanation for an observation that is testable by a scientific investigation. You **test the hypothesis** by conducting a scientific investigation to see whether the hypothesis is supported.

Try It

1. Read and complete a lab safety form.

2. Form a hypothesis that answers the question in the title of the lab. Write your hypothesis in your Science Journal.

3. Copy the data table in your Science Journal.

4. Use a triple-beam balance to measure 5 g of table salt (NaCl). Dissolve the 5 g of table salt in 50 mL of distilled water.

5. Place 40 mL of distilled water in one large test tube. Place 40 mL of the salt-water mixture in a second large test tube.

6. Measure and record the temperature of the liquids in each test tube.

7. Place both test tubes into a large foam cup filled with crushed ice-salt slush. Gently rotate the thermometers in the test tubes. Record the temperature in each test tube every minute until the temperature remains the same for several minutes.

Apply It

8. How does the data tell you when the freezing point of the liquid has been reached?

9. Do your results support your hypothesis? Why or why not?

10. 🔑 **Key Concept** Explain your observations in terms of how temperature affects particle motion and how a liquid changes to a solid.

Water	Time (min)	0	1	2	3	4	5	6	7	8
	Temperature (°C)										
Salt water	Time (min)	0	1	2	3	4	5	6	7	8
	Temperature (°C)										

The Behavior of Gases

Reading Guide

Key Concepts 🗝
ESSENTIAL QUESTIONS

- How does the kinetic molecular theory describe the behavior of a gas?

- How are temperature, pressure, and volume related in Boyle's law?

- How is Boyle's law different from Charles's law?

Vocabulary

kinetic molecular theory

pressure

Boyle's law

Charles's law

 Multilingual eGlossary

Video

What's Science Got to do With It?

 AID S1.2b, S2.2a, S2.2b, S2.2c, S2.2d, S2.2e, S2.3a, S2.3b, S3.1a, S3.1b, S3.2a, S3.2g, S3.2h, S3.3; IS 1.1, 3.1; ICT 2.3; PS 3.1c

Inquiry Survival Gear?

Why do some pilots wear oxygen masks? Planes fly at high altitudes where the atmosphere has a lower pressure and gas molecules are less concentrated. If the pressure is not adjusted inside the airplane, a pilot must wear an oxygen mask to inhale enough oxygen to keep the body functioning.

Stocktrek Images/Getty Images

Are volume and pressure of a gas related? 🚗 🧪 ✋

Pressure affects gases differently than it affects solids and liquids. How do pressure changes affect the volume of a gas?

1 Read and complete a lab safety form.

2 Stretch and blow up a **small balloon** several times.

3 Finally, blow up the balloon to a diameter of about 5 cm. Twist the neck, and stretch the mouth of the balloon over the opening of a **plastic bottle. Tape** the neck of the balloon to the bottle.

4 Squeeze and release the bottle several times while observing the balloon. Record your observations in your Science Journal.

Think About This

1. Why doesn't the balloon deflate when you attach it to the bottle?

2. What caused the balloon to inflate when you squeezed the bottle?

3. 🔑 **Key Concept** Using this lab as a reference, do you think pressure and volume of a gas are related? Explain.

Understanding Gas Behavior

Pilots do not worry as much about solids and liquids at high altitudes as they do gases. That is because gases behave differently than solids and liquids. Changes in temperature, pressure, and volume affect the behavior of gases more than they affect solids and liquids.

The explanation of particle behavior in solids, liquids, and gases is based on the kinetic molecular theory. The **kinetic molecular theory** *is an explanation of how particles in matter behave.* Some basic ideas in this theory are

- small particles make up all matter;

- these particles are in constant, random motion;

- the particles collide with other particles, other objects, and the walls of their container;

- when particles collide, no energy is lost.

You have read about most of these, but the last two statements are very important in explaining how gases behave.

✓ **Key Concept Check** How does the kinetic molecular theory describe the behavior of a gas?

ACADEMIC VOCABULARY

theory
(noun) an explanation of things or events that is based on knowledge gained from many observations and investigations

Hutchings Photography/Digital Light Source

Greatest volume, least pressure

Less volume, more pressure

Least volume, most pressure

Figure 15 🔑 As pressure increases, the volume of the gas decreases.

What is pressure?

Particles in gases move constantly. As a result of this movement, gas particles constantly collide with other particles and their container. When particles collide with their container, pressure results. **Pressure** *is the amount of force applied per unit of area.* For example, gas in a cylinder, as shown in **Figure 15,** might contain trillions of gas particles. These particles exert forces on the cylinder each time they strike it. When a weight is added to the plunger, the plunger moves down, compressing the gas in the cylinder. With less space to move around, the particles that make up the gas collide with each other more frequently, causing an increase in pressure. The more the particles are compressed, the more often they collide, increasing the pressure.

Pressure and Volume

Figure 15 also shows the relationship between pressure and volume of gas at a constant temperature. What happens to pressure if the volume of a container changes? Notice that when the volume is greater, the particles have more room to move. This additional space results in fewer collisions within the cylinder, and pressure is less. The gas particles in the middle cylinder have even less volume and more pressure. In the cylinder on the right, the pressure is greater because the volume is less. The particles collide with the container more frequently. Because of the greater number of collisions within the container, pressure is greater.

WORD ORIGIN · · · · · · · · · · · ·

pressure
from Latin *pressura*, means
"to press"

FOLDABLES

Fold a sheet of notebook paper to make a three-tab Foldable and label as shown. Use your Foldable to compare two important gas laws.

Boyle's Law
Both
Charles's Law

Boyle's Law

You read that the pressure and volume of a gas are related. Robert Boyle (1627–1691), a British scientist, was the first to describe this property of gases. **Boyle's law** *states that pressure of a gas increases if the volume decreases and pressure of a gas decreases if the volume increases, when temperature is constant.* This law can be expressed mathematically as shown to the left.

 Key Concept Check What is the relationship between pressure and volume of a gas if temperature is constant?

Boyle's Law in Action

You have probably felt Boyle's law in action if you have ever traveled in an airplane. While on the ground, the air pressure inside your middle ear and the pressure of the air surrounding you are equal. As the airplane takes off and begins to increase in altitude, the air pressure of the surrounding air decreases. However, the air pressure inside your middle ear does not decrease. The trapped air in your middle ear increases in volume, which can cause pain. These pressure changes also occur when the plane is landing. You can equalize this pressure difference by yawning or chewing gum.

Graphing Boyle's Law

This relationship is shown in the graph in **Figure 16.** Pressure is on the *x*-axis, and volume is on the *y*-axis. Notice that the line decreases in value from left to right. This shows that as the pressure of a gas increases, the volume of the gas decreases.

Figure 16 The graph shows that as pressure increases, volume decreases. This is true only if the temperature of the gas is constant.

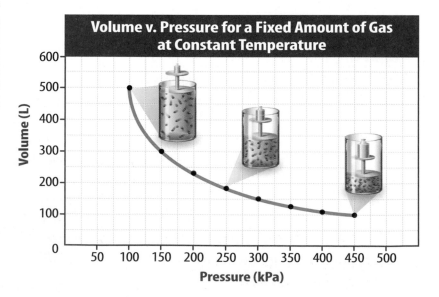

Lower temperature, less volume

Higher temperature, greater volume

Figure 17 As the temperature of a gas increases, the kinetic energy of the particles increases. The particles move farther apart, and volume increases.

Temperature and Volume

Pressure and volume changes are not the only factors that affect gas behavior. Changing the temperature of a gas also affects its behavior, as shown in **Figure 17.** The gas in the cylinder on the left has a low temperature. The average kinetic energy of the particles is low, and they move closer together. The volume of the gas is less. When thermal energy is added to the cylinder, the gas particles move faster and spread farther apart. This increases the pressure from gas particles, which push up the plunger. This increases the volume of the container.

Charles's Law

Jacque Charles (1746–1823) was a French scientist who described the relationship between temperature and volume of a gas. **Charles's law** *states that the volume of a gas increases with increasing temperature, if the pressure is constant.* Charles's practical experience with gases was most likely the result of his interest in balloons. Charles and his colleague were the first to pilot and fly a hydrogen-filled balloon in 1783.

Key Concept Check How is Boyle's law different from Charles's law?

(Inquiry) **MiniLab** 20 minutes

How does temperature affect the volume? 🥽 🧤 🧹 ✋

You can observe Charles's law in action using a few lab supplies.

1 Read and complete a lab safety form.

2 Stretch and blow up a **small balloon** several times.

3 Finally, blow up the balloon to a diameter of about 5 cm. Twist the neck and stretch the mouth of the balloon over the opening of an **ovenproof flask.**

4 Place the flask on a cold **hot plate.** Turn on the hot plate to low, and gradually heat the flask. Record your observations in your Science Journal.

5 ⚠ Use **tongs** to remove the flask from the hot plate. Allow the flask to cool for 5 min. Record your observations.

6 Place the flask in a **bowl of ice water.** Record your observations.

Analyze and Conclude

Key Concept What is the effect of temperature changes on the volume of a gas?

Charles's Law in Action

You have probably seen Charles's law in action if you have ever taken a balloon outside on a cold winter day. Why does a balloon appear slightly deflated when you take it from a warm place to a cold place? When the balloon is in cold air, the temperature of the gas inside the balloon decreases. Recall that a decrease in temperature is a decrease in the average kinetic energy of particles. As a result, the gas particles slow down and begin to get closer together. Fewer particles hit the inside of the balloon. The balloon appears partially deflated. If the balloon is returned to a warm place, the kinetic energy of the particles increases. More particles hit the inside of the balloon and push it out. The volume increases.

Reading Check What happens when you warm a balloon?

Graphing Charles's Law

The relationship described in Charles's law is shown in the graph of several gases in **Figure 18.** Temperature is on the *x*-axis and volume is on the *y*-axis. Notice that the lines are straight and represent increasing values. Each line in the graph is extrapolated to −273°C. *Extrapolated* means the graph is extended beyond the observed data points. This temperature also is referred to as 0 K (kelvin), or absolute zero. This temperature is theoretically the lowest possible temperature of matter. At absolute zero, all particles are at the lowest possible energy state and do not move. The particles contain a minimal amount of thermal energy (potential energy + kinetic energy).

Figure 18 The volume of a gas increases when the temperature increases at constant pressure.

Visual Check What do the dashed lines mean?

 Key Concept Check Which factors must be constant in Boyle's law and in Charles's law?

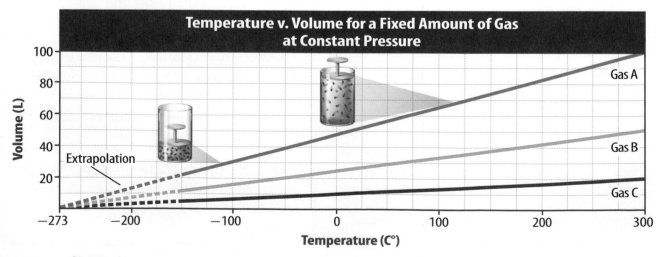

Temperature v. Volume for a Fixed Amount of Gas at Constant Pressure

Gas A

Gas B

Gas C

Extrapolation

Volume (L)

Temperature (C°)

Lesson 3 Review

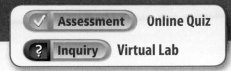
Visual Summary

The explanation of particle behavior in solids, liquids, and gases is based on the kinetic molecular theory.

As volume of a gas decreases, the pressure increases when at constant temperature.

At constant pressure, as the temperature of a gas increases, the volume also increases.

FOLDABLES

Use your lesson Foldable to review the lesson. Save your Foldable for the project at the end of the chapter.

What do you think NOW?

You first read the statements below at the beginning of the chapter.

5. Changes in temperature and pressure affect gas behavior.

6. If the pressure on a gas increases, the volume of the gas also increases.

Did you change your mind about whether you agree or disagree with the statements? Rewrite any false statements to make them true.

Use Vocabulary

1 **List** the basic ideas of the kinetic molecular theory.

2 _____ is force applied per unit area.

Understand Key Concepts

3 Which is held constant when a gas obeys Boyle's law?
A. motion
C. temperature
B. pressure
D. volume

4 **Describe** how the kinetic molecular theory explains the behavior of a gas.

5 **Contrast** Charles's law with Boyle's law.

6 **Explain** how temperature, pressure, and volume are related in Boyle's law.

Interpret Graphics

7 **Explain** what happens to the particles to the right when more weights are added.

8 **Identify** Copy and fill in the graphic organizer below to list three factors that affect gas behavior.

Critical Thinking

9 **Describe** what would happen to the pressure of a gas if the volume of the gas doubles while at a constant temperature.

Math Skills

 Review
— Math Practice —

10 **Calculate** The pressure on 400 mL of a gas is raised from 20.5 kPa to 80.5 kPa. What is the final volume of the gas?

Design an Experiment to Collect Data

Materials

triple-beam balance

50-mL graduated cylinders

beakers

test tubes

thermometers

distilled water

Also needed: ice, salt

Safety

In this chapter, you have learned about the relationship between the motion of particles in matter and change of state. How might you use your knowledge of particles in real life? Suppose that you work for a state highway department in a cold climate. Your job is to test three products. You must determine which is the most effective in melting existing ice, the best at keeping melted ice from refreezing, and the best product to buy.

Question

How can you compare the products? What might make one product better than another? Consider how you can describe and compare the effect of each product on both existing ice and the freezing point of water. Think about controls, variables, and the equipment you have available.

Procedure

1. Read and complete a lab safety form.

2. In your Science Journal, write a set of procedures you will use to answer your questions. Include the materials and steps you will use to test the effect of each product on existing ice and on the freezing point of water. How will you record your data? Draw any data tables, such as the example below, that you might need. Have your teacher approve your procedures.

Distilled Water	Time (min)	0	1	2	3	4	5	6	7	8
	Temperature (°C)									
Product A	Time (min)	0	1	2	3	4	5	6	7	8
	Temperature (°C)									
Product B	Time (min)	0	1	2	3	4	5	6	7	8
	Temperature (°C)									
Product C	Time (min)	0	1	2	3	4	5	6	7	8
	Temperature (°C)									

3. Begin by observing and recording your observations on how each product affects ice. Does it make ice melt or melt faster?

4. Test the effect of each product on the freezing point of water. Think about how you will ensure that each product is tested in the same way.

5. Add any additional tests you think you might need to make your recommendation.

Hutchings Photography/Digital Light Source

Analyze and Conclude

6 **Analyze the data** you have collected. Which product was most effective in melting existing ice? How do you know?

7 **Determine** which product was most effective in lowering the freezing point of water.

8 **Draw or make a model** to show the effect of dissolved solids on water molecules.

9 **Recognize Cause and Effect** In terms of particles, what causes dissolved solids to lower the freezing point of water?

10 **Draw Conclusions** In terms of particles, why are some substances more effective than others in lowering the freezing point of water?

11 **The Big Idea** Why is the kinetic molecular theory important in understanding how and why matter changes state?

Communicate Your Results

You are to present your recommendations to the road commissioners. Create a graphic presentation that clearly displays your results and justifies your recommendations about which product to buy.

In some states, road crews spray liquid deicer on the roads. If your teacher approves, you may enjoy testing liquids, such as alcohol, corn syrup, or salad oil.

Lab Tips

☑ To ensure fair testing, add the same mass of each product to the ice cubes at the same time.

☑ Be sure to add the same mass of each solid to the same volume of water. About 1 g of solid in 10 mL of water is a good ratio.

☑ Keep adding crushed ice/salt slush to the cup so that the liquid in the test tubes remains below the surface.

Remember to use scientific methods.

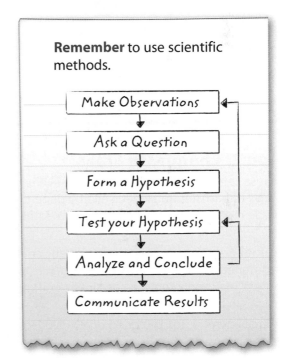

Make Observations
↓
Ask a Question
↓
Form a Hypothesis
↓
Test your Hypothesis
↓
Analyze and Conclude
↓
Communicate Results

Chapter 4 Study Guide

As matter changes from one state to another, the distances and the forces between the particles change, and the amount of thermal energy in the matter changes.

Key Concepts Summary 🔑

	Vocabulary
Lesson 1: Solids, Liquids, and Gases • Particles vibrate in **solids.** They move faster in **liquids** and even faster in **gases.** • The force of attraction among particles decreases as matter goes from a solid, to a liquid, and finally to a gas.  **Solid** **Liquid** **Gas**	solid liquid viscosity surface tension gas vapor
Lesson 2: Changes in State • Because **temperature** is defined as the average **kinetic energy** of particles and kinetic energy depends on particle motion, temperature is directly related to particle motion. • **Thermal energy** includes both the kinetic energy and the potential energy of particles in matter. However, temperature is only the average kinetic energy of particles in matter. • Thermal energy must be added or removed from matter for a change of state to occur.	kinetic energy temperature thermal energy vaporization evaporation condensation sublimation deposition
Lesson 3: The Behavior of Gases • The **kinetic molecular theory** states basic assumptions that are used to describe particles and their interactions in gases and other states of matter. • **Pressure** of a gas increases if the volume decreases, and pressure of a gas decreases if the volume increases, when temperature is constant. • **Boyle's law** describes the behavior of a gas when pressure and volume change at constant temperature. **Charles's law** describes the behavior of a gas when temperature and volume change, and pressure is constant. 	kinetic molecular theory pressure Boyle's law Charles's law

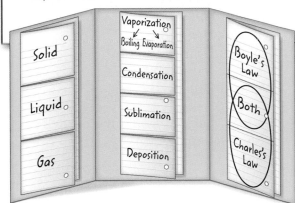

FOLDABLES® **Chapter Project**

Assemble your lesson Foldables as shown to make a Chapter Project. Use the project to review what you have learned in this chapter.

Use Vocabulary

Replace the underlined word with the correct term.

1 Matter with a definite shape and a definite volume is known as a <u>gas</u>.

2 <u>Surface tension</u> is a measure of a liquid's resistance to flow.

3 The gas state of a substance that is normally a solid or a liquid at room temperature is a <u>pressure</u>.

4 <u>Boiling</u> is vaporization that occurs at the surface of a liquid.

5 <u>Boyle's law</u> is an explanation of how particles in matter behave.

6 When graphing a gas obeying <u>Boyle's law</u>, the line will be a straight line with a positive slope.

Link Vocabulary and Key Concepts

Concepts in Motion Interactive Concept Map

Copy this concept map, and then use vocabulary terms from the previous page to complete the concept map.

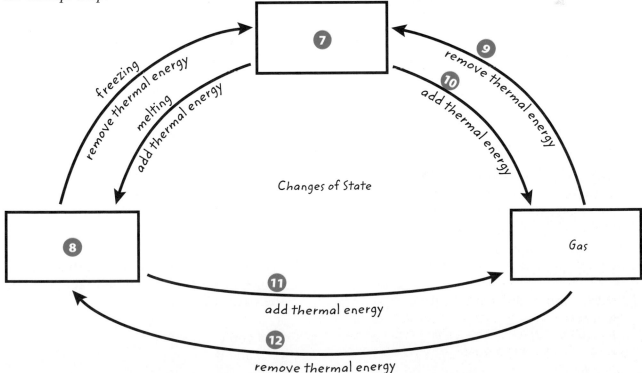

Understand Key Concepts 🔑

1 What would happen if you tried to squeeze a gas into a smaller container?
  A. The attractive forces between the particles would increase.
  B. The force of the particles would prevent you from doing it.
  C. The particles would have fewer collisions with the container.
  D. The repulsive forces of the particles would pull on the container.

2 Which type of motion in the figure below best represents the movement of gas particles?

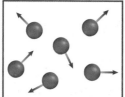
Motion 1

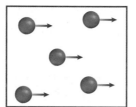
Motion 2

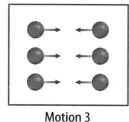
Motion 3

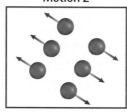
Motion 4

  A. motion 1
  B. motion 2
  C. motion 3
  D. motion 4

3 A pile of snow slowly disappears into the air, even though the temperature remains below freezing. Which process explains this?
  A. condensation
  B. deposition
  C. evaporation
  D. sublimation

4 Which unit is a density unit?
  A. cm^3
  B. cm^3/g
  C. g
  D. g/cm^3

5 Which is a form of vaporization?
  A. condensation
  B. evaporation
  C. freezing
  D. melting

6 When a needle is placed on the surface of water, it floats. Which idea best explains why this happens?
  A. Boyle's law
  B. molecular theory
  C. surface tension
  D. viscosity theory

7 In which material would the particles be most closely spaced?
  A. air
  B. brick
  C. syrup
  D. water

Use the graph below to answer questions 8 and 9.

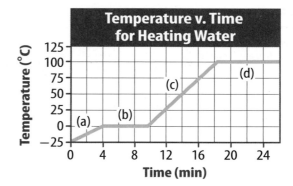

8 Which area of the graph above shows melting of a solid?
  A. a
  B. b
  C. c
  D. d

9 Which area or areas of the graph above shows a change in the potential energy of the particles?
  A. a
  B. a and c
  C. b and d
  D. c

Critical Thinking

10 **Explain** how the distances between particles in a solid, a liquid, and a gas help determine the densities of each.

11 **Describe** what would happen to the volume of a balloon if it were submerged in hot water.

12 **Assess** The particles of an unknown liquid have very weak attractions for other particles in the liquid. Would you expect the liquid to have a high or low viscosity? Explain your answer.

13 **Rank** these liquids from highest to lowest viscosity: honey, rubbing alcohol, and ketchup.

14 **Evaluate** Each beaker below contains the same amount of water. The thermometers show the temperature in each beaker. Explain the kinetic energy differences in each beaker.

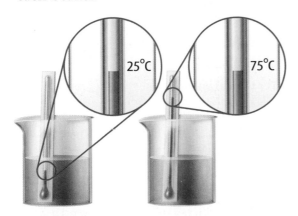

15 **Summarize** A glass with a few milliliters of water is placed on a counter. No one touches the glass. Explain what happens to the water after a few days.

Writing in Science

16 **Write** a paragraph that describes how you could determine the melting point of a substance from its heating or cooling curve.

REVIEW THE BIG IDEA

17 During springtime in Alaska, frozen rivers thaw and boats can navigate the rivers again. What physical changes and energy changes occur to the ice molecules when ice changes to water? Explain the process in which water in the river changes to water vapor.

18 In the photo below, explain how the average kinetic energy of the particles changes as the molten glass cools. What instrument could you use to verify the change in the average kinetic energy of the particles?

Math Skills

Review

— Math Practice —

Solve Equations

19 The pressure on 1 L of a gas at a pressure of 600 kPa is lowered to 200 kPa. What is the final volume of the gas?

20 A gas has a volume of 30 mL at a pressure of 5000 kPa. What is the volume of the gas if the pressure is lowered to 1,250 kPa?

Standardized Test Practice

Record your answers on the answer sheet provided by your teacher or on a separate sheet of paper.

Multiple Choice

1 Which property applies to matter that consists of particles vibrating in place?

A has a definite shape

B takes the shape of the container

C flows easily at room temperature

D particles far apart

Use the figure below to answer questions 2 and 3.

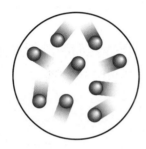

2 Which state of matter is represented above?

A amorphous solid

B crystalline solid

C gas

D liquid

3 Which best describes the attractive forces between particles shown in the figure?

A The attractive forces keep the particles vibrating in place.

B The particles hardly are affected by the attractive forces.

C The attractive forces keep the particles close together but still allow movement.

D The particles are locked in their positions because of the attractive forces between them.

4 What happens to matter as its temperature increases?

A The average kinetic energy of its particles decreases.

B The average thermal energy of its particles decreases.

C The particles gain kinetic energy.

D The particles lose potential energy.

Use the figure to answer question 5.

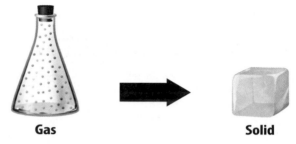

Gas   Solid

5 Which process is represented in the figure?

A deposition

B freezing

C sublimation

D vaporization

6 Which is a fundamental assumption of the kinetic molecular theory?

A All atoms are composed of subatomic particles.

B The particles of matter move in predictable paths.

C No energy is lost when particles collide with one another.

D Particles of matter never come into contact with one another.

7 Which is true of the thermal energy of particles?

A Thermal energy includes the potential and the kinetic energy of the particles.

B Thermal energy is the same as the average kinetic energy of the particles.

C Thermal energy is the same as the potential energy of particles.

D Thermal energy is the same as the temperature of the particles.

Use the graph below to answer question 8.

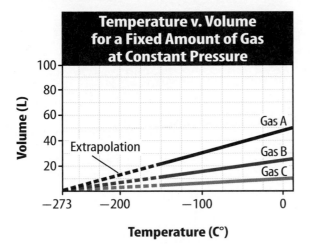

8 Which relationship is shown in the graph?

A Boyle's law

B Charles's law

C kinetic molecular theory

D definition of thermal energy

Constructed Response

9 Some people say that something that does not move very quickly is "as slow as molasses in winter." What property of molasses is described by the saying? Based on the saying, how do you think this property changes with temperature?

Use the graph to answer questions 10 and 11.

A scientist measured the temperature of a sample of frozen mercury as thermal energy is added to the sample. The graph below shows the results.

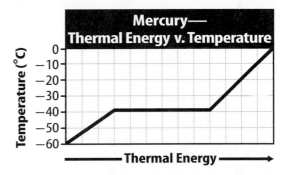

10 At what temperature does mercury melt? How do you know?

11 Describe the motion and arrangement of mercury atoms while the temperature is constant.

12 Atmospheric pressure is greater at the base of a mountain than at its peak. A hiker drinks from a water bottle at the top of a mountain. The bottle is capped tightly. At the base of the mountain, the water bottle has collapsed slightly. What happened to the gas inside the bottle? Assume constant temperature. Explain.

NEED EXTRA HELP?												
If You Missed Question...	1	2	3	4	5	6	7	8	9	10	11	12
Go to Lesson...	1	1	1	2	2	3	2	3	1	1	2	3

Chapter 5

AID M2.1a, S1.1b, S1.2a, S1.4, S2.1a, S2.1b, S2.1c, S2.1d, S3.1a, S3.2c, S3.2d, T1.1a, T1.2a, T1.3a, T1.3b, T1.4a, T1.5a, T1.5b; IS 1.1, 1.3, 3.1; ICT 6.1, 6.2; IPS 1.2, 1.3, 2.1; PS 3.1a, 4.1d, 4.1e, 4.2a, 4.2b, 4.2d

Thermal Energy

THE BIG IDEA How can thermal energy be used?

Inquiry What are these colors?

This image shows the thermal energy of cars moving in traffic. The white indicates regions of high thermal energy, and the dark blue indicates regions of low thermal energy.

- What is thermal energy?
- How does thermal energy relate to temperature and heat?
- How can thermal energy be used?

Tyrone Turner/National Geographic Stock

Get Ready to Read

What do you think?

Before you read, decide if you agree or disagree with each of these statements. As you read this chapter, see if you change your mind about any of the statements.

1 Temperature is the same as thermal energy.

2 Heat is the movement of thermal energy from a hotter object to a cooler object.

3 It takes a large amount of energy to significantly change the temperature of an object with a low specific heat.

4 The thermal energy of an object can never be increased or decreased.

5 Car engines create energy.

6 Refrigerators cool food by moving thermal energy from inside the refrigerator to the outside.

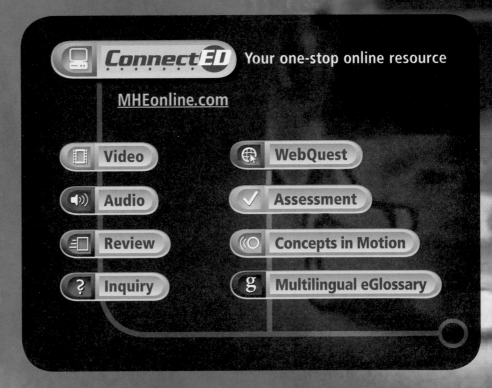

ConnectED Your one-stop online resource

MHEonline.com

- Video
- Audio
- Review
- Inquiry
- WebQuest
- Assessment
- Concepts in Motion
- Multilingual eGlossary

Lesson 1

Reading Guide

Key Concepts 🗝
ESSENTIAL QUESTIONS

- How are temperature and kinetic energy related?
- How do heat and thermal energy differ?

Vocabulary
thermal energy

temperature

heat

g Multilingual eGlossary

 AID S1.2a, S1.4, S2.1a, S2.1b, S2.1c, S2.1d, S3.1a, S3.2c, S3.2d; PS 4.1d, 4.1e, 4.2a

Thermal Energy, Temperature, and Heat

inquiry How hot is it?

Forty gallons of sugar-maple sap must be heated to a very high temperature for several days to produce 1 gallon of maple syrup. What kind of energy is needed to achieve this very high temperature? Is there a difference between heat, temperature, and thermal energy?

Philip Scalia/Alamy

How can you describe temperature?

Have you ever used Fahrenheit or Celsius to describe the temperature? Why can't you just make up your own temperature scale?

1. Read and complete a lab safety form.

2. Use a **ruler** and a **permanent marker** to divide a **clear plastic straw** into 12 equal parts. Number the lines. Give your scale a name.

3. Add a room-temperature **colored alcohol-water mixture** to an **empty plastic water bottle** until it is about $\frac{1}{4}$ full.

4. Place one end of the straw into the bottle with the tip just below the surface of the liquid. Seal the straw onto the bottle top with **clay.**

5. Place the bottle in a **hot water bath**, and observe the liquid in your straw.

Think About This

1. Why is it important for scientists to use the same scale to measure temperature?

2. 🔑 **Key Concept** What are some ways to make the liquid in your thermometer rise or fall?

Kinetic and Potential Energy

What do a soaring soccer ball and the particles that make up hot maple syrup have in common? They all have energy, or the ability to cause change. What type of energy does a moving soccer ball have? Recall that any moving object has kinetic energy. When the athlete in **Figure 1** kicks the ball and puts it in motion, the ball has kinetic energy.

In addition to kinetic energy, when the soccer ball is in the air, it has potential energy. Potential energy is stored energy due to the interaction between two objects. For example, think of Earth as one object and the ball as another. When the ball is in the air, it is attracted to Earth due to gravity. This attraction is called gravitational potential energy. In other words, since the ball has the potential to change, it has potential energy. And, the higher the ball is in the air, the greater the potential energy of the ball.

You also might recall that the potential energy plus the kinetic energy of an object is the mechanical energy of the object. When a soccer ball is flying through the air, you could describe the mechanical energy of the ball by describing both its kinetic and potential energy. On the next page, you will read about how the particles that make up maple syrup have energy, just like a soaring soccer ball.

✓ **Reading Check** How could you describe the energy of a moving object?

(t)Hutchings Photography/Digital Light Source, (b)Jamie Sabau/Getty Images

REVIEW VOCABULARY · · · · ·

kinetic energy
the energy an object or a particle has because it is moving

potential energy
stored energy

Figure 1 This soccer ball has both kinetic energy and potential energy.

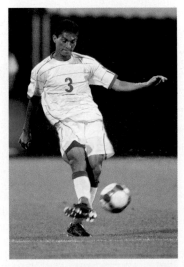

What is thermal energy?

Every solid, liquid, and gas is made up of trillions of tiny particles that are constantly moving. Moving particles make up the books you read, the air you breathe, and the maple syrup you pour on your pancakes. For example, the particles that make up a book, or any solid, vibrate in place. The particles that make up the air around you, or any gas, are spread out and move freely and quickly. Because particles are in motion, they have kinetic energy, like the soaring soccer ball in **Figure 2.** The faster particles move, the more kinetic energy they have.

The particles that make up matter also have potential energy. Like the interaction between a soccer ball and Earth, particles that make up matter interact with and are attracted to one another. The particles that make up solids usually are held very close together by attractive forces. The particles that make up a liquid are slightly farther apart than those that make up a solid. And, the particles that make up a gas are much more spread out than those that make up either a solid or a liquid. The greater the average distance between particles, the greater the potential energy of the particles.

Recall that a flying soccer ball has mechanical energy, which is the sum of its potential energy and its kinetic energy. The particles that make up the soccer ball, or any material, have a similar kind of energy called thermal energy. **Thermal energy** *is the sum of the kinetic energy and the potential energy of the particles that make up a material.* Thermal energy describes the energy of the particles that make up a solid, a liquid, or a gas.

Reading Check How are thermal energy and mechanical energy similar? How are they different?

Figure 2 The potential energy of the soccer ball depends on the distance between the ball and Earth. The potential energy of the particles of matter depends on their distance from one another.

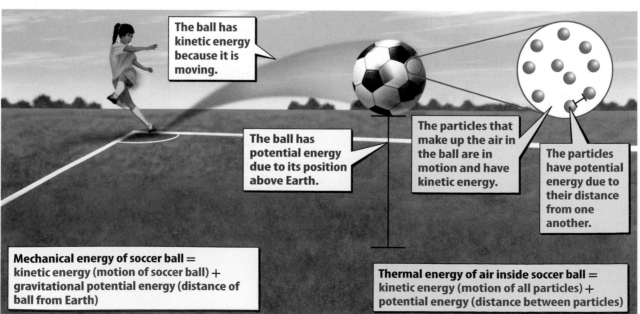

The ball has kinetic energy because it is moving.

The ball has potential energy due to its position above Earth.

The particles that make up the air in the ball are in motion and have kinetic energy.

The particles have potential energy due to their distance from one another.

Mechanical energy of soccer ball = kinetic energy (motion of soccer ball) + gravitational potential energy (distance of ball from Earth)

Thermal energy of air inside soccer ball = kinetic energy (motion of all particles) + potential energy (distance between particles)

Figure 3 🗝 The air's temperature depends on how fast the particles in the air move.

Visual Check What happens to the motion of the particles in the air as temperature increases?

((O)) **Concepts in Motion**
Animation

What is temperature?

When you think of temperature, you probably think of it as a measurement of how warm or cold something is. However, scientists define temperature in terms of kinetic energy.

Average Kinetic Energy and Temperature

The particles that make up the air inside and outside the house in **Figure 3** are moving. However, they are not moving at the same speed. The particles in the air in the warm house move faster and have more kinetic energy than those outside on a cold winter evening. **Temperature** *represents the average kinetic energy of the particles that make up a material.*

The greater the average kinetic energy of particles, the greater the temperature. The temperature of the air inside the house is higher than the temperature of the air outside the house. This is because the particles that make up the air inside the house have greater average kinetic energy than those outside. In other words, the particles of air inside the house are moving at a greater average speed than those outside.

🗝 **Key Concept Check** How are temperature and kinetic energy related?

Thermal Energy and Temperature

Temperature and thermal energy are related, but they are not the same. For example, as a frozen pond melts, both ice and water are present and they have the same temperature. Therefore, the particles that make up the ice and the water have the same average kinetic energy, or speed. However, the particles do not have the same thermal energy. This is because the average distance of the particles that make up liquid water and ice are different. The particles that make up the liquid and the solid water have different potential energies and, therefore, different thermal energies.

WORD ORIGIN · · · · · · ·

temperature
from Latin *temperatura*, means "moderating, tempering"

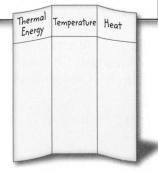

FOLDABLES

Make a vertical three-column chart book. Label it as shown. Use it to organize your notes on the properties of heat, temperature, and thermal energy.

Thermal Energy	Temperature	Heat

itpow/Getty Images

Convert Between Temperature Scales

To convert Fahrenheit to Celsius, use the following equation:

$$°C = \frac{(°F - 32)}{1.8}$$

For example, to convert **176°F** to Celsius:

1. Always perform the operation in parentheses first.

$$176 - 32 = 144$$

2. Divide the answer from Step 1 by 1.8.

$$\frac{144}{1.8} = 80°C$$

To convert Celsius to Fahrenheit, follow the same steps using the following equation:

$$°F = (°C \times 1.8) + 32$$

Practice

1. Convert 86°F to Celsius.

2. Convert 37°C to Fahrenheit.

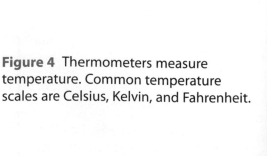

- **Math Practice**
- **Personal Tutor**

Measuring Temperature

How can you measure temperature? It would be impossible to measure the kinetic energy of individual particles and then calculate their average kinetic energy to determine the temperature. Instead, you can use thermometers, such as the ones in **Figure 4,** to measure temperature.

A common type of thermometer is a bulb thermometer. A bulb thermometer is a glass tube connected to a bulb that contains a liquid such as alcohol. When the temperature of the alcohol increases, the alcohol expands and rises in the glass tube. When the temperature of the alcohol decreases, the alcohol contracts back into the bulb. The height of the alcohol in the tube indicates the temperature.

There are other types of thermometers too, such as an electronic thermometer. This thermometer measures changes in the resistance of an electric circuit and converts this measurement to a temperature.

Temperature Scales

You might have seen the temperature in a weather report given in degrees Fahrenheit and degrees Celsius. On the Fahrenheit scale, water freezes at 32° and boils at 212°. On the Celsius scale, water freezes at 0° and boils at 100°. The Celsius scale is used by scientists worldwide.

Scientists also use the Kelvin scale. On the Kelvin scale, water freezes at 273 K and boils at 373 K. The lowest possible temperature for any material is 0 K. This is known as absolute zero. If a material were at 0 K, the particles in that material would not be moving and would no longer have kinetic energy. Scientists have not been able to cool any material to 0 K.

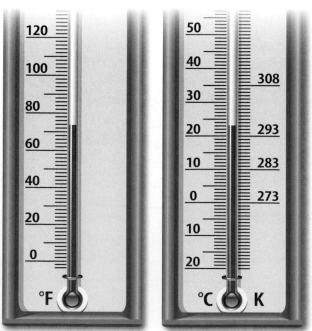

Figure 4 Thermometers measure temperature. Common temperature scales are Celsius, Kelvin, and Fahrenheit.

The hot cocoa has a high temperature. Thermal energy is transferred from the mug to its surroundings.

The heat from the hot cocoa transferred to the air is greater than the heat transferred from the hot cocoa to the girl's hands. This is because the temperature difference is greater from the hot cocoa to the air.

Figure 5 The hot cocoa heats the air and the girl's hands.

What is heat?

Have you ever held a cup of hot cocoa on a cold day like the girl in **Figure 5?** When you do, thermal energy moves from the warm cup to your hands. *The movement of thermal energy from a warmer object to a cooler object is called* **heat.** Another way to say this is that thermal energy from the cup heats your hands, or the cup is heating your hands.

Just as temperature and thermal energy are not the same thing, neither are heat and thermal energy. All objects have thermal energy. However, you heat something when thermal energy transfers from one object to another. The girl in **Figure 5** heats her hands because thermal energy transfers from the hot cocoa to her hands.

Key Concept Check How do heat and thermal energy differ?

The rate at which heating occurs depends on the difference in temperatures between the two objects. The difference in temperatures between the hot cocoa and the air is greater than the difference in temperatures between the hot cocoa and the cup. The hot cocoa heats the air more than it heats the cup. Heating continues until all objects in contact are the same temperature.

inquiry MiniLab
10 minutes

How do temperature scales compare?

If someone told you it was 2°C or 300 K outside, would you know whether it was warm or cold?

	Celsius (°C)	Fahrenheit (°F)	Kelvin (K)
Room temperature			
Light jacket weather			
Hot summer day			

1. Copy the table into your Science Journal.
2. Lay a **ruler** across **Figure 4** so that it lines up with the temperatures at which water freezes. Record the temperatures
3. Repeat step 2 for the three values in the table.

Analyze and Conclude

1. **Estimate** Imagine that it is snowing outside. What might the temperature be in degrees Celsius? In kelvin?

2. **Key Concept** Why doesn't the Kelvin scale include negative numbers?

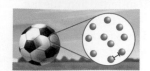

Visual Summary

The greater the distance between two particles or two objects, the greater the potential energy.

Heat is the movement of thermal energy from a warmer object to a cooler object.

When thermal energy moves between a material and its environment, the material's temperature changes.

FOLDABLES®

Use your lesson Foldable to review the lesson. Save your Foldable for the project at the end of the chapter.

What do you think NOW?

You first read the statements below at the beginning of the chapter.

1. Temperature is the same as thermal energy.

2. Heat is the movement of thermal energy from a hotter object to a cooler object.

Did you change your mind about whether you agree or disagree with the statements? Rewrite any false statements to make them true.

Use Vocabulary

1 The sum of kinetic energy and potential energy of the particles in a material is _____.

2 **Relate** temperature to the average kinetic energy in a material.

Understand Key Concepts

3 **Differentiate** between thermal energy and heat.

4 Which increases the kinetic energy of the particles that make up a bowl of soup?
   A. dividing the soup in half
   B. putting the soup in a refrigerator
   C. heating the soup for 1 min on a stove
   D. decreasing the distance between the particles that make up the soup

5 **Infer** Suppose a friend tells you he has a temperature of 38°C. Your temperature 37°C. Do the particles that make up your body or your friend's body have a greater average kinetic energy? Explain.

Interpret Graphics

6 **Identify** Copy and fill in the following graphic organizer to show the forms of energy that make up thermal energy.

Thermal Energy

Critical Thinking

7 **Explain** How could you increase the kinetic thermal energy of a liquid?

Math Skills ✕÷
— Math Practice —

8 Maple sap boils at 104°C. At what Fahrenheit temperature does the sap boil?

Summer Jones/Alamy

How do different materials affect thermal energy transfer?

Materials

cardboard

100-mL graduated cylinder

2 thermometers

Also Needed

1-L square plastic container, test containers (metal, polystyrene, ceramic, glass, plastic), large rubber band, hot water

Safety

You might have noticed that thermal energy moves more easily through some substances than others. For example, juice stays colder in a foam cup than in a can. How does the container's material affect how quickly thermal energy moves through it?

Learn It

To **form a hypothesis** is to propose an explanation for an observation. The explanation should be testable. One way to **test a hypothesis** is by gathering data that shows whether the hypothesis is correct.

Try It

1 Read and complete a lab safety form.

2 Observe the test containers. Write a hypothesis in your Science Journal that explains why you think a certain material will slow the transfer of thermal energy more than others.

3 Copy the table below.

4 Each lab group will test one container. Stand your test container in the center of a 1-L plastic container.

5 Add 125 mL of hot water to the test container. Measure and record the water's temperature.

6 Add room-temperature water to the plastic container until the level in both containers is equal. Measure and record the room-temperature water's temperature.

7 Place a cardboard square over the test container. Use two thermometers to take the temperature of the water in both containers every 2 min for 20 min. Record your data in your table.

8 Compare your data with the data gathered by the other teams. Rank the test containers from slowest to fastest thermal energy transfer in your Science Journal.

Apply It

9 **Analyze Data** Did your data support your hypothesis? Why or why not?

10 🔑 **Key Concept** What happened to the thermal energy of the water in the test container? Why did this happen?

°C	0 min	2 min	4 min	6 min	8 min	10 min	12 min	14 min	16 min	18 min	20 min
Temp in test container											
Temp in outer container											

Reading Guide

Key Concepts
ESSENTIAL QUESTIONS

- What is the effect of having a small specific heat?

- What happens to a material when it is heated?

- In what ways can thermal energy be transferred?

Vocabulary

radiation

conduction

thermal conductor

thermal insulator

specific heat

thermal contraction

thermal expansion

convection

convection current

 Multilingual eGlossary

Video **Science Video**

 AID M2.1a, S1.1b; IS 1.1, 1.3; PS 3.1a, 4.2b, 4.2d

Thermal Energy Transfers

Inquiry Keeping Warm?

Imagine camping in the mountains on a cold winter night. Your survival could depend on keeping warm. There are many things you could do to get warm and stay warm. In this picture, how is thermal energy transferred from the fire to the camper? Why does his coat keep him from losing thermal energy?

Johner Images/Getty Images

How hot is it?

When you touch an ice cube, you sense that it is cold. When you get inside a car on a warm day, you sense that it is hot. How accurate is your sense of touch in predicting temperature?

1. Read and complete a lab safety form.

2. Place the palm of one hand flat against a piece of **metal** and the other hand against a piece of **wood.** Observe which material feels colder, and record it in your Science Journal.

3. Repeat step 2 with other materials, including **cardboard, glass, plastic,** and **foam.**

4. Rank the materials from coldest to warmest in your Science Journal.

5. Place a **liquid crystal thermometer** on each material. Record the temperature of each material in your Science Journal.

Think About This

1. Were you able to accurately rank the materials by temperature only by touching them?

2. 🔑 **Key Concept** Why might some of the materials in this experiment feel cooler than others even though they are in the same room?

How is thermal energy transferred?

Have you ever gotten into a car, such as the one in **Figure 6,** on a hot summer day? You can guess that the inside of the car is hot even before you touch the door handle. You open the door and hot air seems to pour out of the car. When you touch the metal safety-belt buckle, it is hot. How is thermal energy transferred between objects? Thermal energy is transferred in three ways—by radiation, conduction, and convection.

Radiation

The transfer of thermal energy from one material to another by electromagnetic waves is called **radiation.** All matter, including the Sun, fire, you, and even ice, transfers thermal energy by radiation. Warm objects emit more radiation than cold objects do. For example, when you place your hands near a fire, you can more easily feel the transfer of thermal energy by radiation than when you place your hands near a block of ice.

Thermal energy from the Sun heats the inside of the car in **Figure 6** by radiation. In fact, radiation is the only way thermal energy can travel from the Sun to Earth. This is because space is a **vacuum.** However, radiation also transfers thermal energy through solids, liquids, and gases.

✓ **Reading Check** How does the Sun heat the inside of a car?

SCIENCE USE V. COMMON USE

vacuum

Science Use a space that contains little or no matter

Common Use a device for cleaning carpets and rugs that uses suction

Figure 6 The Sun heats this car by radiation.

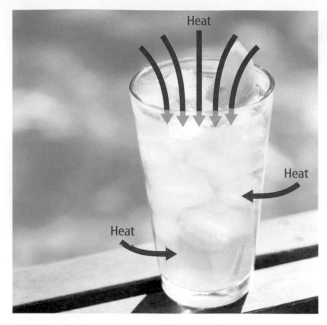

Figure 7 🔑 The hot air transfers thermal energy to, or heats, the cool lemonade by conduction. Eventually the kinetic thermal energy and temperature of the air and the lemonade will be equal.

(⦿) Concepts in Motion Animation

FOLDABLES®

Make a vertical three-column chart book. Label it as shown. Use it to describe the ways thermal energy is transferred.

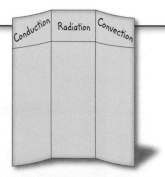

Conduction

Suppose it's a hot day and you have a cold glass of lemonade, such as the one in **Figure 7.** The lemonade has a lower temperature than the surrounding air. Therefore, the particles that make up the lemonade have less kinetic energy than the particles that make up the air. When particles with different kinetic energies collide, the particles with higher kinetic energy transfer energy to particles with lower kinetic energy.

In **Figure 7,** the particles that make up the air collide with and transfer kinetic energy to the particles that make up the lemonade. As a result, the average kinetic energy, or temperature, of the particles that make up the lemonade increases. Since kinetic energy is being transferred, thermal energy is being transferred. *The transfer of thermal energy between materials by the collisions of particles is called* **conduction.** Conduction continues until the thermal energy of all particles in contact is equal.

Thermal Conductors and Insulators

On a hot day, why does a metal safety-belt buckle in a car feel hotter than the safety belt? Both the buckle and safety belt receive the same amount of thermal energy from the Sun. The metal that makes up the buckle is a good thermal conductor. *A* **thermal conductor** *is a material through which thermal energy flows easily.* Atoms in good thermal conductors have electrons that move easily. These electrons transfer kinetic energy when they collide with other electrons and atoms. Metals are better thermal conductors than nonmetals. The cloth that makes up a safety belt is a good thermal insulator. *A* **thermal insulator** *is a material through which thermal energy does not flow easily.* The electrons in the atoms of a good thermal insulator do not move easily. These materials do not transfer thermal energy easily because fewer collisions occur between electrons and atoms.

Specific Heat

The amount of thermal energy required to increase the temperature of 1 kg of a material by 1°C is called **specific heat.** Every material has a specific heat. It does not take much energy to change the temperature of a material with a low specific heat but it can take a lot of energy to change the temperature of a material with high specific heat.

Thermal conductors, such as the metal safety-belt buckle in **Figure 8,** have a lower specific heat than thermal insulators, such as the cloth safety belt. This means it takes less thermal energy to increase the buckle's temperature than it takes to increase the temperature of the cloth safety belt by the same amount.

The specific heat of water is particularly high. It takes a large amount of energy to increase the temperature of water. The high specific heat of water has many beneficial effects. For example, much of your body is water. Water's high specific heat helps prevent your body from overheating. The high specific heat of water is one of the reasons why pools, lakes, and oceans stay cool in summer. Water's high specific heat also makes it ideal for cooling machinery, such as car engines and rock-cutting saws.

 Key Concept Check What does it mean if a material has a low specific heat?

ACADEMIC VOCABULARY

specific
(*adjective*) precise and detailed; belonging to a distinct category

Specific Heat 🔑

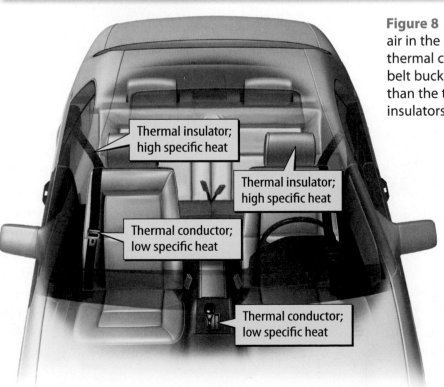

Thermal insulator; high specific heat

Thermal insulator; high specific heat

Thermal conductor; low specific heat

Thermal conductor; low specific heat

Figure 8 On a hot summer day, the air in the car is hot. The temperature of thermal conductors, such as the safety-belt buckles, increases more quickly than the temperature of thermal insulators, such as the seat material.

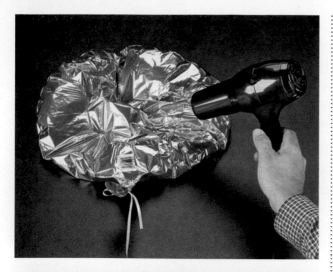

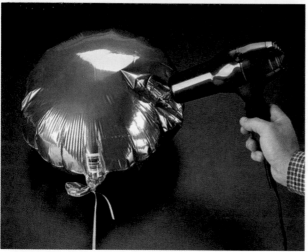

▲ **Figure 9** Air inside the balloon increases in volume when the temperature increases.

▲ **Figure 10** Sidewalks can withstand thermal expansion and contraction because of control joints.

Thermal Expansion and Contraction

What happens if you take an inflated balloon outside on a cold day? Thermal energy transfers from the particles that make up the air inside the balloon to the particles that make up the balloon material and then to the cold outside air. As the particles that make up the air in the balloon lose thermal energy, which includes kinetic energy, they slow down and get closer together. This causes the volume of the balloon to decrease. **Thermal contraction** *is a decrease in a material's volume when its temperature decreases.*

How could you reinflate the balloon? You could heat the air inside the balloon with a hair dryer, like in **Figure 9.** The particles that make up the hot air coming out of the hair dryer transfer thermal energy, which includes kinetic energy, to the particles that make up the air inside the balloon. As the average kinetic energy of the particles increases, the air temperature increases. Also, as the average kinetic energy of the particles increases, they speed up and spread out, increasing the volume of air inside the balloon. **Thermal expansion** *is an increase in a material's volume when its temperature increases.*

Thermal expansion and contraction are most noticeable in gases, less noticeable in liquids, and the least noticeable in solids.

Key Concept Check What happens to the volume of a gas when it is heated?

Sidewalk Gaps

In many places, outdoor temperatures become very hot in the summer. High temperatures can cause thermal expansion in structures, such as concrete sidewalks. If the concrete expands too much or expands unevenly, it could crack. Therefore, control joints are cut into sidewalks, as shown in **Figure 10.** If the sidewalk does crack, it should crack smoothly at the control joint.

Hot-Air Balloons

How do hot-air balloons work? As shown in **Figure 11**, a burner heats the air in the balloon, causing thermal expansion. The particles that make up the air inside the balloon move faster and faster. As the particles collide with one another, some are forced outside the balloon through the opening at the bottom. Now, there are fewer particles in the balloon than in the same volume of air outside the balloon. The balloon is less dense, and it begins to rise through denser outside air.

To land a hot-air balloon, the balloonist allows the air inside the balloon to gradually cool. The air undergoes thermal contraction. However, the balloon itself does not contract. Instead, denser air from outside the balloon fills the space inside. As the density of the balloon increases, it slowly descends.

Ovenproof Glass

If you put an ordinary drinking glass into a hot oven, the glass might break or shatter. However, an ovenproof glass dish would not be damaged in a hot oven. Why is this so?

Different parts of ordinary glass expand at different rates when heated. This causes it to crack or shatter. Ovenproof glass is designed to expand less than ordinary glass when heated, which means that it usually does not crack in the oven.

Figure 11 Hot-air balloonists control their balloons using thermal expansion and contraction.

New York FYI

Why Ice Expands One important exception to this general rule is water. Because of the forces that act between water molcules, water expands when it becomes ice.

---

inquiry MiniLab

20 minutes

How does adding thermal energy affect a wire?

How could thermal energy help you remove a metal lid from a glass jar?

1. Read and complete a lab safety form.

2. Set up **two ring stands** so that the rings are 1–2 m apart. Tie the ends of a **2-m length of wire** to the rings so that the wire is straight and tight.

3. Use **thread** to tie a **weight** to the middle of the wire.

4. Use a **ruler** to measure the distance from the bottom of the weight to the table. Record your data in your Science Journal.

5. Using **matches** light two **candles.** Move the candle flames back and forth under the wire. Repeat step 4 every minute for 5 min. Blow out the candles.

6. Repeat step 4 again every minute for 5 min as the wire cools.

Analyze and Conclude

1. **Predict** What would happen if you continued to heat the wire? Explain.

2. **Apply** How could you use this idea to help you remove a metal lid from a glass jar?

3. **Key Concept** What happens to the particles that make up the wire when the wire is heated? How do you know?

Review

Personal Tutor

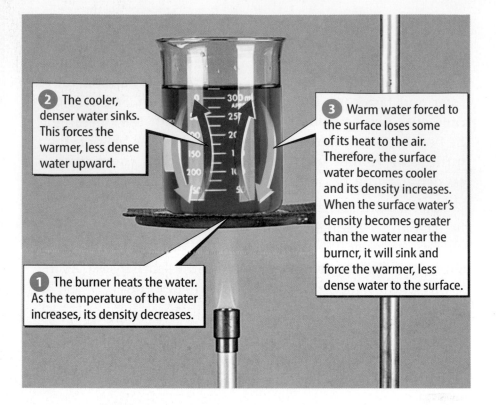

2 The cooler, denser water sinks. This forces the warmer, less dense water upward.

3 Warm water forced to the surface loses some of its heat to the air. Therefore, the surface water becomes cooler and its density increases. When the surface water's density becomes greater than the water near the burner, it will sink and force the warmer, less dense water to the surface.

1 The burner heats the water. As the temperature of the water increases, its density decreases.

Convection

When you heat a pan of water on the stove, the burner heats the pan by conduction. This process, shown in **Figure 12**, involves the movement of thermal energy within a fluid. The particles that make up liquids and gases move around easily. As they move, they transfer thermal energy from one location to another. **Convection** *is the transfer of thermal energy by the movement of particles from one part of a material to another.* Convection only occurs in fluids, such as water, air, magma, and maple syrup.

 Key Concept Check What are the three processes that transfer thermal energy?

Density, Thermal Expansion, and Thermal Contraction

In **Figure 12**, the burner transfers thermal energy to the beaker, which transfers thermal energy to the water. Thermal expansion occurs in water nearest the bottom of the beaker. Heating increases the water's volume making it less dense.

At the same time, water molecules at the water's surface transfer thermal energy to the air. This causes cooling and thermal contraction of the water on the surface. The denser water at the surface sinks to the bottom, forcing the less dense water upward. This cycle continues until all the water in the beaker is at the same temperature.

WORD ORIGIN

convection
from Latin *convectionem*, means "the act of carrying"

Matt Meadows

Convection Currents in Earth's Atmosphere

The movement of fluids in a cycle because of convection is a **convection current.** Convection currents circulate the water in Earth's oceans and other bodies of water. They also circulate the air in a room, and the materials in Earth's interior. Convection currents also move matter and thermal energy from inside the Sun to its surface.

On Earth, convection currents move air between the equator and latitudes near 30°N and 30°S. This plays an important role in Earth's climates, as shown in **Figure 13.**

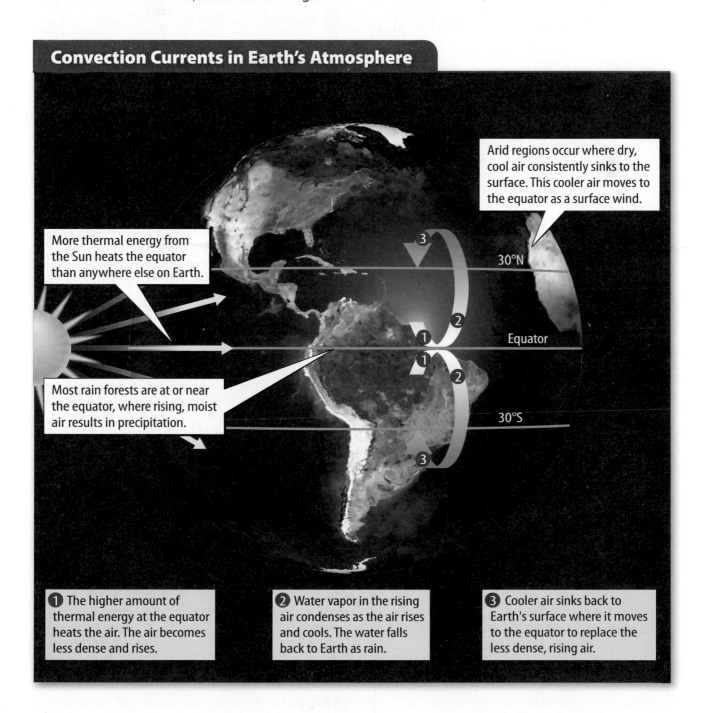

Convection Currents in Earth's Atmosphere

Arid regions occur where dry, cool air consistently sinks to the surface. This cooler air moves to the equator as a surface wind.

More thermal energy from the Sun heats the equator than anywhere else on Earth.

Most rain forests are at or near the equator, where rising, moist air results in precipitation.

30°N

Equator

30°S

❶ The higher amount of thermal energy at the equator heats the air. The air becomes less dense and rises.

❷ Water vapor in the rising air condenses as the air rises and cools. The water falls back to Earth as rain.

❸ Cooler air sinks back to Earth's surface where it moves to the equator to replace the less dense, rising air.

Visual Summary

When a material has a low specific heat, transferring a small amount of energy to the material increases its temperature significantly.

Thermal energy can be transferred through radiation, conduction, or convection.

When a material is heated, the thermal energy of the material increases and the material expands.

FOLDABLES®

Use your lesson Foldable to review the lesson. Save your Foldable for the project at the end of the chapter.

What do you think NOW?

You first read the statements below at the beginning of the chapter.

3. It takes a large amount of energy to significantly change the temperature of an object with a low specific heat.

4. The thermal energy of an object can never be increased or decreased.

Did you change your mind about whether you agree or disagree with the statements? Rewrite any false statements to make them true.

Use Vocabulary

1 The transfer of thermal energy by electromagnetic waves is _____.

2 **Define** *convection* in your own words.

Understand Key Concepts 🔑

3 **Contrast** radiation with conduction.

4 Why do hot-air balloons rise?
A. thermal conduction
B. thermal convection
C. thermal expansion
D. thermal radiation

5 **Infer** why the sauce on a hot pizza burns your mouth but the crust of the pizza does not burn your mouth.

Interpret Graphics

6 **Analyze** Two cubes with the same mass and volume are heated in the same pan of water. The graph below shows the change in temperature with time. Which cube has the higher specific heat?

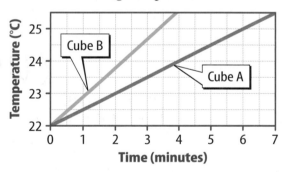

7 **Organize** Copy and fill in the graphic organizer to show how thermal energy is transferred.

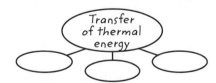

Critical Thinking

8 **Explain** Why do you use a pot holder when taking hot food out of the oven?

Matt Meadows

Insulating the Home

It's what's between the walls that matters.

The first requirement of a shelter is to protect you from the weather. If the weather where you live is mild year-round, almost any kind of shelter will do. However, basic shelters, such as huts and tents, are not comfortable during cold winters or hot summers. Over many centuries, societies have experimented with thermal insulators that keep the inside of a shelter warm during winter and cool during summer.

One of the first thermal insulators used in shelters was air. Because air is a poor conductor of thermal energy, using cavity walls became a common form of insulating homes in the United States.

An air gap was not the perfect solution, however. Convection currents in the cavity carried some thermal energy across the gap. At first, no one seemed to mind. But, in the 1970s, the cost of heating and cooling homes suddenly increased. People began looking for a better way to reduce the transfer of thermal energy between the outside and the inside.

To meet the growing demand for better insulation, scientists began researching to find better insulation materials. If you could stop the convection currents, they reasoned, you could stop the transfer of thermal energy. One way was to use materials such as polymer foam or fiberglass. Each of these trapped air between the walls and held it there.

But how do you install insulation if your house is already built? You poke holes in the walls and blow it in! This process has little effect on your home's structure, and it decreases the cost of heating and cooling the house.

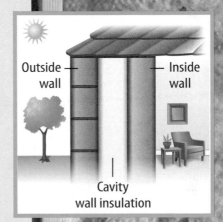

Outside wall — Inside wall

Cavity wall insulation

It's Your Turn

MAKE A POSTER A material's insulating ability is rated with an R-value. Find out what an R-value is. Then make a poster showing the ratings of common materials.

Lesson 3

Reading Guide

Key Concepts 🔑
ESSENTIAL QUESTIONS

- How does a thermostat work?
- How does a refrigerator keep food cold?
- What are the energy transformations in a car engine?

Vocabulary

heating appliance

thermostat

refrigerator

heat engine

 Multilingual eGlossary

 AID T1.1a, T1.2a, T1.3a, T1.3b, T1.4a, T1.5a, T1.5b; IS 1.3, 3.1; ICT 6.1, 6.2; IPS 1.2, 1.3, 2.1

Using Thermal Energy

Inquiry Concentrating Energy?

This power plant uses mirrors to focus light toward a tower. The tower then transforms some of the light into thermal energy. In what ways do we use thermal energy?

How can you transform energy?

If you rub your hands together very quickly, do they become warm? Where does the thermal energy come from?

1. Read and complete a lab safety form.
2. Copy the table into your Science Journal.
3. Place a **thermometer strip** on the surface of a **block of wood.** Record the temperature after the thermometer stops changing color.

	Starting temp (°C)	Ending temp (°C)
30 s		
60 s		

4. Remove the thermometer and rub the wood vigorously with **sandpaper** for 30 seconds. Quickly replace the thermometer, and record the temperature.
5. Repeat steps 3 and 4 on another part of the wood. This time, sand the wood for 60 seconds.

Think About This

1. Did the temperature of the wood change? Why or why not?
2. When did the wood have the highest temperature? Explain this result.
3. 🔑 **Key Concept** What energy transformations take place in this activity?

Thermal Energy Transformations

You can convert other forms of energy into thermal energy. Repeatedly stretching a rubber band makes it hot. Burning wood heats the air. A toaster gets hot when you turn it on.

You also can convert thermal energy into other forms of energy. Burning coal can generate electricity. Thermostats transform thermal energy into mechanical energy that switch heaters on and off. When you convert energy from one form to another, you can use the energy to perform useful tasks.

Remember that energy cannot be created or destroyed. Even though many devices transform energy from one form to another or transfer energy from one place to another, the total amount of energy does not change.

Heating Appliances

A device that converts electric energy into thermal energy is a **heating appliance.** Curling irons, coffeemakers, and clothes irons are some examples of heating appliances.

Other devices, such as computers and cell phones, also become warm when you use them. This is because some electric energy always is converted to thermal energy in an electronic device. However, the thermal energy that most electronic devices generate is not used for any purpose.

FOLDABLES

Make a vertical four-tab book. Label it as shown. Use it to explain the energy transformation that occurs in each device.

Heating Appliances
Heat Engines
Refrigerators
Thermostats

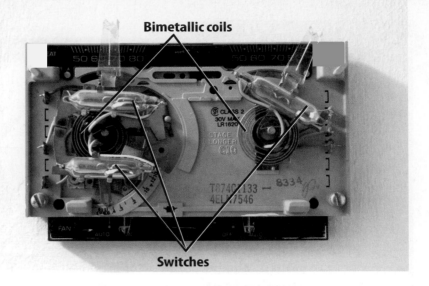

Figure 14 🔑 The coil in a thermostat contains two different metals that expand at two different rates.

Bimetallic coils

Switches

WORD ORIGIN

thermostat
from Greek *therme*, meaning "heat"; and *statos*, meaning "a standing"

Thermostats

You might have heard the furnace in your house or in your classroom turn on in the winter. After the room warms, the furnace turns off. *A* **thermostat** *is a device that regulates the temperature of a system.* Kitchen refrigerators, toasters, and ovens are all equipped with thermostats.

Most thermostats used in home heating systems contain a bimetallic coil. A bimetallic coil is made of two types of metal joined together and bent into a coil, as shown in **Figure 14.** The metal on the inside of the coil expands and contracts more than the metal on the outside of the coil. After the room warms, the thermal energy in the air causes the bimetallic coil to uncurl slightly. This moves a switch that turns off the furnace. As the room cools, the metal on the inside of the coil contracts more than the metal on the outside, curling the coil tighter. This moves the switch in the other direction, turning on the furnace.

 Key Concept Check How does the bimetallic coil in a thermostat respond to heating and cooling?

Refrigerators

A device that uses electric energy to transfer thermal energy from a cooler location to a warmer location is called a **refrigerator.** Recall that thermal energy naturally flows from a warmer area to a cooler area. The opposite might seem impossible. But, that is exactly how your refrigerator works. So, how does a refrigerator move thermal energy from its cold inside to the warm air outside? Pipes that surround the refrigerator are filled with a fluid, called a coolant, that flows through the pipes. Thermal energy from inside the refrigerator transfers to the coolant, keeping the inside of the refrigerator cold.

Derrick Alderman/Alamy

Vaporizing the Coolant

A coolant is a substance that evaporates at a low temperature. In a refrigerator, a coolant is pumped through pipes on the inside and the outside of the refrigerator. The coolant, which begins as a liquid, passes through an expansion valve and cools. As the cold gas flows through pipes inside the refrigerator, it absorbs thermal energy from the refrigerator compartment and vaporizes. The coolant gas becomes warmer, and the inside of the refrigerator becomes cooler.

Condensing the Coolant

The coolant flows to an electric compressor at the bottom of the refrigerator. Here, the coolant is compressed, or forced into a smaller space, which increases its thermal energy. Then, the gas is pumped through condenser coils. In the coils, the thermal energy of the gas is greater than that of the surrounding air. This causes thermal energy to flow from the coolant gas to the air behind the refrigerator. As thermal energy is removed from the gas, it condenses, or becomes liquid. Then, the liquid coolant is pumped up through the expansion valve. The cycle repeats.

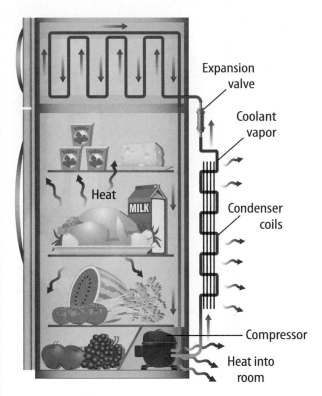

Figure 15 Coolant in a refrigerator moves thermal energy from inside to outside the refrigerator.

Key Concept Check How does a refrigerator keep food cold?

Inquiry MiniLab   **10 minutes**

Can thermal energy be used to do work?

You know you can raise the thermal energy of a substance by doing work on it. Is the opposite true? Can thermal energy cause something to move?

1. Read and complete a lab safety form.
2. Add 10 mL of water to a **100-mL beaker.**
3. Place a **small square of aluminum foil** over the top of the beaker.
4. Place the beaker on a **hot plate,** and turn it on. Observe the results and record them in your Science Journal.

Analyze and Conclude

1. **Infer** Is thermal energy used to do work in this lab? Explain your answer.

2. **Key Concept** Is thermal energy transformed into another form of energy in this experiment? If so, what is the other form of energy?

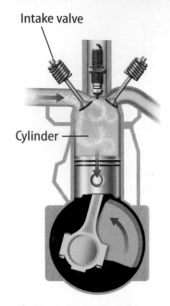

Intake valve

Cylinder

① The intake valve opens as the piston moves downward, drawing a mixture of gasoline and air into the cylinder.

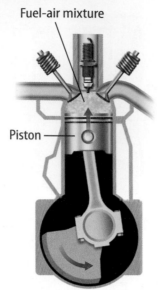

Fuel-air mixture

Piston

② The intake valve closes as the piston moves upward, compressing the fuel-air mixture.

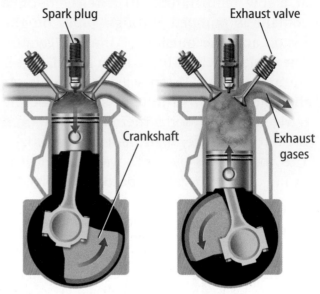

Spark plug

Exhaust valve

Crankshaft

Exhaust gases

③ A spark plug ignites the fuel-air mixture. As the mixture burns, hot gases expand, pushing the piston down.

④ As the piston moves up, the exhaust valve opens, and the hot gases are pushed out of the cylinder.

Figure 16 Internal combustion engines transform the chemical energy from fuel to thermal energy, which then produces mechanical energy.

Heat Engines

A typical automobile engine is a heat engine. *A* **heat engine** *is a machine that converts thermal energy into mechanical energy.* When a heat engine converts thermal energy into mechanical energy, the mechanical energy moves the vehicle. Most cars, buses, boats, trucks, and lawn mowers use a type of heat engine called an internal combustion engine. **Figure 16** shows how one type of internal combustion engine converts thermal energy into mechanical energy.

Perhaps you have heard someone refer to a car as having a six-cylinder engine. A cylinder is a tube with a piston that moves up and down. At one end of the cylinder a spark ignites a fuel-air mixture. The ignited fuel-air mixture expands and pushes the piston down. This action occurs because the fuel's chemical energy converts to thermal energy. Some of the thermal energy immediately converts to mechanical energy.

A heat engine is not efficient. Most automobile engines only convert about 20 percent of the chemical energy in gasoline into mechanical energy. The remaining energy from the gasoline is lost to the environment.

Key Concept Check What is one form of energy that is output from a heat engine?

Visual Summary

A bimetallic coil inside a thermostat controls a switch that turns a heating or cooling device on or off.

A refrigerator keeps food cold by moving thermal energy from the inside of the refrigerator out to the refrigerator's surroundings.

In a car engine, chemical energy in fuel is transformed into thermal energy. Some of this thermal energy is then transformed into mechanical energy.

FOLDABLES

Use your lesson Foldable to review the lesson. Save your Foldable for the project at the end of the chapter.

What do you think NOW?

You first read the statements below at the beginning of the chapter.

5. Car engines create energy.

6. Refrigerators cool food by moving thermal energy from inside the refrigerator to the outside.

Did you change your mind about whether you agree or disagree with the statements? Rewrite any false statements to make them true.

Use Vocabulary

1 A _____ is a device that converts electric energy into thermal energy.

2 **Explain** how an internal combustion engine works.

Understand Key Concepts

3 **Describe** the path of thermal energy in a refrigerator.

4 Which sequence describes the energy transformation in an automobile engine?
A. chemical→thermal→mechanical
B. thermal→kinetic→potential
C. thermal→mechanical→potential
D. thermal→chemical→mechanical

5 **Explain** how a thermostat uses electric energy, mechanical energy, and thermal energy.

Interpret Graphics

6 **Predict** Suppose you pointed a hair dryer at the device pictured below and turned on the hair dryer. What would happen?

7 **Sequence** Copy the graphic organizer below. Use it to show the steps involved in one cycle of an internal combustion engine.

Critical Thinking

8 **Explain** how two of the devices you read about in this chapter could be used in one appliance.

Design an Insulated Container

Materials

aluminum foil

self-sealing plastic bag

triple-beam balance

creative building materials

office supplies

Also Needed
frozen fruit pop, foam packing peanuts, rubber bands

Safety

Many refrigerated or frozen food products must be kept cold as they are transported long distances. Meat or fresh fruits might travel from South America to grocery stores in the United States. Imagine that you have been hired to design a container that will keep a frozen fruit pop from melting for as long as possible.

Ask a Question

How can you construct a container that will prevent a frozen fruit pop inside a plastic bag from melting? Think about thermal energy transfer by conduction, convection, and radiation. You will begin with a shoe box, but you can modify it in any way. Consider the materials you have available. Ask yourself what material you can bring from home that might slow the melting of a frozen fruit pop.

Make Observations

1 Read and complete a lab safety form.

2 In your Science Journal, write your ideas about

- how you can you reduce the amount of thermal energy moving by conduction, convection, and radiation;
- what materials you will use inside and outside your box;
- what materials you will need to bring from home.

3 Outline the steps in preparing for your box. Have your teacher check your procedures. Decide who will obtain which materials before the next lab period. Design a logo for your container.

4 As a class, decide how many hours you will wait before checking the condition of your frozen fruit pop.

Form a Hypothesis

5 Formulate a hypothesis explaining why the materials you use inside your bag will be effective in insulating the frozen fruit pop. Remember, your hypothesis should be a testable explanation based on observations.

Test Your Hypothesis

6 On the second lab day, follow the steps you have outlined and prepare your container. Check it over one more time to be sure you have accounted for all ways that thermal energy could enter or leave the box.

7 Obtain a frozen fruit pop. Place it inside a self-sealing plastic bag. Seal the bag. Quickly measure and record its mass. Attach your logo and return the pop to the freezer.

8 On the third lab day, remove your frozen fruit pop from the freezer. Do not open the plastic bag. Place your frozen fruit pop in your container and seal it. Place your container in a location assigned by your teacher.

9 After the set amount of time, remove the fruit pop from the container. Open the plastic bag, and pour off any melted juice. Reseal the bag. Measure and record the mass.

Analyze and Conclude

10 **Calculate** What percentage of your fruit pop remained frozen? How long do you think it would take for the fruit pop to completely melt in your container? Justify your answer.

11 **Analyze** What are some possible ways thermal energy entered your bag? How could you improve the package on another try?

12 **The Big Idea** How would you modify your design to keep something hot inside the bag? Explain your answer.

Lab Tips

☑ Keep in mind that you are trying to keep thermal energy out of the package.

☑ The length of the test time you decide on should be long enough to allow some of the fruit pop to melt.

Remember to use scientific methods.

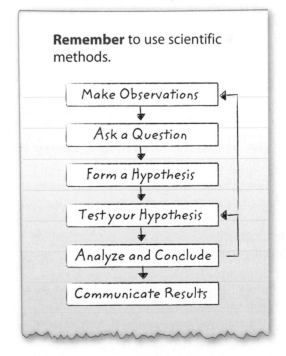

```
Make Observations
      ↓
Ask a Question
      ↓
Form a Hypothesis
      ↓
Test your Hypothesis
      ↓
Analyze and Conclude
      ↓
Communicate Results
```

Communicate Your Results

Make a class graph showing the percentages of the different frozen fruit pops remaining. Discuss why some packages were more or less effective.

Inquiry Extension

Explore designs for portable coolers. What are the most effective portable packages that keep things hot or cold without external cooling or heating?

Chapter 5 Study Guide

Thermal energy can be transferred by conduction, radiation, and convection. Thermal energy also can be transformed into other forms of energy and used in devices such as thermostats, refrigerators, and automobile engines.

Key Concepts Summary

Vocabulary

Lesson 1: Thermal Energy, Temperature, and Heat

- The **temperature** of a material is the average kinetic energy of the particles that make up the material.

- **Heat** is the movement of **thermal energy** from a material or area with a higher temperature to a material or area with a lower temperature.

- When a material is heated, the material's temperature changes.

thermal energy
temperature
heat

Lesson 2: Thermal Energy Transfers

- When a material has a low **specific heat,** transferring a small amount of energy to the material increases its temperature significantly.

- When a material is heated, the thermal energy of the material increases and the material expands.

- Thermal energy can be transferred by **conduction, radiation,** or **convection.**

radiation
conduction
thermal conductor
thermal insulator
specific heat
thermal contraction
thermal expansion
convection
convection current

Lesson 3: Using Thermal Energy

- The two different metals in a bimetallic coil inside a **thermostat** expand and contract at different rates. The bimetallic coil curls and uncurls, depending on the thermal energy of the air, pushing a switch that turns a heating or cooling device on or off.

- A **refrigerator** keeps food cold by moving thermal energy from inside the refrigerator out to the refrigerator's surroundings.

- In a car engine, chemical energy in fuel is transformed into thermal energy. Some of this thermal energy is then transformed into mechanical energy.

heating appliance
thermostat
refrigerator
heat engine

FOLDABLES® Chapter Project

Assemble your lesson Foldables as shown to make a Chapter Project. Use the project to review what you have learned in this chapter.

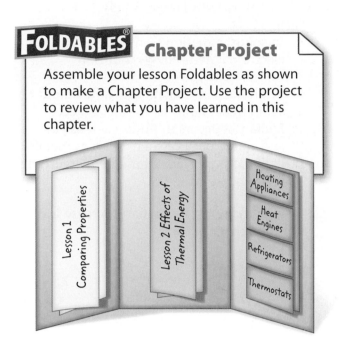

Use Vocabulary

1 When you increase the _____ of a cup of hot cocoa, you increase the average kinetic energy of the particles that make up the hot cocoa.

2 The increase in volume of a material when heated is _____ _____.

3 A(n) _____ is used to control the temperature in a room.

4 Thermal energy is transferred by _____ between two objects that are touching.

5 A fluid moving in a circular pattern because of changes in density is a _____.

6 Define *heating appliance* in your own words.

Link Vocabulary and Key Concepts

((O)) **Concepts in Motion** Interactive Concept Map

Copy this concept map, and then use vocabulary terms from the previous page to complete the concept map.

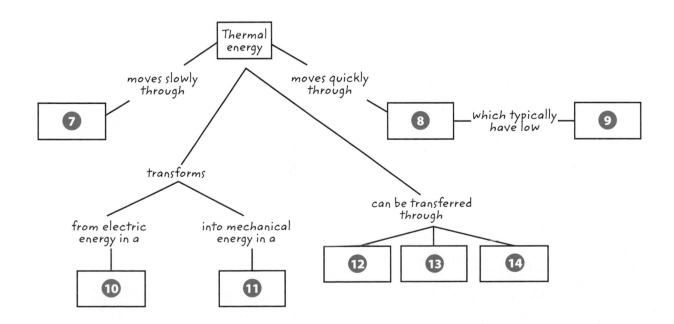

Understand Key Concepts

1 Which would decrease a material's thermal energy?

A. heating the material

B. increasing the kinetic energy of the particles that make up the material

C. increasing the temperature of the material

D. moving the material to a location where the temperature is lower

2 You put a metal spoon in a bowl of hot soup. Why does the spoon feel hotter than the outside of the bowl?

A. The bowl is a better conductor than the spoon.

B. The bowl has a lower specific heat than the spoon.

C. The spoon is a good thermal insulator.

D. The spoon transfers thermal energy better than the bowl does.

3 In the picture to the right, thermal energy moves from the

A. glass to the air.

B. lemonade to the air.

C. ice to the lemonade.

D. air to the lemonade.

4 Which has the lowest specific heat?

A. an object that is made out of metal

B. an object that does not transfer thermal energy easily

C. an object with electrons that do not move easily

D. an object that requires a lot of energy to change its temperature

5 Which does NOT occur in an internal combustion engine?

A. Most of the thermal energy is wasted.

B. Thermal energy forces the piston downward.

C. Thermal energy is converted into chemical energy.

D. Thermal energy is converted into mechanical energy.

6 Which statement about radiation is correct?

A. In solids, radiation transfers electromagnetic energy, but not thermal energy.

B. Cooler objects radiate the same amount of thermal energy as warmer objects.

C. Radiation occurs in fluids such as gas and water, but not solids such as metals.

D. Radiation transfers thermal energy from the Sun to Earth.

7 The device below detects an increase in room temperature as

A. an increase in thermal energy causes a bimetallic coil to curl.

B. an increase in thermal energy causes a bimetallic coil to uncurl.

C. a switch causes a bimetallic coil to curl.

D. a switch causes a bimetallic coil to uncurl

8 Which is the lowest temperature?

A. 0°C

B. 0°F

C. 32°F

D. 273 K

9 Which energy conversion typically occurs in a heating appliance?

A. chemical energy to thermal energy

B. electric energy to thermal energy

C. thermal energy to chemical energy

D. thermal energy to mechanical energy

Critical Thinking

10 Compare A swimming pool with a temperature of 30°C has more thermal energy than a cup of soup with a temperature of 60°C. Explain why this is so.

11 Contrast A spoon made of aluminum and a spoon made of steel have the same mass. The aluminum spoon has a higher specific heat than the steel spoon. Which spoon becomes hotter more quickly when placed in a pan of boiling water?

12 Describe How do convection currents influence Earth's climate?

13 Diagram A room has a heater on one side and an open window letting in cool air on the opposite side. Diagram the convection current in the room. Label the warm air and the cool air.

14 Evaluate When engineers build bridges, they separate sections of the roadway with expansion joints such as the one below that allow movement between the sections. Why are expansion joints necessary?

15 Explain Why is conduction slower in a gas than in a liquid or a solid?

Writing in Science

16 Research various types of heat engines that have been developed throughout history. Write 3–5 paragraphs explaining the energy transformations in one of these engines.

REVIEW THE BIG IDEA

17 Describe each of the three ways thermal energy can be transferred. Give an example of each.

18 What do the different colors in this photograph indicate?

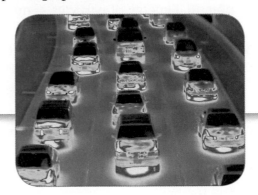

Math Skills

Review
Math Practice

Convert Between Temperature Scales

19 If water in a bath is at 104°F, then what is the temperature of the water in degrees Celsius?

20 Convert −40°C to degrees Fahrenheit.

Standardized Test Practice

Record your answers on the answer sheet provided by your teacher or on a sheet of paper.

Multiple Choice

1 Which statement describes the thermal energy of an object?

  A kinetic energy of particles + potential energy of particles

  B kinetic energy of particles ÷ number of particles

  C potential energy of particles ÷ number of particles

  D kinetic energy of particles ÷ (kinetic energy of particles + potential energy of particles)

2 Which term describes a transfer of thermal energy?

  A heat

  B specific heat

  C temperature

  D thermal energy

Use the figures below to answer question 3.

   Sample X   **Sample Y**

3 The figures show two different samples of air. In what way do they differ?

  A Sample X is at a higher temperature than sample Y.

  B Sample X has a higher specific heat than sample Y.

  C Particles of sample Y have a higher average kinetic energy than those of sample X.

  D Particles of sample Y have a higher average thermal energy than those of sample X.

Use the table below to answer question 4.

Material	Specific Heat (in J/g·K)
Air	1.0
Copper	0.4
Water	4.2
Wax	2.5

4 The table shows the specific heat of four materials. Which statement can be concluded from the information in the table?

  A Copper is a thermal insulator.

  B Wax is a thermal conductor.

  C Air takes the most thermal energy to change its temperature.

  D Water takes the most thermal energy to change its temperature.

5 Which term describes what happens to a cold balloon when placed in a hot car?

  A thermal conduction

  B thermal contraction

  C thermal expansion

  D thermal insulation

6 A girl stirs soup with a metal spoon. Which process causes her hand to get warmer?

  A conduction

  B convection

  C insulation

  D radiation

7 In a thermostat's coil, what causes the two metals in the strip to curl and uncurl?

  A They contract at the same rate when cooled.

  B They expand at different rates when heated.

  C They have the same specific heat.

  D They melt at different temperatures.

Use the figure to below to answer questions 8–10.

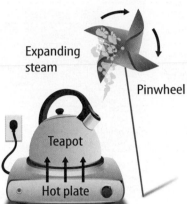

8 Which term describes the transfer of thermal energy between the hot plate and the teapot?

   A conduction

   B convection

   C insulation

   D radiation

9 Which energy transformations are taking place in this system?

   A electrical → thermal → chemical

   B electrical → thermal → mechanical

   C thermal → electrical → chemical

   D thermal → electrical → mechanical

10 What kind of machine is represented by the hot plate, the teapot, the steam, and the pinwheel working together?

   A bimetallic coil

   B heat engine

   C refrigerator

   D thermostat

Constructed Response

Use the figure to answer questions 11 and 12.

11 The foam cooler and the metal pan both contain ice. Describe the energy transfers that cause the ice to melt in each container.

12 After 1 hour, the ice in the metal pan had melted more than the ice in the foam cooler. What is it about the containers that could explain the difference in the melting rates?

13 What causes the air around a refrigerator to become warmer as the refrigerator is cooling the air inside it?

14 How does a car's internal combustion engine convert thermal energy to mechanical energy?

NEED EXTRA HELP?														
If You Missed Question...	1	2	3	4	5	6	7	8	9	10	11	12	13	14
Go to Lesson...	1	1	1	2	2	2	3	2	3	3	2	2	3	3

AID S2.1a, S2.1b, S2.1c, S2.1d, S3.2f; IS 1.1;
ICT 2.1; IPS 1.1, 1.4, 2.1; PS 4.1d, 4.4a, 4.4b

Waves, Light, and Sound

THE BIG IDEA

How do waves transfer energy through matter and through empty space?

Inquiry — What do the colors mean?

Have you ever seen weather reports that show a map with colorful images? Clear skies produce a clear weather map, but watch out if you see lots of blue, green, yellow, and red on the map!

- What do the different colors on the map mean?
- How do meteorologists get the information they display on a weather map?
- How do waves transfer energy through matter and through empty space?

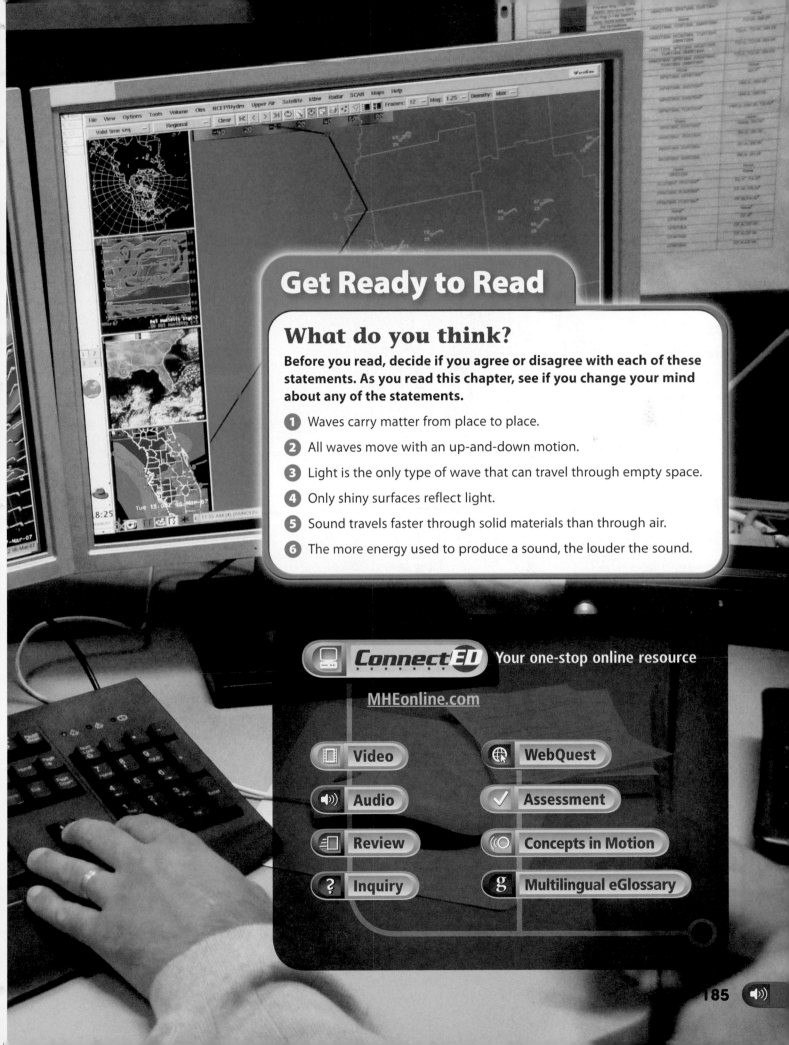

Get Ready to Read

What do you think?

Before you read, decide if you agree or disagree with each of these statements. As you read this chapter, see if you change your mind about any of the statements.

1. Waves carry matter from place to place.

2. All waves move with an up-and-down motion.

3. Light is the only type of wave that can travel through empty space.

4. Only shiny surfaces reflect light.

5. Sound travels faster through solid materials than through air.

6. The more energy used to produce a sound, the louder the sound.

ConnectED Your one-stop online resource

MHEonline.com

- Video
- Audio
- Review
- Inquiry
- WebQuest
- Assessment
- Concepts in Motion
- Multilingual eGlossary

Lesson 1

Waves

Reading Guide

Key Concepts 🔑
ESSENTIAL QUESTIONS

- What are waves, and how are waves produced?
- How can you describe waves by their properties?
- What are some ways in which waves interact with matter?

Vocabulary

mechanical wave

electromagnetic wave

transverse wave

longitudinal wave

frequency

amplitude

refraction

 Multilingual eGlossary

 Video **Science Video**

 AID S2.1a, S2.1b, S2.1c, S2.1d, S3.2f

Inquiry What causes the waves?

Have you ever watched a surfer ride the waves? Ocean waves are produced by winds far out at sea. By the time they reach shore, some waves have so much energy that they are taller than a person or even a house. Why do waves get taller as they approach the shore? What properties do water waves have in common with other types of waves?

redbrickstock.com/Alamy

How do waves form?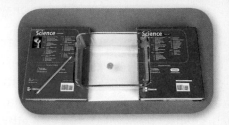

You probably have seen water waves on the surface of a lake or a swimming pool. How are the waves produced?

1. Read and complete a lab safety form.

2. Place **books** under opposite edges of a **glass pan**. Add about 5 mm of water to the pan. Place a **sheet of white paper** under the pan. Wait until the water is still.

3. Place a **cork** in the water about halfway between the center and the edge of the pan. Dip your **pencil** tip into the center of the water one time. What happens to the cork? Record your observations of the water and the cork in a data table in your Science Journal.

4. Repeatedly tap your pencil tip on the surface of the water slowly. Record your observations.

5. Repeat step 4, tapping your pencil tip faster this time. Record your observations.

Think About This

1. How are the waves you produced in steps 3 and 4 alike? How are they different?

2. How does the behavior of the cork change in steps 4 and 5?

3. **Key Concept** What do you think is the source of the waves that you made?

What are waves?

A flag waves in the breeze. Ocean waves break onto a beach. You wave your hand at a friend. All of these actions have something in common. Waves always begin with a source of energy that causes a back-and-forth or up-and-down disturbance, or movement. In **Figure 1,** energy of the wind causes a disturbance in the flag. This disturbance moves along the length of the flag as a wave. A wave is a disturbance that transfers energy from one place to another without transferring matter.

Key Concept Check What are waves?

Energy Transfer

Wind transfers energy to the fabric in the flag. The flag ripples back and forth as the energy travels along the fabric. Notice that each point on the flag moves back and forth, but the fabric does not move along with the wave. Recall, waves only transfer energy, not matter, from place to place.

When you lift a pebble, you transfer energy to it. Suppose you drop the pebble into a pond. The pebble's energy transfers to the water. Waves carry the energy away from the point where the pebble hit the water. The water itself moves up and down as the wave passes, but the water does not move along with the wave.

Figure 1 The wave is a disturbance that transfers energy along the flag.

▲ **Figure 2** 🔑 The energy of the falling pebble produces a mechanical wave

Table 1 Electromagnetic waves are always transverse. Mechanical waves can be either transverse, longitudinal, or a combination of both. ▼

Two Main Types of Waves

Some waves carry energy only through matter. Other types of waves can carry energy through matter or empty space.

Mechanical Waves *A wave that travels only through matter is a* **mechanical wave.** A medium is the matter through which a mechanical wave travels. A mechanical wave forms when a source of energy causes particles that make up a medium to vibrate. For example, a pebble falling into water transfers its kinetic energy to particles of the water, as shown in **Figure 2.** The water particles vibrate and push against nearby particles, transferring the energy outward. After each particle pushes the next particle, it returns to its original rest position. Energy is transferred, but the water particles are not.

Electromagnetic Waves *A wave that can travel through empty space or through matter is an* **electromagnetic wave.** This type of wave forms when a charged particle, such as an electron, vibrates. For example, electromagnetic waves transfer the Sun's energy to Earth through empty space. Once the waves reach Earth, they travel through matter, such as the atmosphere or a glass window of your house.

🔑 **Key Concept Check** How are waves produced?

Describing Wave Motion

Some waves move particles of a medium up and down or side to side, **perpendicular** to the direction the wave travels. For example, the waves in a flag move side to side, perpendicular to the direction the wind. Other wave disturbances move particles of the medium forward then backward in same direction, or parallel, to the motion of the wave. And last, some waves are a combination of both of these two types of motion. **Table 1** summarizes these three types of wave motion—transverse, longitudinal, or a combination of both.

Table 1 Types of Wave Motion		
Type of Wave Motion	**Mechanical Waves**	**Electromagnetic Waves**
Transverse—perpendicular to the direction the wave travels	✓ example: flag waving in a breeze	✓ example: light waves
Longitudinal—parallel to the direction the wave travels	✓ example: sound waves	
Combination—both transverse and longitudinal	✓ example: water waves	

Don Farrall/Getty Images

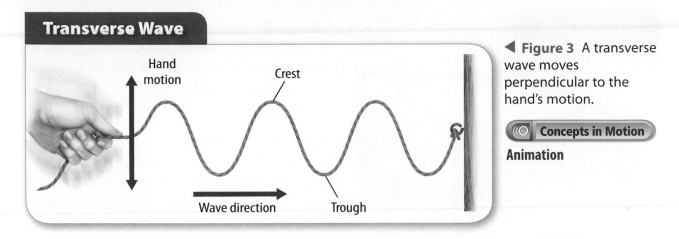

Transverse Wave

Hand motion

Crest

Wave direction

Trough

◀ **Figure 3** A transverse wave moves perpendicular to the hand's motion.

Concepts in Motion
Animation

Transverse Waves *A wave in which the disturbance is perpendicular to the direction the wave travels is a* **transverse wave.** A breeze produces transverse waves in a flag. You can make transverse waves by attaching one end of a rope to a hook and holding the other end, as in **Figure 3.** When you move your hand up and down, transverse waves travel along the rope. High points on a wave are called crests. Low points are called troughs.

Recall that a vibrating charge, such as an electron, produces an electromagnetic wave. Electromagnetic waves are transverse waves. The electric and magnetic wave disturbances are perpendicular to the motion of the vibrating charge. You read that light is a form of energy transferred by transverse electromagnetic waves. X-rays and radio waves are two other examples.

Longitudinal Waves *A wave that makes the particles of a medium move back and forth parallel to the direction the wave travels is a* **longitudinal wave.** Longitudinal waves are mechanical waves. Like a transverse wave, a longitudinal wave disturbance passes energy from particle to particle of a medium. For example, when you knock on a door, energy of your hand transfers to the particles that make up the door. The energy of the vibrating particles of the door is then transferred to the air in the next room. Also, you can make a longitudinal wave by pushing or pulling on a coiled spring toy, as in **Figure 4.** Pushing moves the coils closer together. Pulling spreads the coils apart.

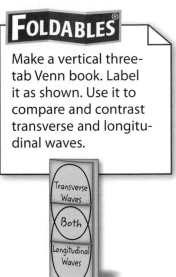

FOLDABLES

Make a vertical three-tab Venn book. Label it as shown. Use it to compare and contrast transverse and longitudinal waves.

Transverse Waves

Both

Longitudinal Waves

Longitudinal Wave

Concepts in Motion **Animation**

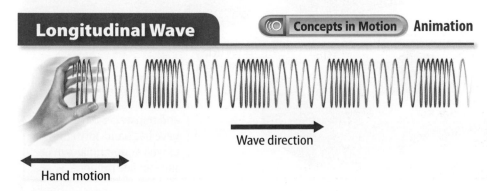

Wave direction

Hand motion

◀ **Figure 4** The back-and-forth motion of the hand causes a back-and-forth motion in the spring. The longitudinal waves move parallel to the hand's motion.

Water Waves

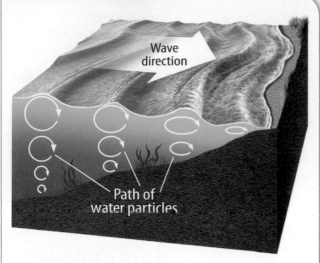

Wave direction

Path of water particles

Figure 5 Waves cause water particles to move in small circles.

⦿ **Visual Check** How is the path of the water particles near the water's surface different from the path near the ocean floor?

Figure 6 Seismic waves can be longitudinal, transverse, or a combination of the two. ▼

⦿ **Visual Check** Which seismic wave is similar to a water wave?

⦿ **Concepts in Motion** **Animation**

Waves in Nature

Waves are common in nature because so many different energy sources produce waves. Two common waves in nature are water waves and seismic waves.

Water Waves Although water waves look like transverse waves, water particles move in circles, as shown in **Figure 5.** Water waves are a combination of transverse and longitudinal waves. Water particles move forward and backward. They also move up and down. The result is a circular path that gets smaller as the wave approaches land.

Water waves form because there is friction between the wind at sea and the water. Energy from the wind transfers to the water as the water moves toward land. Like all waves, water waves only transport energy. Because the waves move only through matter, water waves are mechanical waves.

Seismic Waves When layers of rock of Earth's crust suddenly shift, an earthquake occurs. The movement of rock sends out waves that travel to Earth's surface. An earthquake wave is called a seismic wave. As shown in **Figure 6,** there are different types of seismic waves. Seismic waves are mechanical waves because they move through matter.

Seismic Waves

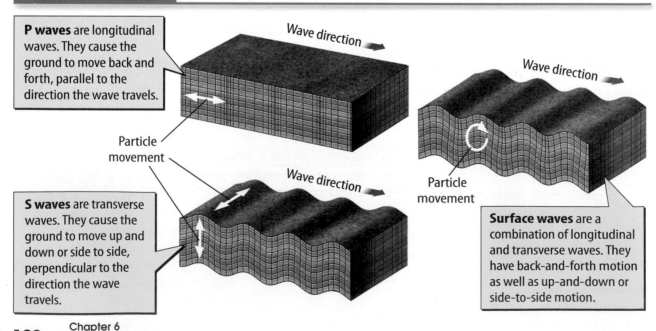

P waves are longitudinal waves. They cause the ground to move back and forth, parallel to the direction the wave travels.

Wave direction

Particle movement

S waves are transverse waves. They cause the ground to move up and down or side to side, perpendicular to the direction the wave travels.

Wave direction

Wave direction

Particle movement

Surface waves are a combination of longitudinal and transverse waves. They have back-and-forth motion as well as up-and-down or side-to-side motion.

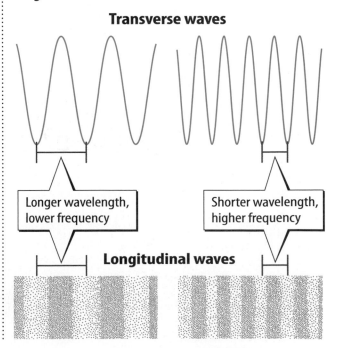

Inquiry MiniLab

15 minutes

How can you make waves with different properties?

Waves traveling through a spring can have different wavelengths and frequencies.

1. Read and complete a lab safety form.

2. Use **tape** to secure one end of a **spring toy** to your desk and the other end to the floor. Tie pieces of **string** to the spring 1/4, 1/2, and 3/4 of the way between the floor and the desk.

3. Pull a few of the lowest coils on the spring toy to the right. Release. Record your observations in your Science Journal.

4. Slowly tap the bottom of the spring toward the right. Repeat, this time doubling your rate of tapping. Record your observations.

5. Push down the bottom 5 cm of the spring toy. Release. Repeat, this time pushing down the bottom 10 cm. Record your observations.

Analyze and Conclude

1. **Compare** the movement of the pieces of string in step 4 and in step 5.

2. **Classify** the types of waves you made in steps 3–5 as transverse or longitudinal.

3. **Key Concept** What do the waves transfer up and down the spring toy?

Properties of Waves

How could you describe water waves at a beach? You might describe properties such as the height or the speed of the wave. When scientists describe waves, they describe the properties of wavelength and frequency.

Wavelength

The distance between a point on one wave, such as the crest, and the same point on the next wave is called the wavelength. Different types of waves can have wavelengths that range from thousands of kilometers to less than the size of an atom!

Frequency

The number of wavelengths that pass a point each second is a wave's **frequency**. Frequency is measured in hertz (Hz). One hertz equals one wave per second. As shown in **Figure 7**, the longer the wavelength, the lower the frequency. As the distance between the crests gets shorter, the number of waves passing a point each second increases.

✓ **Reading Check** What is frequency?

Figure 7 You can describe the wavelength and the frequency of both transverse and longitudinal waves.

Transverse waves

Longer wavelength, lower frequency

Shorter wavelength, higher frequency

Longitudinal waves

Table 2 Wave Speeds	
Type of Wave	**Typical wave speed (m/s)**
Ocean wave	25
Sound wave in air	340
Transverse seismic wave (S wave)	1,000 to 8,000
Longitudinal seismic wave (P wave)	1,000 to 14,000
Electromagnetic wave through empty space	300,000,000

▲ **Table 2** The speed of a wave depends on the type of wave and the medium through which the wave travels.

Wave Speed

A wave's speed depends on the medium, or type of material, through which it travels. Electromagnetic waves always travel through empty space at the same speed, 3×10^8 m/s. That's 300 million meters each second! They travel slower through a medium, or matter, because they must interact with particles. Mechanical waves also travel slower through matter because the waves transfer energy from one particle to another. For example, sound waves travel about one-millionth the speed of light waves. The speed of water waves depends on the strength of the wind that produces them. **Table 2** compares the speeds of different types of waves.

Amplitude and Energy

Different waves carry different amounts of energy. Some earthquakes, for example, are catastrophic because they carry so much energy. A shift in Earth's crust can cause particles in the crust to vibrate back and forth very far from their rest positions, producing seismic waves. In January 2010, seismic waves in Haiti transferred enough energy to destroy entire cities.

A wave's **amplitude** *is the maximum distance a wave varies from its rest position.* For mechanical waves, amplitude is the maximum distance the particles of the medium move from their rest positions as a wave passes. The more energy a mechanical wave has, the larger its amplitude. The amplitude of a transverse mechanical wave is shown in **Figure 8.**

 Key Concept Check How can you describe waves?

Figure 8 As more energy is used to produce a mechanical wave, particles of a medium vibrate farther from their rest positions. ▶

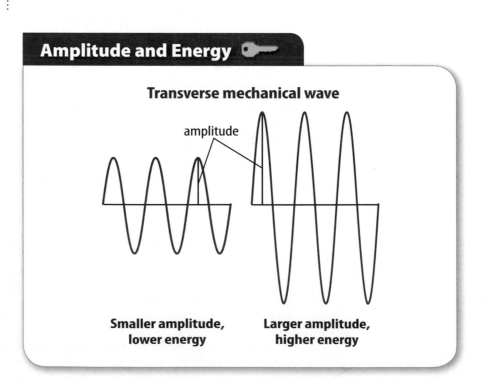

Amplitude and Energy

Transverse mechanical wave

amplitude

Smaller amplitude, lower energy

Larger amplitude, higher energy

Wave Interaction with Matter

You have read that when you knock on a door, longitudinal sound waves transfer the energy of the knock through the door. However, when a person in the next room hears the knock, it is not as loud as the sound on your side of the door. The sound is weaker after it passes through the door because the waves interact with the matter that makes up the door.

Transmission

Some of the sound from your knock passes through the door. The waves transmit, or carry, the energy all the way through the door. The energy then passes into air particles, and the person on the other side hears the knock.

Absorption

Some of the sound is absorbed by the particles that make up the door. Instead of passing through the door, the energy increases the motion of the particles of the wood. The sound energy changes to thermal energy within the door. Therefore, less sound energy passes into the air in the next room.

Reflection

Some of the energy you used to knock on the door reflects, or bounces back, into the room you are in. Sound waves in the air transfer sound back to your ears. **Figure 9** shows how the energy of electromagnetic waves can also be transmitted, absorbed, or reflected.

 Reading Check What are transmission, absorption, and reflection?

Transmission, Absorption, and Reflection 🔑

Figure 9 As waves travel, some of the energy they carry is transmitted, some is absorbed, and some is reflected by the particles in matter.

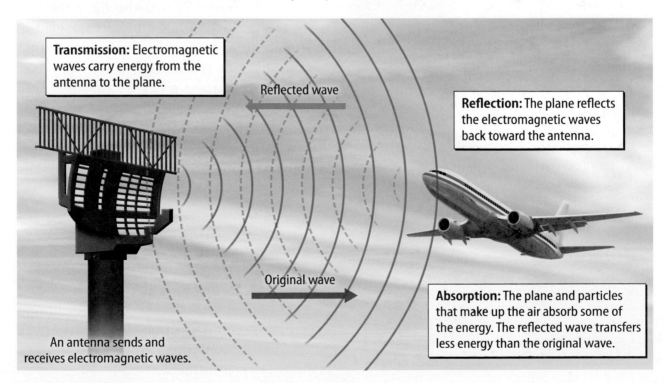

Transmission: Electromagnetic waves carry energy from the antenna to the plane.

Reflected wave

Reflection: The plane reflects the electromagnetic waves back toward the antenna.

Original wave

Absorption: The plane and particles that make up the air absorb some of the energy. The reflected wave transfers less energy than the original wave.

An antenna sends and receives electromagnetic waves.

✔ **Visual Check** Does all of the energy reflected from the plane return to the antenna? Why or why not?

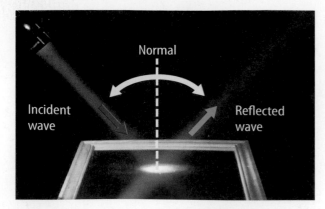

▲ **Figure 10** 🔑 The law of reflection describes the direction of a reflected wave.

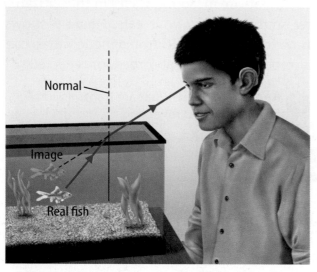

▲ **Figure 11** 🔑 Refraction causes the fish to appear in a place different from its real location.

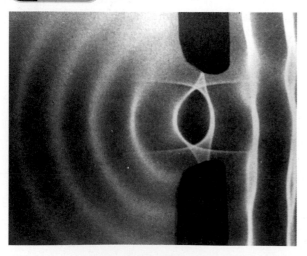

▲ **Figure 12** 🔑 Diffraction causes waves to spread around barriers and through openings.

Law of Reflection

You can predict how waves will reflect from a smooth surface. The red arrow in **Figure 10** represents a light wave approaching a surface at an angle. This is called the incident wave. The blue arrow represents the reflected wave. The dotted line perpendicular to the surface at the point where the wave hits the surface is the normal. The law of reflection states that the angle between the incident wave and the normal always equals the angle between the reflected wave and the normal. If the incident angle in **Figure 10** increases, the reflected angle also increases.

Refraction

The change in direction of a wave as it changes speed, moving from one medium into another, is called **refraction.** The image of the fish in **Figure 11** is an example. Light reflects off the fish in all directions. The light speeds up as it moves from water into air. Notice that the light refracts away from the normal, or the line perpendicular to the surface at which the wave moves from one medium to other. This is the light the boy sees. His brain assumes the light traveled in a straight line. The light seems to come from the position of the image. Note that waves only refract if they move at an angle into another medium. They do not refract if they move straight into a medium. Waves refract toward the normal if they slow down when entering a medium and away from the normal if they speed up.

Diffraction

Diffraction is the change in direction of a wave when it travels past the edge of an object or through an opening. If you walk down a school hall and hear sound coming from an open classroom door, the sound waves have diffracted around the corner to your ears. Diffraction is illustrated in **Figure 12.**

🔑 **Key Concept Check** What are some ways in which waves interact with matter?

Lesson 1 Review

Visual Summary

A wave is a disturbance that transfers energy from one place to another without transferring matter.

A wave can have a disturbance parallel or perpendicular to the direction the wave travels. Some waves are a combination of the two directions.

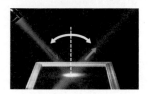

Waves can interact with matter by reflection, refraction, and diffraction.

FOLDABLES

Use your lesson Foldable to review the lesson. Save your Foldable for the project at the end of the chapter.

What do you think NOW?

You first read the statements below at the beginning of the chapter.

1. Waves carry matter from place to place.

2. All waves move with an up-and-down motion.

Did you change your mind about whether you agree or disagree with the statements? Rewrite any false statements to make them true.

Use Vocabulary

1 **Define** *longitudinal wave* in your own words.

2 A wave that can travel through both matter and empty space is a(n) _____.

Understand Key Concepts

3 In which type of wave does the medium travel in a circular motion?

A. electromagnetic C. transverse

B. longitudinal D. water

4 **Identify** what produces a mechanical wave. An electromagnetic wave?

5 **Compare and contrast** how transmission, reflection, and absorption affect a wave.

Interpret Graphics

6 **Identify** The picture below shows a light ray bouncing off a flat surface. What is the correct scientific term for this interaction?

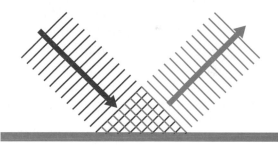

7 **Organize** Copy and fill in the graphic organizer below. In each oval, list a way in which waves can interact with matter.

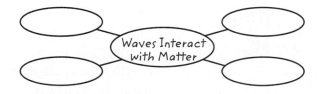

Waves Interact with Matter

Critical Thinking

8 **Decide** A forest fire makes a loud roaring sound. The explosive processes that release energy from the Sun occur at a much higher temperature. Why don't you hear a roaring sound from the Sun?

How do water waves interact with matter?

You can use a ripple tank to observe waves with different properties. Think about how waves interact with matter and with each other. How can you change the properties of the waves?

Materials

9-in. × 13-in. glass pan

sponges cut into thin strips

plastic snap-together blocks

adhesive putty

2-cm wooden dowel

Also needed: 2 books, white paper

Safety

Learn It

Scientists **observe** items and events and then record what they see. When you make observations, you should carefully look for details and then record your observations accurately and completely.

Try It

1. Read and complete a lab safety form.

2. Make a ripple tank by placing books under opposite edges of a glass pan. Secure the edges with putty. Pour water into the pan until it is about 5 mm deep. Place a sheet of white paper under the pan. Lay strips of sponge inside the short ends of the pan to absorb wave energy. Lay a dowel in the opposite end of the pan.

3. Tap the dowel with your finger to make a series of waves. Observe properties of the waves. Increase and decrease the wavelength of your waves. Explain in your Science Journal how you changed the wavelength.

4. Make barriers from snap-together blocks. Place the barriers end-to-end in your ripple tank at an angle to the dowel, as shown in the photo. What will happen to waves that hit against the barrier? Try it, and then change the angle of the barrier and repeat. Record your observations.

5. Place the barrier in the middle of the pan, parallel to the dowel, with a small space between the two parts. Demonstrate diffraction by making waves with different frequencies move through the space between the barriers. Observe how the waves change when they move through the space. Repeat, increasing the distance between the barriers. Record your observations.

Apply It

6. **Describe** How does changing the barrier's angle change the waves?

7. **Draw a diagram** of the waves passing between the two barriers.

8. **Predict** Place the barriers in a new formation in your tank. Predict the behavior of the waves. Draw a diagram of your setup and your prediction. How well were you able to foresee what the waves were going to do?

9. **Key Concept** Summarize your observations of wave reflection and diffraction in your investigation.

4

Light

Reading Guide

Key Concepts
ESSENTIAL QUESTIONS

- How does light differ from other forms of electromagnetic waves?

- What are some ways in which light interacts with matter?

- How do eyes change light waves into the images you see?

Vocabulary

radio wave

infrared wave

ultraviolet wave

transparent

translucent

opaque

intensity

 Multilingual eGlossary

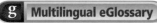 **Video**

- BrainPOP®
- Science Video
- What's Science Got to do With It?

ICT 2.1; IPS 1.1; PS 4.1d, 4.4a, 4.4b

Design Pics/Don Hammond

Inquiry Spreading Light?

Thick trees in a forest can block much of the sunlight, but some light still shines through. Why do you see bands of dim and bright light? Like all electromagnetic waves, light travels in straight lines. But light that moves past the trees can scatter and spread out.

Can you see the light?

When light travels through a medium, it interacts with the particles of the medium. Each material affects light differently.

1. Read and complete a lab safety form.

2. Obtain a **collection of materials** from your teacher. Make a two-column data table in your Science Journal. Write the headings *Material* above the left column and *Estimated Percentage of Light That Passes Through* above the right column. List each of your materials in the left column.

3. Shine a **flashlight** through one of the materials. Observe how much of the light passes through.

4. Estimate the percentage of light that passes through the material. Record your estimate in the data table.

5. Repeat steps 3 and 4 for each of the remaining materials.

6. Rank each material in order from the one that allows the most light to pass through to the one that allows the least amount of light to pass through.

Think About This

1. Which material allows the most light to pass through? Why?

2. What happens to the light when you shine your flashlight on the material you ranked number 3?

3. **Key Concept** Summarize ways in which you think the materials affect the light.

What are light waves?

You have read that there are two main types of waves—mechanical and electromagnetic. Mechanical waves move only through matter, but electromagnetic waves can move through matter and through empty space. Now you will read about different types of electromagnetic waves. The most familiar type of electromagnetic wave is light.

Recall that vibrating charged particles produce electromagnetic waves with many different wavelengths. Only a narrow **range** of these wavelengths are detected by most people's eyes. This small range of electromagnetic waves is what is known as light. Light waves and other forms of electromagnetic waves differ in wavelength and frequency.

An object that produces light is a luminous object. The Sun is Earth's major source of visible light. Almost half the Sun's energy that reaches Earth is visible light. Other luminous objects include lightbulbs and objects that produce light as they burn, such as a campfire.

Key Concept Check How does light differ from other forms of electromagnetic waves?

ACADEMIC VOCABULARY

range
(noun) a set of values from least to greatest

Hutchings Photography/Digital Light Source

The Electromagnetic Spectrum

Light is just a one type of electromagnetic wave. There is a wide range of electromagnetic waves that make up the electromagnetic spectrum, shown in **Figure 13.** Besides light, you encounter several other types of electromagnetic waves every day, and they probably play an important role in your life.

Types of Electromagnetic Waves

The electromagnetic spectrum consists of seven main types of waves. These waves range from low-energy, long-wavelength radio waves to very high-energy, short-wavelength gamma rays. Notice the relationship between wavelength, frequency, and energy indicated by the arrows in **Figure 13.** As the wavelength of electromagnetic waves decreases, the wave frequency increases. Low-frequency electromagnetic waves carry low amounts of energy, and high-frequency waves carry high amounts of energy.

Radio Waves *A low-frequency, low-energy electromagnetic wave that has a wavelength longer than about 30 cm is called a* **radio wave.** Radio waves have the least amount of energy of any electromagnetic wave. On Earth, radio and television transmitters produce radio waves that carry radio and television signals.

Microwaves You might use microwaves to cook your food. Microwaves also carry cell phone signals. Wavelengths of microwaves range from about 1 mm to 30 cm. Microwaves easily pass through smoke, light rain, and clouds, which makes them useful for transmitting information by satellites. Weather radar systems reflect microwaves off rain or storm clouds to detect and calculate the storm's distance and motion. Then, these calculations are used to make weather maps like the one shown on the first page of this chapter.

The Electromagnetic Spectrum   Review   Personal Tutor

Figure 13 Electromagnetic waves have different wavelengths, frequencies, and energy.

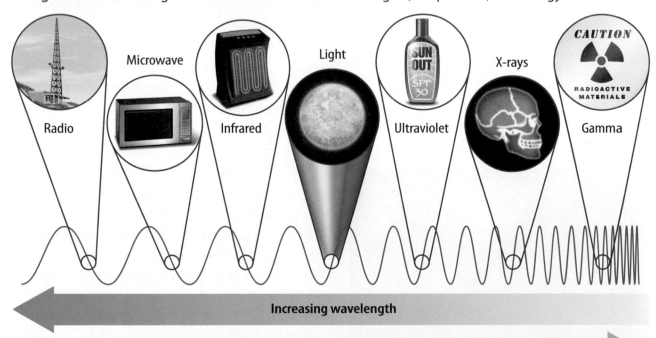

▲ **Figure 14** Infrared waves travel outward in all directions from the campfire.

WORD ORIGIN · · · · · · · · · · · · · · · · · · ·

infrared
from Latin *infra*, means "below"; and *ruber*, means "red"

ultraviolet
from Latin *ultra*, means "beyond"; and *viola*, means "violet"
· ·

Figure 15 The ozone layer protects Earth from the most dangerous ultraviolet waves from the Sun. ▼

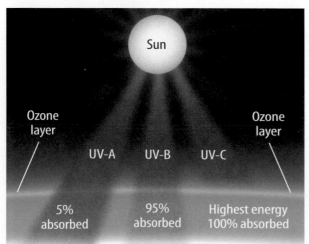

Light When you turn on a lamp or stand in sunshine, you probably don't think about waves entering your eyes. However, as you have read, light is a type of electromagnetic wave that the eyes detect. Light includes a range of wavelengths. You will read later in this lesson how this range of wavelengths relates to various properties of light.

Infrared Waves *An electromagnetic wave with a wavelength shorter than a microwave but longer than light is an* **infrared wave.** When you sit near a heater or a campfire, as in **Figure 14,** infrared waves transfer energy to your skin, and you feel warm. The Sun is Earth's major source of infrared waves. However, vibrating molecules in any type of matter, including your body, emit infrared waves.

Reading Check How do infrared waves and microwaves differ?

Ultraviolet Waves *An electromagnetic wave with a slightly shorter wavelength and higher frequency than light is an* **ultraviolet wave.** Electromagnetic waves with shorter wavelengths carry more energy than those with longer wavelengths and, therefore, can be harmful to living things. You might have heard that ultraviolet waves, or UV rays, from the Sun can be dangerous. These waves carry enough energy to cause particles of matter to combine or break apart and form other types of matter. Exposure to high levels of these waves can damage your skin.

Ultraviolet waves from the Sun are sometimes labeled UV-A, UV-B, or UV-C based on their wavelengths. UV-A have the longest wavelengths and the least energy. UV-C are the most dangerous because they have the shortest wavelengths and carry the most energy. As shown in **Figure 15,** the ozone layer in Earth's atmosphere blocks the Sun's most harmful UV rays from reaching Earth.

Reading Check Why can ultraviolet waves be dangerous?

X-rays High-energy electromagnetic waves that have slightly shorter wavelengths and higher frequencies than ultraviolet waves are X-rays. These waves can be very powerful. They have enough energy to pass through skin and muscle, but denser bone can stop them. This makes them useful for taking pictures of the inside of the body. Airport scanners, as in **Figure 16,** sometimes use X-rays to take pictures of the contents of luggage.

Gamma Rays Electromagnetic waves produced by vibrations within the nucleus of an atom are called gamma rays. They have shorter wavelengths and higher frequencies than any other form of electromagnetic wave. Gamma rays carry so much energy that they can penetrate about 10 cm of lead, one of the densest elements. On Earth, gamma rays are produced by radioactive elements and nuclear reactions.

Reading Check Why do you think gamma rays cannot be used for communication in the same way radio waves are used?

Electromagnetic Waves from the Sun

The Sun produces an enormous amount of energy that is carried outward in all directions as electromagnetic waves. Because Earth is so far from the Sun, Earth receives less than one-billionth of the Sun's energy. However, if all the Sun's energy that reaches Earth in a 20-minute period could be transformed to useful energy, it could power the entire Earth for a year!

As shown in **Figure 17,** about 44 percent of the Sun's energy that reaches Earth is carried by light waves, and about 49 percent is carried by infrared waves. About 7 percent is carried by ultraviolet waves. Radio waves, microwaves, X-rays, and gamma rays carry less than 1 percent of the Sun's energy.

▲ **Figure 16** X-rays are useful for security scans because they have enough energy to pass through soft parts of luggage.

Visual Check How do the views of hard parts and soft parts of luggage differ in this X-ray image?

Figure 17 Infrared waves, light, and ultraviolet waves carry almost all of the Sun's energy. ▼

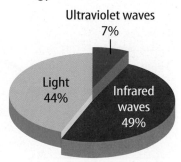

Ultraviolet waves
7%

Light
44%

Infrared
waves
49%

Speed, Wavelength, and Frequency

How could you describe the light from stars or the lights in a city at night? You might use words like *bright* or *dim*, or you might describe the color of the lights. You also could say how easily the light moves through a material. People use properties to describe light and to distinguish one color of light from another.

Like all types of electromagnetic waves, light travels at a speed of 3×10^8 m/s in empty space. When light enters a medium, or matter, it slows down. This is because of the interaction between the waves and the particles that make up the matter.

The wavelength and the frequency of a light wave determine the color of the light. The average human eye can distinguish among millions of wavelengths, or colors. Reds have the longest wavelengths and the lowest frequencies of light. Colors at the violet end of the visible light spectrum have the shortest wavelengths and the highest frequencies.

Light and Matter Interact

In Lesson 1, you read that matter can transmit, absorb, or reflect waves. How do these interactions affect light that travels from a source to your eyes?

Transmission

Air and clear glass, as shown in **Figure 18**, transmit light with little or no distortion. *A material that allows almost all of the light striking it to pass through, and through which objects can be seen clearly is* **transparent.**

Materials such as waxed paper or frosted glass also transmit light, but you cannot see through them clearly. *A material that allows most of the light that strikes it to pass through, but through which objects appear blurry is* **translucent.**

Absorption

Some materials absorb most of the light that strikes them. They transmit no light. Therefore, you cannot see objects through them. *A material through which light does not pass is* **opaque.**

Interactions of Light and Matter 🔑

Figure 18 Materials transmit, absorb, and reflect different amounts of light. This determines whether the material is transparent, translucent, or opaque.

Transparent
You can see clearly through a material such as this window glass because it is transparent. Light moves through the material without being scattered.

Opaque
You cannot see through the window frame because the material is opaque. All of the light that strikes the material is either absorbed or reflected.

Translucent
The lower part of this window contains panes of translucent frosted glass. Light that moves through the glass is scattered. Sometimes you can see colors and vague images through translucent materials, but it is difficult to determine what the shapes are.

Reflection

Why can you see your reflection clearly in a mirror, but not in the wall of your room? Recall that waves reflect off surfaces according to the law of reflection. Parallel rays that reflect from a smooth surface remain parallel and form a clear image. Light that reflects from a bumpy surface scatters in many directions. A wall seems smooth, but up close it is too bumpy to form a clear image.

Different types of matter interact with light in different ways. For example, the window in **Figure 18** both transmits and reflects light. Some of the light that strikes an opaque object, such as a book, is absorbed and reflected at the same time. Reflected light allows an object to be seen.

 Key Concept Check How does light interact with matter?

Color

The colors of an object depends on the wavelengths of light that enters the eye. A luminous object, such as a campfire, is the color of light that it emits. If an object is not luminous, its perceived color depends on other factors.

Opaque Objects Suppose white light strikes an American flag. The blue background absorbs all wavelengths of light except blue. The blue wavelengths reflect back to your eye. The red stripes absorb all colors but red, and red reflects to your eye. The white stars and stripes reflect all colors. You see white. An opaque object is the color it reflects, as shown in **Figure 19.**

Transparent and Translucent Objects If you look at a white lightbulb through a filter of red plastic wrap, only red wavelengths are transmitted through the plastic. The red plastic absorbs other wavelengths. Therefore, the lightbulb appears to be red. .

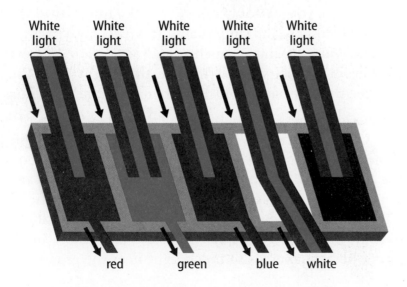

White light   White light   White light   White light   White light

red   green   blue   white

Figure 19 The color of an opaque object is the color of the light that reflects off the object. White objects reflect all colors of light. Black objects absorb all colors. Common black objects are visible because they actually reflect a small amount of light.

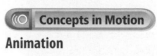 **Concepts in Motion**

Animation

What color is the puppet? 🔒 🧪 🧤 ✂️ 🖐️

An object's color depends on the materials it is made of. Does the color of light shining on an object have any effect?

1. Read and complete a lab safety form.

2. Copy the data table into your Science Journal.

3. Make a red filter by adding three drops of **red food coloring** to 100 mL of water in a **beaker.** Make blue and green filters using **blue and green food coloring.** With **scissors,** cut puppets out of **white and green paper.**

4. Turn off the lights. Shine a **flashlight** through the red water filter onto the white puppet. Record the puppet's color in the table.

5. Repeat step 4 using the colored filters listed in the table. When using more than one color of light, align the beakers so light moves through both and onto the puppet. Record your observations in the data table.

Analyze and Conclude

1. **Model** Draw a picture showing whether each color of light was reflected or absorbed by the green puppet.

2. 🔑 **Key Concept** How does the interaction of light and matter affect the puppet colors?

Light	Original Puppet Color	Observed Puppet Color
Red	White	
Green	White	
Blue	White	
Red	Green	
Green	Green	
Blue	Green	
Red and blue	White	
Red and blue	Green	
Red and green	White	
Red and green	Green	

Figure 20 Light from nearby buildings and other sources can prevent you from seeing stars in the sky.

Intensity of Light

Another property you can use to describe light is intensity. **Intensity** *is the amount of energy that passes through a square meter of space in one second.* Intensity depends on the amount of energy a source emits. Light from a flashlight, for example, has a much lower intensity than light from the Sun. Intensity also depends on the light's distance from the source. When near a lamp, you probably notice that the intensity of the light is greater closer to the lamp than it is farther away. Many of the stars in **Figure 20** emit as much energy as the Sun. However, the light from the stars is less intense than light from the Sun, because the stars are so much farther away than the Sun.

The brightness of a light is a person's perception of intensity. One person's eyes might be more sensitive to light than someone else's eyes. As a result, different people might describe the intensity of a light differently. In addition, eyes are more sensitive to some colors than others. The environment also can affect the brightness of a light. Many stars are visible in the bottom photo of **Figure 20.** Few stars are visible in the top photo because there is so much light near the ground.

Interaction of Sunlight and Matter

Have you ever wondered why the sky is blue or the Sun is yellow? The interaction of light and matter causes interesting effects such as these when sunlight travels through air.

Scattering of Sunlight

As sunlight moves through Earth's atmosphere, most of the light reaches the ground. However, blue wavelengths are shorter than red wavelengths. The particles that make up the air scatter the shorter blue wavelengths more than they scatter longer wavelengths. The sky appears blue because the blue wavelengths spread out in every direction. They eventually reach the eye from all parts of the sky.

A light source, such as the Sun, that emits all colors of light should appear white. Why does the Sun often appear yellow instead of white? As shown in **Figure 21,** after the blue wavelengths of light scatter, the remaining colors appear yellow.

✓ **Reading Check** Why is the sky blue? Why is the Sun yellow?

Refraction of Sunlight

Another interesting effect of sunlight occurs because of refraction. Recall that light changes speed as it travels from one medium into another. If light enters a new medium at an angle, the light wave refracts, or changes direction.

As shown in **Figure 22,** the refraction of light can affect the appearance of the setting Sun. The Sun's rays slow down when they enter Earth's atmosphere. The light rays refract toward Earth's surface. The brain assumes the rays that reach your eyes have traveled in a straight line, and the Sun seems to be higher in the sky than it actually is. This refraction causes you to see the Sun even after it has set below Earth's horizon.

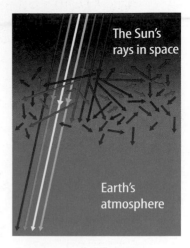

▲ **Figure 21** The Sun appears yellow because only longer wavelengths of light travel through the air in a straight line.

FOLDABLES

Make a vertical two-tab book using the labels shown. Use it to organize your notes on scattering and refraction.

Scattering

Refraction

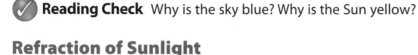

Figure 22 After the Sun actually sets, its light rays refract, and you see the Sun above the horizon.

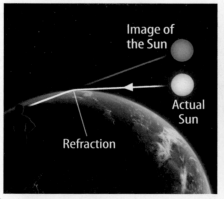

Image of the Sun

Actual Sun

Refraction

Alan Bolesta/Index Stock/age fotostock

Vision and the Eye

Light enables objects to be seen. Light from luminous objects travels directly from the object to the viewer. Objects also are seen when they reflect light to the eyes. What happens to light after it enters the eyes? How do eyes and the brain transform light waves into information about people, places, and things?

As shown in **Figure 23**, light enters the eye through the cornea. The cornea and the lens focus light onto the retina. Cells in the retina absorb the light and send signals about the light to the brain. Follow the steps in **Figure 23** to learn more about how the eye works.

Key Concept Check How do eyes change light waves into the images you see?

The Eye

Concepts in Motion Animation

Figure 23 The parts of the eye work together to change light waves into signals your brain interprets as images.

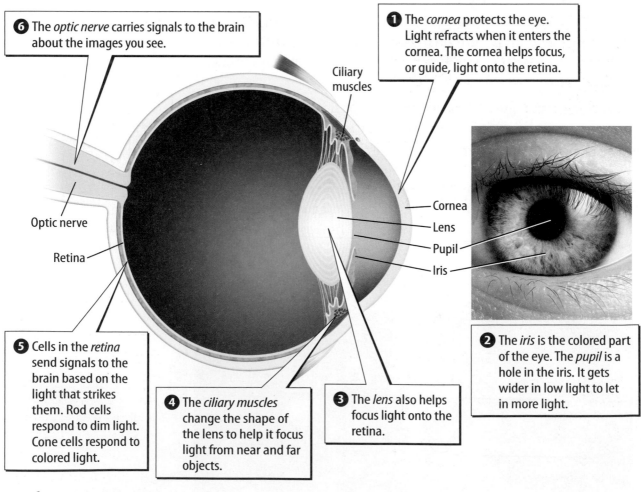

6 The *optic nerve* carries signals to the brain about the images you see.

1 The *cornea* protects the eye. Light refracts when it enters the cornea. The cornea helps focus, or guide, light onto the retina.

Ciliary muscles

Optic nerve

Retina

Cornea
Lens
Pupil
Iris

5 Cells in the *retina* send signals to the brain based on the light that strikes them. Rod cells respond to dim light. Cone cells respond to colored light.

4 The *ciliary muscles* change the shape of the lens to help it focus light from near and far objects.

3 The *lens* also helps focus light onto the retina.

2 The *iris* is the colored part of the eye. The *pupil* is a hole in the iris. It gets wider in low light to let in more light.

Visual Check What part of the eye responds to color?

Lesson 2 Review

Visual Summary

The different types of electromagnetic waves play important roles in your life.

Materials transmit, absorb, and reflect different amounts of light.

Interaction with matter produces interesting effects in sunlight. You can see the Sun even after it sets below the horizon.

FOLDABLES®

Use your lesson Foldable to review the lesson. Save your Foldable for the project at the end of the chapter.

What do you think NOW?

You first read the statements below at the beginning of the chapter.

3. Light is the only type of wave that can travel through empty space.

4. Only shiny surfaces reflect light.

Did you change your mind about whether you agree or disagree with the statements? Rewrite any false statements to make them true.

Use Vocabulary

1. **Contrast** radio waves, infrared waves, and ultraviolet waves.

2. **Explain** the difference between a transparent and a translucent material.

Understand Key Concepts

3. Which eye part responds to colored light?
   - **A.** cones
   - **B.** cornea
   - **C.** iris
   - **D.** lens

4. **Compare** the ways light interacts with a red book and a red stained-glass window.

5. **Describe** how light waves and ultraviolet waves differ.

Interpret Graphics

6. **Explain** the diagram below in terms of the interaction of light waves with matter.

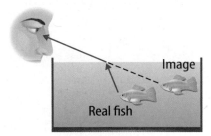

Image

Real fish

7. **Sequence** Copy and fill in a graphic organizer like the one below that shows the sequence of wave types in the electromagnetic spectrum. Add boxes as necessary.

Critical Thinking

8. **Decide** If you turn on an electric stove and stand to the side of it, what type of electromagnetic wave causes you to feel heat from the burner?

9. **Construct** a drawing of the major parts of the eye and describe how each part helps turn light waves into visual information.

Light

Is it keeping you from sleeping at night?

This image was created using data gathered by satellites. It shows light pollution generated by human populations around the world.

◄ The lights used to keep this road safe contribute to light pollution.

Imagine trying to sleep in this house! Light shining in bedroom windows at night is a form of light pollution. ►

Trash on the sidewalk, automobile exhaust in the air, and fertilizer in a river's water are all types of pollution. But did you know that light also can be considered pollution? Light pollution is a serious problem in many urban areas worldwide.

Artificial lighting can be very useful. It can help keep areas free from crime and allow people to work and drive safely after dark. However, the lights people use often shine out into surrounding areas or up into the night sky. This is called light pollution.

Light pollution is a term that refers to the negative effects of artificial lighting. For example, light pollution can disrupt the daily cycles of nocturnal animals. Also, light that escapes into the atmosphere is wasted energy. In some areas, observing the night sky is very difficult because of light pollution.

Awareness of light pollution is increasing. Groups such as the American Medical Association (AMA) have recognized the negative impact of light pollution. The AMA has passed resolutions advocating energy-efficient, fully shielded streetlight design. Individuals can take steps to decrease light pollution by carefully choosing outdoor lights with light-pollution reduction in mind.

It's Your Turn

OBSERVE AND DRAW Observe the night sky near your home, and make a drawing of what you observe. Then, discuss how light pollution in your area might compare with light pollution in other parts of the country.

Lesson 3

Reading Guide

Key Concepts 🔑
ESSENTIAL QUESTIONS

- What are some properties of sound waves?

- How do ears enable people to hear sounds?

Vocabulary

compression

rarefaction

pitch

decibel

g Multilingual eGlossary

▊ **Video** Science Video

IS 1.1; IPS 1.4, 2.1

Sound

Inquiry How does it make sounds?

Have you ever stood nearby as a marching band plays or carefully watched musicians during a concert? The notes they play can be high or low, loud or soft, or anything in between. Why are the sounds so different? How are sounds perceived?

Sean Justice/Digital Vision/Getty Images

Launch Lab

How can you change the sound of a straw?

Sounds are longitudinal waves that travel through matter. If you blow across a straw, you can make different wavelengths of sound. How do different wavelengths change the sounds you hear?

1 Read and complete a lab safety form.

2 Using **scissors,** cut a **straw** in half. Cut one of the halves into two equal parts. Cut one of those parts into two equal parts.

3 Blow across the top of each straw. How do the sounds differ? Make a data table in your Science Journal, and then record your observations in your data table.

4 Repeat step 3, this time covering the bottom of each straw with your finger.

Think About This

1. What is the source of energy that creates the sound waves?

2. How does covering the bottom of the straw change the sound?

3. 🔑 **Key Concept** How do the sounds made by a long straw and a short straw differ? Why do you think this is?

What are sound waves?

Just as light is a type of wave that can be seen, sounds are a type of wave that can be heard. Sound waves are longitudinal mechanical waves. Unlike light waves, sound waves must travel through a medium.

Audible Vibrations

Suppose you strike two metal pans together. Now, suppose you strike two pillows together. How would the two sounds differ? Sound waves are vibrations the ear can detect. You hear a loud sound when you hit the pans together because they vibrate so much. You barely hear the pillows because they vibrate so little. Healthy, young humans can hear sound waves produced by vibrations with frequencies between about 20 Hz and 20,000 Hz. As people age, their ability to hear the higher and lower frequencies of sound decreases. The human ear is most sensitive to frequencies between 1,000 Hz and 4,000 Hz.

Animals have ranges of hearing that help them catch prey or avoid predators. For example, elephants hear sounds as low as 15 Hz. Chickens hear sounds between 125 Hz and 2,000 Hz. Porpoises can hear sounds between 75 Hz and 150,000 Hz! Ranges for other animals are listed in **Figure 24.**

Figure 24 People and animals hear different ranges of sound frequencies.

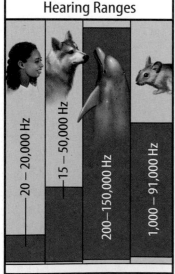

Hearing Ranges

20 – 20,000 Hz   15 – 50,000 Hz   200–150,000 Hz   1,000 – 91,000 Hz

Human   Dog   Dolphin   Mouse

Figure 25 A sound wave produces compressions and rarefactions as it passes through matter.

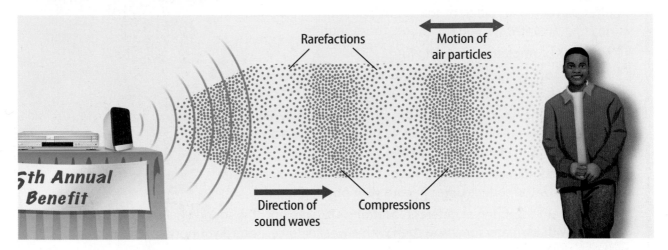

Rarefactions

Motion of air particles

Direction of sound waves

Compressions

5th Annual Benefit

Compressions and Rarefactions

Sound waves usually travel to your ears through air. Air particles are in constant motion. As the particles bounce off objects, they exert a force, or pressure. **Figure 25** shows how sound waves moving through air change the air pressure by causing air particles to move toward and then away from each other.

Suppose you pluck a guitar string. As the string springs back, it pushes air particles forward, forcing them closer together. This increases the air pressure near the string. *A* **compression** *is the region of a longitudinal wave where the particles of the medium are closest together.* As the string vibrates, it moves in the other direction. This leaves behind a region with lower pressure. *A* **rarefaction** *is the region of a longitudinal wave where the particles are farthest apart.*

✓ **Reading Check** How do compressions and rarefactions differ?

Properties of Sound Waves

A sound wave is described by its wavelength, frequency, amplitude, and speed. These properties of sound waves depend on the compressions and rarefactions of the sound waves.

Wavelength, Frequency, and Pitch

Recall that the wavelength of a wave becomes shorter as the wave's frequency increases. How does the frequency of a sound wave affect what is heard?

The perception of how high or low a sound seems is called **pitch.** The higher the frequency, the higher the pitch of the sound. For example, a female voice generally produces higher-pitched sounds than a male voice. This is because the female voice has a higher range of frequencies. **Figure 26** shows the range of frequencies produced by several instruments and voices.

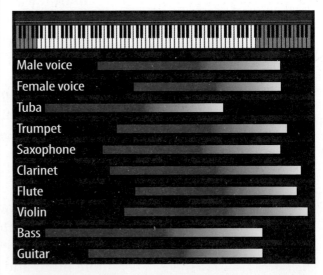

Male voice
Female voice
Tuba
Trumpet
Saxophone
Clarinet
Flute
Violin
Bass
Guitar

▲ **Figure 26** People and instruments have different ranges of sound frequencies.

Can you make different sounds with string?

A guitar player makes different sounds by holding and plucking the strings in different ways. You can model these sounds.

1. Read and complete a lab safety form.

2. Use **scissors** to cut a piece of **string** 1 m long. Attach one end securely to the leg of a desk.

3. Hold the other end, and stretch the string horizontally. Pluck the string several times, and observe the sound. Record your observations in your Science Journal.

4. Continue holding the string at various locations and plucking it. Notice how the sounds differ. Record your observations.

5. Again, hold the string at different locations. Observe how the sound changes as you pull the string with a greater force and then with a weaker force. Record your observations.

Analyze and Conclude

1. **Interpret** How does pulling the string tighter or changing its length affect the string's sound?

2. 🔑 **Key Concept** Explain how you changed the frequency, wavelength, pitch, amplitude, and energy of the sound you made with the string.

SCIENCE USE v. COMMON USE

rest position
Science Use position of an undisturbed particle; particles are still in motion here

Common Use the state of something not moving

Amplitude and Energy

You use more energy to shout than to whisper. The more energy you put into your voice, the farther the particles of air move as they vibrate. The distance a vibrating particle moves from its **rest position** is the amplitude. The more energy used to produce the sound wave, the greater the amplitude.

Speed

Sound waves travel much slower than electromagnetic waves. With sound, the transmitted energy must pass from particle to particle. The type of medium and the temperature affect the speed of sound.

Type of Medium Gas particles are far apart and collide less often than particles in a liquid or a solid. As shown in **Table 3,** a gas takes longer to transfer sound energy between particles.

Temperature Particles move faster and collide more often as the temperature of a gas increases. This increase in the number of collisions transfers more energy in less time. Temperature has the opposite effect on liquids and sounds. As liquids and solids cool, the molecules move closer together. They collide more often and transfer energy faster.

🔑 **Key Concept Check** What are some properties of sound waves?

Table 3 The Speed of Sound	
Material	**Speed (m/s)**
Air (0°C)	331
Air (20°C)	343
Water (20°C)	1,481
Water (0°C)	1,500
Seawater (25°C)	1,533
Ice (0°C)	3,500
Iron	5,130
Glass	5,640

Intensity and Loudness

Generally, the greater the amplitude of a sound wave, the louder the sound seems. But what happens if you move away from a sound source? As you move away, the wave's amplitude decreases and the sound seems quieter. This is because as a sound wave moves farther from the source, more and more particles collide, and the energy from the wave spreads out among more particles. Therefore, the farther you move from the source, the less energy present in the same area of space. Recall that the amount of energy that passes through a square meter of space in one second is the intensity of a wave. Loudness is your ear's perception of intensity.

The Decibel Scale

The unit used to measure sound intensity, or loudness, is the **decibel (dB).** The decibel levels of common sounds are shown in **Figure 27.** Each increase of 10 dB causes a sound about twice as loud. As the decibel level goes up, the amount of time you can listen to the sound without risking hearing loss gets shorter and shorter. People who work around loud sounds wear protective hearing devices to prevent hearing loss.

Decibel Levels

Figure 27 The decibel scale helps you understand safe limits of different types of sounds.

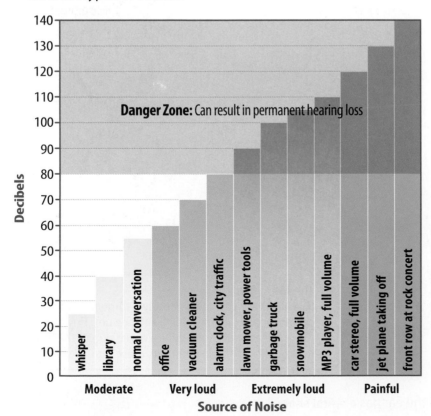

Use a Fraction

Because sound energy travels out in all directions from the source, the intensity of the sound decreases as you move away. You can calculate the fraction by which the sound intensity changes. The fraction $= \left(\dfrac{r_1}{r_2}\right)^2$, where r_1 is the starting distance and r_2 is the ending distance from the source. For example, by what fraction does sound intensity decrease if you move from **3 m** to **6 m** from a source?

1 Replace the variables with given values.
fraction $= \left(\dfrac{3}{6}\right)^2$

2 Solve the problem.
$\left(\dfrac{3}{6}\right)^2 = \left(\dfrac{1}{2}\right)^2 = \dfrac{1}{4}$, so the intensity decreases to $\dfrac{1}{4}$ of its original value.

Practice

You are standing at a distance of 2 m from a sound source. How does the sound intensity change if you move to a distance of 6 m?

📖 **Review**

- **Math Practice**
- **Personal Tutor**

WORD ORIGIN · · · · · · · · · · ·

decibel
from Latin *decibus,* means "tenth"

Hearing and the Ear

Typically, objects are seen when light enters the eyes. Similarly, sound waves enter the ears with information about the environment. The human ear has three main parts, as shown in **Figure 28.** First, the external outer ear collects sound waves. Next, the middle ear amplifies, or intensifies, the sound waves. The middle ear includes the ear drum and three small bones—the hammer, the anvil, and the stirrup, Finally, the inner ear contains the cochlea (KOH klee uh). The cochlea converts sound waves to nerve signals. These nerve signals are typically processed by the brain, creating the perception of sound.

Key Concept Check How do your ears enable you to hear sounds?

Parts of the Human Ear

 **Concepts in Motion** Animation

Figure 28 The different parts of the ear work together to gather and interpret sound waves.

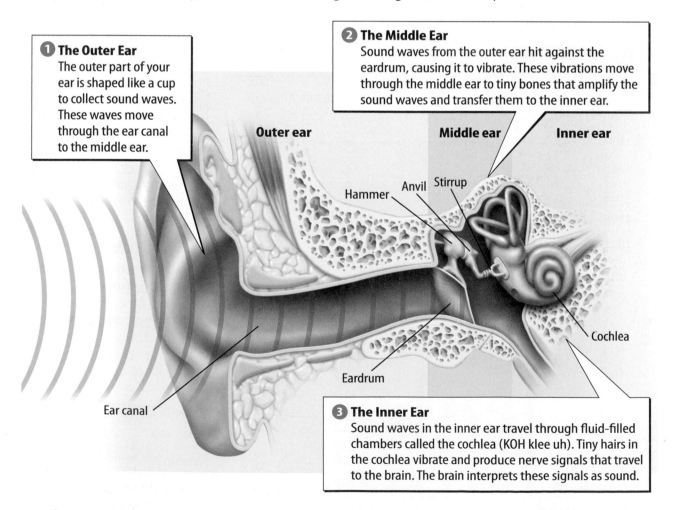

❶ The Outer Ear
The outer part of your ear is shaped like a cup to collect sound waves. These waves move through the ear canal to the middle ear.

❷ The Middle Ear
Sound waves from the outer ear hit against the eardrum, causing it to vibrate. These vibrations move through the middle ear to tiny bones that amplify the sound waves and transfer them to the inner ear.

Outer ear   Middle ear   Inner ear

Hammer   Anvil   Stirrup

Eardrum

Ear canal

Cochlea

❸ The Inner Ear
Sound waves in the inner ear travel through fluid-filled chambers called the cochlea (KOH klee uh). Tiny hairs in the cochlea vibrate and produce nerve signals that travel to the brain. The brain interprets these signals as sound.

Visual Check Which part of the ear has a spiral shape?

Lesson 3 Review

Visual Summary

Sound waves are produced when an energy source causes matter to vibrate.

Sound waves are compressions and rarefactions that move away from a sound source.

You hear sounds when your ears capture sound waves and produce signals that travel to your brain.

FOLDABLES

Use your lesson Foldable to review the lesson. Save your Foldable for the project at the end of the chapter.

What do you think NOW?

You first read the statements below at the beginning of the chapter.

5. Sound travels faster through solid materials than through air.

6. The more energy used to produce a sound, the louder the sound.

Did you change your mind about whether you agree or disagree with the statements? Rewrite any false statements to make them true.

Use Vocabulary

1 The property of a sound wave that relates to a high or low musical note is the sound's _____.

2 **Explain** the difference between a compression and a rarefaction in a sound wave.

Understand Key Concepts

3 Which property of a sound wave describes the amount of energy that passes through a square meter of space each second?
   A. amplitude   C. intensity
   B. frequency   D. wavelength

4 **Describe** how the three main parts of the ear enable people to hear.

Interpret Graphics

5 **Sequence** Copy and fill in a graphic organizer like the one below to describe the path of a sound wave from when it is produced by a source until is interpreted by the brain. Describe the function of each part of the path.

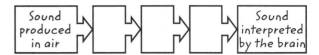

Critical Thinking

6 **Construct** a diagram of four sound waves. Two of the waves should have the same amplitude but different frequencies. The other two waves should have the same wavelength but different amplitudes. Label the properties of the waves.

Math Skills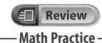

Review
—— Math Practice ——

7 A student is standing a distance of 4 m from the school bell. If the student moves to a distance 20 m away, what fraction of the original intensity of the bell's sound will the student hear?

Check the sound! Cue the lights!

Materials

coiled spring toy

snap-together plastic blocks

food coloring

flashlights

string

scissors

Also needed:
variety of beakers, dowel, large glass pan, colored paper, sponge, water, white paper, office supplies

Safety

You are part of an entertainment firm that creates sound and light shows like the kind you see during a music concert or at halftime of a sports event. You have been asked to produce an exciting and entertaining wave show that is between 2 and 4 minutes long. The show must use at least three types of waves, and you must be able to identify at least three properties or behaviors of waves. Unfortunately, you do not have a big budget or high-tech equipment like professional show designers. You can use only the materials you have used in other labs in this chapter, as well as any materials your teacher approves.

Question

How can you use different waves to build an exciting and entertaining show?

Procedure

1. Read and complete a lab safety form.
2. As a group, decide on a concept or idea around which you will focus your show.
3. Develop a script for the show. Assign the different roles to the members of your group.
4. Make a table of the different waves in your show, as shown below. Consider the source of the wave and the medium through which the wave travels.
5. Create a list of the different physical concepts related to waves that you will include in your show.
6. Build all the instruments and lighting equipment required for your show. Practice your show so that everyone in your group is able to smoothly perform the different parts together for the class.

Title of the show: _____

Wave	Source	Medium
1.		
2.		
3.		
4.		
5.		

7. Show the script of your show to another group. Ask the group to evaluate how well you use different waves and wave properties. Get feedback on ways to make your show even more entertaining.

8. As a group, think about how you can use the suggestions you received from the other group. Consider what supplies you will need and how you will make the changes.

9. Record these suggestions and your ideas about how to make modifications to your setup in your Science Journal.

10. Make modifications to your show based on your ideas. You might need to test different parts to see how ideas work. When you have made all the changes, perform your entire show.

Analyze and Conclude

11. **Explain** How did you incorporate three types of waves into your show?

12. **Assess** What are some benefits and some challenges of using waves to create a show?

13. **The Big Idea** How did you use the physical properties of waves in your show?

Communicate Your Results

Perform your show for your class. After your show, have your class give you feedback on how well you used different types of waves and different properties of waves to create an exciting and entertaining show.

Inquiry Extension

What were some of the problems you encountered because of the limited materials that were available for making your show? What kind of equipment would you have liked to use? Write a proposal that you might submit to a client to explain why you would like to have the funds to purchase improved sound and light equipment. Explain how a larger budget might improve the show and make people pay to see your show.

Lab Tips

☑ Be sure to decide on a theme around which to focus your show. For example, will it be a music concert? A sideshow at a sports event? A display at a theme park?

☑ Look back at the labs for this chapter for ideas on how to use waves.

☑ Try to make your show as creative as possible. How can you make your show exciting?

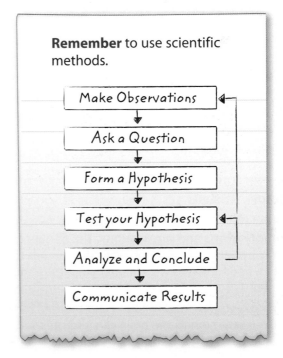

Remember to use scientific methods.

Make Observations

Ask a Question

Form a Hypothesis

Test your Hypothesis

Analyze and Conclude

Communicate Results

Chapter 6 Study Guide

THE BIG IDEA

Mechanical waves transfer energy from particle to particle in matter. Electromagnetic waves transfer energy through either matter or empty space.

Key Concepts Summary 🔑	Vocabulary
Lesson 1: Waves  • Waves are disturbances that transfer energy from place to place. A **mechanical wave** forms when a source of energy causes particles of a medium to vibrate. A vibrating electric charge produces an **electromagnetic wave.** • You can describe wavelength, **frequency,** speed, **amplitude,** and energy of waves. • Matter can transmit, absorb, or reflect a wave. It also can change a wave's direction by **refraction** or diffraction.	**mechanical wave** **electromagnetic wave** **transverse wave** **longitudinal wave** **frequency** **amplitude** **refraction**
Lesson 2: Light  • Light differs from other forms of electromagnetic waves by its frequency, wavelength, and energy. Light is the type of electromagnetic wave that is visible with the human eye. • Matter can transmit, absorb, and reflect light. These interactions differ in how much light the matter transmits and how it changes the direction of light. • Cells in the retina of the eyes change light into electric signals that travel to the brain.	**radio wave** **infrared wave** **ultraviolet wave** **transparent** **translucent** **opaque** **intensity**
Lesson 3: Sound  • Sound waves travel through matter as a series of **compressions** and **rarefactions.** The frequency and wavelength of a sound wave determines the **pitch.** Sound waves with greater amplitude sound louder. • Ears collect and amplify sound and then convert it to signals the brain can interpret.	**compression** **rarefaction** **pitch** **decibel**

(t)Don Farrall/Getty Images; (b)Design Pics/Don Hammond

FOLDABLES® **Chapter Project**

Assemble your lesson Foldables as shown to make a Chapter Project. Use the project to review what you have learned in this chapter.

Transverse Waves

Both

Longitudinal Waves

Scattering

Refraction

Wavelength

Frequency

Amplitude

Speed

Properties of Sound Waves

Use Vocabulary

1 The property of waves that is measured in hertz (Hz) is _____.

2 A change in direction, or _____, can occur as a wave moves into a medium.

3 A material that transmits light but through which objects appear blurry is _____.

4 An object that does not allow light to pass through it is _____.

5 The portion of a sound wave with higher-than-normal pressure is called a(n) _____.

6 A unit that describes the intensity or loudness of sound is the _____.

Link Vocabulary and Key Concepts

 **Concepts in Motion** **Interactive Concept Map**

Copy this concept map, and then use vocabulary terms from the previous page to complete the concept map.

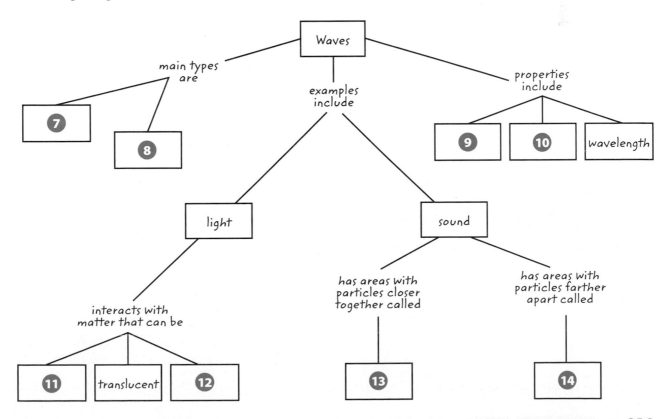

Waves

main types are

7

8

examples include

properties include

9

10

wavelength

light

sound

interacts with matter that can be

11

translucent

12

has areas with particles closer together called

13

has areas with particles farther apart called

14

Understand Key Concepts

1 As a water wave passes, the particles that make up the water move
  A. back and forth, parallel to the wave.
  B. in circles around the same point.
  C. up and down at right angles to the wave.
  D. whichever direction the wave moves.

2 The refraction of a wave is caused by a change in
  A. amplitude.
  B. frequency.
  C. speed.
  D. wavelength.

3 Which is always a transverse wave?
  A. microwave
  B. seismic wave
  C. sound wave
  D. water wave

4 Wave frequency is measured in
  A. decibels.
  B. hertz.
  C. meters.
  D. seconds.

5 The arrow in the diagram below shows a point on a light wave that stops as it interacts with matter. Which type of interaction does the arrow represent?

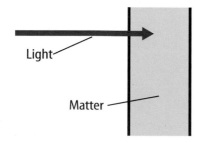

  A. absorption
  B. reflection
  C. refraction
  D. transmission

6 The distance between one point on a wave and the nearest point just like it is the
  A. amplitude.
  B. frequency.
  C. pitch.
  D. wavelength.

7 Which interactions of light with matter are taking place in the picture below?

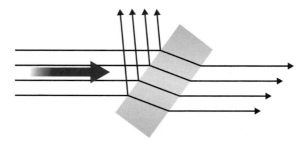

  A. diffraction, reflection, and absorption
  B. reflection, refraction, and transmission
  C. reflection, scattering, and diffraction
  D. translucent, transparent, and opaque

8 Which of the following colors of light has the longest wavelength?
  A. red
  B. green
  C. violet
  D. yellow

9 You turn up the volume on the car radio. Which of the following properties of the sound changes?
  A. amplitude
  B. frequency
  C. speed
  D. wavelength

10 If a sound is loud and low-pitched, the sound wave also has which of the following properties?
  A. low frequency and high amplitude
  B. low frequency and low amplitude
  C. high frequency and high amplitude
  D. high frequency and low amplitude

Critical Thinking

11 **Construct** Make a diagram that shows how interactions of light waves with matter cause a flower to appear orange.

12 **Synthesize** An MP3 player at maximum volume produces sound at 110 dB. The table shows the time exposure before a risk of hearing damage. How many hours a day could you listen to your MP3 player at full volume before a hearing loss risk? Explain.

Recommended Noise Exposure Limits	
Sound Level (dB)	Time Permitted (h)
90	8
95	4
100	2
105	1

13 **Summarize** What is the process by which an object can be seen and recognized? Be sure to include the interactions of light waves and matter in your summary.

14 **Hypothesize** Why does a 200-W lightbulb appear brighter than a 100-W lightbulb? Mention properties of light in your explanation.

15 **Apply** The passage of lightning through air produces thunder. Why is lightning seen before thunder is heard?

16 **Compare and Contrast** How does the motion of the medium in transverse mechanical waves, longitudinal waves, water waves, and seismic waves differ?

Writing in Science

17 **Write** a paragraph describing an example of sound waves and an example of light most people use each day. Identify a way you could change the properties of each wave.

REVIEW **THE BIG IDEA**

18 Explain various ways in which waves transfer energy through matter and empty space. Include correct terms to describe the various interactions of waves with matter.

19 Using the picture below, describe how the transfer of energy through matter and empty space helps a meteorologist predict the weather.

Math Skills ×÷

 Review

—— **Math Practice** ——

Use a Fraction

20 By what fraction does the sound intensity change if you move from 2 m away from a source to 10 m away from the source?

21 You are standing 3 m from someone who is using a lawn mower. How will the sound intensity change if the person moves the mower to a distance 12 m from you?

22 A car 5 m away from you beeps its horn. How would the intensity of the beep change if you moved to a distance 40 m from the car?

Standardized Test Practice

Record your answers on the answer sheet provided by your teacher or on a sheet of paper.

Multiple Choice

Use the figure to answer questions 1–3.

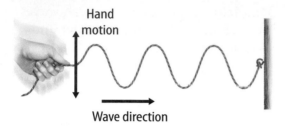

1 The figure above shows waves generated on a rope. Which type of waves are shown in the figure?

  A combination

  B electromagnetic

  C longitudinal

  D mechanical

2 Which statement best describes the correct relationship for the wave shown in the figure?

  A The disturbance is parallel to the direction the wave travels.

  B The disturbance is perpendicular to the direction the wave travels.

  C The disturbance carries matter and energy in the same direction along the wave.

  D The disturbance has both back-and-forth and up-and-down motion.

3 Which describes how the wave would change if the person's hand moved at a faster rate?

  A The amplitude would decrease.

  B The amplitude would increase.

  C The frequency would decrease.

  D The frequency would increase.

4 If two waves are traveling at the same speed, which description is most accurate?

  A The wave with the longer wavelength has the higher frequency.

  B The wave with the shorter wavelength has the higher frequency.

  C Both waves must have equal wavelengths.

  D Both waves must have equal frequencies.

5 Wood is opaque. Which describes how light waves can interact with wood?

  A absorption and reflection

  B diffraction and transmission

  C reflection and refraction

  D transmission and refraction

6 Which property is unique to electromagnetic waves?

  A the ability to interact with matter

  B the ability to travel through matter

  C the ability to have different intensities

  D the ability to travel through empty space

Use the table to answer question 7.

Incoming Light	Color of Filter	Outgoing Light
white	red	red
red	blue	none
white	blue	blue
green	green	?

7 The table above shows the interactions of different colors of light with different colors of filters. Which is the correct color to complete the table?

  A green

  B none

  C red

  D white

8 Which must be true of the cornea for the eye to work properly in sending a message to the brain?

A It must absorb light.

B It must block out light.

C It must reflect light.

D It must transmit light.

Use the table to answer question 9.

Material	Speed of Sound (m/s)
Air (0°C)	331
Air (20°C)	343
Water (0°C)	1,500
Water (20°C)	1,481
Ice (0°C)	3,500
Iron	5,130

9 Based on the data in the table, which of the following statements is most likely true?

A Sound travels fastest through gases because they are less dense.

B Sound travels fastest through liquids because they are most fluid.

C Sound travels fastest through solids because they are most dense.

D Sound travels fastest through materials that have higher temperatures.

10 Which color of light could you shine on a green object to make it appear black?

A green

B red

C white

D yellow

Constructed Response

11 You are standing outside and hear a jet flying overhead. You look up toward the direction of the sound, but you notice that the jet is far ahead of where the sound seems to come from. Explain why you can hear a jet only after it passes overhead.

Use the figure to answer question 12.

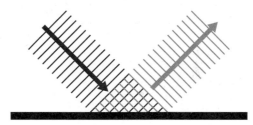

12 The figure above shows light rays striking a flat surface. Describe how the figure would change if the surface the light rays hit against were bumpy instead of flat.

13 People sometimes confuse the pitch of a sound with the sound's intensity. How would you explain the difference between these two properties to a classmate?

14 What roles do the outer ear, the middle ear, and the inner ear play in hearing?

NEED EXTRA HELP?														
If You Missed Question...	1	2	3	4	5	6	7	8	9	10	11	12	13	14
Go to Lesson...	1	1	1	1	2	2	2	2	3	2	3	2	3	3

Chapter 7

AID S1.2a, S1.2b, S1.3, S2.1a, S2.1c, S2.1d, T1.4a; ICT 1.2, 1.4, 2.1, 2.2; PS 2.1a, 2.1c, 2.1d, 2.1j, 2.2i, 2.2j

Our Planet—Earth

THE BIG IDEA How can you describe Earth?

Inquiry   What can you see?

From space, it's easy to see why Earth is called the blue planet. But there's more to Earth than oceans of water.

- What other parts of Earth can you see in the photo?

- How would you describe Earth to a friend?

Get Ready to Read

What do you think?

Before you read, decide if you agree or disagree with each of these statements. As you read this chapter, see if you change your mind about any of the statements.

1 Earth is a simple system made of rocks.

2 Most of Earth is covered by one large ocean.

3 Earth's interior is made of distinct layers.

4 The water cycle begins in the ocean.

5 Earth's air contains solids, liquids, and gases.

6 Rocks are made of minerals.

 **Connect ED** Your one-stop online resource

MHEonline.com

 Video   WebQuest

 Audio   Assessment

 Review   Concepts in Motion

 Inquiry   Multilingual eGlossary

Earth Systems

Reading Guide

Key Concepts
ESSENTIAL QUESTIONS

- What are the composition and the structure of the atmosphere?
- How is water distributed in the hydrosphere?
- What are Earth's systems?
- What are the composition and the structure of the geosphere?

Vocabulary
biosphere
atmosphere
hydrosphere
groundwater
geosphere
mineral
rock

 Multilingual eGlossary

Video

- **BrainPOP®**
- **Science Video**
- **What's Science Got to do With It?**

 PS 2.1a, 2.1c, 2.1d

Inquiry A Hot Mix?

Earth is made of more than soil, minerals, and melted rocks flowing out of volcanoes. What other parts of Earth do you see in the photo? How do these parts interact?

Philippe Bourseiller/Getty Images

How can you describe Earth? ✂

When you look out the window, you might see wispy white clouds, birds in the trees, and rolling hills in the distance. All these things are part of Earth. What else makes up Earth?

living **rock** plants
air **Earth**
water oxygen
animals **mineral** soil
ice **energy**

1 Read and complete a lab safety form.

2 With your partner, brainstorm a list of words that describe Earth. Limit the list to 20 words. Be creative! Record the list in your Science Journal.

3 Use **markers** to rewrite your list of words using different colors and letter shapes. Use **scissors** to cut out each word.

4 Group the words that you think relate to each other. Use a **glue stick** to fix the words to a piece of **colored paper.**

Think About This

1. What words did you use to describe Earth?

2. How did your list compare to those of other students?

3. 🔑 **Key Concept** What things do you think make up Earth?

What is Earth?

The puffy, white clouds over your head and the hard ground under your feet are both parts of Earth. The water in the oceans and the fish that live there are also parts of Earth. The planet Earth is more than a solid ball in space. It includes air molecules that float near the boundaries of outer space and molten rock that churns deep below Earth's surface.

Earth is a complex place. People often divide complex things into smaller parts in order to study them. Scientists divide Earth into four systems to help better understand the planet. The systems contain different materials and work in different ways, but they all interact. What happens in one system affects the others.

Earth's Air

The outermost Earth system is an invisible layer of gases that surrounds the planet. Even though you cannot see air, you can feel it when the wind blows. Moving air is blowing the tree in **Figure 1.**

Figure 1 Even though you cannot see air, you can see its power when it makes objects move.

©C.I. Aguera/Corbis

Earth's Water

Below the layer of air is the system that contains Earth's water. Like air, water can move from place to place. Some of the water is salty, and some is fresh. Fresh river water flows into the salty Pacific Ocean in Hawaii, as shown in **Figure 2.**

The Solid Earth

The next system is the solid part of Earth. It contains a thin layer of soil covering a rocky center. It is by far the largest Earth system. Because it is solid, materials in this system move more slowly than air or water. But they do move, and over time, landforms rise up and then wear away. It took millions of years for the canyon shown in **Figure 2** to form.

Life on Earth

The Earth system that contains all living things is the **biosphere.** Living things are found in air, water, and soil. So, the biosphere has no distinct boundaries; it is found within the other Earth systems. The living things shown in **Figure 2** are part of the biosphere. You will learn more about the biosphere when you study life science, or biology. The rest of this chapter will describe the three Earth systems made of nonliving things.

✓ **Reading Check** Why doesn't the biosphere have distinct boundaries?

Figure 2 Air, water, rocks, and living things are all part of Earth.

(l)Chris Close/Getty Images, (tr)Pixtal/age fotostock, (br)Joseph Sohm-Visions of America/Getty Images

The Atmosphere

The force of Earth's gravity pulls molecules of gases into a layer surrounding the planet. *This mixture of gases forms a layer around Earth called the* **atmosphere.** The atmosphere is denser near Earth's surface and becomes less dense farther from Earth. It keeps Earth warm by trapping thermal energy from the Sun that bounces back from Earth's surface. If the atmosphere did not regulate temperature, life as it is on Earth could not exist.

WORD ORIGIN

atmosphere
from Greek *atmos-*, means "vapor"; and Greek *spharia,* means "sphere"

What makes up the atmosphere?

The atmosphere contains a mixture of nitrogen, oxygen, and smaller amounts of other gases. The graph in **Figure 3** shows the percentages of these gases. The most common gas is nitrogen, which makes up 78 percent of the atmosphere. Most of the remaining gas is oxygen.

The other gases are called trace gases because they make up only 1 percent, or a trace, of the atmosphere. Nonetheless, trace gases are important. Carbon dioxide, methane, and water vapor help regulate Earth's temperature. Note that **Figure 3** shows the percentages of gases in dry air. The atmosphere also contains water vapor. The amount of water vapor in the atmosphere generally ranges from 0 to 4 percent.

Along with gases and water vapor, the atmosphere contains small amounts of solids. Particles of dust float along with the gases and water vapor. Sometimes you can see these tiny specks as sunlight reflects off them as it shines through a window.

Key Concept Check What is the composition of the atmosphere?

Figure 3 Dry air contains a mixture of gases. Though the atmosphere is made mainly of nitrogen and oxygen, trace gases are also important.

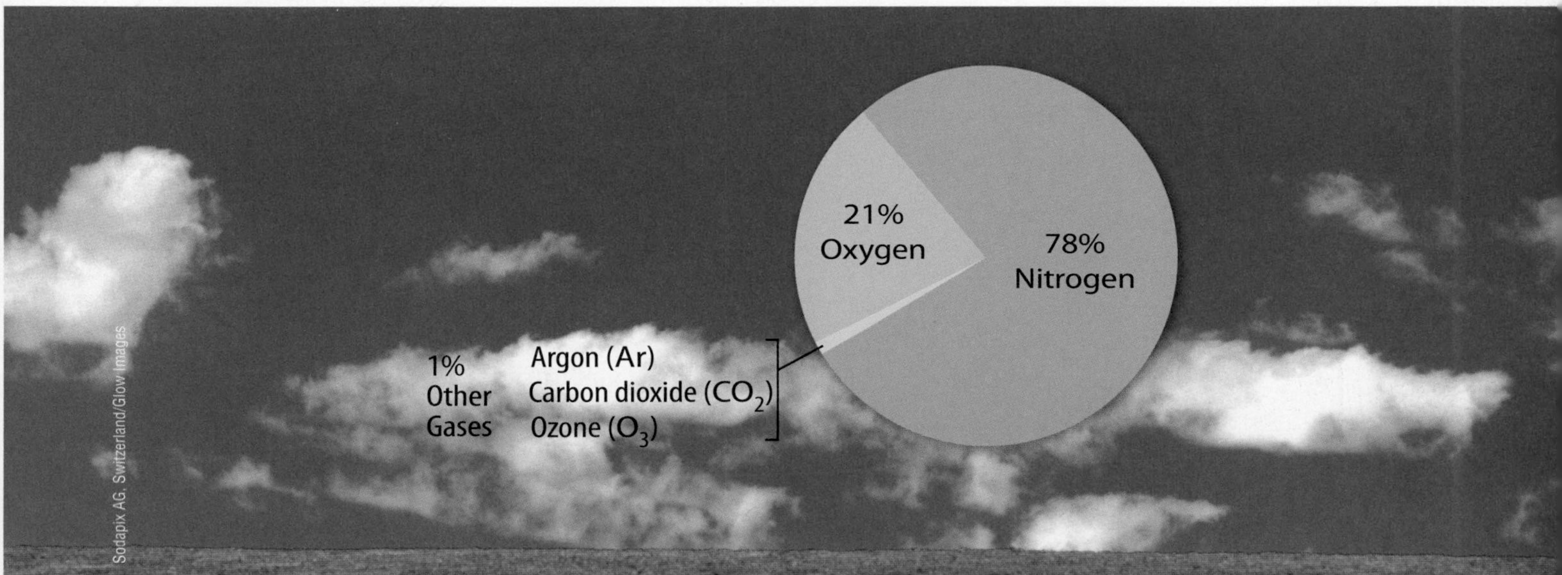
21%
Oxygen
78%
Nitrogen
1%
Other
Gases
Argon (Ar)
Carbon dioxide (CO2)
Ozone (O3)
Sodapix AG, Switzerland/Glow Images

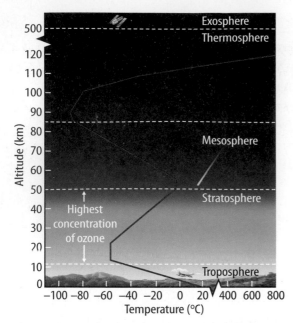

Figure 4 The atmosphere is divided into layers according to differences in temperature.

Visual Check Summarize how temperature changes as altitude increases.

Concepts in Motion Animation

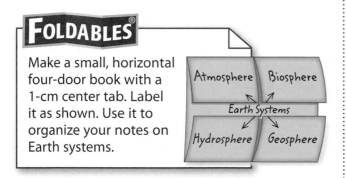

Atmosphere   Biosphere

Earth Systems

Hydrosphere   Geosphere

Layers of the Atmosphere

The composition of the atmosphere does not change much over time. However, the temperature of the atmosphere does change. Radiant energy from the Sun heats Earth's atmosphere; however, different parts of the atmosphere absorb or reflect the Sun's energy in different ways. The red line in **Figure 4** shows changes in temperature as altitude increases. These temperature changes are used to distinguish layers in the atmosphere.

The Troposphere If you have ever hiked up a mountain, you might have noticed that the temperature decreases as you climb higher. In the bottom layer of the atmosphere, called the troposphere, temperature decreases as you move upward from Earth's surface. Gases flow and swirl in the troposphere, causing weather. Although the troposphere does not extend very far upward, it contains most of the mass in the atmosphere.

The Stratosphere Above the troposphere is the stratosphere. Unlike gases in the troposphere, gases in the stratosphere do not swirl around. They are more stable and form flat layers. Within the stratosphere is a layer of ozone, a form of oxygen. This ozone layer protects Earth's surface from harmful radiation from the Sun. It acts like a layer of sunscreen, protecting the biosphere. Because ozone absorbs solar radiation, temperatures increase in the stratosphere.

Upper Layers Above the stratosphere is the mesosphere. Temperature decreases in this layer, then increases again in the next layer, the thermosphere. The last layer of Earth's atmosphere is the exosphere. The lowest density of gas molecules is in this layer. Beyond the exosphere is outer space.

Key Concept Check What are the layers of the atmosphere?

The Hydrosphere

Water is one of the most common and important substances on Earth. *The system containing all Earth's water is called the* **hydrosphere.** Most water is stored on Earth's surface, but some is located below the surface or within the atmosphere and biosphere. The hydrosphere contains more than 1.3 billion km^3 of water. The amount of water does not change. But like the gases in the atmosphere, water in the hydrosphere flows. It moves from one location to another over time. Water also changes state. It is found as a liquid, a solid, and a gas on Earth.

 Reading Check How much water is in the hydrosphere?

Ocean

Scientists call the natural locations where water is stored reservoirs (REH zuh vworz). The largest reservoir on Earth is the world ocean. Though the oceans have separate names, they are all connected, making one large ocean. Water flows freely throughout the world ocean. About 97 percent of Earth's water is in the ocean, as shown in **Figure 5.**

Many minerals dissolve easily in water. As water in rivers and underground reservoirs flows toward the ocean, it dissolves materials from the solid Earth. These dissolved minerals make ocean water salty. Most plants and animals that live on land, including humans, cannot use salt water. They need **freshwater** to survive.

REVIEW VOCABULARY

freshwater
water that contains less than 0.2 percent dissolved salts

Distribution of Earth's Water 🗝

Figure 5 Water in the hydrosphere is found in several different reservoirs.

Visual Check Where is most water on Earth located?

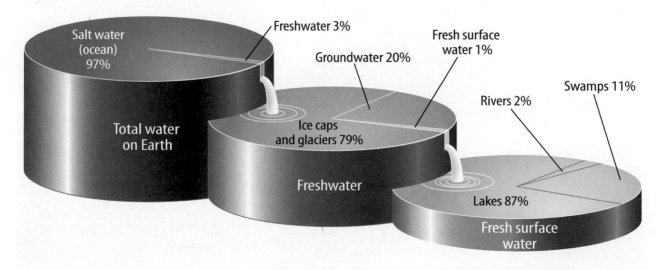

Lakes and Rivers

Less than 1 percent of freshwater is easily accessible on Earth's surface. This small percentage of Earth's total water must meet the needs of people and other organisms that require freshwater. Rain and snow supply water to the surface reservoirs—lakes and rivers. Water in these reservoirs moves through the water cycle much faster than water frozen in glaciers and ice caps.

Groundwater

Ice, lakes, and rivers hold about 80 percent of Earth's freshwater. Where is the remaining 20 percent? It is beneath the ground. Some rain and snow seep into the ground and collect in small cracks and open spaces called pores. **Groundwater** *is water that is stored in cracks and pores beneath Earth's surface.* As shown in **Figure 6,** groundwater collects in layers. Many people get their water by drilling wells down into these layers of groundwater.

 Key Concept Check How is water distributed in the hydrosphere?

The Cryosphere

Did you know that most of Earth's freshwater is frozen? The frozen portion of water on Earth's surface is called the cryosphere. About 79 percent of the planet's freshwater is in the cryosphere. The cryosphere consists of snow, glaciers, and icebergs. Water can be stored as ice for thousands of years before melting and becoming liquid water in other reservoirs.

Figure 6 Freshwater in lakes, rivers, and glaciers is visible on Earth's surface, but large amounts of groundwater are hidden below the surface.

Groundwater

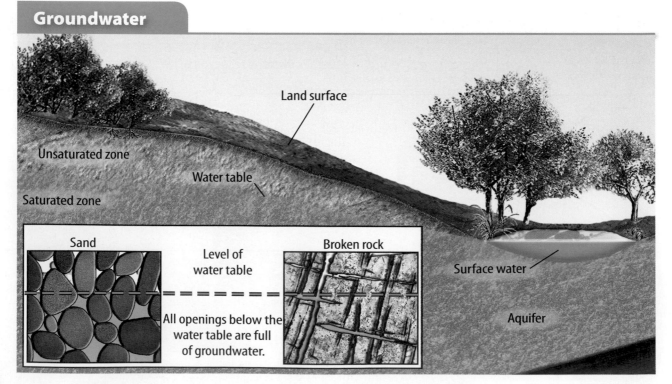

Land surface

Unsaturated zone

Water table

Saturated zone

Sand

Level of water table

Broken rock

Surface water

Aquifer

All openings below the water table are full of groundwater.

The Geosphere

The last nonliving Earth system is the geosphere. *The geosphere is the solid part of Earth.* It includes a thin layer of soil and broken rock material along with the underlying layers of rock. The rocks and soil on land and beneath the oceans are part of the geosphere.

 Key Concept Check What are Earth systems?

Materials in the Geosphere

The geosphere is made of soil, rock, and metal. All of these materials are composed of smaller particles.

Minerals Have you ever seen a sparkling diamond ring? Diamond is a mineral that is mined and then later cut and polished. **Minerals** *are naturally occurring, inorganic solids that have crystal structures and definite chemical compositions.*

To be considered a mineral, a material must have all five characteristics listed above. For example, materials that are made by people are not minerals because they did not form naturally. Materials that were once alive are organic and cannot be minerals. A mineral must be solid, so liquids and gases are not minerals. The atoms in minerals must be arranged in an orderly, repeating pattern. Finally, each mineral has a unique composition made of specific elements.

Minerals are identified by their physical properties, which include color, streak, hardness, luster, and crystal shape. Streak is the color of a mineral's powder. Even though some minerals have different colors, the color of the streak is the same. Hardness describes how easily a mineral can be scratched. Luster describes how a mineral reflects light. Usually, you must test several properties to identify a mineral. Examples of minerals with different properties are shown in **Figure 7.**

(l)©José Manuel Sanchis Calvete/Corbis; (r)Mark A. Schneider/Photo Researchers, Inc.

 New York FYI

The Lithosphere Earth's thin crust of soil and rock forms a nearly continuous shell around Earth. Earth's crust and the uppermost portion of the mantle is called the lithosphere. The majority of the lithosphere is covered by the hydrosphere.

Figure 7 Minerals have different properties. The quartz shown on the left has a visible crystal structure. The olivine shown on the right has a striking color.

 **Review**

Personal Tutor

Figure 8 Diorite (top) is an igneous rock. Gneiss (center) is metamorphic. The conglomerate (bottom) is sedimentary.

Rocks Minerals are the building blocks of rocks. *A rock is a naturally occurring solid composed of minerals and sometimes other materials such as organic matter.* Scientists classify rocks according to how they formed. As shown in **Figure 8,** there are three major rock types: igneous, sedimentary, and metamorphic.

Igneous rocks form when molten material, called magma, cools and hardens. Often magma is found deep inside Earth, but sometimes it erupts from volcanoes and flows onto Earth's surface as lava. So, igneous rocks can form inside Earth or on Earth's surface.

Sedimentary rocks form when forces such as water, wind, and ice break down rocks into small pieces called sediment. These same forces carry and deposit the sediment in layers. The bottom layers of sediment are compressed and then cemented together by natural substances to form rocks.

Metamorphic rocks form when extreme temperatures and pressure within Earth change existing rocks into new rocks. The rocks do not melt. Instead, their compositions or their structures change.

Inquiry MiniLab   **20 minutes**

What makes the geosphere unique?

Rocks and minerals, minerals and rocks—they always seem to go together. Can you have one without the other?

1. Read and complete a lab safety form.

2. Select a set of samples. You should have eight **minerals** and one **rock.** Identify which samples are minerals and which is the rock. Check with your teacher before moving on to step 3.

3. Use a **magnifying lens** to examine each mineral carefully. Note its color and other properties. Record your observations in your Science Journal.

4. Now, examine the rock. Do you recognize any of the minerals in the rock? Make two sets of samples—minerals that are present in the rock and minerals that are not.

Analyze and Conclude

1. **Summarize** the mineral and rock properties you observed.

2. **Generalize** What general statement can you make about the differences between rocks and minerals?

3. 🔑 **Key Concept** Based on your observations, what kinds of materials make up the geosphere?

(tl)©Susan E. Degginger/Alamy; (cl)Dr. Parvinder Sethi; (bl)sonsam/Getty Images; (br)Hutchings Photography/Digital Light Source

Structure of the Geosphere 🔑

Figure 9 Earth's major layers include the crust, the mantle, and the core.

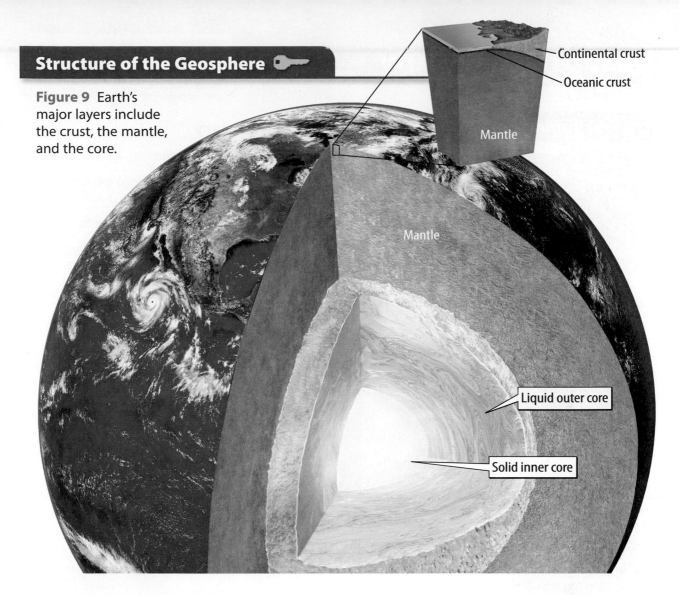

Continental crust
Oceanic crust
Mantle
Mantle
Liquid outer core
Solid inner core

Structure

Earth's internal structure is layered like the layers of a hard-cooked egg. The three basic layers of the geosphere are shown in **Figure 9.** Similar to an egg, each layer of the geosphere has a different composition.

Crust The brittle outer layer of the geosphere is much thinner than the inner layers, like the shell on a hard-cooked egg. This thin layer of rock is called the crust. The crust is found under the soil on continents and under the ocean. Oceanic crust is thinner and denser than continental crust. This is due to their different compositions. Continental crust is made of igneous, sedimentary, and metamorphic rocks. Oceanic crust is made of only igneous rock.

Mantle The middle and largest layer of the geosphere is the mantle. Like the crust, the mantle is made of rock; however, mantle rocks are hotter and denser than those in the crust. In parts of the mantle, temperatures are so high that rocks flow, a bit like partially melted plastic.

Core The center of Earth is the core. If you use a hard-cooked egg as a model of Earth, then the yolk would be the core. Unlike the crust and the mantle, the core is not made of rock. Instead, it is made mostly of the metal iron and small amounts of nickel. The core is divided into two parts. The outer core is liquid. The inner core is a dense ball of solid iron.

Key Concept Check What are the composition and the structure of the geosphere?

Visual Summary

Earth is made of interacting systems: the atmosphere, the hydrosphere, the cryosphere, the geosphere, and the biosphere.

The atmosphere is made mainly of gases and has a layered structure. The geosphere is made of rock, soil, and metal and also has a layered structure.

Most water in the hydrosphere is in the world ocean.

FOLDABLES®

Use your lesson Foldable to review the lesson. Save your Foldable for the project at the end of the chapter.

What do you think NOW?

You first read the statements below at the beginning of the chapter.

1. Earth is a simple system made of rocks.

2. Most of Earth is covered by one large ocean.

3. Earth's interior is made of distinct layers.

Did you change your mind about whether you agree or disagree with the statements? Rewrite any false statements to make them true.

Use Vocabulary

1 **Use the term** *atmosphere* in a sentence.

2 **Distinguish** between the geosphere and the hydrosphere.

3 **Define** *mineral* in your own words.

Understand Key Concepts 🔑

4 Which Earth system contains living things?

A. atmosphere **C.** geosphere
B. biosphere **D.** hydrosphere

5 **Compare** the structure of the geosphere to that of a hard-cooked egg.

6 **Organize** the reservoirs in the hydrosphere according to how much water they hold. Begin with the reservoir that holds the most water.

7 **Distinguish** among Earth systems based on the states of matter found in each system.

Interpret Graphics

8 **Describe** How are Earth systems interacting in the photo shown here?

9 **Summarize** Copy and fill in the graphic organizer below to identify Earth systems.

Earth systems

Critical Thinking

10 **Hypothesize** Earth systems interact with and affect one another. What might happen to your local hydrosphere and geosphere if conditions in the troposphere caused rain for several weeks?

Desalination

Taking the Salt out of Salt Water

Anyone who's been toppled by a big ocean wave knows salt water doesn't taste like the water we drink. People can't drink salt water. It's about 200 times more salty than freshwater. About 97 percent of Earth's water is salty. Most freshwater is frozen in glaciers and ice caps, leaving less than 1 percent of the planet's water available for 6.7 billion people and countless other organisms that require freshwater to live.

The need for freshwater has scientists searching for efficient ways to take the salt out of salt water. One solution is a desalination plant, where dissolved salts are separated from seawater through a process called reverse osmosis. This is how it works:

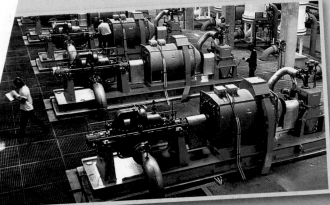

▲ **Desalination plants are found all over the world, including the United States.**

❶ Salt water is pumped from the ocean.

❷ High pressure forces water through a semipermeable membrane.

❸ The semipermeable membrane acts as a filter, allowing the water, but not the salt, to pass through.

❺ Water containing the waste salts flows out of the tank.

❹ Clean freshwater is collected in a separate tank.

Because it takes a lot of energy to change salt water into freshwater, desalination plants are expensive to operate. But desalination is used in places such as Saudi Arabia and Japan, where millions of people have few freshwater resources.

AFP/Getty Images

It's Your Turn

RESEARCH What is the cost of desalinated water for households? How does it compare to the cost of water for households in your area? Present your findings to the class.

AMERICAN MUSEUM OF NATURAL HISTORY

Lesson 2

Interactions of Earth Systems

Reading Guide

Key Concepts 🗝️
ESSENTIAL QUESTIONS

- How does the water cycle show interactions of Earth systems?

- How does weather show interactions of Earth systems?

- How does the rock cycle show interactions of Earth systems?

Vocabulary

water cycle

evaporation

transpiration

condensation

precipitation

weather

climate

rock cycle

uplift

 Multilingual eGlossary

 Video BrainPOP®

 AID S1.2a, S1.2b, S1.3, S2.1a, S2.1c, S2.1d, T1.4a; ICT 1.2, 1.4, 2.1, 2.2; PS 2.1j, 2.2i, 2.2j

Inquiry All Systems Go?

A storm is moving from over the ocean toward land. Waves are crashing against the shore. All Earth systems are affected by the storm. How does water in clouds enter the atmosphere? How are Earth systems interacting in this storm?

Oxford Scientific/Photolibrary/Getty Images

How do some Earth systems interact?

Earth's systems constantly interact with each other. In this activity, you'll model some common interactions.

1. Read and complete a lab safety form.

2. Place a **plastic container** on a sheet of **newspaper.** In one end of the container, mold about 5 cups of **soil** into a landform of your choice.

3. Hold a **hair dryer** about 20 cm from the model landform. Using the hair dryer set on low, blow air across the model landscape for 1 min. Be careful not to blow the soil out of the container. Record your observations in your Science Journal.

4. Using a **spray bottle,** spray water onto your landform. Record your observations.

Think About This

1. How did you use the materials in this activity to model Earth's systems?

2. How could you improve your model? What changes would you make?

3. 🔑 **Key Concept** Describe how Earth systems interacted in your model.

The Water Cycle

You read that the amount of water on Earth does not change. The water that you drink has been on Earth for a long time. Millions of years ago, a dinosaur might have swallowed the same water that you are drinking today. Or, that water might have raged down a river, flooding an ancient city. How does water move from place to place as time passes?

The **water cycle** *is the continuous movement of water on, above, and below Earth's surface.* The Sun provides the energy that drives the water cycle and moves water from place to place. As this occurs, liquid water can change state to a gas or a solid and then back again to a liquid. The change of state requires either an input or an output of thermal energy. **Figure 10** illustrates how energy is absorbed during evaporation and released during condensation.

Because the water cycle is continuous, there is no beginning or end. You will start your investigation of the water cycle in the hydrosphere's largest reservoir, the world ocean.

✓ **Reading Check** What is the source of energy for the water cycle?

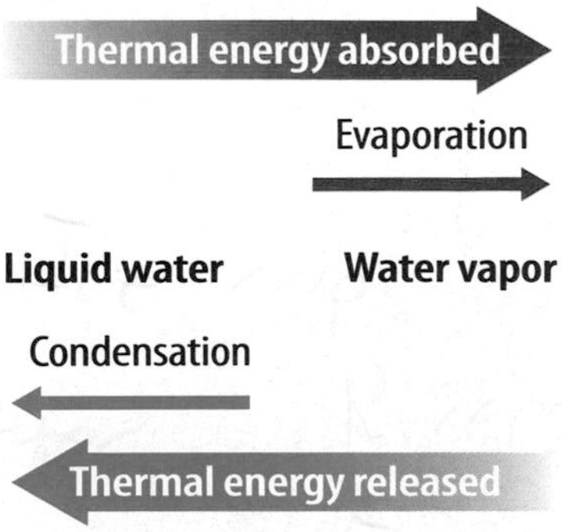

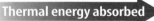

Thermal energy absorbed

Evaporation

Liquid water   Water vapor

Condensation

Thermal energy released

Figure 10 When water changes state from a gas to a liquid, thermal energy is released. Thermal energy is absorbed when liquid water changes into water vapor.

Review

Personal Tutor

Hutchings Photography/Digital Light Source

Evaporation

When the Sun shines on an ocean, water near the surface absorbs energy and becomes warmer. As a molecule of water absorbs energy, it begins to vibrate faster. When it has enough energy, it breaks away from the other water molecules in the ocean. It rises into the atmosphere as a molecule of gas called water vapor. **Evaporation** *is the process by which a liquid, such as water, changes into a gas.* Water vapor, like other gases in the atmosphere, is invisible.

Transpiration and Respiration

Oceans hold most of Earth's water, so they are major sources of water vapor. But, water also evaporates from rivers, lakes, puddles, and even soil. These sources, along with oceans, account for 90 percent of the water that enters the atmosphere. Most of the remaining 10 percent is produced by transpiration. **Transpiration** *is the process by which plants release water vapor through their leaves.*

Some water vapor also comes from organisms through cellular respiration. Cellular respiration takes place in many cells. Water and carbon dioxide are produced during cellular respiration. When animals breathe, they release carbon dioxide and water vapor from their lungs into the atmosphere. The blue arrows in **Figure 11** show how water vapor enters the atmosphere.

 Reading Check How are transpiration and respiration similar? How are they different?

Water Cycle 🔑

 **Concepts in Motion** Animation

Figure 11 In the water cycle, water moves through the hydrosphere, the atmosphere, the lithosphere, and the biosphere.

✅ **Visual Check**
Through which processes does water vapor enter the atmosphere?

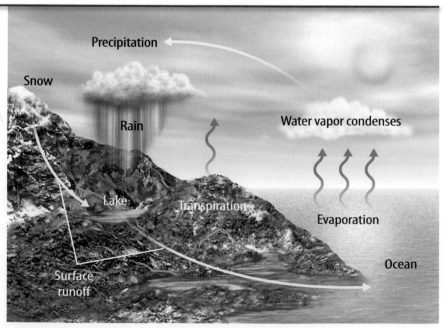

Condensation

Recall that the temperatures of the troposphere decrease with increasing altitude. So, as water vapor rises through the troposphere, it becomes cooler. Eventually it loses so much thermal energy that it returns to the liquid state. *The process by which a gas changes to a liquid is* **condensation.** Tiny droplets of liquid water join to form larger drops. When millions of water droplets come together, a cloud forms.

Precipitation

Eventually, drops of water in the clouds become so large and heavy that they fall to Earth's surface. *Moisture that falls from clouds to Earth's surface is* **precipitation.** Rain and snow are forms of precipitation.

More than 75 percent of precipitation falls into the ocean, and the rest falls onto land. Some of this water evaporates and goes back into the atmosphere. Some flows into lakes or rivers, and the rest seeps into soil and rocks.

In the water cycle, water continually moves between the hydrosphere, the atmosphere, the biosphere, and the geosphere. As water flows across the land, it interacts with soil and rocks in the geosphere. You will learn more about these interactions when you read about the rock cycle.

WORD ORIGIN · · · · · · · · · · ·

precipitation
from Latin *praecipitationem,*
means "act or fact of falling headlong"

 Key Concept Check How do Earth systems interact in the water cycle?

Inquiry MiniLab   **20 min**

How do plants contribute to the water cycle?

You have learned how water moves through Earth systems. How does the biosphere contribute to the water cycle?

1. Read and complete a lab safety form.
2. Choose a **potted plant.**
3. Carefully slide the plant into a **self-sealing plastic bag.** Close the bag tightly.
4. Place your bag on a sunny windowsill and leave it undisturbed overnight.
5. Observe the plant and the bag. Record your observations in your Science Journal.

Analyze and Conclude

1. **Recognize** Where did the moisture in the bag come from?

2. **Identify** What process of the water cycle did you model?

3. **Key Concept** How does your model show interactions among Earth systems?

Math Skills

Use a Formula

The amount of water vapor in air is called vapor density. Relative humidity (RH) compares the actual vapor density in air to the amount of water vapor the air could contain at that temperature. For example, at 15°C, air can contain a maximum of **12.8 g/m³** of water vapor. If the air contains 10.0 g/m³ of water vapor, what Is the RH?

1. Use the formula:

$$RH = \left(\frac{\text{actual vapor density}}{\text{maximum vapor density}} \right) \times 100$$

2. Work out the equation.

$$RH = \left(\frac{10.0 \text{ g/m}^3}{12.8 \text{ g/m}^3} \right) \times 100$$

$$RH = 0.781 \times 100 = 78.1\%$$

Practice

At 0°C, air can contain 4.85 g/m³ of water vapor. Assume the actual water vapor content is 0.970 g/m³. What is the RH?

Review

- **Math Practice**
- **Personal Tutor**

Changes in the Atmosphere

The atmosphere is continually changing. These changes take place mainly within the troposphere, which contains most of the gases in the atmosphere. Some changes occur within hours or days. Others can take decades or even centuries.

Weather

When you wake up in the morning and get ready for school, you might look outside to check the weather. **Weather** *is the state of the atmosphere at a certain time and place.* In most places, the weather changes to some degree every day. How do scientists describe weather and its changes?

Describing Weather Scientists use several factors to describe weather, as shown in **Figure 12.** Air temperature is a measure of the average amount of energy produced by the motion of air molecules. Air **pressure** is the force exerted by air molecules in all directions. Wind is the movement of air caused by differences in air pressure. Humidity is the amount of water vapor in a given volume of air. High humidity makes it more likely that clouds will form and precipitation will fall.

Interactions Weather is influenced by conditions in the atmosphere, the geosphere, and the hydrosphere. For example, air masses take on the characteristics of the area over which they form. So, an air mass that forms over a cool ocean will bring cool, moist air. In addition to these interactions, the hydrosphere provides much of the water for cloud formation and precipitation. Warm tropical waters provide the thermal energy that produces hurricanes.

 Key Concept Check How does weather show interactions of Earth systems?

Figure 12 Scientists describe weather using air temperature and pressure, wind speed and direction, and humidity.

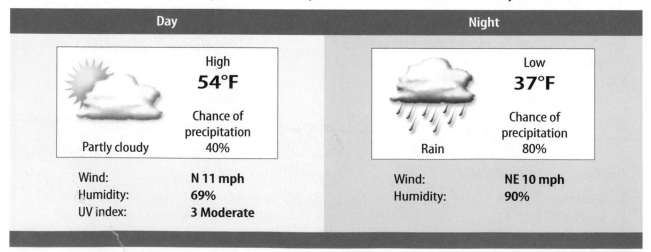

Day		Night	
Partly cloudy	High **54°F** Chance of precipitation 40%	Rain	Low **37°F** Chance of precipitation 80%
Wind:	N 11 mph	Wind:	NE 10 mph
Humidity:	69%	Humidity:	90%
UV index:	3 Moderate		

Climate

The weather in the area where you live might change each day, but weather patterns can remain nearly the same from season to season. For example, the weather might differ each day in the summer. But overall, summer is warm. These weather patterns are called climate. **Climate** *is the average weather pattern for a region over a long period of time.* Earth has many climates. Climates differ in part because of interactions between the atmosphere and other Earth systems.

 Reading Check How does weather differ from climate?

Mountains Recall that air temperature decreases with altitude. So the climate near the top of a mountain often is cooler than the climate near the mountain's base. Mountains also can affect the amount of precipitation an area receives—a phenomenon known as the rain-shadow effect. As shown in **Figure 13,** warm, wet air rises and cools as it moves up the windward side of a mountain. Clouds form and precipitation falls, giving this side of the mountain a wet climate. The air, now dry, continues to move over the mountain's peak and down the leeward side of the mountain. This side of the mountain often has a dry climate.

Ocean Currents As wind blows over an ocean, it creates surface currents in the water. Surface currents are like rivers in an ocean—the water flows in a predictable pattern. These currents transport thermal energy in water from place to place. For example, the Gulf Stream carries warm waters from tropical regions to northern Europe, making the climate of northern Europe warmer than it would be without these warm water currents.

SCIENCE USE V. COMMON USE

pressure
Science Use the force exerted over an area

Common Use the burden of physical or mental distress

Rain-Shadow Effect

Figure 13 Moist air on the windward side of mountains cools as it rises. Rain falls on this side of the mountain, resulting in a wet climate. This leaves little precipitation for the leeward side of the mountain, resulting in a dry climate.

 Visual Check How can mountains affect the amount of precipitation an area receives?

Rain shadow

Wind

Windward (wet)

Leeward (dry)

The Rock Cycle

In the water cycle, water moves throughout the hydrosphere, the atmosphere, the biosphere, and the geosphere. Another natural cycle is the rock cycle. *The **rock cycle** is the series of processes that transport and continually change rocks into different forms.* This cycle, shown in **Figure 14,** takes place in the geosphere, but it is affected by interactions with the other Earth systems.

As rocks move through the rock cycle, they might become igneous rocks, sedimentary rocks, or metamorphic rocks. At times they might not be rocks at all. Instead, they might take the form of sediments or hot, flowing magma. Like the water cycle, the rock cycle has no beginning or end. Some processes in this cycle take place on Earth's surface, and others take place deep within the geosphere.

Cooling and Crystallization

As shown in **Figure 14,** magma is located inside the geosphere. When magma flows out onto Earth's surface, it is called lava. Mineral crystals form as magma cools below the surface or as lava cools on the surface. This crystallization changes the molten material into igneous rock.

Uplift

Even rocks formed deep within Earth can eventually be exposed at the surface. **Uplift** *is the process that moves large bodies of Earth materials to higher elevations.* Uplift is often associated with mountain building. After millions of years of uplift, rocks that formed deep below Earth's surface could move up to the surface.

✓ **Reading Check** How can a rock buried deep within Earth eventually reach the surface?

The Rock Cycle 🔑

 **Concepts in Motion** Animation

Figure 14 As rocks move slowly through the rock cycle, they change from one form to another.

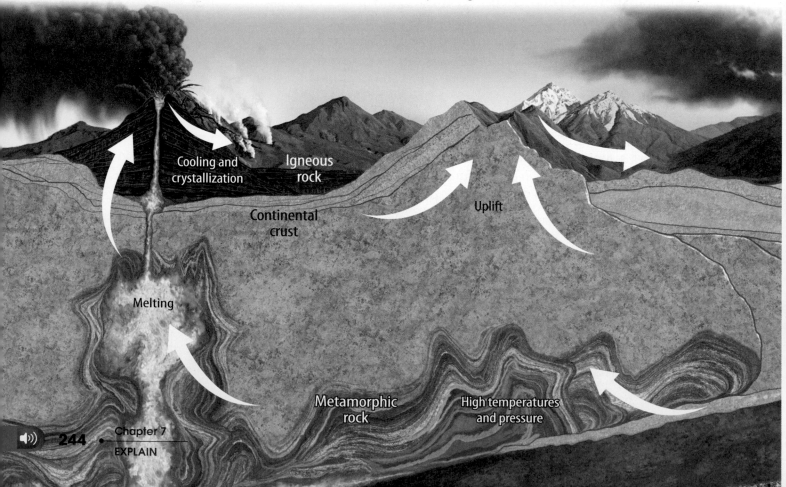

Cooling and crystallization

Igneous rock

Continental crust

Uplift

Melting

Metamorphic rock

High temperatures and pressure

Weathering and Erosion

Rocks on Earth's surface are exposed to the atmosphere, the hydrosphere, and the biosphere. Glaciers, wind, and rain, along with the activities of some organisms, break down rocks into sediment. This **process** is called weathering. In **Figure 14,** weathering is shown in the mountains, where uplift has exposed rocks. Weathering of rocks into sediments is often accompanied by erosion. Erosion occurs when the sediments are carried by agents of erosion—water, wind, or glaciers—to new locations.

Deposition

Eventually, agents of erosion lose their energy and slow down or stop. When this occurs, eroded sediments are deposited, or laid down, in new places. Deposition forms layers of sediment. Over time, more and more layers are deposited.

Compaction and Cementation

As more layers of sediment are deposited, their weight pushes down on underlying layers. The deeper layers are compacted. Minerals dissolved in surrounding water crystallize between grains of sediment and cement the sediments together. Compaction and cementation produce sedimentary rocks.

ACADEMIC VOCABULARY

process
(noun) a natural phenomenon marked by gradual changes that lead toward a particular result

Visual Check How do weathering and erosion change rocks?

Weathering and erosion

Deposition

Compaction and cementation

Sedimentary rock

Oceanic crust

Mantle

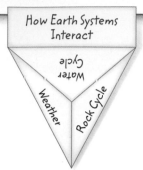

High Temperatures and Pressure

Metamorphic rocks form when rocks are subjected to high temperatures and pressure. This usually occurs far beneath Earth's surface. Igneous, sedimentary, and even metamorphic rocks can become new metamorphic rocks. Then, uplift can bring the rocks to the surface. There, the rocks are broken down and continue moving through the rock cycle.

Most interactions between the geosphere, the hydrosphere, and the atmosphere occur on Earth's surface. The atmosphere and hydrosphere alter rocks in the geosphere, and the geosphere in turn alters the other Earth systems. For example, energy from the Sun reaches Earth. The energy is reflected by Earth's surface and heats the atmosphere.

These are just a few examples of different interactions among Earth's systems. You have read about four different Earth systems in this chapter. But as **Figure 15** shows, the systems interact and function together as one unified system—planet Earth.

Key Concept Check How do Earth systems interact in the rock cycle?

Figure 15 Earth is a unified system made of four interacting subsystems.

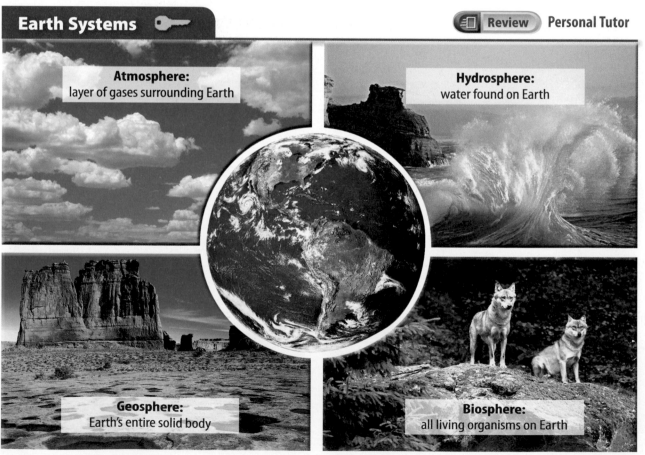

Earth Systems

Review   Personal Tutor

Atmosphere: layer of gases surrounding Earth

Hydrosphere: water found on Earth

Geosphere: Earth's entire solid body

Biosphere: all living organisms on Earth

(t)Brand X Pictures/PunchStock, (tr)Gary Vestal/Getty Images, (c)NASA, (bl)Corbis/SuperStock, (br)age fotostock/SuperStock

Visual Summary

In the water cycle, water continually moves through the hydrosphere, the atmosphere, the geosphere, and the biosphere.

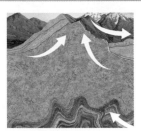

Weather and climate are influenced by interactions between the atmosphere and the other Earth systems.

In the rock cycle, rocks continually change from one form to another.

FOLDABLES®

Use your lesson Foldable to review the lesson. Save your Foldable for the project at the end of the chapter.

What do you think NOW?

You first read the statements below at the beginning of the chapter.

4. The water cycle begins in the ocean.

5. Earth's air contains solids, liquids, and gases.

6. Rocks are made of minerals.

Did you change your mind about whether you agree or disagree with the statements? Rewrite any false statements to make them true.

Use Vocabulary

1 **Distinguish** between weather and climate.

2 **Define** the *water cycle* in your own words.

3 The process that changes liquid water to water vapor is _____.

Understand Key Concepts

4 Which is an example of an interaction between the atmosphere and the geosphere?
   A. breathing   **C.** storms
   B. ocean currents   **D.** weathering

5 **Outline** Make an outline about the rock cycle. Include information about processes, rock types, and interactions with Earth systems.

6 **Compare** how the hydrosphere affects weather and how it affects climate.

Interpret Graphics

7 **Organize Information** Copy and fill in the graphic organizer below. Identify the processes of the water cycle.

Critical Thinking

8 **Design** a model that shows an interaction between two Earth systems.

9 **Assess** Some gasoline was spilled in a driveway. Could the pollutant pose a problem for the hydrosphere? Why or why not?

Math Skills ×÷
── Math Practice ──

10 Air at 20°C has a vapor density of 8.65 g/m³. The maximum amount of vapor density at that temperature is 17.3 g/m³. What is the relative humidity?

Inquiry Lab

Materials

water

lamp

sand

table fan

Safety

How do Earth's systems interact?

You've learned about the rock cycle and the water cycle. These are just two examples of how Earth systems work together. Each system interacts with the others to help maintain an ecological balance on Earth. What happens if one system is disrupted?

Ask a Question

How does a change in one system affect other systems? How can you model interactions among Earth systems?

Make Observations

1. Read and complete a lab safety form.

2. Think about Earth's four systems and how they interact with each other. In your Science Journal, describe a real-world scenario that shows these interactions. The photos on the next page show examples of real-world scenarios.

3. Use the materials shown here, or make a list of your own materials. Then, design a model of your scenario. Think about the following as you plan your model:

- How can you represent each of Earth's systems?

- How will you show the systems interacting?

- Will your model be self-contained or open to the air?

4. After your teacher approves your design, build your model according to your design plans.

(t to b)McGraw-Hill Education; (2-3)Ken Cavanagh/McGraw-Hill Education; (4) Jules Frazier/Getty Images; (r)Hutchings Photography/Digital Light Source

Form a Hypothesis

5 After building your model, formulate a hypothesis on how a change in one system might affect the other systems.

Test Your Hypothesis

6 Add or take away something in your model to cause one system to change. Is the change realistic? Could this happen in real life?

7 Observe and record the results immediately after the change occurs. Examine your model again on the following day. Be sure to record the results.

Analyze and Conclude

8 **Identify** Which parts of your model represent each system?

9 **Summarize** how the change you made to one system affected the others.

10 **Interpret** Was the change you modeled helpful or harmful? Was it caused by human activities or natural events? Explain.

11 **The Big Idea** Earth is sometimes described as a rocky planet. Based on what you observed in this lab, does that statement accurately describe Earth? Why or why not?

Communicate Your Results

Take your classmates on a "tour" of your model. Point out each Earth system, explain your hypothesis, recreate the change you introduced, and describe your results. Invite your classmates to ask questions and offer suggestions about improving your model.

 **Extension**

Conduct research to locate a place where the change you observed in your model has occurred. Find out what impact it had on the living things in the area. Determine if the change is still impacting life in the area.

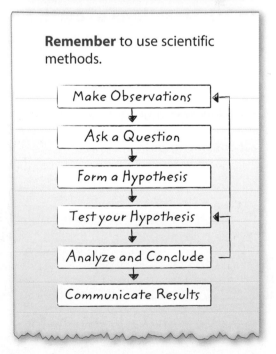

Remember to use scientific methods.

Make Observations

Ask a Question

Form a Hypothesis

Test your Hypothesis

Analyze and Conclude

Communicate Results

Chapter 7 Study Guide

Earth is a unified system that can be modeled by dividing it into four interacting subsystems: the biosphere, the atmosphere, the hydrosphere, and the geosphere.

Key Concepts Summary 🔑

Vocabulary

Lesson 1: Earth Systems

- Earth is made of the **biosphere,** the **atmosphere,** the **hydrosphere,** and the **geosphere.**
- The atmosphere has a layered structure that includes the troposphere, the stratosphere, the mesosphere, the thermosphere, and the exosphere. It is made of nitrogen, oxygen, and trace gases.
- Water is found on Earth in oceans, lakes, rivers, and as ice and **groundwater.** Small amounts of water are also found within the atmosphere and the biosphere.
- The geosphere is made of soil, metal, and **rock.** It has a layered structure that includes the crust, the mantle, and the core.

biosphere
atmosphere
hydrosphere
groundwater
geosphere
mineral
rock

Lesson 2: Interactions of Earth Systems

- The **water cycle** shows how water moves between reservoirs of the hydrosphere, the atmosphere, the geosphere, and the biosphere.
- **Weather** and **climate** are influenced by transfers of water and energy among the atmosphere, the geosphere, and the hydrosphere.
- Rocks continually change form as they move through the **rock cycle.** Processes such as weathering and erosion are examples of interactions among Earth systems.

water cycle
evaporation
transpiration
condensation
precipitation
weather
climate
rock cycle
uplift

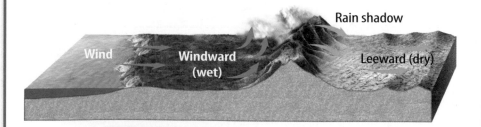

Rain shadow

Wind   Windward
(wet)   Leeward (dry)

Pixtal/age fotostock

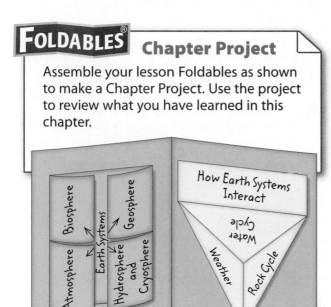

FOLDABLES® **Chapter Project**

Assemble your lesson Foldables as shown to make a Chapter Project. Use the project to review what you have learned in this chapter.

Use Vocabulary

1 The Earth system containing all living things is the _____.

2 Use the term *mineral* in a sentence.

3 Distinguish between rocks and minerals.

4 Conditions in the atmosphere at a given time and place are called _____.

5 Define the word *uplift* in your own words.

6 Distinguish between condensation and precipitation.

Link Vocabulary and Key Concepts

⬛ **Concepts in Motion** **Interactive Concept Map**

Copy this concept map, and then use vocabulary terms from the previous page to complete the concept map.

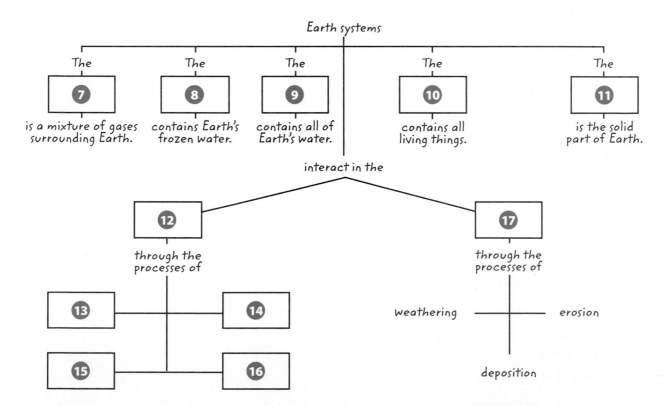

Understand Key Concepts 🔑

1 Which are two characteristics of minerals?
- A. artificial and organic
- B. liquid and gas
- C. living and inorganic
- D. solid and natural

2 What are the major gases of the atmosphere?
- A. carbon dioxide and water vapor
- B. nitrogen and carbon dioxide
- C. nitrogen and oxygen
- D. oxygen and water vapor

3 Which reservoir holds the largest amount of freshwater?
- A. groundwater
- B. ice
- C. lakes
- D. rivers

4 The diagram below shows the water cycle. Which number represents precipitation?

- A. 1
- B. 2
- C. 3
- D. 4

5 In which layer of the atmosphere does weather occur?
- A. hydrosphere
- B. mesosphere
- C. stratosphere
- D. troposphere

6 What does the hydrosphere contain?
- A. air
- B. plants
- C. soil
- D. water

7 The diagram below shows the layers of the atmosphere. The arrow is pointing to which layer?

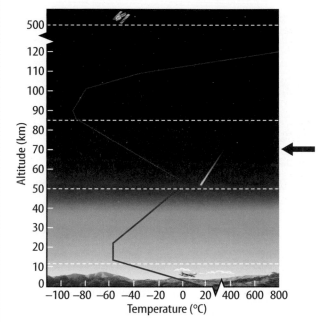

- A. troposphere
- B. mesosphere
- C. stratosphere
- D. exosphere

8 What is the middle layer of the geosphere?
- A. inner core
- B. crust
- C. mantle
- D. core

9 Rocks are classified according to _____ .
- A. color.
- B. formation.
- C. size.
- D. structure.

Critical Thinking

10 **Give** an example of how the water cycle impacts the rock cycle.

11 **Construct** Describe how you might construct a terrarium that models Earth systems.

12 **Design** Based on what you have learned about the water cycle, design a device for turning salt water into freshwater.

13 **Assess** How does the geosphere affect organisms that live in an ocean?

14 **Infer** How might the distribution of freshwater on Earth change if surface temperatures decreased?

15 **Evaluate** the relationship between weathering and erosion. How do the processes work together to change Earth's surface? How might the surface be different if only one of these processes occurred?

16 **Simplify** The diagram below shows the path of one rock through the rock cycle. What terms are missing from the diagram? Use the terms to describe how the rock changed.

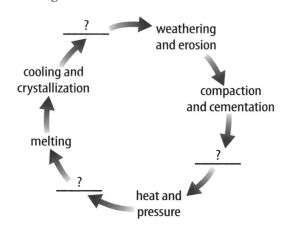

Writing in Science

17 **Create** A haiku is a poem with three lines. The lines contain five, seven, and five syllables respectively. Create a haiku that describes interactions among Earth systems.

REVIEW THE B!G IDEA

18 How would you describe Earth to a younger student?

19 What Earth systems do you see in the photo? What does each system include?

Math Skills ×÷+

◀ Review
─ Math Practice ─

Use a Formula

Use the data in the table below to answer questions 20–22.

Temperature (°C)	Maximum Vapor Density (g/m³)
10	9.4
24	23.0
30	30.4

20 The current temperature is 24°C. The water vapor in the air has a density of 5.75 g/m³. What is the relative humidity?

21 At a temperature of 30°C, the air contains 22.8 g/m³ of water vapor. What is the relative humidity?

22 Based on the data in the table, what is the relationship between the temperature and the amount of water vapor air can contain?

StockTrek/Getty Images

Record your answers on the answer sheet provided by your teacher or on a sheet of paper.

Multiple Choice

1 Which of Earth's systems includes the crust, the mantle, and the core?

  A atmosphere

  B biosphere

  C geosphere

  D hydrosphere

2 How much of Earth's water is freshwater?

  A 1 percent

  B 3 percent

  C 79 percent

  D 97 percent

Use the diagram below to answer question 3.

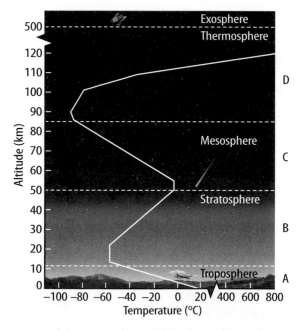

3 Earth's ozone layer absorbs solar radiation, protecting the biosphere. Which atmospheric layer includes the ozone layer?

  A A

  B B

  C C

  D D

4 Through which process does water leave the hydrosphere and enter the atmosphere?

  A condensation

  B deposition

  C evaporation

  D precipitation

5 Though the geosphere is described as the solid part of the Earth, which part is liquid?

  A crust

  B inner core

  C mantle

  D outer core

Use the image below to answer question 6.

6 Which process is occurring in the area circled in the figure?

  A condensation

  B deposition

  C precipitation

  D transpiration

7 Which process recycles water from the biosphere to the atmosphere?

   A condensation

   B deposition

   C precipitation

   D transpiration

8 Which sequence accurately shows the events that form sedimentary rock?

   A compaction → cementation → melting

   B erosion → volcanic eruption → weathering

   C volcanic eruption → cooling → crystallization

   D weathering → erosion → deposition

Use the diagram below to answer question 9.

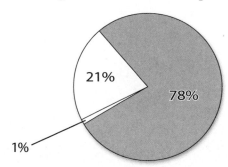

9 Which gas is represented by the shaded portion on the pie chart?

   A carbon dioxide

   B nitrogen

   C oxygen

   D water vapor

Constructed Response

10 Describe the path an igneous rock could take through the rock cycle. Begin and end with an igneous rock.

Use the figure below to answer questions 11 and 12.

11 Use the figure to describe why the weather differs on the left and right sides of the mountains.

12 Describe how the hydrosphere, the atmosphere, and the geosphere interact to produce the rain-shadow effect in the figure.

13 Millions of years ago, a dinosaur might have drunk the same water that you drink today. Explain how this is possible.

14 Describe how the hydrosphere, the atmosphere, the biosphere, and the geosphere interact in the rock cycle to form sedimentary rock.

NEED EXTRA HELP?														
If You Missed Question...	1	2	3	4	5	6	7	8	9	10	11	12	13	14
Go to Lesson...	1	1	1	2	1	2	2	2	1	2	2	2	2	2

AID M2.1a, S1.1a, S1.2a, S1.2b, S2.1a,
S2.1b, S2.1c, S2.1d, S2.2b, S2.2c, S2.2d,
T1.4a; ICT 1.4, 2.1, 2.2; PS 2.1a, 2.1b, 2.2k,
2.2n, 2.2p, 2.2r

Earth's Atmosphere

THE BIG IDEA

How does Earth's atmosphere affect life on Earth?

Inquiry · What's in the atmosphere?

Earth's atmosphere is made up of gases and small amounts of liquid and solid particles. Earth's atmosphere surrounds and sustains life.

- What type of particles make up clouds in the atmosphere?

- How do conditions in the atmosphere change as height above sea level increases?

- How does Earth's atmosphere affect life on Earth?

Daniel H. Bailey/Alamy

Get Ready to Read

What do you think?

Before you read, decide if you agree or disagree with each of these statements. As you read this chapter, see if you change your mind about any of the statements.

1 Air is empty space.

2 Earth's atmosphere is important to living organisms.

3 All the energy from the Sun reaches Earth's surface.

4 Earth emits energy back into the atmosphere.

5 Uneven heating in different parts of the atmosphere creates air circulation patterns.

6 Warm air sinks and cold air rises.

7 If no humans lived on Earth, there would be no air pollution.

8 Pollution levels in the air are not measured or monitored.

ConnectED Your one-stop online resource

MHEonline.com

Video

WebQuest

Audio

Assessment

Review

Concepts in Motion

Inquiry

Multilingual eGlossary

Reading Guide

Key Concepts 🔑
ESSENTIAL QUESTIONS

- How did Earth's atmosphere form?
- What is Earth's atmosphere made of?
- What are the layers of the atmosphere?
- How do air pressure and temperature change as altitude increases?

Vocabulary

atmosphere

water vapor

troposphere

stratosphere

ozone layer

ionosphere

 Multilingual eGlossary

 AID S1.1a; PS 2.1a, 2.1b

Describing Earth's Atmosphere

Inquiry Why is the atmosphere important?

What would Earth be like without its atmosphere? Earth's surface would be scarred with craters created from the impact of meteorites. Earth would experience extreme daytime-to-nighttime temperature changes. How would changes in the atmosphere affect life? What effect would atmospheric changes have on weather and climate?

©Corbis

Where does air apply pressure?

With the exception of Mercury, most planets in the solar system have some type of atmosphere. However, Earth's atmosphere provides what the atmospheres of other planets cannot: oxygen and water. Oxygen, water vapor, and other gases make up the gaseous mixture in the atmosphere called air. In this activity, you will explore air's effect on objects on Earth's surface.

1. Read and complete a lab safety form.
2. Add **water** to a **cup** until it is two-thirds full.
3. Place a large **index card** over the opening of the cup so that it is completely covered.
4. Hold the cup over a tub or a large bowl.
5. Place one hand on the index card to hold it in place as you quickly turn the cup upside down. Remove your hand.

Think About This

1. What happened when you turned the cup over?

2. How did air play a part in your observation?

3. 🔑 **Key Concept** How do you think these results might differ if you repeated the activity in a vacuum?

Importance of Earth's Atmosphere

The photo on the previous page shows Earth's atmosphere as seen from space. How would you describe the atmosphere? *The* **atmosphere** (AT muh sfihr) *is a thin layer of gases surrounding Earth.* Earth's atmosphere is hundreds of kilometers high. However, when compared to Earth's size, it is about the same relative thickness as an apple's skin to an apple.

The atmosphere contains the oxygen, carbon dioxide, and water necessary for life on Earth. Earth's atmosphere also acts like insulation on a house. It helps keep temperatures on Earth within a range in which living organisms can survive. Without it, daytime temperatures would be extremely high and nighttime temperatures would be extremely low.

The atmosphere helps protect living organisms from some of the Sun's harmful rays. It also helps protect Earth's surface from being struck by meteors. Most meteors that fall toward Earth burn up before reaching Earth's surface. Friction with the atmosphere causes them to burn. Only the very largest meteors strike Earth.

✓ **Reading Check** Why is Earth's atmosphere important to life on Earth?

WORD ORIGIN ....

atmosphere
from Greek *atmos*, means "vapor"; and Latin *sphaera*, means "sphere"

Origins of Earth's Atmosphere

Most scientists agree that when Earth formed, it was a ball of molten rock. As Earth slowly cooled, its outer surface hardened. Erupting volcanoes emitted hot gases from Earth's interior. These gases surrounded Earth, forming its atmosphere.

Ancient Earth's atmosphere was thought to be water vapor with a little carbon dioxide (CO_2) and nitrogen. **Water vapor** *is water in its gaseous form.* This ancient atmosphere did not have enough oxygen to support life as we know it. As Earth and its atmosphere cooled, the water vapor condensed into **liquid.** Rain fell and then evaporated from Earth's surface repeatedly for thousands of years. Eventually, water accumulated on Earth's surface, forming oceans. Most of the original CO_2 that dissolved in rain is in rocks on the ocean floor. Today the atmosphere has more nitrogen than CO_2.

Earth's first organisms could undergo photosynthesis, which changed the atmosphere. Recall that photosynthesis uses light energy to produce sugar and oxygen from carbon dioxide and water. The organisms removed CO_2 from the atmosphere and released oxygen into it. Eventually the levels of CO_2 and oxygen supported the development of other organisms.

 Key Concept Check How did Earth's present atmosphere form?

Inquiry MiniLab
20 minutes

Why does the furniture get dusty?

Have you ever noticed that furniture gets dusty? The atmosphere is one source for dirt and dust particles. Where can you find dust in your classroom?

1. Read and complete a lab safety form.
2. Choose a place in your classroom to collect a sample of dust.
3. Using a **duster,** collect dust from about a 50-cm² area.
4. Examine the duster with a **magnifying lens.** Observe any dust particles. Some might be so small that they only make the duster look gray.
5. Record your observations in your Science Journal.
6. Compare your findings with those of other members of your class.

Analyze and Conclude

1. **Analyze** how the area surrounding your collection site might have influenced how much dust you observed on the duster.

2. **Infer** the source of the dust.

3. **Key Concept** Other than gases and water droplets, predict what Earth's atmosphere might contain.

Figure 1 Oxygen and nitrogen make up most of the atmosphere, with the other gases making up only 1 percent. ▼

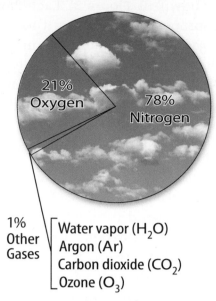

21% Oxygen

78% Nitrogen

1% Other Gases

Water vapor (H_2O)
Argon (Ar)
Carbon dioxide (CO_2)
Ozone (O_3)

☑ **Visual Check** What percent of the atmosphere is made up of oxygen and nitrogen?

▲ **Figure 2** One way solid particles enter the atmosphere is from volcanic eruptions.

Composition of the Atmosphere

Today's atmosphere is mostly made up of invisible gases, including nitrogen, oxygen, and carbon dioxide. Some solid and liquid particles, such as ash from volcanic eruptions and water droplets, are also present.

Gases in the Atmosphere

Study **Figure 1.** Which gas is the most abundant in Earth's atmosphere? Nitrogen makes up about 78 percent of Earth's atmosphere. About 21 percent of Earth's atmosphere is oxygen. Other gases, including argon, carbon dioxide, and water vapor, make up the remaining 1 percent of the atmosphere.

The amounts of water vapor, carbon dioxide, and ozone vary. The concentration of water vapor in the atmosphere ranges from 0 to 4 percent. Carbon dioxide is 0.038 percent of the atmosphere. A small amount of ozone is at high altitudes. Ozone also occurs near Earth's surface in urban areas.

Solids and Liquids in the Atmosphere

Tiny solid particles are also in Earth's atmosphere. Many of these, such as pollen, dust, and salt, can enter the atmosphere through natural processes. **Figure 2** shows another natural source of particles in the atmosphere—ash from volcanic eruptions. Some solid particles enter the atmosphere because of human activities, such as driving vehicles that release soot.

The most common liquid particles in the atmosphere are water droplets. Although microscopic in size, water droplets are visible when they form clouds. Other atmospheric liquids include acids that result when volcanoes erupt and fossil fuels are burned. Sulfur dioxide and nitrous oxide combine with water vapor in the air and form the acids.

🔑 **Key Concept Check** What is Earth's atmosphere made of?

Layers of Atmosphere

Concepts in Motion Animation

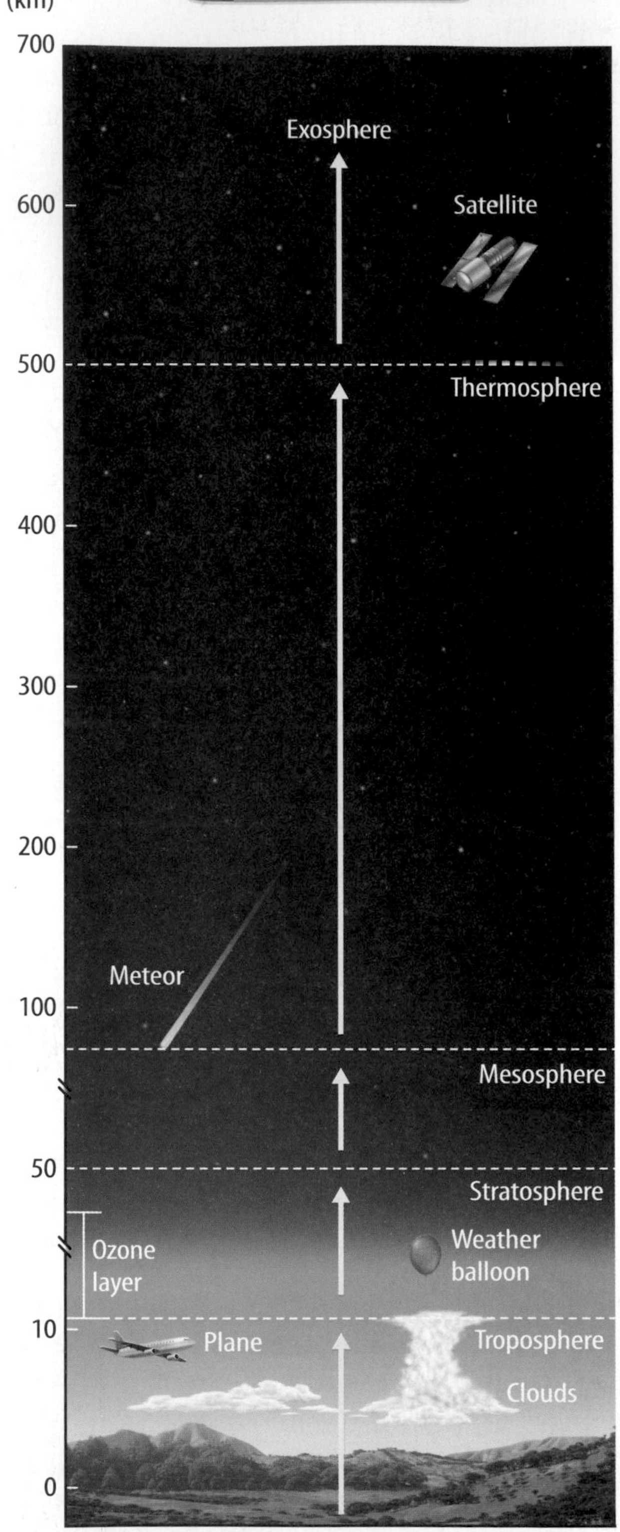

(km)
700
600
500
400
300
200
100
50
10
0
Exosphere
Satellite
Thermosphere
Meteor
Mesosphere
Stratosphere
Ozone layer
Weather balloon
Plane
Troposphere
Clouds

Figure 3 Scientists divide Earth's atmosphere into different layers.

Visual Check In which layer of the atmosphere do planes fly?

Layers of the Atmosphere

The atmosphere has several different layers, as shown in **Figure 3.** Each layer has unique properties, including the composition of gases and how temperature changes with altitude. Notice that the scale between 0–100 km in **Figure 3** is not the same as the scale from 100–700 km. This is so all the layers can be shown in one image.

Troposphere

The atmospheric layer closest to Earth's surface is called the **troposphere** (TRO puh sfihr). Most people spend their entire lives within the troposphere. It extends from Earth's surface to altitudes between 8–15 km. Its name comes from the Greek word *tropos,* which means "change." The temperature in the troposphere decreases as you move away from Earth. The warmest part of the troposphere is near Earth's surface. This is because most sunlight passes through the atmosphere and warms Earth's surface. The warmth is radiated to the troposphere, causing weather.

Reading Check Describe the troposphere.

Stratosphere

The atmospheric layer directly above the troposphere is the **stratosphere** (STRA tuh sfihr). The stratosphere extends from about 15 km to about 50 km above Earth's surface. The lower half of the stratosphere contains the greatest amount of ozone gas. *The area of the stratosphere with a high concentration of ozone is referred to as the* **ozone layer.** The presence of the ozone layer causes increasing stratospheric temperatures with increasing altitude.

An ozone (O_3) molecule differs from an oxygen (O_2) molecule. Ozone has three oxygen atoms instead of two. This difference is important because ozone absorbs the Sun's ultraviolet rays more effectively than oxygen does. Ozone protects Earth from ultraviolet rays that can kill plants, animals, and other organisms and cause skin cancer in humans.

Mesosphere and Thermosphere

As shown in **Figure 3,** the mesosphere extends from the stratosphere to about 85 km above Earth. The thermosphere can extend from the mesopshere to more than 500 km above Earth. Combined, these layers are much broader than the troposphere and the stratosphere, yet only 1 percent of the atmosphere's gas molecules are found in the mesosphere and the thermosphere. Most meteors burn up in these layers instead of striking Earth.

Ionosphere *The ionosphere is a region within the mesosphere and thermosphere that contains ions.* Between 60 km and 500 km above Earth's surface, the ionosphere's ions reflect AM radio waves transmitted at ground level. After sunset when ions recombine, this reflection increases. **Figure 4** shows how AM radio waves can travel long distances, especially at night, by bouncing off Earth and the ionosphere.

Radio Waves and the Ionosphere

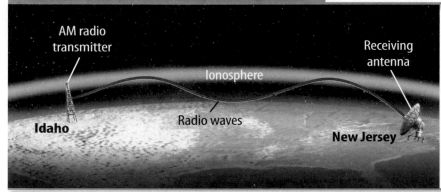

AM radio transmitter

Ionosphere

Receiving antenna

Radio waves

Idaho

New Jersey

Figure 4 Radio waves can travel long distances in the atmosphere.

Auroras The ionosphere is where stunning displays of colored lights called auroras occur, as shown in **Figure 5.** Auroras are most frequent in the spring and fall, but are best seen when the winter skies are dark. Auroras occur when ions from the Sun strike air molecules, causing them to emit vivid colors of light. People who live in the higher latitudes, nearer to the North Pole and the South Pole, are most likely to see auroras.

Exosphere

The exosphere is the atmospheric layer farthest from Earth's surface. Here, pressure and density are so low that individual gas molecules rarely strike one another. The molecules move at incredibly fast speeds after absorbing the Sun's radiation. The atmosphere does not have a definite edge, and molecules that are part of it can escape the pull of gravity and travel into space.

 Key Concept Check What are the layers of the atmosphere?

▲ **Figure 5** Auroras occur in the ionosphere.

Per Breiehagen/Getty Images

Figure 6 Molecules in the air are closer together near Earth's surface than they are at higher altitudes. ▼

Increasing altitude

Air Pressure and Altitude

Gravity is the force that pulls all objects toward Earth. When you stand on a scale, you can read your weight. This is because gravity is pulling you toward Earth. Gravity also pulls the atmosphere toward Earth. The pressure that a column of air exerts on anything below it is called air pressure. Gravity's pull on air increases its density. At higher altitudes, the air is less dense. **Figure 6** shows that air pressure is greatest near Earth's surface because the air molecules are closer together. This dense air exerts more force than the less dense air near the top of the atmosphere. Mountain climbers sometimes carry oxygen tanks at high altitudes because fewer oxygen molecules are in the air at high altitudes.

Reading Check How does air pressure change as altitude increases?

Temperature and Altitude

Figure 7 shows how temperature changes with altitude in the different layers of the atmosphere. If you have ever been hiking in the mountains, you have experienced the temperature cooling as you hike to higher elevations. In the troposphere, temperature decreases as altitude increases. Notice that the opposite effect occurs in the stratosphere. As altitude increases, temperature increases. This is because of the high concentration of ozone in the stratosphere. Ozone absorbs energy from sunlight, which increases the temperature in the stratosphere.

In the mesosphere, as altitude increases, temperature again decreases. In the thermosphere and exosphere, temperatures increase as altitude increases. These layers receive large amounts of energy from the Sun. This energy is spread across a small number of particles, creating high temperatures.

Figure 7 Temperature differences occur within the layers of the atmosphere. ▼

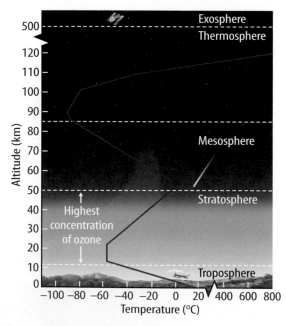

Exosphere
Thermosphere

500
120
110
100
90
80
70
60
50
40
30
20
10
0

Altitude (km)

Mesosphere

Stratosphere

Highest concentration of ozone

Troposphere

−100 −80 −60 −40 −20 0 20 400 600 800
Temperature (°C)

Visual Check Which temperature pattern is most like the troposphere's?

Key Concept Check How does temperature change as altitude increases?

Lesson 1 Review

Visual Summary

Earth's atmosphere consists of gases that make life possible.

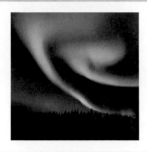

Layers of the atmosphere include the troposphere, the stratosphere, the mesosphere, the thermosphere, and the exosphere.

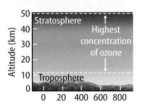

The ozone layer is the area in the stratosphere with a high concentration of ozone.

FOLDABLES

Use your lesson Foldable to review the lesson. Save your Foldable for the project at the end of the chapter.

What do you think NOW?

You first read the statements below at the beginning of the chapter.

1. Air is empty space.

2. Earth's atmosphere is important to living organisms.

Did you change your mind about whether you agree or disagree with the statements? Rewrite any false statements to make them true.

Use Vocabulary

① The _____ is a thin layer of gases surrounding Earth.

② The area of the stratosphere that helps protect Earth's surface from harmful ultraviolet rays is the _____.

③ **Define** Using your own words, define *water vapor*.

Understand Key Concepts

④ Which atmospheric layer is closest to Earth's surface?
   A. mesosphere   C. thermosphere
   B. stratosphere   D. troposphere

⑤ **Identify** the two atmospheric layers in which temperature decreases as altitude increases.

Interpret Graphics

⑥ **Contrast** Copy and fill in the graphic organizer below to contrast the composition of gases in Earth's early atmosphere and its present-day atmosphere.

Atmosphere	Gases
Early	
Present-day	

⑦ **Determine** the relationship between air pressure and the water in the glass in the photo below.

Critical Thinking

⑧ **Explain** three ways the atmosphere is important to living things.

A Crack in Earth's Shield

AMERICAN MUSEUM of NATURAL HISTORY

Scientists discover an enormous hole in the ozone layer that protects Earth.

The ozone layer is like sunscreen, protecting Earth from the Sun's ultraviolet rays. But not all of Earth is covered. Every spring since 1985, scientists have been monitoring a growing hole in the ozone layer above Antarctica.

This surprising discovery was the outcome of years of research from Earth and space. The first measurements of polar ozone levels began in the 1950s, when a team of British scientists began launching weather balloons in Antarctica. In the 1970s, NASA started using satellites to measure the ozone layer from space. Then, in 1985 a close examination of the British team's records indicated a large drop in ozone levels during the Antarctic spring. The levels were so low that the scientists checked and rechecked their instruments before they reported their findings. NASA scientists quickly confirmed the discovery—an enormous hole in the ozone layer over the entire continent of Antarctica. They reported that the hole might have originated as far back as 1976.

Human-made compounds found mostly in chemicals called chlorofluorocarbons, or CFCs, are destroying the ozone layer. During cold winters, molecules released from these compounds are transformed into new compounds by chemical reactions on ice crystals that form in the ozone layer over Antarctica. In the spring, warming by the Sun breaks down the new compounds and releases chlorine and bromine. These chemicals break apart ozone molecules, slowly destroying the ozone layer.

In 1987, CFCs were banned in many countries around the world. Since then, the loss of ozone has slowed and possibly reversed, but a full recovery will take a long time. One reason is that CFCs stay in the atmosphere for more than 40 years. Still, scientists predict the hole in the ozone layer will eventually mend.

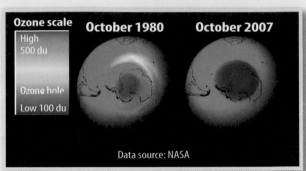

Ozone scale — High 500 du — Ozone hole — Low 100 du — October 1980 — October 2007

Data source: NASA

▲ **A hole in the ozone layer has developed over Antarctica. Even though it has gotten worse over the years, the hole has not grown as fast as scientists initially thought it would.**

Global Warming and the Ozone

Drew Shindell is a NASA scientist investigating the connection between the ozone layer in the stratosphere and the buildup of greenhouse gases throughout the atmosphere. Surprisingly, while these gases warm the troposphere, they are actually causing temperatures in the stratosphere to become cooler. As the stratosphere cools above Antarctica, more clouds with ice crystals form—a key step in the process of ozone destruction. While the buildup of greenhouse gases in the atmosphere may slow the recovery, Shindell still thinks that eventually the ozone layer will heal itself.

It's Your Turn

NEWSCAST Work with a partner to develop three questions about the ozone layer. Research to find the answers. Take the roles of reporter and scientist. Present your findings to the class in a newscast format.

Lesson 2

Reading Guide

Key Concepts
ESSENTIAL QUESTIONS

- How does energy transfer from the Sun to Earth and the atmosphere?

- How are air circulation patterns within the atmosphere created?

Vocabulary
radiation

conduction

convection

stability

temperature inversion

g **Multilingual eGlossary**

 AID M2.1a; ICT 1.4

Energy Transfer in the Atmosphere

Inquiry What's really there?

Mirages are created as light passes through layers of air that have different temperatures. How does energy create the reflections? What other effects does energy have on the atmosphere?

John King/Alamy

Launch Lab

15 minutes

What happens to air as it warms?

Light energy from the Sun is converted to thermal energy on Earth. Thermal energy powers the weather systems that impact your everyday life.

1 Read and complete a lab safety form.

2 Turn on a **lamp** with an incandescent lightbulb.

3 Place your hands under the light near the lightbulb. What do you feel?

4 Dust your hands with **powder.**

5 Place your hands below the lightbulb and clap them together once.

6 Observe what happens to the particles.

Think About This

1. How might the energy in step 3 move from the lightbulb to your hand?

2. How did the particles move when you clapped your hands?

3. 🔑 **Key Concept** How did particle motion show you how the air was moving?

Hutchings Photography/Digital Light Source

Energy from the Sun

The Sun's energy travels 148 million km to Earth in only 8 minutes. How does the Sun's energy get to Earth? It reaches Earth through the process of radiation. **Radiation** *is the transfer of energy by electromagnetic waves.* Ninety-nine percent of the radiant energy from the Sun consists of visible light, ultraviolet light, and infrared radiation.

ACADEMIC VOCABULARY

process
(noun) an ordered series of actions

Visible Light

The majority of sunlight is visible light. Recall that visible light is light that you can see. The atmosphere is like a window to visible light, allowing it to pass through. At Earth's surface it is converted to thermal energy, commonly called heat.

Near-Visible Wavelengths

The wavelengths of ultraviolet (UV) light and infrared radiation (IR) are just beyond the range of visibility to human eyes. UV light has short wavelengths and can break chemical bonds. Excess exposure to UV light will burn human skin and can cause skin cancer. Infrared radiation (IR) has longer wavelengths than visible light. You can sense IR as thermal energy or warmth. Earth absorbs energy from the Sun and then radiates it into the atmosphere as IR.

✓ **Reading Check** Contrast visible light and ultraviolet light.

Energy on Earth

As the Sun's energy passes through the atmosphere, some of it is absorbed by gases and particles, and some of it is reflected back into space. As a result, not all the energy coming from the Sun reaches Earth's surface.

Absorption

Study **Figure 8.** Gases and particles in the atmosphere absorb about 20 percent of incoming solar radiation. Oxygen, ozone, and water vapor all absorb incoming ultraviolet light. Water and carbon dioxide in the troposphere absorb some infrared radiation from the Sun. Earth's atmosphere does not absorb visible light. Visible light must be converted to infrared radiation before it can be absorbed.

Reflection

Bright surfaces, especially clouds, **reflect** incoming radiation. Study **Figure 8** again. Clouds and other small particles in the air reflect about 25 percent of the Sun's radiation. Some radiation travels to Earth's surface and is then reflected by land and sea surfaces. Snow-covered, icy, or rocky surfaces are especially reflective. As shown in **Figure 8,** this accounts for about 5 percent of incoming radiation. In all, about 30 percent of incoming radiation is reflected into space. This means that, along with the 20 percent of incoming radiation that is absorbed in the atmosphere, Earth's surface only receives and absorbs about 50 percent of incoming solar radiation.

SCIENCE USE v. COMMON USE

reflect

Science Use to return light, heat, sound, and so on, after it strikes a surface

Common Use to think quietly and calmly

Figure 8 Some of the energy from the Sun is reflected or absorbed as it passes through the atmosphere.

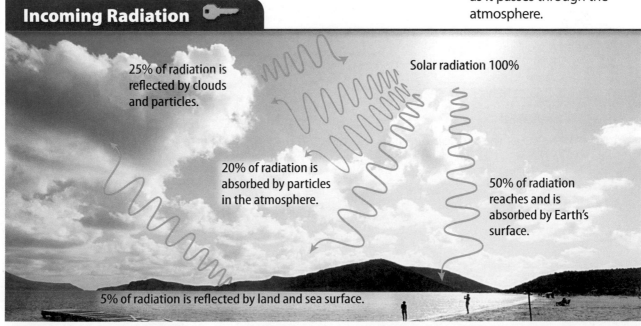

Incoming Radiation 🔑

25% of radiation is reflected by clouds and particles.

Solar radiation 100%

20% of radiation is absorbed by particles in the atmosphere.

50% of radiation reaches and is absorbed by Earth's surface.

5% of radiation is reflected by land and sea surface.

Visual Check What percent of incoming radiation is absorbed by gases and particles in the atmosphere?

Eric James/Alamy

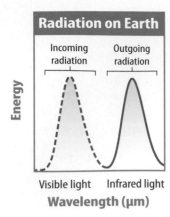

Radiation on Earth

Incoming radiation   Outgoing radiation

Energy

Visible light   Infrared light

Wavelength (µm)

▲ **Figure 9** The amount of solar energy absorbed by Earth and its atmosphere is equal to the amount of energy Earth radiates back into space.

Radiation Balance

The Sun's radiation heats Earth. So, why doesn't Earth get hotter and hotter as it continues to receive radiation from the Sun? There is a balance between the amount of incoming radiation from the Sun and the amount of outgoing radiation from Earth.

The land, water, plants, and other organisms absorb solar radiation that reaches Earth's surface. The radiation absorbed by Earth is then re-radiated, or bounced back, into the atmosphere. Most of the energy radiated from Earth is infrared radiation, which heats the atmosphere. **Figure 9** shows that the amount of radiation Earth receives from the Sun is the same as the amount Earth radiates into the outer atmosphere. Earth absorbs the Sun's energy and then radiates that energy away until a balance is achieved.

The Greenhouse Effect

As shown in **Figure 10,** the glass of a greenhouse allows light to pass through, where it is converted to infrared energy. The glass prevents the IR from escaping and it warms the greenhouse. Some of the gases in the atmosphere, called greenhouse gases, act like the glass of a greenhouse. They allow sunlight to pass through, but they prevent some of Earth's IR energy from escaping. Greenhouse gases in Earth's atmosphere trap IR and direct it back to Earth's surface. This causes an additional buildup of thermal energy at Earth's surface. The gases that trap IR best are water vapor (H_2O), carbon dioxide (CO_2), and methane (CH_4).

 Reading Check Describe the greenhouse effect.

The Greenhouse Effect

 **Concepts in Motion**   **Animation**

Figure 10 Some of the outgoing radiation is directed back toward Earth's surface by greenhouse gases.

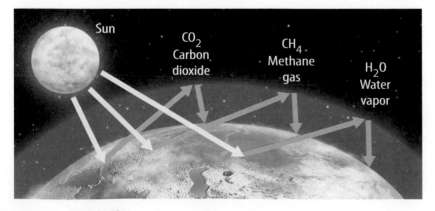

Thermal Energy Transfer

Recall that there are three types of thermal energy transfer—radiation, conduction, and convection. All three occur in the atmosphere. Recall that radiation is the process that transfers energy from the Sun to Earth.

Conduction

Thermal energy always moves from an object with a higher temperature to an object with a lower temperature. **Conduction** *is the transfer of thermal energy by collisions between particles of matter.* Particles must be close enough to touch to transfer energy by conduction. Touching the pot of water, shown in **Figure 11,** would transfer energy from the pot to your hand. Conduction occurs where the atmosphere touches Earth.

Convection

As molecules of air close to Earth's surface are heated by conduction, they spread apart, and air becomes less dense. Less dense air rises, transferring thermal energy to higher altitudes. *The transfer of thermal energy by the movement of particles within matter is called* **convection.** Convection can be seen in **Figure 11** as the boiling water circulates and steam rises.

Latent Heat

More than 70 percent of Earth's surface is covered by a highly unique substance—water! Water is the only substance that can exist as a solid, a liquid, and a gas within Earth's temperature ranges. Recall that latent heat is exchanged when water changes from one phase to another, as shown in **Figure 12.** Latent heat energy is transferred from Earth's surface to the atmosphere.

 Key Concept Check How does energy transfer from the Sun to Earth and the atmosphere?

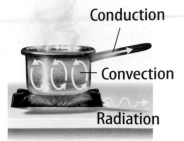

▲ **Figure 11** Energy is transferred through conduction, convection, and radiation.

 Review

Personal Tutor

WORD ORIGIN · · · · · · · · · · ·

conduction
from Latin *conducere*, means "to bring together"

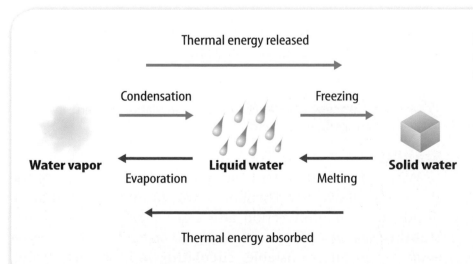

Thermal energy released

Condensation

Freezing

Water vapor

Liquid water

Solid water

Evaporation

Melting

Thermal energy absorbed

Figure 12 Water releases or absorbs thermal energy during phase changes.

Figure 13 Rising warm air is replaced by cooler, denser air that sinks beside it.

Cold air

Cold air

Hot air

Figure 14 Lens-shaped lenticular clouds form when air rises with a mountain wave. ▼

Mountain Wave

Circulating Air

You've read that energy is transferred through the atmosphere by convection. On a hot day, air that is heated becomes less dense. This creates a pressure difference. Cool, denser air pushes the warm air out of the way. The warm air is replaced by the more dense air, as shown in **Figure 13.** The warm air is often pushed upward. Warmer, rising air is always accompanied by cooler, sinking air.

Air is constantly moving. For example, wind flowing into a mountain range rises and flows over it. After reaching the top, the air sinks. This up-and-down motion sets up an atmospheric phenomenon called a mountain wave. The upward moving air within mountain waves creates lenticular (len TIH kyuh lur) clouds, shown in **Figure 14.** Circulating air affects weather and climate around the world.

🔑 **Key Concept Check** How are air circulation patterns within the atmosphere created?

Stability

When you stand in the wind, your body forces some of the air to move above you. The same is true for hills and buildings. Conduction and convection also cause air to move upward. **Stability** *describes whether circulating air motions will be strong or weak.* When air is unstable, circulating motions are strong. During stable conditions, circulating motions are weak.

(t)Ingram Publishing; (b)James Brunker/Alamy

Cold air

Warm air

Normal conditions

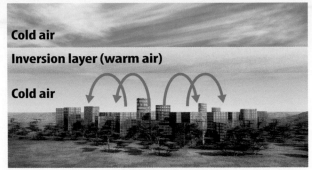

Cold air

Inversion layer (warm air)

Cold air

Temperature inversion

Unstable Air and Thunderstorms Unstable conditions often occur on warm, sunny afternoons. During unstable conditions, ground-level air is much warmer than higher-altitude air. As warm air rises rapidly in the atmosphere, it cools and forms large, tall clouds. Latent heat, released as water vapor changes from a gas to a liquid, adds to the instability, and produces a thunderstorm.

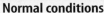 **Reading Check** Relate unstable air to the formation of thunderstorms.

Stable Air and Temperature Inversions Sometimes ground-level air is nearly the same temperature as higher-altitude air. During these conditions, the air is stable, and circulating motions are weak. A temperature inversion can occur under these conditions. *A* **temperature inversion** *occurs in the troposphere when temperature increases as altitude increases.* During a temperature inversion, a layer of cooler air is trapped by a layer of warmer air above it, as shown in **Figure 15.** Temperature inversions prevent air from mixing and can trap pollution in the air close to Earth's surface.

Figure 15 A temperature inversion occurs when cooler air is trapped beneath warmer air.

Visual Check How do conditions during a temperature inversion differ from normal conditions?

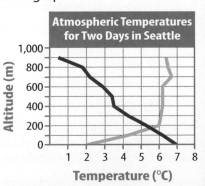

Visual Summary

Not all radiation from the Sun reaches Earth's surface.

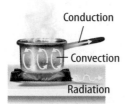

Conduction

Convection

Radiation

Thermal energy transfer in the atmosphere occurs through radiation, conduction, and convection.

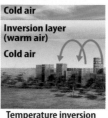

Cold air

Inversion layer (warm air)

Cold air

Temperature inversion

Temperature inversions prevent air from mixing and can trap pollution in the air close to Earth's surface.

FOLDABLES

Use your lesson Foldable to review the lesson. Save your Foldable for the project at the end of the chapter.

What do you think NOW?

You first read the statements below at the beginning of the chapter.

3. All of the energy from the Sun reaches Earth's surface.

4. Earth emits energy back into the atmosphere.

Did you change your mind about whether you agree or disagree with the statements? Rewrite any false statements to make them true.

Use Vocabulary

1 The property of the atmosphere that describes whether circulating air motions will be strong or weak is called _____.

2 **Define** *conduction* in your own words.

3 _____ is the transfer of thermal energy by the movement of particles within matter.

Understand Key Concepts

4 Which statement is true?
  A. The Sun's energy is completely blocked by Earth's atmosphere.
  B. The Sun's energy passes through the atmosphere without warming it significantly.
  C. The Sun's IR energy is absorbed by greenhouse gases.
  D. The Sun's energy is primarily in the UV range.

5 **Distinguish** between conduction and convection.

Interpret Graphics

6 **Explain** how greenhouses gases affect temperatures on Earth.

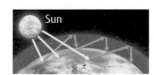

7 **Sequence** Copy and fill in the graphic organizer below to describe how energy from the Sun is absorbed in Earth's atmosphere.

Energy Absorption

Critical Thinking

8 **Suggest** a way to keep a parked car cool on a sunny day.

9 **Relate** temperature inversions to air stability.

Eric James/Alamy

Materials

candle

---

metal rod

---

glass rod

---

wooden dowel

500-mL beaker

ice

bowls (2)

lamp

glass cake pan

food coloring

250-mL beaker

Safety

Can you conduct, convect, and radiate?

After solar radiation reaches Earth, the molecules closest to Earth transfer thermal energy from molecule to molecule by conduction. The newly warmed air becomes less dense and moves through the process of convection.

Learn It

When you **compare and contrast** two or more things, you look for similarities and differences between them. When you **compare** two things, you look for the similarities, or how they are the same. When you **contrast** them, you look for how they are different from each other.

Try It

1. Read and complete a lab safety form.

2. Drip a small amount of melted candle wax onto one end of a metal rod, a glass rod, and a wooden dowel.

3. Place a 500-mL beaker on the lab table. Have your teacher add 350 mL of very hot water. Place the ends of the rods without candle wax in the water. Set aside.

4. Place an ice cube into each of two small bowls labeled A and B.

5. Place bowl A under a lamp with a 60- or 75-watt lightbulb. Place the light source 10 cm above the bowl. Turn on the lamp. Set bowl B aside.

6. Fill a glass cake pan with room-temperature water to a level of 2 cm. Put 2–3 drops of red food coloring into a 250-mL beaker of very hot water. Put 2–3 drops of blue food coloring into a 250-mL beaker of very cold water and ice cubes. Carefully pour the hot water into one end of the pan. Slowly pour the very cold water into the same end of the pan. Observe what happens from the side of the pan. Record your observations in your Science Journal.

7. Observe the candle wax on the rods in the hot water and the ice cubes in the bowls.

Apply It

8. What happened to the candle wax? Identify the type of energy transfer.

9. Which ice cube melted the most in the bowls? Identify the type of energy transfer that melted the ice.

10. Compare and contrast how the hot and cold water behaved in the pan. Identify the type of energy transfer.

11. 🔑 **Key Concept** Explain how each part of the lab models radiation, conduction, or convection.

Reading Guide

Key Concepts
ESSENTIAL QUESTIONS

- How does uneven heating of Earth's surface result in air movement?
- How are air currents on Earth affected by Earth's spin?
- What are the main wind belts on Earth?

Vocabulary

wind

trade winds

westerlies

polar easterlies

jet stream

sea breeze

land breeze

 g **Multilingual eGlossary**

Video

What's Science Got to do With It?

AID T1.4a; ICT 2.2; PS 2.2k, 2.2n, 2.2p

Air Currents

Inquiry How does air push these blades?

If you have ever ridden a bicycle into a strong wind, you know the movement of air can be a powerful force. Some areas of the world have more wind than others. What causes these differences? What makes wind?

GYRO PHOTOGRAPHY/amanaimagesRF/Getty Images

Why does air move?

Early sailors relied on wind to move their ships around the world. Today, wind is used as a renewable source of energy. In the following activity, you will explore what causes air to move.

1. Read and complete a lab safety form.
2. Inflate a **balloon.** Do not tie it. Hold the neck of the balloon closed.
3. Describe how the inflated balloon feels.
4. Open the neck of the balloon without letting go of the balloon. Record your observations of what happens in your Science Journal.

Think About This

1. What caused the inflated balloon surface to feel the way it did when the neck was closed?

2. What caused the air to leave the balloon when the neck was opened?

3. **Key Concept** Why didn't outside air move into the balloon when the neck was opened?

Global Winds

There are great wind belts that circle the globe. The energy that causes this massive movement of air originates at the Sun. However, wind patterns can be global or local.

Unequal Heating of Earth's Surface

The Sun's energy warms Earth. However, the same amount of energy does not reach all of Earth's surface. The amount of energy an area gets depends largely on the Sun's angle. For example, energy from the rising or setting Sun is not very intense. But Earth heats up quickly when the Sun is high in the sky.

In latitudes near the equator—an area referred to as the tropics—sunlight strikes Earth's surface at a high angle—nearly 90°—year round. As a result, in the tropics there is more sunlight per unit of surface area. This means that the land, the water, and the air at the equator are always warm.

At latitudes near the North Pole and the South Pole, sunlight strikes Earth's surface at a low angle. Sunlight is now spread over a larger surface area than in the tropics. As a result, the poles receive very little energy per unit of surface area and are cooler.

Recall that differences in density cause warm air to rise. Warm air puts less pressure on Earth than cooler air. Because it's so warm in the tropics, air pressure is usually low. Over colder areas, such as the North Pole and the South Pole, air pressure is usually high. This difference in pressure creates wind. **Wind** *is the movement of air from areas of high pressure to areas of low pressure.* Global wind belts influence both climate and weather on Earth.

Key Concept Check How does uneven heating of Earth's surface result in air movement?

Hutchings Photography/Digital Light Source

Figure 16 Three cells in each hemisphere move air through the atmosphere.

✓ **Visual Check** Which wind belt do you live in?

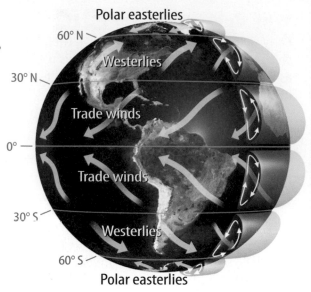

Polar easterlies
60° N
Westerlies
30° N
Trade winds
0°
Trade winds
30° S
Westerlies
60° S
Polar easterlies

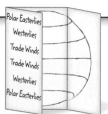

FOLDABLES

Make a shutterfold. As illustrated, draw Earth and the three cells found in each hemisphere on the inside of the shutterfold. Describe each cell and explain the circulation of Earth's atmosphere. On the outside, label the global wind belts.

Polar Easterlies
Westerlies
Trade Winds
Trade Winds
Westerlies
Polar Easterlies

Global Wind Belts

Figure 16 shows the three-cell model of circulation in Earth's atmosphere. In the northern hemisphere, hot air in the cell nearest the equator moves to the top of the troposphere. There, the air moves northward until it cools and moves back to Earth's surface near 30° latitude. Most of the air in this convection cell then returns to Earth's surface near the equator.

The cell at the highest northern latitudes is also a convection cell. Air from the North Pole moves toward the equator along Earth's surface. The cooler air pushes up the warmer air near 60° latitude. The warmer air then moves northward and repeats the cycle. The cell between 30° and 60° latitude is not a convection cell. Its motion is driven by the other two cells, in a motion similar to a pencil that you roll between your hands. Three similar cells exist in the southern hemisphere. These cells help generate the global wind belts.

The Coriolis Effect

What happens when you throw a ball to someone across from you on a moving merry-go-round? The ball appears to curve because the person catching the ball has moved. Similarly, Earth's rotation causes moving air and water to appear to move to the right in the northern hemisphere and to the left in the southern hemisphere. This is called the Coriolis effect. The contrast between high and low pressure and the Coriolis effect creates distinct wind patterns, called prevailing winds.

🔑 **Key Concept Check** How are air currents on Earth affected by Earth's spin?

Prevailing Winds

The three global cells in each hemisphere create northerly and southerly winds. When the Coriolis effect acts on the winds, they blow to the east or the west, creating relatively steady, predictable winds. Locate the trade winds in **Figure 16.** *The* **trade winds** *are steady winds that flow from east to west between 30°N latitude and 30°S latitude.*

At about 30°N and 30°S air cools and sinks. This creates areas of high pressure and light, calm winds at the equator called the doldrums. Sailboats without engines can be stranded in the doldrums.

The prevailing **westerlies** *are steady winds that flow from west to east between latitudes 30°N and 60°N, and 30°S and 60°S.* This region is also shown in **Figure 16.** *The* **polar easterlies** *are cold winds that blow from the east to the west near the North Pole and the South Pole.*

 Key Concept Check What are the main wind belts on Earth?

Jet Streams

Near the top of the troposphere is a narrow band of high winds called the **jet stream.** Shown in **Figure 17,** jet streams flow around Earth from west to east, often making large loops to the north or the south. Jet streams influence weather as they move cold air from the poles toward the tropics and warm air from the tropics toward the poles. Jet streams can move at speeds up to 300 km/h and are more unpredictable than prevailing winds.

Figure 17 Jet streams are thin bands of high wind speed. The clouds seen here have condensed within a cooler jet stream.

Review **Personal Tutor**

Inquiry) MiniLab   **20 minutes**

Can you model the Coriolis effect? ✂

Earth's rotation causes the Coriolis effect. It affects the movement of water and air on Earth.

1. Read and complete a lab safety form.
2. Draw dot A in the center of a piece of **foamboard.** Draw dot B along the outer edge of the foamboard.
3. Roll a **table-tennis ball** from dot A to dot B. Record your observations in your Science Journal.
4. Center the foamboard on a **turntable**. Have your partner rotate the foamboard at a medium speed. Roll the ball along the same path. Record your observations.

Analyze and Conclude

1. **Contrast** the path of the ball when the foamboard was not moving to when it was spinning.

2. 🔑 **Key Concept** How might air moving from the North Pole to the equator travel due to Earth's rotation?

Local Winds

You have just read that global winds occur because of pressure differences around the globe. In the same way, local winds occur whenever air pressure is different from one location to another.

Sea and Land Breezes

Anyone who has spent time near a lake or an ocean shore has probably experienced the connection between temperature, air pressure, and wind. *A **sea breeze** is wind that blows from the sea to the land due to local temperature and pressure differences.* **Figure 18** shows how sea breezes form. On sunny days, land warms up faster than water does. The air over the land warms by conduction and rises, creating an area of low pressure. The air over the water sinks, creating an area of high pressure because it is cooler. The differences in pressure over the warm land and the cooler water result in a cool wind that blows from the sea onto land.

*A **land breeze** is a wind that blows from the land to the sea due to local temperature and pressure differences.* **Figure 18** shows how land breezes form. At night, the land cools more quickly than the water. Therefore, the air above the land cools more quickly than the air over the water. As a result, an area of lower pressure forms over the warmer water. A land breeze then blows from the land toward the water.

✓ **Reading Check** Compare and contrast sea breezes and land breezes.

Figure 18 Sea breezes and land breezes are created as part of a large reversible convection current.

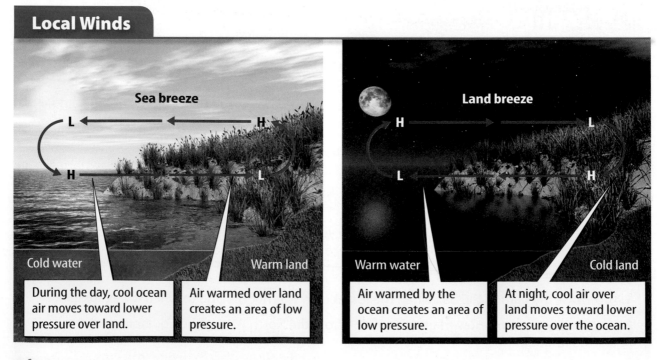

Local Winds

Sea breeze

Cold water — During the day, cool ocean air moves toward lower pressure over land.

Warm land — Air warmed over land creates an area of low pressure.

Land breeze

Warm water — Air warmed by the ocean creates an area of low pressure.

Cold land — At night, cool air over land moves toward lower pressure over the ocean.

✓ **Visual Check** Sequence the steps involved in the formation of a land breeze.

Lesson 3 Review

Visual Summary

Wind is created by pressure differences between one location and another.

Prevailing winds in the global wind belts are the trade winds, the westerlies, and the polar easterlies.

Sea breeze

Sea breezes and land breezes are examples of local winds.

FOLDABLES

Use your lesson Foldable to review the lesson. Save your Foldable for the project at the end of the chapter.

What do you think NOW?

You first read the statements below at the beginning of the chapter.

5. Uneven heating in different parts of the atmosphere creates air circulation patterns.

6. Warm air sinks and cold air rises.

Did you change your mind about whether you agree or disagree with the statements? Rewrite any false statements to make them true.

Use Vocabulary

1 The movement of air from areas of high pressure to areas of low pressure is _____.

2 A(n) _____ is wind that blows from the sea to the land due to local temperature and pressure differences.

3 **Distinguish** between westerlies and trade winds.

Understand Key Concepts

4 Which does NOT affect global wind belts?
  A. air pressure
  B. land breezes
  C. the Coriolis effect
  D. the Sun

5 **Relate** Earth's spinning motion to the Coriolis effect.

Interpret Graphics

Use the image below to answer question 6.

6 **Explain** a land breeze.

7 **Organize** Copy and fill in the graphic organizer below to summarize Earth's global wind belts.

Wind Belt	Description
Trade winds	
Westerlies	
Polar easterlies	

Critical Thinking

8 **Infer** what would happen without the Coriolis effect.

9 **Explain** why the wind direction is often the same in Hawaii as it is in Greenland.

Can you model global wind patterns?

In each hemisphere, air circulates in specific patterns. Recall that scientists use the three-cell model to describe these circulation cells. General circulation of the atmosphere produces belts of prevailing winds around the world. In this activity, you will make a **model** of the main circulation cells in Earth's atmosphere.

Materials

ribbons

globe

permanent marker

scissors

transparent tape

Safety

Learn It

Making a **model** can help you visualize how a process works. Scientists use models to represent processes that may be difficult to see in real time. Sometimes a model represents something too small to see with the unaided eye, such as a model of an atom. Other models, such as one of the solar system, represent something that is too large to see from one location.

Try It

1. Read and complete a lab safety form.

2. Refer to **Figure 16** to make your model.

3. Choose one color of ribbon for the circulation cells. Make a separate loop of ribbon long enough to cover the latitude boundaries of each cell. Draw arrows on each ribbon to show the direction that the air flows in that cell. Make one loop for each cell in the northern hemisphere and one for each in the southern hemisphere. Tape your "cells" onto the globe.

4. Choose different-colored ribbons to model each of these wind belts: trade winds, westerlies, and polar easterlies, in both hemispheres. Draw arrows on each ribbon to show the direction that the wind blows. Tape the ribbons on the globe.

5. Create a color key to identify each cell and its corresponding wind type.

Apply It

6. Explain how your model represents the three-cell model used by scientists. How does your model differ from actual air movement in the atmosphere?

7. Explain why you cannot accurately model the global winds with this model.

8. **Key Concept** Explain how latitude affects global winds.

Lesson 4

Air Quality

Reading Guide

Key Concepts
ESSENTIAL QUESTIONS

- How do humans impact air quality?
- Why do humans monitor air quality standards?

Vocabulary

air pollution

acid precipitation

photochemical smog

particulate matter

 Multilingual eGlossary

Video BrainPOP®

 AID S1.2a, S1.2b, S2.1a, S2.1b, S2.1c, S2.1d, S2.2b, S2.2c, S2.2d, S2.2r, T1.4a; ICT 2.1, 2.2

Inquiry How did this happen?

Air pollution can be trapped near Earth's surface during a temperature inversion. This is especially common in cities located in valleys and surrounded by mountains. What do you think the quality of the air is like on a day like this one? Where does pollution come from?

© Martin Thomas/Reuters/Corbis

How does acid rain form? 🥽 🧤 🧴

Vehicles, factories, and power plants release chemicals into the atmosphere. When these chemicals combine with water vapor, they can form acid rain.

1. Read and complete a lab safety form.
2. Half-fill a **plastic cup** with **distilled water.**
3. Dip a strip of **pH paper** into the water. Use a **pH color chart** to determine the pH of the distilled water. Record the pH in your Science Journal.
4. Use a **dropper** to add **lemon juice** to the water until the pH equals that of acid rain. Swirl and test the pH each time you add 5 drops of the lemon juice to the mixture.

Think About This

1. A strong acid has a pH between 0 and 2. How does the pH of lemon juice compare to the pH of other substances? Is acid rain a strong acid?

2. 🔑 **Key Concept** Why might scientists monitor the pH of rain?

Substances	pH
Hydrochloric acid	0.0
Lemon juice	2.3
Vinegar	2.9
Tomato juice	4.1
Coffee (black)	5.0
Acid rain	5.6
Rainwater	6.5
Milk	6.6
Distilled water	7.0
Blood	7.4
Baking soda solution	8.4
Toothpaste	9.9
Household ammonia	11.9
Sodium hydroxide	14.0

Sources of Air Pollution

The contamination of air by harmful substances including gases and smoke is called **air pollution.** Air pollution is harmful to humans and other living things. Years of exposure to polluted air can weaken a human's immune system. Respiratory diseases such as asthma can be caused by air pollution.

Air pollution comes from many sources. Point-source pollution is pollution that comes from an identifiable source. Examples of point sources include smokestacks of large factories, such as the one shown in **Figure 19,** and electric power plants that burn fossil fuels. They release tons of polluting gases and particles into the air each day. An example of natural point-source pollution is an erupting volcano.

Nonpoint-source pollution is pollution that comes from a widespread area. One example of pollution from a nonpoint-source is air pollution in a large city. This is considered non-point-source pollution because it cannot be traced back to one source. Some bacteria found in swamps and marshes are examples of natural sources of nonpoint-source pollution.

🔑 **Key Concept Check** Compare point-source and nonpoint-source pollution.

Figure 19 One example of point-source pollution is a factory smoke stack.

C. Sherburne/PhotoLink/Getty Images

Causes and Effects of Air Pollution

The harmful effects of air pollution are not limited to human health. Some pollutants, including ground-level ozone, can damage plants. Air pollution can also cause serious damage to human-made structures. Sulfur dioxide pollution can discolor stone, corrode metal, and damage paint on cars.

Acid Precipitation

When sulfur dioxide and nitrogen oxides combine with moisture in the atmosphere and form precipitation that has a pH lower than that of normal rainwater, it is called **acid precipitation.** Acid precipitation includes acid rain, snow, and fog. It affects the chemistry of water in lakes and rivers. This can harm the organisms living in the water. Acid precipitation damages buildings and other structures made of stone. Natural sources of sulfur dioxide include volcanoes and marshes. However, the most common sources of sulfur dioxide and nitrogen oxides are automobile exhausts and factory and power plant smoke.

Smog

Photochemical smog *is air pollution that forms from the interaction between chemicals in the air and sunlight.* Smog forms when nitrogen dioxide, released in gasoline engine exhaust, reacts with sunlight. A series of chemical reactions produces ozone and other compounds that form smog. Recall that ozone in the stratosphere helps protect organisms from the Sun's harmful rays. However, ground-level ozone can damage the tissues of plants and animals. Ground-level ozone is the main component of smog. Smog in urban areas reduces visibility and makes air difficult to breathe. **Figure 20** shows New York City on a clear day and on a smoggy day.

 Key Concept Check How do humans impact air quality?

Figure 20 Smog can be observed as haze or a brown tint in the atmosphere.

Smog

MICHAEL S. YAMASHITA/National Geographic Image Collection

Particulate Pollution

Although you can't see them, over 10,000 solid or liquid particles are in every cubic centimeter of air. A cubic centimeter is about the size of a sugar cube. This type of pollution is called particulate matter. **Particulate** (par TIH kyuh lut) **matter** *is a mixture of dust, acids, and other chemicals that can be hazardous to human health.* The smallest particles are the most harmful. These particles can be inhaled and can enter your lungs. They can cause asthma, bronchitis, and lead to heart attacks. Children and older adults are most likely to experience health problems due to particulate matter.

Particulate matter in the atmosphere absorbs and scatters sunlight. This can create haze. Haze particles scatter light, make things blurry, and reduce visibility.

Movement of Air Pollution

Wind can influence the effects of air pollution. Because air carries pollution with it, some wind patterns cause more pollution problems than others. Weak winds or no wind prevents pollution from mixing with the surrounding air. During weak wind conditions, pollution levels can become dangerous.

For example, the conditions in which temperature inversions form are weak winds, clear skies, and longer winter nights. As land cools at night, the air above it also cools. Calm winds, however, prevent cool air from mixing with warm air above it. **Figure 21** shows how cities located in valleys experience a temperature inversion. Cool air, along with the pollution it contains, is trapped in valleys. More cool air sinks down the sides of the mountain, further preventing layers from mixing. The pollution in the photo at the beginning of the lesson was trapped due to a temperature inversion.

WORD ORIGIN

particulate
from Latin *particula*, means "small part"

Figure 21 At night, cool air sinks down the mountain sides, trapping pollution in the valley below.

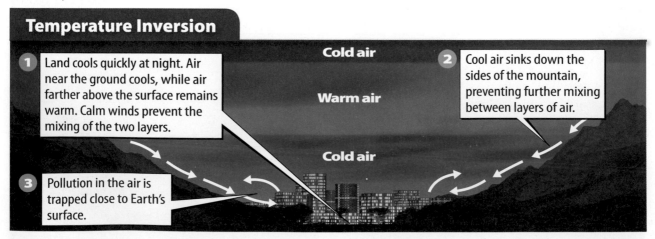

Temperature Inversion

1 Land cools quickly at night. Air near the ground cools, while air farther above the surface remains warm. Calm winds prevent the mixing of the two layers.

3 Pollution in the air is trapped close to Earth's surface.

2 Cool air sinks down the sides of the mountain, preventing further mixing between layers of air.

Cold air

Warm air

Cold air

Visual Check How is pollution trapped by a temperature inversion?

Maintaining Healthful Air Quality

Preserving the quality of Earth's atmosphere requires the cooperation of government officials, scientists, and the public. The Clean Air Act is an example of how government can help fight pollution. Since the Clean Air Act became law in 1970, steps have been taken to reduce automobile emissions. Pollutant levels have decreased significantly in the United States. Despite these advances, serious problems still remain. The amount of ground-level ozone is still too high in many large cities. Also, acid precipitation produced by air pollutants continues to harm organisms in lakes, streams, and forests.

Air Quality Standards

The Clean Air Act gives the U.S. government the power to set air quality standards. The standards protect humans, animals, plants, and buildings from the harmful effects of air pollution. All states are required to make sure that pollutants, such as carbon monoxide, nitrogen oxides, particulate matter, ozone, and sulfur dioxide, do not exceed harmful levels.

 Reading Check What is the Clean Air Act?

Monitoring Air Pollution

Pollution levels are continuously monitored by hundreds of instruments in all major U.S. cities. If the levels are too high, authorities may advise people to limit outdoor activities.

 MiniLab   **15 minutes**

Can being out in fresh air be harmful to your health?

Are you going to be affected if you play tennis for a couple hours, go biking with your friends, or even just lie on the beach? Even if you have no health problems related to your respiratory system, you still need to be aware of the quality of air in your area of activity for the day.

Analyze and Conclude

1. Which values on the AQI indicate that the air quality is good?

2. At what value is the air quality unhealthful for anyone who may have allergies and respiratory disorders?

3. Which values would be considered as warnings of emergency conditions?

4. 🔑 **Key Concept** The quality of air in different areas changes throughout the day. Explain how you can use the AQI to help you know when you should limit your outdoor activity.

Air Quality Index (AQI) Values	Levels of Health Concern
0 to 50	Good
51 to 100	Moderate
101 to 150	Unhealthful for Sensitive Groups
151 to 200	Unhealthful
201 to 300	Very Unhealthful
301 to 500	Hazardous

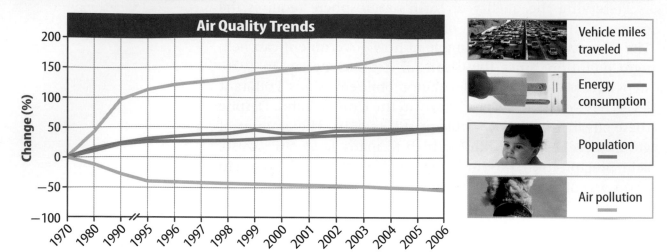

Figure 22 Pollution emissions have declined, even though the population is increasing.

(t to b)Digital Vision Ltd./SuperStock; (2)Testra Images/Getty Images; (3)©Arthur Tilley/Creatas/PictureQuest; (4)C. Sherburne/PhotoLink/Getty Images

Math Skills

Use Graphs

The graph above shows the percent change in four different pollution factors from 1970 through 2006. All values are based on the 0 percent amount in 1970. For example, from 1970 to 1990, the number of vehicle miles driven increased by 100 percent, or the vehicle miles doubled. Use the graph to infer which factors might be related.

Practice

1. What was the percent change in population between 1970 and 2006?

2. What other factor changed by about the same amount during that period?

 Review

- **Math Practice**
- **Personal Tutor**

Air Quality Trends

Over the last several decades, air quality in U.S. cities has improved, as shown in **Figure 22.** Even though some pollution-producing processes have increased, such as burning fossil fuels and traveling in automobiles, levels of certain air pollutants have decreased. Airborne levels of lead and carbon monoxide have decreased the most. Levels of sulfur dioxide, nitrogen oxide, and particulate matter have also decreased.

However, ground-level ozone has not decreased much. Why do ground-level ozone trends lag behind those of other pollutants? Recall that ozone can be created from chemical reactions involving automobile exhaust. The increase in the amount of ground-level ozone is because of the increase in the number of miles traveled by vehicles.

Key Concept Check Why do humans monitor air quality standards?

Indoor Air Pollution

Not all air pollution is outdoors. The air inside homes and other buildings can be as much as 50 times more polluted than outdoor air! The quality of indoor air can impact human health much more than outdoor air quality.

Indoor air pollution comes from many sources. Tobacco smoke, cleaning products, pesticides, and fireplaces are some common sources. Furniture upholstery, carpets, and foam insulation also add pollutants to the air. Another indoor air pollutant is radon, an odorless gas given off by some soil and rocks. Radon leaks through cracks in a building's foundation and sometimes builds up to harmful levels inside homes. Harmful effects of radon come from breathing its particles.

Visual Summary

Air pollution comes from point sources, such as factories, and nonpoint sources, such as automobiles.

Photochemical smog contains ozone, which can damage tissues in plants and animals.

FOLDABLES

Use your lesson Foldable to review the lesson. Save your Foldable for the project at the end of the chapter.

What do you think NOW?

You first read the statements below at the beginning of the chapter.

7. If no humans lived on Earth, there would be no air pollution.

8. Pollution levels in the air are not measured or monitored.

Did you change your mind about whether you agree or disagree with the statements? Rewrite any false statements to make them true.

Use Vocabulary

❶ **Define** *acid precipitation* in your own words.

❷ _____ forms when chemical reactions combine pollution with sunlight.

❸ The contamination of air by harmful substances, including gases and smoke, is _____.

Understand Key Concepts 🔑

❹ Which is NOT true about smog?
   A. It contains nitrogen oxide.
   B. It contains ozone.
   C. It reduces visibility.
   D. It is produced only by cars.

❺ **Describe** two ways humans add pollution to the atmosphere.

❻ **Assess** whether urban or rural areas are more likely to have high levels of smog.

❼ **Identify** and describe the law designed to reduce air pollution.

Interpret Graphics

❽ **Compare and Contrast** Copy and fill in the graphic organizer below to compare and contrast details of smog and acid precipitation.

	Similarities	Differences
Smog		
Acid Precipitation		

Critical Thinking

❾ **Describe** how conduction and convection are affected by paving over a grass field.

Math Skills ×∹⁺   🖳 **Review**

—— **Math Practice** ——

❿ Based on the graph on the opposite page, what was the total percent change in air pollution between 1970 and 2006?

(t)C. Sherburne/PhotoLink/Getty Images; (b)MICHAEL S. YAMASHITA/National Geographic Image Collection

Materials

thermometer

sand

500-mL beaker

lamp

stopwatch

paper towels

spoon

potting soil

clay

Safety

Radiant Energy Absorption

Ultimately, the Sun is the source of energy for Earth. Energy from the Sun moves through the atmosphere and is absorbed and reflected from different surfaces on Earth. Light surfaces reflect energy, and dark surfaces absorb energy. Both land and sea surfaces absorb energy from the Sun, and air in contact with these surfaces is warmed through conduction.

Ask a Question

Which surfaces on Earth absorb the most energy from the Sun?

Make Observations

① Read and complete a lab safety form.

② Make a data table in your Science Journal to record your observations of energy transfer. Include columns for Type of Surface, Temperature Before Heating, and Temperature After Heating.

③ Half-fill a 500-mL beaker with sand. Place a thermometer in the sand and carefully add enough sand to cover the thermometer bulb—about 2 cm deep. Keep the bulb under the sand for 1 minute. Record the temperature in the data table.

④ Place the beaker under the light source. Record the temperature after 10 minutes.

⑤ Repeat steps 3 and 4 using soil and water.

Form a Hypothesis

⑥ Use the data in your table to form a hypothesis stating which surfaces on Earth, such as forests, wheat fields, lakes, snowy mountain tops, and deserts, will absorb the most radiant energy.

Test Your Hypothesis

7 Decide what materials could be used to mimic the surfaces on Earth from your hypothesis.

8 Repeat the experiment with materials approved by the teacher to test your hypothesis.

9 Examine your data. Was your hypothesis supported? Why or why not?

Analyze and Conclude

10 **Infer** which types of areas on Earth absorb the most energy from the Sun.

11 **Think Critically** When areas of Earth are changed so they become more likely to reflect or absorb energy from the Sun, how might these changes affect conduction and convection in the atmosphere?

12 **The Big Idea** Explain how thermal energy from the Sun being received by and reflected from Earth's surface is related to the role of the atmosphere in maintaining conditions suitable for life.

Communicate Your Results

Display data from your initial observations to compare your findings with your classmates' findings. Explain your hypothesis, experiment results, and conclusions to the class.

Inquiry Extension

What could you add to this investigation to show how cloud cover changes the amount of radiation that will reach Earth's surfaces? Design a study that could test the effect of cloud cover on radiation passing through Earth's atmosphere. How could you include a way to show that clouds also reflect radiant energy from the Sun?

6

Lab Tips

☑ If possible, use leaves, straw, shaved ice, and other natural materials to test your hypothesis.

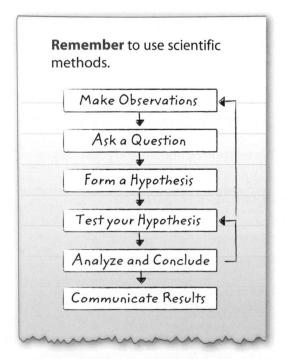

Remember to use scientific methods.

Make Observations
↓
Ask a Question
↓
Form a Hypothesis
↓
Test your Hypothesis
↓
Analyze and Conclude
↓
Communicate Results

Chapter 8 Study Guide

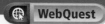
 THE BIG IDEA The gases in Earth's atmosphere, some of which are needed by organisms to survive, affect Earth's temperature and the transfer of thermal energy to the atmosphere.

Key Concepts Summary 🔑	**Vocabulary**
Lesson 1: Describing Earth's Atmosphere • Earth's **atmosphere** formed as Earth cooled and chemical and biological processes took place. • Earth's atmosphere consists of nitrogen, oxygen, and a small amount of other gases, such as CO_2 and **water vapor.** • The atmospheric layers are the **troposphere,** the **stratosphere,** the mesosphere, the thermosphere, and the exosphere. • Air pressure decreases as altitude increases. Temperature either increases or decreases as altitude increases, depending on the layer of the atmosphere.  21% Oxygen 78% Nitrogen	atmosphere water vapor troposphere stratosphere ozone layer ionosphere
Lesson 2: Energy Transfer in the Atmosphere  Conduction · Convection · Radiation • The Sun's energy is transferred to Earth's surface and the atmosphere through **radiation, conduction, convection,** and latent heat. • Air circulation patterns are created by convection currents.	radiation conduction convection stability temperature inversion
Lesson 3: Air Currents • Uneven heating of Earth's surface creates pressure differences. **Wind** is the movement of air from areas of high pressure to areas of low pressure. • Air currents curve to the right or to the left due to the Coriolis effect. • The main wind belts on Earth are the **trade winds,** the **westerlies,** and the **polar easterlies.**	wind trade winds westerlies polar easterlies jet stream sea breeze land breeze
Lesson 4: Air Quality • Some human activities release pollution into the air. • Air quality standards are monitored for the health of organisms and to determine if anti-pollution efforts are successful. 	air pollution acid precipitation photochemical smog particulate matter

FOLDABLES® Chapter Project

Assemble your lesson Foldables® as shown to make a Chapter Project. Use the project to review what you have learned in this chapter.

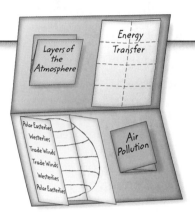

Use Vocabulary

1 Radio waves travel long distances by bouncing off electrically charged particles in the _____.

2 The Sun's thermal energy is transferred to Earth through space by _____.

3 Rising currents of warm air transfer energy from Earth to the atmosphere through _____.

4 A narrow band of winds located near the top of the troposphere is a(n) _____.

5 _____ are steady winds that flow from east to west between 30°N latitude and 30°S latitude.

6 In large urban areas, _____ forms when pollutants in the air interact with sunlight.

7 A mixture of dust, acids, and other chemicals that can be hazardous to human health is called _____.

Link Vocabulary and Key Concepts

Concepts in Motion Interactive Concept Map

Copy this concept map, and then use vocabulary terms from the previous page to complete the concept map.

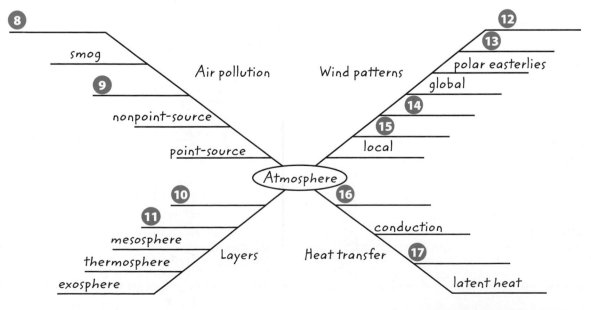

Understand Key Concepts

1 Air pressure is greatest
A. at a mountain base.
B. on a mountain top.
C. in the stratosphere.
D. in the ionosphere.

2 In which layer of the atmosphere is the ozone layer found?
A. troposphere
B. stratosphere
C. mesosphere
D. thermosphere

Use the image below to answer question 3.

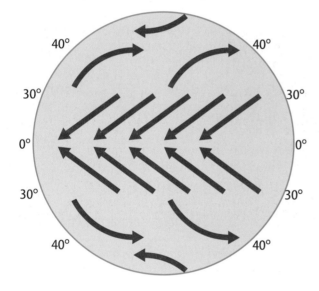

3 This diagram represents the atmosphere's
A. air masses.
B. global wind belts.
C. inversions.
D. particulate motion.

4 The Sun's energy
A. is completely absorbed by the atmosphere.
B. is completely reflected by the atmosphere.
C. is in the form of latent heat.
D. is transferred to the atmosphere after warming Earth.

5 Which type of energy is emitted from Earth to the atmosphere?
A. ultraviolet radiation
B. visible radiation
C. infrared radiation
D. aurora borealis

6 Which is a narrow band of high winds located near the top of the troposphere?
A. polar easterly
B. a jet stream
C. a sea breeze
D. a trade wind

7 Which helps protect people, animals, plants, and buildings from the harmful effects of air pollution?
A. primary pollutants
B. secondary pollutants
C. ozone layer
D. air quality standards

Use the photo below to answer question 8.

8 This photo shows a potential source of
A. ultraviolet radiation.
B. indoor air pollution.
C. radon.
D. smog.

Critical Thinking

9 **Predict** how atmospheric carbon dioxide levels might change if more trees were planted on Earth. Explain your prediction.

10 **Compare** visible and infrared radiation.

11 **Assess** whether your home is heated by conduction or convection.

12 **Sequence** how the unequal heating of Earth's surface leads to the formation of wind.

13 **Evaluate** whether a sea breeze could occur at night.

14 **Interpret Graphics** What are the top three sources of particulate matter in the atmosphere? What could you do to reduce particulate matter from any of the sources shown here?

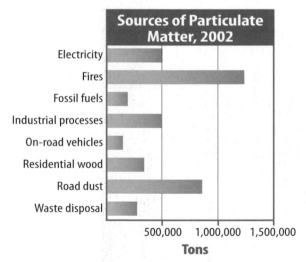

Sources of Particulate Matter, 2002

- Electricity
- Fires
- Fossil fuels
- Industrial processes
- On-road vehicles
- Residential wood
- Road dust
- Waste disposal

500,000 1,000,000 1,500,000

Tons

15 **Diagram** how acid precipitation forms. Include possible sources of sulfur dioxide and nitrogen oxide and organisms that can be affected by acid precipitation.

Writing in Science

16 **Write** a paragraph explaining whether you think it would be possible to permanently pollute the atmosphere with particulate matter.

REVIEW THE BIG IDEA

17 Review the title of each lesson in the chapter. List all of the characteristics and components of the troposphere and the stratosphere that affect life on Earth. Describe how life is impacted by each one.

18 Discuss how energy is transferred from the Sun throughout Earth's atmosphere.

Math Skills ×÷ —   ⊟ Review

Use Graphs ————— **Math Practice** ——

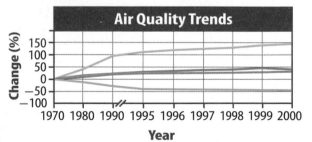

Air Quality Trends

Change (%)

150
100
50
0
−50
−100

1970 1980 1990 1995 1996 1997 1998 1999 2000

Year

— Vehicle miles — Energy consumption
— Air polution — Population

19 What was the percent change in energy use between 1996 and 1999?

20 What happened to energy use between 1999 and 2000?

21 What was the total percentage change between vehicle miles traveled and air pollution from 1970 to 2000?

Record your answers on the answer sheet provided by your teacher or on a sheet of paper.

Multiple Choice

1 What causes the phenomenon known as a mountain wave?

  A radiation imbalance

  B rising and sinking air

  C temperature inversion

  D the greenhouse effect

Use the diagram below to answer question 2.

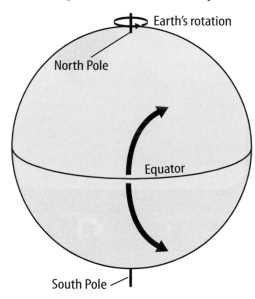

2 What phenomenon does the diagram above illustrate?

  A radiation balance

  B temperature inversion

  C the Coriolis effect

  D the greenhouse effect

3 Which do scientists call greenhouse gases?

  A carbon dioxide, hydrogen, nitrogen

  B carbon dioxide, methane gas, water vapor

  C carbon monoxide, oxygen, argon

  D carbon monoxide, ozone, radon

4 In which direction does moving air appear to turn in the northern hemisphere?

  A down

  B up

  C right

  D left

Use the diagram below to answer question 5.

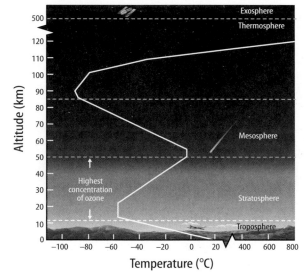

5 Which layer of the atmosphere has the widest range of temperatures?

  A mesosphere

  B stratosphere

  C thermosphere

  D troposphere

6 Which was the main component of Earth's original atmosphere?

  A carbon dioxide

  B nitrogen

  C oxygen

  D water vapor

7 Which is the primary cause of the global wind patterns on Earth?

   A ice cap melting

   B uneven heating

   C weather changing

   D waves breaking

Use the diagram below to answer question 8.

Energy Transfer Methods

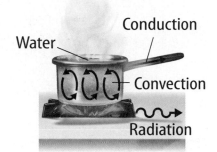

8 In the diagram above, which transfers thermal energy in the same way the Sun's energy is transferred to Earth?

   A the boiling water

   B the burner flame

   C the hot handle

   D the rising steam

9 Which substance in the air of U.S. cities has decreased least since the Clean Air Act began?

   A carbon monoxide

   B ground-level ozone

   C particulate matter

   D sulfur dioxide

Constructed Response

Use the table below to answer questions 10 and 11.

Layer	Significant Fact

10 In the table above, list in order the layers of Earth's atmosphere from lowest to highest. Provide one significant fact about each layer.

11 Explain how the first four atmospheric layers are important to life on Earth.

Use the table below to answer question 12.

Heat Transfer	Explanation
Conduction	
Convection	
Latent heat	
Radiation	

12 Complete the table to explain how heat energy transfers from the Sun to Earth and its atmosphere.

13 What are temperature inversions? How do they form? What is the relationship between temperature inversions and air pollution?

NEED EXTRA HELP?													
If You Missed Question...	1	2	3	4	5	6	7	8	9	10	11	12	13
Go to Lesson...	2	3	2	3	1	1	3	2	4	1	1	2	2, 4

Chapter 9

Weather

THE BIG IDEA How do scientists describe and predict weather?

Inquiry Is this a record snowfall?

Buffalo, New York, is famous for its snowstorms, averaging 3 m of snow each year. Other areas of the world might only get a few centimeters of snow a year. In some parts of the world, it never snows.

- Why do some areas get less snow than others?

- How do scientists describe and predict weather?

George Frey/Getty Images

Get Ready to Read

What do you think?

Before you read, decide if you agree or disagree with each of these statements. As you read this chapter, see if you change your mind about any of the statements.

1 Weather is the long-term average of atmospheric patterns of an area.

2 All clouds are at the same altitude within the atmosphere.

3 Precipitation often occurs at the boundaries of large air masses.

4 There are no safety precautions for severe weather, such as tornadoes and hurricanes.

5 Weather variables are measured every day at locations around the world.

6 Modern weather forecasts are done using computers.

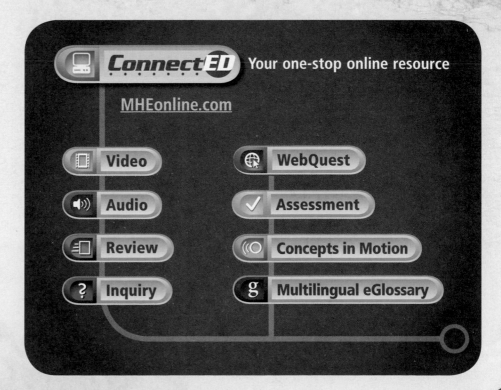

ConnectED Your one-stop online resource

MHEonline.com

- Video
- Audio
- Review
- Inquiry
- WebQuest
- Assessment
- Concepts in Motion
- Multilingual eGlossary

Lesson 1

Reading Guide

Key Concepts 🔑
ESSENTIAL QUESTIONS

- What is weather?
- What variables are used to describe weather?
- How is weather related to the water cycle?

Vocabulary

weather
air pressure
humidity
relative humidity
dew point
precipitation
water cycle

 Multilingual eGlossary

 Video
- **BrainPOP®**
- **Science Video**

 AID M1.1b, M1.1c, M2.1a, M2.1b; PS 2.1j, 2.2i, 2.2k, 2.2l

Describing Weather

Inquiry Why are clouds different?

If you look closely at the photo, you'll see that there are different types of clouds in the sky. How do clouds form? If all clouds consist of water droplets and ice crystals, why do they look different? Are clouds weather?

Peter de Clercq/Alamy

Can you make clouds in a bag?

When water vapor in the atmosphere cools, it condenses.
The resulting water droplets make up clouds.

1 Read and complete a lab safety form.

2 Half-fill a **500-mL beaker** with **ice** and **cold water.**

3 Pour 125 mL of **warm water** into a **resealable plastic bag** and seal the bag.

4 Carefully lower the bag into the ice water. Record your observations in your Science Journal.

Think About This

1. What did you observe when the warm water in the bag was put into the beaker?

2. What explanation can you give for what happened?

3. **Key Concept** What could you see in the natural world that results from the same process?

What is weather?

Everybody talks about the weather. "Nice day, isn't it?" Talking about weather is so common that we even use weather terms to describe unrelated topics. "That homework assignment was a breeze." Or "I'll take a rain check."

Weather *is the atmospheric conditions, along with short-term changes, of a certain place at a certain time.* Weather is caused by the uneven heating of Earth's surface. If you have ever been caught in a rainstorm on what began as a sunny day, you know the weather can change quickly. Sometimes it changes in just a few hours. But other times your area might have the same sunny weather for several days in a row.

Weather Variables

Perhaps some of the first things that come to mind when you think about weather are temperature and rainfall. As you dress in the morning, you need to know what the temperature will be throughout the day to help you decide what to wear. If it is raining, you might cancel your picnic.

Temperature and rainfall are just two of the **variables** used to describe weather. Meteorologists, scientists who study and predict weather, use several specific variables that describe a variety of atmospheric conditions. These variables include air temperature, air pressure, wind speed and direction, humidity, cloud coverage, and precipitation.

Key Concept Check What is weather?

Hutchings Photography/Digital Light Source

REVIEW VOCABULARY

variable
a quantity that can change

Air Temperature

The measure of the average **kinetic energy** of molecules in the air is air temperature. When the temperature is high, molecules have a high kinetic energy. Therefore, molecules in warm air move faster than molecules in cold air. Air temperatures vary with time of day, season, location, and altitude.

Air Pressure

The force that a column of air applies on the air or a surface below it is called **air pressure.** Study **Figure 1.** Is air pressure at Earth's surface more or less than air pressure at the top of the atmosphere? Air pressure decreases as altitude increases. Therefore, air pressure is greater at low altitudes than at high altitudes.

You might have heard the term *barometric pressure* during a weather forecast. Barometric pressure refers to air pressure. Air pressure is measured with an instrument called a barometer, shown in **Figure 2.** Air pressure is typically measured in millibars (mb). Knowing the barometric pressure of different areas helps meteorologists predict the weather.

 Reading Check What instrument measures air pressure?

Wind

As air moves from areas of high pressure to areas of low pressure, it creates wind. Wind direction is the direction from which the wind is blowing. For example, winds that blow from west to east are called westerlies. Meteorologists measure wind speed using an instrument called an anemometer (a nuh MAH muh tur). An anemometer is also shown in **Figure 2.**

Humidity

The amount of water vapor in the air is called **humidity** (hyew MIH duh tee). Humidity can be measured in grams of water per cubic meter of air (g/m^3). When the humidity is high, there is more water vapor in the air. On a day with high humidity, your skin might feel sticky, and sweat might not evaporate from your skin as quickly.

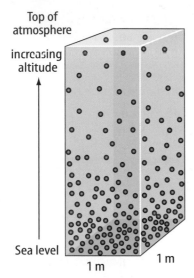

Top of atmosphere

increasing altitude

Sea level

1 m   1 m

Figure 1 Increasing air pressure comes from having more molecules overhead.

Visual Check What happens to air pressure as altitude decreases?

Figure 2 Barometers, left, and anemometers, right, are used to measure weather variables.

Relative Humidity

Think about how a sponge can absorb water. At some point, it becomes full and cannot absorb any more water. In the same way, air can only contain a certain amount of water vapor. When air is saturated, it contains as much water vapor as possible. Temperature determines the maximum amount of water vapor air can contain. Warm air can contain more water vapor than cold air. *The amount of water vapor present in the air compared to the maximum amount of water vapor the air could contain at that temperature is called* **relative humidity.**

Relative humidity is measured using an instrument called a psychrometer and is given as a percent. For example, air with a relative humidity of 100 percent cannot contain any more moisture and dew or rain will form. Air that contains only half the water vapor it could hold has a relative humidity of 50 percent.

 Reading Check Compare and contrast humidity and relative humidity.

Dew Point

When a sponge becomes saturated with water, the water starts to drip from the sponge. Similarly, when air becomes saturated with water vapor, the water vapor will condense and form water droplets. When air near the ground becomes saturated, the water vapor in air will condense to a liquid. If the temperature is above 0°C, dew forms. If the temperature is below 0°C, ice crystals, or frost, form. Higher in the atmosphere clouds form. The graph in **Figure 3** shows the total amount of water vapor that air can contain at different temperatures.

When the temperature decreases, the air can hold less moisture. As you just read, the air becomes saturated, condensation occurs, and dew forms. *The temperature at which air is saturated and condensation can occur is called the* **dew point.**

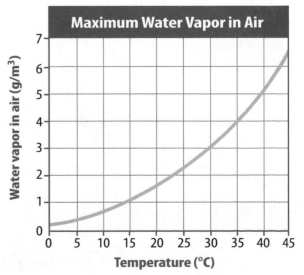

Figure 3 As air temperature increases, the air can contain more water vapor.

Figure 4 Clouds have different shapes and can be found at different altitudes.

Stratus clouds
- flat, white, and layered
- altitude up to 2,000 m

Cumulus clouds
- fluffy, heaped, or piled up
- 2,000 to 6,000 m altitude

Cirrus clouds
- wispy
- above 6,000 m

WORD ORIGIN

precipitation
from Latin *praecipitationem*, means "act or fact of falling headlong"

FOLDABLES®

Make a horizontal two-tab book and label the tabs as illustrated. Use it to collect information on clouds and fog. Find similarities and differences.

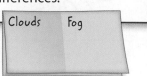

Clouds   Fog

Clouds and Fog

When you exhale outside on a cold winter day, you can see the water vapor in your breath condense into a foggy cloud in front of your face. This also happens when warm air containing water vapor cools as it rises in the atmosphere. When the cooling air reaches its dew point, water vapor condenses on small particles in the air and forms droplets. Surrounded by thousands of other droplets, these small droplets block and reflect light. This makes them visible as clouds.

Clouds are water droplets or ice crystals suspended in the atmosphere. Clouds can have different shapes and be present at different altitudes within the atmosphere. Different types of clouds are shown in **Figure 4.** Because we observe that clouds move, we recognize that water and thermal energy are transported from one location to another. Recall that clouds are also important in reflecting some of the Sun's incoming radiation.

A cloud that forms near Earth's surface is called fog. Fog is a suspension of water droplets or ice crystals close to or at Earth's surface. Fog reduces visibility, the distance a person can see into the atmosphere.

 Reading Check What is fog?

Precipitation

Recall that droplets in clouds form around small solid particles in the atmosphere. These particles might be dust, salt, or smoke. Precipitation occurs when cloud droplets combine and become large enough to fall back to Earth's surface. **Precipitation** *is water, in liquid or solid form, that falls from the atmosphere.* Examples of precipitation—rain, snow, sleet, and hail—are shown in **Figure 5.**

Rain is precipitation that reaches Earth's surface as droplets of water. Snow is precipitation that reaches Earth's surface as solid, frozen crystals of water. Sleet may originate as snow. The snow melts as it falls through a layer of warm air and refreezes when it passes through a layer of below-freezing air. Other times it is just freezing rain. Hail reaches Earth's surface as large pellets of ice. Hail starts as a small piece of ice that is repeatedly lifted and dropped by an updraft within a cloud. A layer of ice is added with each lifting. When it finally becomes too heavy for the updraft to lift, it falls to Earth.

 Key Concept Check What variables are used to describe weather?

The Water Cycle

Precipitation is an important process in the water cycle. Evaporation and condensation are phase changes that are also important to the water cycle. *The* **water cycle** *is the series of natural processes by which water continually moves among oceans, land, and the atmosphere.* As illustrated in **Figure 6,** most water vapor enters the atmosphere when water at the ocean's surface is heated and evaporates. Water vapor cools as it rises in the atmosphere and condenses back into a liquid. Eventually, droplets of liquid and solid water form clouds. Clouds produce precipitation, which falls to Earth's surface and later evaporates, continuing the cycle.

 Key Concept Check How is weather related to the water cycle?

Types of Precipitation

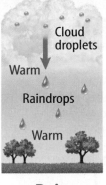

Rain   **Snow**

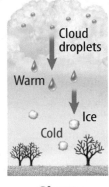
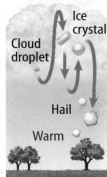

Sleet   **Hail**

▲ **Figure 5** Rain, snow, sleet, and hail are forms of precipitation.

 Visual Check What is the difference between snow and sleet?

The Water Cycle   **Review**   **Personal Tutor**

Figure 6 The Sun's energy powers the water cycle, which is the continual movement of water between the ocean, the land, and the atmosphere.

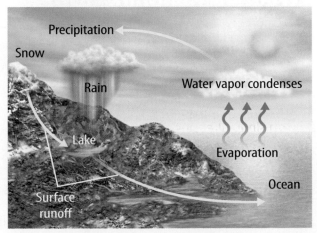

Lesson 1 Review

Assessment   Online Quiz

Visual Summary

Weather is the atmospheric conditions, along with short-term changes, of a certain place at a certain time.

Meteorologists use weather variables to describe atmospheric conditions.

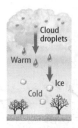

Forms of precipitation include rain, sleet, snow, and hail.

FOLDABLES

Use your lesson Foldable to review the lesson. Save your Foldable for the project at the end of the chapter.

What do you think NOW?

You first read the statements below at the beginning of the chapter.

1. Weather is the long-term average of atmospheric patterns of an area.

2. All clouds are at the same altitude within the atmosphere.

Did you change your mind about whether you agree or disagree with the statements? Rewrite any false statements to make them true.

Use Vocabulary

1. **Define** *humidity* in your own words.

2. **Use the term** *precipitation* in a sentence.

3. _____ is the pressure that a column of air exerts on the surface below it.

Understand Key Concepts

4. Which is NOT a standard weather variable?
   A. air pressure
   B. moon phase
   C. temperature
   D. wind speed

5. **Identify** and describe the different variables used to describe weather.

6. **Relate** humidity to cloud formation.

7. **Describe** how processes in the water cycle are related to weather.

Interpret Graphics

8. **Identify** Which type of precipitation is shown in the diagram below? How does this precipitation form?

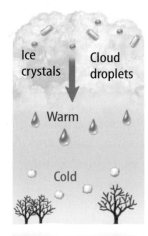

Critical Thinking

9. **Analyze** Why would your ears pop if you climbed a tall mountain?

10. **Differentiate** among cloud formation, fog formation, and dew point.

(t)WIN-Initiative/Getty Images; (b)Jan Tadeusz/Alamy

EVALUATE

Flooding caused widespread devastation in New Orleans, a city that lies below sea level. The storm surge broke through levees that had protected the city.

Is there a link between hurricanes and global warming?

Scientists worry that hurricanes might be getting bigger and happening more often.

On August 29, 2005, Hurricane Katrina roared through New Orleans, Louisiana. The storm destroyed homes and broke through levees, flooding most of the low-lying city. In the wake of the disaster, many wondered whether global warming was responsible. If warm oceans are the fuel for hurricanes, could rising temperatures cause stronger or more frequent hurricanes?

Climate scientists have several ways to investigate this question. They examine past hurricane activity, sea surface temperature, and other climate data. They compare these different types of data and look for patterns. Based on the laws of physics, they put climate and hurricane data into equations. A computer solves these equations and makes computer models. Scientists analyze the models to see whether there is a connection between hurricane activity and different climate variables.

What have scientists learned? So far they have not found a link between warming oceans and the frequency of hurricanes. However, they have found a connection between warming oceans and hurricane strength. Models suggest that rising ocean temperatures might create more destructive hurricanes with stronger winds and more rainfall.

The warm waters of the Gulf of Mexico fueled Hurricane Katrina as it spun toward Louisiana.

But global warming is not the only cause of warming oceans. As the ocean circulates, it goes through cycles of warming and cooling. Data show that the Atlantic Ocean has been in a warming phase for the past few decades.

Whether due to global warming or natural cycles, ocean temperatures are expected to rise even more in coming years. While rising ocean temperatures might not produce more hurricanes, climate research shows they could produce more powerful hurricanes. Perhaps the better question is not what caused Hurricane Katrina, but how we can prepare for equal-strength or more destructive hurricanes in the future.

It's Your Turn

DIAGRAM With a partner, create a storyboard with each frame showing one step in hurricane formation. Label your drawings. Share your storyboard with the class.

(t)NASA/Jeff Schmaltz, MODIS Land Rapid Response Team, (b)Jocelyn Augustino/FEMA

Weather Patterns

Reading Guide

Key Concepts

ESSENTIAL QUESTIONS

- What are two types of pressure systems?
- What drives weather patterns?
- Why is it useful to understand weather patterns?
- What are some examples of severe weather?

Vocabulary

high-pressure system

low-pressure system

air mass

front

tornado

hurricane

blizzard

 Multilingual eGlossary

 Video

What's Science Got to do With It?

 AID M1.1b, S3.2e; PS 2.2l, 2.2m, 2.2n, 2.2o, 2.2p, 2.2q

Inquiry What caused this flooding?

Surging waves and rain from Hurricane Katrina caused flooding in New Orleans, Louisiana. Why are flooding and other types of severe weather dangerous? How does severe weather form?

Kyle Niemi/U.S. Coast Guard via Getty Images

How can temperature affect pressure?

Air molecules that have low energy can be packed closely together. As energy is added to the molecules they begin to move and bump into one another.

1. Read and complete a lab safety form.

2. Close a **resealable plastic bag** except for a small opening. Insert a **straw** through the opening and blow air into the bag until it is as firm as possible. Remove the straw and quickly seal the bag.

3. Submerge the bag in a **container** of **ice water** and hold it there for 2 minutes. Record your observations in your Science Journal.

4. Remove the bag from the ice water and submerge it in **warm water** for 2 minutes. Record your observations.

Think About This

1. What do the results tell you about the movement of air molecules in cold air and in warm air?

2. 🔑 **Key Concept** What property of the air is demonstrated in this activity?

Pressure Systems

Weather is often associated with pressure systems. Recall that air pressure is the weight of the molecules in a large mass of air. When air molecules are cool, they are closer together than when they are warm. Cool air masses have high pressure, or more weight. Warm air masses have low pressure.

A **high-pressure system,** shown in **Figure 7,** *is a large body of circulating air with high pressure at its center and lower pressure outside of the system.* Because air moves from high pressure to low pressure, the air inside the system moves away from the center. Dense air sinks, bringing clear skies and fair weather.

A **low-pressure system,** also shown in **Figure 7,** *is a large body of circulating air with low pressure at its center and higher pressure outside of the system.* This causes air inside the low pressure system to rise. The rising air cools and the water vapor condenses, forming clouds and sometimes precipitation—rain or snow.

🔑 **Key Concept Check** Compare and contrast two types of pressure systems.

Figure 7 Air moving from areas of high pressure to areas of low pressure is called wind.

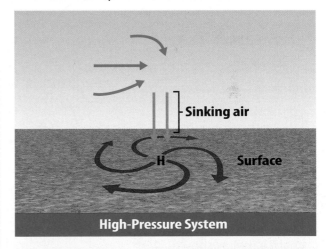

Sinking air

H   **Surface**

High-Pressure System

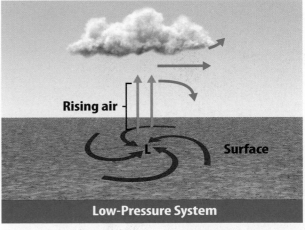

Rising air

L   **Surface**

Low-Pressure System

Figure 8 Five main air masses impact climate across North America.

✔️ **Visual Check** Where does continental polar air come from?

🌐 **New York FYI**

Air Movement Earth's rotation causes moving air to appear to move to the right (west to east) in the northern hemisphere and to the left in the southern hemisphere. This is called the Coriolis effect. The contrast between high and low pressure and the Coriolis effect creates distinct wind patterns, called prevailing winds. The movement of air masses is determined by prevailing winds and upper air currents.

FOLDABLES®

Fold a sheet of paper into thirds along the long axis. Label the outside *Air Masses*. Make another fold about 2 inches from the long edge of the paper to make a three-column chart. Label as shown.

Air masses diagram showing: Maritime polar (Cool, humid); Arctic; Continental polar; Maritime polar (Cool, humid); Dry; Dry, hot; Warm, humid; Warm, humid; Continental tropical; Maritime tropical; Maritime tropical; Maritime tropical

Air Masses

Have you ever noticed that the weather sometimes stays the same for several days in a row? For example, during winter in the northern United States, extremely cold temperatures often last for three or four days in a row. Afterward, several days might follow with warmer temperatures and snow showers.

Air masses are responsible for this pattern. **Air masses** *are large bodies of air that have uniform temperature, humidity, and pressure.* An air mass forms when a large high pressure system lingers over an area for several days. As a high pressure system comes in contact with Earth, the air in the system takes on the temperature and moisture characteristics of the surface below it.

Like high- and low-pressure systems, air masses can extend for a thousand kilometers or more. Sometimes one air mass covers most of the United States. Examples of the main air masses that affect weather in the United States are shown in **Figure 8.**

Air Mass Classification

Air masses are classified by their temperature and moisture characteristics. Air masses that form over land are referred to as continental air masses. Those that form over water are referred to as maritime masses. Warm air masses that form in the equatorial regions are called tropical. Those that form in cold regions are called polar. Air masses near the poles, over the coldest regions of the globe, are called arctic and antarctic air masses.

Arctic Air Masses Forming over Siberia and the Arctic are arctic air masses. They contain bitterly cold, dry air. During winter, an arctic air mass can bring temperatures down to −40°C.

Continental Polar Air Masses Because land cannot transfer as much moisture to the air as oceans can, air masses that form over land are drier than air masses that form over oceans. Continental polar air masses are fast-moving and bring cold temperatures in winter and cool weather in summer. Find the continental polar air masses over Canada in **Figure 8.**

Maritime Polar Air Masses Forming over the northern Atlantic and Pacific Oceans, maritime polar air masses are cold and humid. They often bring cloudy, rainy weather.

Continental Tropical Air Masses Because they form in the tropics over dry, desert land, continental tropical air masses are hot and dry. They bring clear skies and high temperatures. Continental tropical air masses usually form during the summer.

Maritime Tropical Air Masses As shown in **Figure 8,** maritime tropical air masses form over the western Atlantic Ocean, the Gulf of Mexico, and the eastern Pacific Ocean. These moist air masses bring hot, humid air to the southeastern United States during summer. In winter, they can bring heavy snowfall.

Air masses can change as they move over the land and ocean. Warm, moist air can move over land and become cool and dry. Cold, dry air can move over water and become moist and warm.

 Key Concept Check What drives weather patterns?

Math Skills

Conversions

To convert Fahrenheit (°F) units to Celsius (°C) units, use this equation:

$$°C = \frac{(°F - 32)}{1.8}$$

Convert **76°F** to °C

1. Always perform the operation in parentheses first.

   (**76°F** − 32 = **44°F**)

2. Divide the answer from Step 1 by 1.8.

   $$\frac{44°F}{1.8} = 24°C$$

To convert °C to °F, follow the same steps using the following equation:

$$°F = (°C × 1.8) + 32$$

Practice

1. Convert 86°F to °C.
2. Convert 37°C to °F.

Review
- **Math Practice**
- **Personal Tutor**

Inquiry MiniLab   **20 minutes**

How can you observe air pressure?

Although air seems very light, air molecules do exert pressure. You can observe air pressure in action in this activity.

1. Read and complete a lab safety form.
2. Tightly cap the empty **plastic bottle.**
3. Place the bottle in a **bucket of ice** for 10 minutes. Record your observations in your Science Journal.

Analyze and Conclude

1. **Interpret** how air pressure affected the bottle.

2. **Key Concept** Discuss how changing air pressure in Earth's atmosphere affects other things on Earth, such as weather.

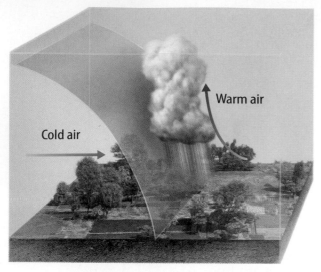

Cold

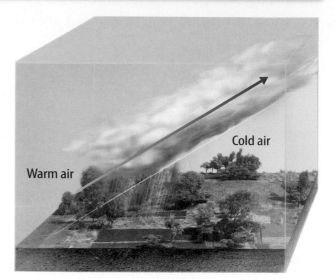

Warm air

Cold air

Warm air

Cold air

Warm

Figure 9 Certain types of fronts are associated with specific weather.

✅ **Visual Check** Describe the difference between a cold front and a warm front.

Science Use v. Common Use

front

Science Use a boundary between two air masses

Common Use the foremost part or surface of something

Fronts

In 1918, Norwegian meteorologist Jacob Bjerknes (BYURK nehs) and his coworkers were busy developing a new method for forecasting the weather. Bjerknes noticed that specific types of weather occur at the boundaries between different air masses. Because he was trained in the army, Bjerknes used a military term to describe this boundary—front.

A military front is the boundary between opposing armies in a battle. *A weather* **front,** *however, is a boundary between two air masses.* Drastic weather changes often occur at fronts. As wind carries an air mass away from the area where it formed, the air mass will eventually collide with another air mass. Changes in temperature, humidity, cloud types, wind, and precipitation are common at fronts.

Cold Fronts

When a colder air mass moves toward a warmer air mass, a cold front forms, as shown in **Figure 9.** The cold air, which is denser than the warm air, pushes underneath the warm air mass. The warm air rises and cools. Water vapor in the air condenses and clouds form. Showers and thunderstorms often form along cold fronts. It is common for temperatures to decrease as much as 10°C when a cold front passes through. The wind becomes gusty and changes direction. In many cases, cold fronts give rise to severe storms.

✅ **Reading Check** What types of weather are associated with cold fronts?

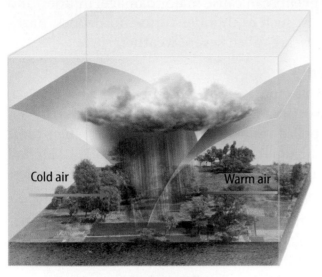

Stationary

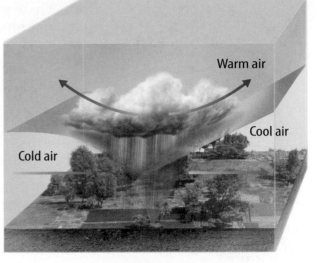

Occluded

Warm Fronts

As shown in **Figure 9,** a warm front forms when less dense, warmer air moves toward colder, denser air. The warm air rises as it glides above the cold air mass. When water vapor in the warm air condenses, it creates a wide blanket of clouds. These clouds often bring steady rain or snow for several hours or even days. A warm front not only brings warmer temperatures, but it also causes the wind to shift directions.

Both a cold front and a warm front form at the edge of an approaching air mass. Because air masses are large, the movement of fronts is used to make weather forecasts. When a cold front passes through your area, temperatures will remain low for the next few days. When a warm front arrives, the weather will become warmer and more humid.

Stationary and Occluded Fronts

Sometimes an approaching front will stall for several days with warm air on one side of it and cold air on the other side. When the boundary between two air masses stalls, the front is called a stationary front. Study the stationary front shown in **Figure 9.** Cloudy skies and light rain are found along stationary fronts.

Cold fronts move faster than warm fronts. When a fast-moving cold front catches up with a slow-moving warm front, an occluded or blocked front forms. Occluded fronts, shown in **Figure 9,** usually bring precipitation.

 Key Concept Check Why is it useful to understand weather patterns associated with fronts?

Severe Weather

Some weather events can cause major damage, injuries, and death. These events, such as thunderstorms, tornadoes, hurricanes, and blizzards, are called severe weather.

Thunderstorms

Also known as electrical storms because of their lightning, thunderstorms have warm temperatures, moisture, and rising air, which may be supplied by a low-pressure system. When these conditions occur, a cumulus cloud can grow into a 10-km-tall thundercloud, or cumulonimbus cloud, in as little as 30 minutes.

A typical thunderstorm has a three-stage life cycle, shown in **Figure 10**. The cumulus stage is **dominated** by cloud formation and updrafts. Updrafts are air currents moving vertically away from the ground. After the cumulus cloud has been created, downdrafts begin to appear. Downdrafts are air currents moving vertically toward the ground. In the mature stage, heavy winds, rain, and lightning dominate the area. Within 30 minutes of reaching the mature stage, the thunderstorm begins to fade, or dissipate. In the dissipation stage, updrafts stop, winds die down, lightning ceases, and precipitation weakens.

Strong updrafts and downdrafts within a thunderstorm cause millions of tiny ice crystals to rise and sink, crashing into each other. This creates positively and negatively charged particles in the cloud. The difference in the charges of particles between the cloud and the charges of particles on the ground eventually creates electricity. This is seen as a bolt of lightning. Lightning can move from cloud to cloud, cloud to ground, or ground to cloud. It can heat the nearby air to more than 27,000°C. Air molecules near the bolt rapidly expand and then contract, creating the sound identified as thunder.

ACADEMIC VOCABULARY

dominate
(verb) to exert the guiding influence on

Figure 10 Thunderstorms have distinct stages characterized by the direction in which air is moving.

Thunderstorms 🔑

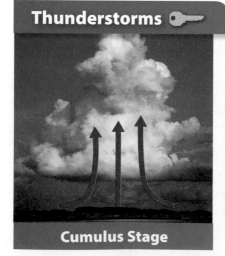
Cumulus Stage

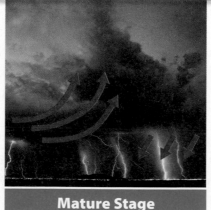
Mature Stage

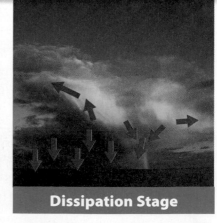
Dissipation Stage

✓ **Visual Check** Describe what happens during each stage of a thunderstorm.

(l)Amazon-Images/Alamy; (c)Mike Olbinski Photography/Getty Images; (r)mediacolor's/Alamy

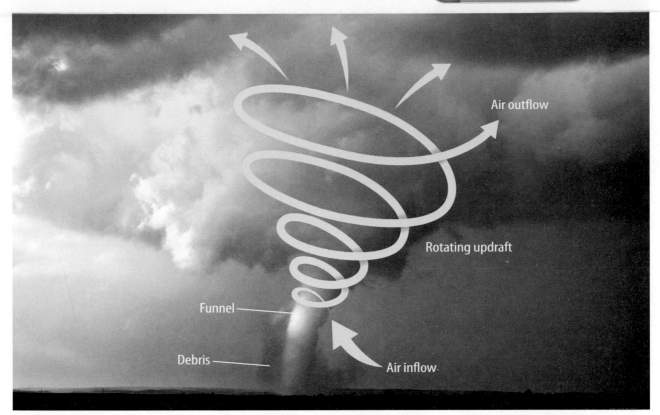

Figure 11 A funnel cloud forms when updrafts within a thunderstorm begin rotating.

Tornadoes

Perhaps you have seen photos of the damage from a tornado. *A **tornado** is a violent, whirling column of air in contact with the ground.* Most tornadoes have a diameter of several hundred meters. The largest tornadoes exceed 1,500 m in diameter. The intense, swirling winds within tornadoes can reach speeds of more than 400 km/h. These winds are strong enough to send cars, trees, and even entire houses flying through the air. Tornadoes usually last only a few minutes. More destructive tornadoes, however, can last for several hours.

Formation of Tornadoes When thunderstorm updrafts begin to rotate, as shown in **Figure 11,** tornadoes can form. Swirling winds spiral downward from the thunderstorm's base, creating a funnel cloud. When the funnel reaches the ground, it becomes a tornado. Although the swirling air is invisible, you can easily see the debris lifted by the tornado.

✅ **Reading Check** How do tornadoes form?

Tornado Alley More tornadoes occur in the United States than anywhere else on Earth. The central United States, from Nebraska to Texas, experiences the most tornadoes. This area has been nicknamed Tornado Alley. In this area, cold air blowing southward from Canada frequently collides with warm, moist air moving northward from the Gulf of Mexico. These conditions are ideal for severe thunderstorms and tornadoes.

Classifying Tornadoes Dr. Ted Fujita developed a method for classifying tornadoes based on the damage they cause. On the modified Fujita intensity scale, F0 tornadoes cause light damage, breaking tree branches and damaging billboards. F1 though F4 tornadoes cause moderate to devastating damage, including tearing roofs from homes, derailing trains, and throwing vehicles in the air. F5 tornadoes cause incredible damage, such as demolishing concrete and steel buildings and pulling the bark from trees.

Figure 12 Hurricanes consist of alternating bands of heavy precipitation and sinking air.

Hurricane Formation

1 As warm, moist air rises into the atmosphere, it cools, water vapor condenses, and clouds form. As more air rises, it creates an area of low pressure over the ocean.

Low pressure

2 As air continues to rise, a tropical depression forms. Tropical depressions bring thunderstorms with winds between 37–62 km/h.

3 Air continues to rise, rotating counterclockwise. The storm builds to a tropical storm with winds in excess of 63 km/h. It produces strong thunderstorms.

4 When winds exceed 119 km/h, the storm becomes a hurricane. Only one percent of tropical storms become hurricanes.

Inside a Hurricane

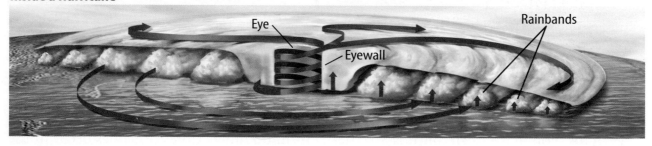

Eye

Eyewall

Rainbands

Visual Check How do hurricanes form?

WORD ORIGIN

hurricane
from Spanish *huracan*, means "tempest"

Hurricanes

An intense tropical storm with winds exceeding 119 km/h is a **hurricane.** Hurricanes are the most destructive storms on Earth. Like tornadoes, hurricanes have a circular shape with intense, swirling winds. However, hurricanes do not form over land. Hurricanes typically form in late summer over warm, tropical ocean water. **Figure 12** sequences the steps in hurricane formation. A typical hurricane is 480 km across, more than 150 thousand times larger than a tornado. At the center of a hurricane is the eye, an area of clear skies and light winds.

Damage from hurricanes occurs as a result of strong winds and flooding. While still out at sea, hurricanes create high waves that can flood coastal areas. As a hurricane crosses the coastline, or makes landfall, strong rains intensify and can flood and devastate entire areas. But once a hurricane moves over land or colder water, it loses its energy and dissipates.

In other parts of the world, these intense tropical storms have other names. In Asia, the same type of storm is called a typhoon. In Australia it is called a tropical cyclone.

StockTrek/Getty Images

Winter Storms

Winter weather can be severe and hazardous. Ice storms, as shown in **Figure 13,** can down power lines and tree branches and make driving dangerous. A **blizzard** *is a violent winter storm characterized by freezing temperatures, strong winds, and blowing snow.* During a blizzard, swirling snow reduces visibility, and freezing temperatures can cause frostbite and hypothermia (hi poh THER mee uh).

Freezing Rain

Figure 13 The weight of ice from freezing rain can cause trees, power lines, and other structures to break.

 Key Concept Check What are examples of severe weather?

Severe Weather Safety

The U.S. National Weather Service issues watches and warnings for different types of severe weather. A watch means that severe weather is possible. A warning means that severe weather is already occurring. Paying close attention to severe weather watches and warnings is important and could save your life.

It is also important to know how to protect yourself during dangerous weather. During thunderstorms, you should stay inside if possible, and stay away from metal objects and electrical cords. If you are outside, stay away from water, high places, and isolated trees. Dressing properly is important in all kinds of weather. When windchill temperatures are below −20°C, you should dress in layers, keep your head and fingers covered, and limit your time outdoors.

Not all weather safety pertains to bad weather. The Sun's ultraviolet (UV) radiation can cause health risks, including skin cancer. The U.S. National Weather Service issues a daily UV Index Forecast. Precautions on sunny days include covering up, using sunscreen, and wearing a hat and sunglasses. Surfaces such as snow, water, and beach sand can double the effects of the Sun's UV radiation.

Lesson 2 Review

Visual Summary

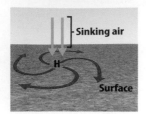

Low-pressure systems, high-pressure systems, and air masses all influence weather.

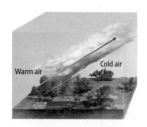

Weather often changes as a front passes through an area.

The National Weather Service issues warnings about severe weather such as thunderstorms, tornadoes, hurricanes, and blizzards.

FOLDABLES

Use your lesson Foldable to review the lesson. Save your Foldable for the project at the end of the chapter.

What do you think NOW?

You first read the statements below at the beginning of the chapter.

3. Precipitation often occurs at the boundaries of large air masses.

4. There are no safety precautions for severe weather, such as tornadoes and hurricanes.

Did you change your mind about whether you agree or disagree with the statements? Rewrite any false statements to make them true.

Use Vocabulary

1 **Distinguish** between an air mass and a front.

2 **Define** *low-pressure system* using your own words.

3 **Use the term** *high-pressure system* in a sentence.

Understand Key Concepts 🔑

4 Which air mass is humid and warm?
   A. continental polar
   B. continental tropical
   C. maritime polar
   D. maritime tropical

5 **Give an example** of cold-front weather.

6 **Compare and contrast** hurricanes and tornadoes.

7 **Explain** how thunderstorms form.

Interpret Graphics

8 **Compare and Contrast** Copy and fill in the graphic organizer below to compare and contrast high-pressure and low-pressure systems.

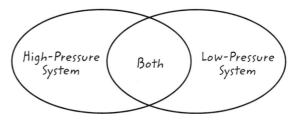

Critical Thinking

9 **Suggest** a reason that low-pressure systems are cloudy and rainy or snowy.

10 **Design** a pamphlet that contains tips on how to stay safe during different types of severe weather.

Math Skills ✕ ÷ +

Review — Math Practice —

11 Convert 212°F to °C.

12 Convert 20°C to °F.

Why does the weather change?

One day it is sunny, the next day it is pouring rain. If you look at only one location, the patterns that cause the weather to change are difficult to see. However, when you look on the large scale, the patterns become apparent.

Learn It

Recognizing cause and effect is an important part of science and conducting experiments. Scientists look for cause-and-effect relationships between variables. The maps below show the movement of fronts and pressure systems over a two-day period. What effect will these systems have on the weather as they move across the United States?

Try It

1 Examine the weather maps below. The thin black lines on each map represent areas where the barometric pressure is the same. The pressure is indicated by the number on the line. The center of a low- or high-pressure system is indicated by the word LOW or HIGH. Identify the location of low- and high- pressure systems on each map. Use the key below the maps to the identify the location of warm and cold fronts.

2 Find locations A, B, C, and where you live on the map. For each location, describe how the systems change positions over the two days.

3 What is the cause of and effect on precipitation and temperature at each location?

Apply It

4 The low-pressure system produced several tornadoes. Which location did they occur closest to? Explain.

5 The weather patterns generally move from west to east. Predict the weather on the third day for each location.

6 One day it is clear and sunny, but you notice that the pressure is less than it was the day before. What weather might be coming? Why?

7 🔑 **Key Concept** How does understanding weather patterns help make predicting the weather more accurate?

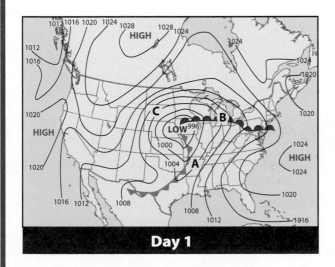

Day 1

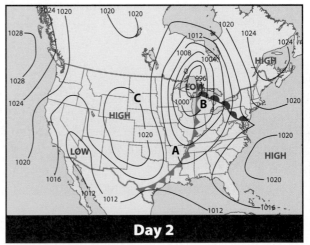

Day 2

▲▲▲ Cold front
●●● Warm front

Weather Forecasts

Reading Guide

Key Concepts 🔑
ESSENTIAL QUESTIONS

- What instruments are used to measure weather variables?
- How are computer models used to predict the weather?

Vocabulary

surface report

upper-air report

Doppler radar

isobar

computer model

 Multilingual eGlossary

 AID M1.1b, M2.1a, S1.2a, S2.3a, S2.3b, S3.1a, S3.1b, S3.2d, S3.2f, S3.2g

Inquiry What's inside?

Information about weather variables is collected by the weather radar station shown here. Data, such as the amount of rain falling in a weather system, help meteorologists make accurate predictions about severe weather. What other instruments do meteorologists use to forecast weather? How do they collect and use data?

Can you understand the weather report?

Weather reports use numbers and certain vocabulary terms to help you understand the weather conditions in a given area for a given time period. Listen to a weather report for your area. Can you record all the information reported?

1 In your Science Journal, make a list of data you would expect to hear in a weather report.

2 Listen carefully to a **recording of a weather report** and jot down numbers and measurements you hear next to those on your list.

3 Listen a second time and make adjustments to your original notes, such as adding more data, if necessary.

4 Listen a third time, then share the weather forecast as you heard it.

Think About This

1. What measurements were difficult for you to apply to understanding the weather report?

2. Why are so many different types of data needed to give a complete weather report?

3. List the instruments that might be used to collect each kind of data.

4. 🔑 **Key Concept** Where do meteorologists obtain the data they use to make a weather forecast?

Measuring the Weather

Being a meteorologist is like being a doctor. Using specialized instruments and visual observations, the doctor first measures the condition of your body. The doctor later combines these measurements with his or her knowledge of medical science. The result is a forecast of your future health, such as, "You'll feel better in a few days if you rest and drink plenty of fluids."

Similarly, meteorologists, scientists who study weather, use specialized instruments to measure conditions in the atmosphere, as you read in Lesson 1. These instruments include thermometers to measure temperature, barometers to measure air pressure, psychrometers to measure relative humidity, and anemometers to measure wind speed.

Surface and Upper-Air Reports

A **surface report** *describes a set of weather measurements made on Earth's surface.* Weather variables are measured by a weather station—a collection of instruments that report temperature, air pressure, humidity, precipitation, and wind speed and direction. Cloud amounts and visibility are often measured by human observers.

An **upper-air report** *describes wind, temperature, and humidity conditions above Earth's surface.* These atmospheric conditions are measured by a radiosonde (RAY dee oh sahnd), a package of weather instruments carried many kilometers above the ground by a weather balloon. Radiosonde reports are made twice a day simultaneously at hundreds of locations around the world.

Hutchings Photography/Digital Light Source

Satellite and Radar Images

Images taken from satellites orbiting about 35,000 km above Earth provide information about weather conditions on Earth. A visible light image, such as the one shown in **Figure 14,** shows white clouds over Earth. The infrared image, also shown in **Figure 14,** shows infrared energy in false color. The infrared energy comes from Earth and is stored in the atmosphere as thermal energy. Monitoring infrared energy provides information about cloud height and atmospheric temperature.

Figure 14 Meteorologists use visible light and infrared satellite images to identify fronts and air masses.

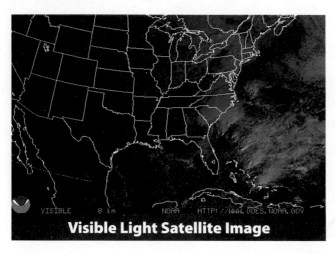

Visible Light Satellite Image

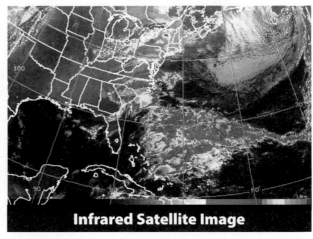

Infrared Satellite Image

✅ **Visual Check** How is an infrared satellite image different from a visible light satellite image?

Radar measures precipitation when radio waves bounce off raindrops and snowflakes. **Doppler radar** *is a specialized type of radar that can detect precipitation as well as the movement of small particles, which can be used to approximate wind speed.* Because the movement of precipitation is caused by wind, Doppler radar can be used to estimate wind speed. This can be especially important during severe weather, such as tornadoes or thunderstorms.

🔑 **Key Concept Check** Identify the weather variables that radiosondes, infrared satellites, and Doppler radar measure.

Weather Maps

Every day, thousands of surface reports, upper-air reports, and satellite and radar observations are made around the world. Meteorologists have developed tools that help them simplify and understand this enormous amount of weather data.

FOLDABLES

Make a horizontal two-tab book and label the tabs as illustrated. Use it to collect information on satellite and radar images. Compare and contrast these information tools.

Weather Satellites | Doppler Radar

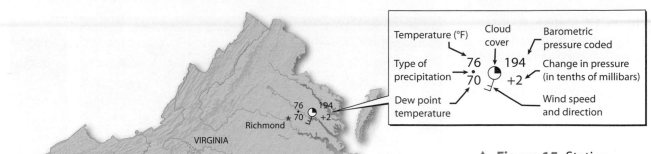

Temperature (°F) | Cloud cover | Barometric pressure coded
Type of precipitation | 76 | 194 | Change in pressure (in tenths of millibars)
70 | +2
Dew point temperature | Wind speed and direction

VIRGINIA

Richmond

76 194
70 +2

▲ **Figure 15** Station models contain information about weather variables.

The Station Model

As shown in **Figure 15,** the station model diagram displays data from many different weather measurements for a particular location. It uses numbers and symbols to display data and observations from surface reports and upper-air reports.

Mapping Temperature and Pressure

In addition to station models, weather maps also have other symbols. For example, **isobars** *are lines that connect all places on a map where pressure has the same value.* Locate an isobar on the map in **Figure 16.** Isobars show the location of high- and low-pressure systems. Isobars also provide information about wind speed. Winds are strong when isobars are close together. Winds are weaker when isobars are farther apart.

In a similar way, isotherms (not shown) are lines that connect places with the same temperature. Isotherms show which areas are warm and which are cold. Fronts are represented as lines with symbols on them, as indicated in **Figure 16.**

✓ **Reading Check** Compare isobars and isotherms.

WORD ORIGIN

isobar
from Greek *isos*, means "equal"; and *baros*, means "heavy"

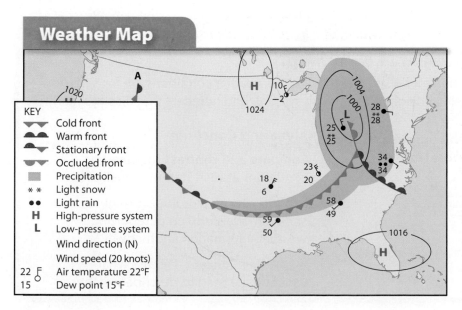

Weather Map

KEY

▼▼▼	Cold front
●●●	Warm front
▼●▼	Stationary front
▼▼●●	Occluded front
▪	Precipitation
✳ ✳	Light snow
●●	Light rain
H	High-pressure system
L	Low-pressure system
	Wind direction (N)
	Wind speed (20 knots)
22	Air temperature 22°F
15	Dew point 15°F

◀ **Figure 16** Weather maps contain symbols that provide information about the weather.

✓ **Visual Check** Which symbols represent high-pressure and low-pressure systems?

Concepts in Motion

Animation

Figure 17 Meteorologists analyze data from various sources—such as radar and computer models—in order to prepare weather forecasts.

Predicting the Weather

Modern weather forecasts are made with the help of computer models, such as the ones shown in **Figure 17. Computer models** *are detailed computer programs that solve a set of complex mathematical formulas.* The formulas predict what temperatures and winds might occur, when and where it will rain and snow, and what types of clouds will form.

Government meteorological offices also use computers and the Internet to exchange weather measurements continuously throughout the day. Weather maps are drawn and forecasts are made using computer models. Then, through television, radio, newspapers, and the Internet, the maps and forecasts are made available to the public.

 Key Concept Check How are computers used to predict the weather?

Inquiry MiniLab   **20 minutes**

How is weather represented on a map?

Meteorologists often use station models to record what the weather conditions are for a particular location. A station model is a diagram containing symbols and numbers that displays many different weather measurements.

Use the **station model legend** provided by your teacher to interpret the data in each station model shown here.

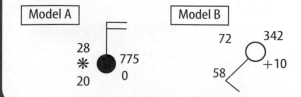

Model A

28
✳
20
775
0

Model B

72   342
58   +10

Analyze and Conclude

1. **Compare and contrast** the weather conditions at each station model.

2. **Explain** why meteorologists might use station models instead of reporting weather information another way.

3. 🔑 **Key Concept** Discuss what variables are used to describe weather.

Lesson 3 Review

Visual Summary

Weather variables are measured by weather stations, radiosondes, satellites, and Doppler radar.

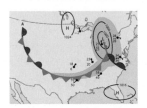

Weather maps contain information in the form of a station model, isobars and isotherms, and symbols for fronts and pressure systems.

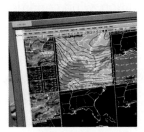

Meteorologists use computer models to help forecast the weather.

FOLDABLES®

Use your lesson Foldable to review the lesson. Save your Foldable for the project at the end of the chapter.

What do you think NOW?

You first read the statements below at the beginning of the chapter.

5. Weather variables are measured every day at locations around the world.

6. Modern weather forecasts are done using computers.

Did you change your mind about whether you agree or disagree with the statements? Rewrite any false statements to make them true.

Use Vocabulary

1 **Define** *computer model* in your own words.

2 A line connecting places with the same pressure is called a(n) _____.

3 **Use the term** *surface report* in a sentence.

Understand Key Concepts 🔑

4 Which diagram shows surface weather measurements?
- A. an infrared satellite image
- B. an upper air chart
- C. a station model
- D. a visible light satellite image

5 **List** two ways that upper-air weather conditions are measured.

6 **Describe** how computers are used in weather forecasting.

7 **Distinguish** between isobars and isotherms.

Interpret Graphics

8 **Identify** Copy and fill in the graphic organizer below to identify the components of a surface map.

Symbol	Meaning
●▽●▽●	
H	

Critical Thinking

9 **Suggest** ways to forecast the weather without using computers.

10 **Explain** why isobars and isotherms make it easier to understand a weather map.

Materials

graph paper

local weather maps

outdoor thermometer

barometer

Can you predict the weather?

Weather forecasts are important—not just so you are dressed right when you leave the house, but also to help farmers know when to plant and harvest, to help cities know when to call in the snow plows, and to help officials know when and where to evacuate in advance of severe weather.

Ask a Question

Can you predict the weather?

Make Observations

1. Read and complete a lab safety form.

2. Collect weather data daily for a period of one week. Temperature and pressure should be recorded as a number, but precipitation, wind conditions, and cloud cover can be described in words. Make your observations at the same time each day.

3. Graph temperature in degrees and air pressure in millibars on the same sheet of paper, placing the graphs side by side, as shown on the next page. Beneath the graphs, for each day, add notes that describe precipitation, wind conditions, and cloud cover.

(t to b)Aaron Haupt; (2-4, r)Hutchings Photography/Digital Light Source

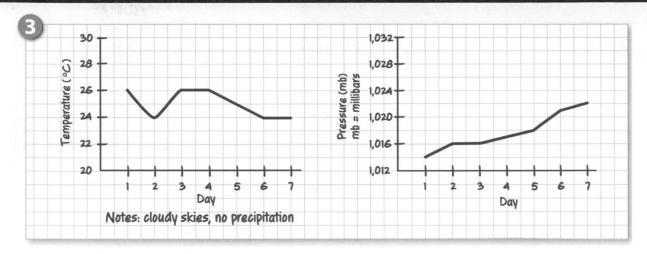

Notes: cloudy skies, no precipitation

Form a Hypothesis

4 Examine your data and the weather maps. Look for factors that appear to be related. For example, your data might suggest that when the pressure decreases, clouds follow.

5 Find three sets of data pairs that seem to be related. Form three hypotheses, one for each set of data pairs.

Test Your Hypothesis

6 Look at your last day of data. Using your hypotheses, predict the weather for the next day.

7 Collect weather data the next day and evaluate your predictions.

8 Repeat steps 6 and 7 for at least two more days.

Analyze and Conclude

9 **Analyze** Compare your hypotheses with the results of your predictions. How successful were you? What additional information might have improved your predictions?

10 **The Big Idea** Scientists have more complex and sophisticated tools to help them predict their weather, but with fairly simple tools, you can make an educated guess. Write a one-paragraph summary of the data you collected and how you interpreted it to predict the weather.

Communicate Your Results

For each hypothesis you generated, make a small poster that states the hypothesis, shows a graph that supports it, and shows the results of your predictions. Write a concluding statement about the reliability of your hypothesis. Share your results with the class.

 **Extension**

Investigate other forms of data you might collect and find out how they would help you to make a forecast. Try them out for a week and see if your ability to make predictions improves.

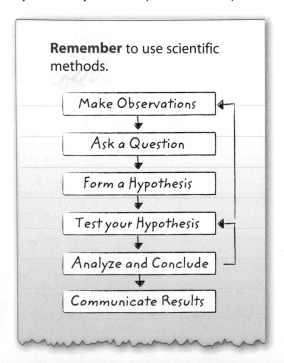

Remember to use scientific methods.

Make Observations
↓
Ask a Question
↓
Form a Hypothesis
↓
Test your Hypothesis
↓
Analyze and Conclude
↓
Communicate Results

Chapter 9 Study Guide

 THE BIG IDEA Scientists use weather variables to describe weather and study weather systems. Scientists use computers to predict the weather.

Key Concepts Summary

| **Vocabulary** |

Lesson 1: Describing Weather

- **Weather** is the atmospheric conditions, along with short-term changes, of a certain place at a certain time.
- Variables used to describe weather are air temperature, **air pressure,** wind, **humidity,** and **relative humidity.**
- The processes in the water cycle—evaporation, condensation, and **precipitation**—are all involved in the formation of different types of weather.

Vocabulary:
- weather
- air pressure
- humidity
- relative humidity
- dew point
- precipitation
- water cycle

Lesson 2: Weather Patterns

- **Low-pressure systems** and **high-pressure systems** are two systems that influence weather.
- Weather patterns are driven by the movement of **air masses.**
- Understanding weather patterns helps make weather forecasts more accurate.
- Severe weather includes thunderstorms, **tornadoes, hurricanes,** and **blizzards.**

Vocabulary:
- high-pressure system
- low-pressure system
- air mass
- front
- tornado
- hurricane
- blizzard

Lesson 3: Weather Forecasts

- Thermometers, barometers, anemometers, radiosondes, satellites, and **Doppler radar** are used to measure weather variables.
- **Computer models** use complex mathematical formulas to predict temperature, wind, cloud formation, and precipitation.

Vocabulary:
- surface report
- upper-air report
- Doppler radar
- isobar
- computer model

FOLDABLES® Chapter Project

Assemble your lesson Foldables as shown to make a Chapter Project. Use the project to review what you have learned in this chapter.

Use Vocabulary

1 The pressure that a column of air exerts on the area below it is called _____.

2 The amount of water vapor in the air is called _____.

3 The natural process in which water constantly moves among oceans, land, and the atmosphere is called the _____.

4 A(n) _____ is a boundary between two air masses.

5 At the center of a(n) _____, air rises and forms clouds and precipitation.

6 A continental polar _____ brings cold temperatures during winter.

7 When the same _____ passes through two locations on a weather map, both locations have the same pressure.

8 The humidity in the air compared to the amount air can hold is the _____.

Link Vocabulary and Key Concepts

Concepts in Motion Interactive Concept Map

Copy this concept map, and then use vocabulary terms from the previous page to complete the concept map.

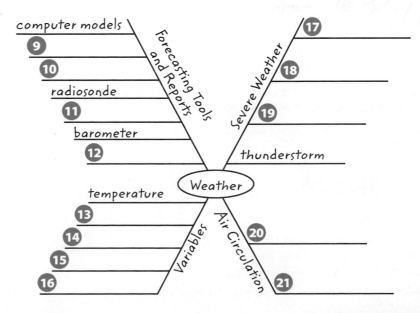

Chapter 9 Review

Understand Key Concepts 🔑

1 Clouds form when water changes from
A. gas to liquid.
B. liquid to gas.
C. solid to gas.
D. solid to liquid.

2 Which type of precipitation reaches Earth's surface as large pellets of ice?
A. hail
B. rain
C. sleet
D. snow

3 Which of these sinking-air situations usually brings fair weather?
A. air mass
B. cold front
C. high-pressure system
D. low-pressure system

4 Which air mass contains cold, dry air?
A. continental polar
B. continental tropical
C. maritime tropical
D. maritime polar

5 Study the front below.

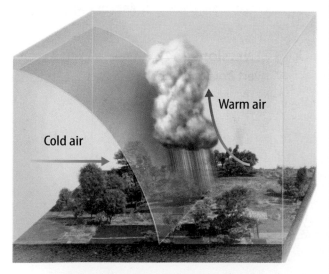

Warm air

Cold air

How does this type of front form?
A. A cold front overtakes a warm front.
B. Cold air moves toward warmer air.
C. The boundary between two fronts stalls.
D. Warm air moves toward colder air.

6 Which is an intense tropical storm with winds exceeding 119 km/h?
A. blizzard
B. hurricane
C. thunderstorm
D. tornado

7 Which contains measurements of temperature, air pressure, humidity, precipitation, and wind speed and direction?
A. a radar image
B. a satellite image
C. a surface report
D. a weather station

8 What does Doppler radar measure?
A. air pressure
B. air temperature
C. the rate at which air pressure changes
D. the speed at which precipitation travels

9 Study the station model below.

81
55
138
3

What is the temperature according to the station model?
A. 3°F
B. 55°F
C. 81°F
D. 138°F

10 Which describes cirrus clouds?
A. flat, white, and layered
B. fluffy, at middle altitudes
C. heaped or piled up
D. wispy, at high altitudes

11 Which instrument measures wind speed?
A. anemometer
B. barometer
C. psychrometer
D. thermometer

Critical Thinking

12 **Predict** Suppose you are on a ship near the equator in the Atlantic Ocean. You notice that the barometric pressure is dropping. Predict what type of weather you might experience.

13 **Compare** a continental polar air mass with a maritime tropical air mass.

14 **Assess** why clouds usually form in the center of a low-pressure system.

15 **Predict** how maritime air masses would change if the oceans froze.

16 **Compare** two types of severe weather.

17 **Interpret Graphics** Identify the front on the weather map below. Predict the weather for areas along the front.

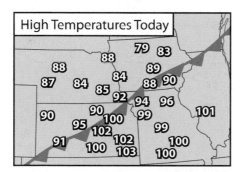

High Temperatures Today

18 **Assess** the validity of the weather forecast: "Tomorrow's weather will be similar to today's weather."

19 **Compare and contrast** surface weather reports and upper-air reports. Why is it important for meterologists to monitor weather variables high above Earth's surface?

Writing in Science

20 **Write** a paragraph about the ways computers have improved weather forecasts. Be sure to include a topic sentence and a concluding sentence.

REVIEW THE **BIG** IDEA

21 Identify the instruments used to measure weather variables.

22 How do scientists use weather variables to describe and predict weather?

23 Describe the factors that influence weather.

24 Use the factors listed in question 23 to describe how a continental polar air mass can change to a maritime polar air mass.

Math Skills ✕ ÷

📖 Review

— Math Practice —

Use Conversions

25 Convert from Fahrenheit to Celsius.
  a. Convert 0°F to °C.
  b. Convert 104°F to °C.

26 Convert from Celsius to Fahrenheit.
  a. Convert 0°C to °F.
  b. Convert −40°C to °F.

27 The Kelvin scale of temperature measurement starts at zero and has the same unit size as Celsius degrees. Zero degrees Celsius is equal to 273 kelvin.

Convert 295 K to Fahrenheit.

Standardized Test Practice

Record your answers on the answer sheet provided by your teacher or on a sheet of paper.

Multiple Choice

1 Which measures the average kinetic energy of air molecules?

  A humidity

  B pressure

  C speed

  D temperature

Use the diagram below to answer question 2.

2 Which weather system does the above diagram illustrate?

  A high pressure

  B hurricane

  C low pressure

  D tornado

3 What causes weather to remain the same several days in a row?

  A air front

  B air mass

  C air pollution

  D air resistance

4 Which lists the stages of a thunderstorm in order?

  A cumulus, dissipation, mature

  B cumulus, mature, dissipation

  C dissipation, cumulus, mature

  D dissipation, mature, cumulus

5 What causes air to reach its dew point?

  A decreasing air currents

  B decreasing humidity

  C dropping air pressure

  D dropping temperatures

6 Which measures air pressure?

  A anemometer

  B barometer

  C psychrometer

  D thermometer

Use the diagram below to answer question 7.

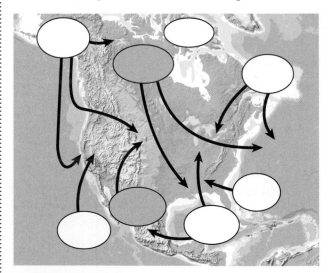

7 Which type of air masses do the shaded ovals in the diagram depict?

  A antarctic

  B arctic

  C continental

  D maritime

8 Which BEST expresses moisture saturation?

  A barometric pressure

  B relative humidity

  C weather front

  D wind direction

Use the diagram below to answer question 9.

Maximum Water Vapor in Air

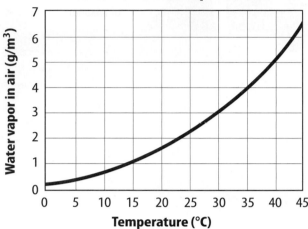

9 What happens to maximum moisture content when air temperatures increase from 15°C to 30°C?

A increases from 1 to 2 g/m³

B increases from 1 to 3 g/m³

C increases from 2 to 3 g/m³

D increases from 2 to 4 g/m³

10 When isobars are close together on a weather map,

A cloud cover is extensive.

B temperatures are high.

C warm fronts prevail.

D winds are strong.

11 Which provides energy for the water cycle?

A air currents

B Earth's core

C ocean currents

D the Sun

Constructed Response

Use the table below to answer question 12.

Weather Variable	Measurement

12 In the table above, list the variables weather scientists use to describe weather. Then describe the unit of measurement for each variable.

Use the diagram below to answer questions 13 and 14.

Cold air   Warm air

13 What does the diagram above depict?

14 Describe the weather conditions associated with the diagram.

15 How do weather fronts form?

NEED EXTRA HELP?															
If You Missed Question...	1	2	3	4	5	6	7	8	9	10	11	12	13	14	15
Go to Lesson...	1	2	2	2	1	1,3	2	1	1	3	1	1	2	2	2

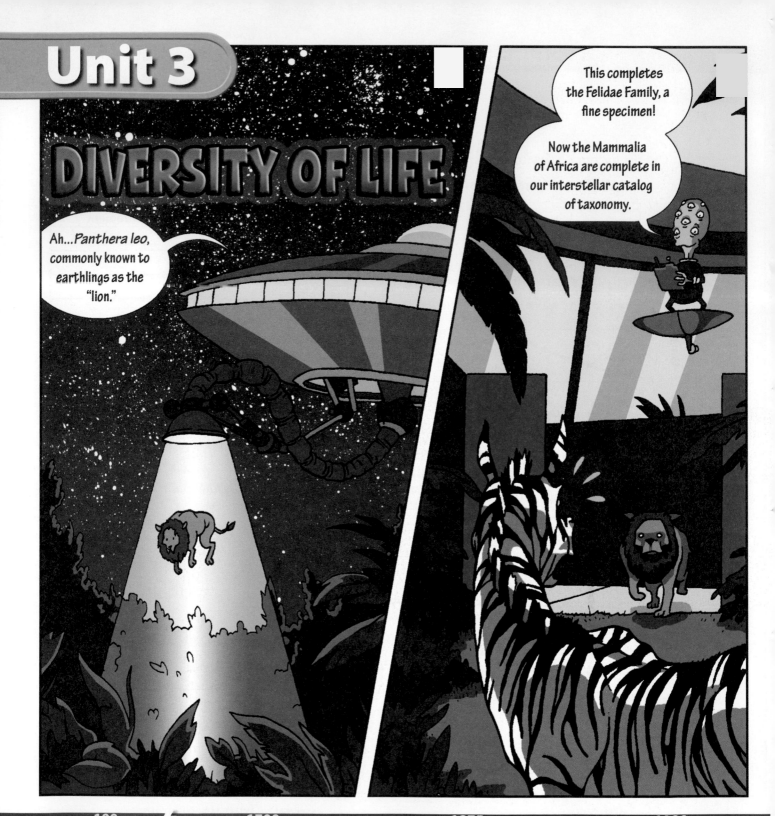

350–341 B.C.

Greek philosopher Aristotle classifies organisms by grouping 500 species of animals into eight classes.

1735

Carl Linnaeus classifies nature within a hierarchy and divides life into three kingdoms: mineral, vegetable, and animal. He uses five ranks: class, order, genus, species and variety. Linnaeus's classification is the basis of modern biological classification.

1859

Charles Darwin publishes *On the Origin of Species,* in which he explains his theory of natural selection.

1866

German biologist Ernst Haeckel coins the term *ecology.*

 Inquiry

Visit ConnectED
for this unit's
STEM activity.

1950

1969
American ecologist Robert
Whittaker is the first to
propose a five-kingdom
taxonomic classification of
the world's biota. The five
kingdoms are Animalia,
Plantae, Fungi, Protista
and Monera.

1973
Konrad Lorenz, Niko
Tinbergen, and Karl
von Frisch are jointly
awarded the Nobel
Prize for their
studies in animal
behavior.

2000

1990
Carl Woese
introduces the three-
domain system that
groups cellular life-
forms into Archaea,
Bacteria, and
Eukaryote domains.

ICT 5.2

Patterns

Have you ever caught a snowflake in your hand or seen one close-up in a book or on TV? You might have heard someone say that no two snowflakes are alike. While this is true, it is also true that all snowflakes have similar patterns. A **pattern** is a consistent plan or model used as a guide for understanding or predicting things. Patterns can be created or occur naturally. The formation of snowflakes is an example of a repeating pattern. They form piece by piece, as water drops in the air freeze into a six-sided crystal.

How Scientists Use Patterns

Studying and using patterns is useful to scientists because it can help explain the natural world or predict future events. A biologist might study patterns in DNA to predict what organisms will look like. A meteorologist might study cloud formation patterns to predict the weather. When doing research, scientists also try to match patterns found in their data with patterns that occur in nature. This helps to determine whether data are accurate and helps to predict outcomes.

Types of Patterns

Cyclic Patterns

A cycle, or repeated series of events, is a form of pattern. An organism's life cycle typically follows the pattern of birth, growth, and death. Scientists study an organism's life cycle to predict the life of its offspring.

Adult

Eggs

Late tadpole

Early tadpole

Physical Patterns

Physical patterns have an artistic or decorative design. Physical patterns can occur naturally, such as the patterns in the colors on butterfly wings or flower petals, or they can be created intentionally, such as a design in a brick wall.

Patterns in Life Science

Why do police detectives or forensic scientists take fingerprints at a crime scene? Forensic scientists know that every fingerprint is unique. Fingerprints contain patterns that can help detectives narrow a list of suspects. The patterns on the fingerprints can then be examined more closely to identify an exact individual. This is because no two humans have the same fingerprint, just as no two zebras have the same stripe pattern.

Patterns are an important key to understanding life science. They are found across all classifications of life and are studied by scientists. Patterns help scientists understand the genetic makeup, lifestyle, and similarities of various species of plants and animals. Zoologists might study the migration patterns of animals to determine the effects climate has on different species. Botanists might study patterns in the leaves of flowering plants to classify the species of the plant and predict the characteristics of the offspring.

Mathematical Patterns

Patterns are applied in mathematics all the time. Whenever you read a number, perform a mathematical operation, or describe a shape or graph, you are using patterns.

$$2, 5, 8, 11, \underline{\quad}, \underline{\quad}, \underline{\quad}$$

What numbers come next in this number pattern?

What will the next shape look like according to the pattern?

Inquiry MiniLab — 15 minutes

Leaf Patterns

Each species of flowering plant has leaves with unique patterns.

Leaf Venation

Pinnate
one main vein with smaller branching veins

Palmate
several main veins that branch from one point

Parallel
veins that do not branch

1. Obtain a collection of leaves.
2. Use the leaves above to identify the venation, or vein patterns, of each leaf.

Analyze and Conclude

1. **Describe** the physical pattern you see in each leaf.

2. **Choose** Besides venation, what other patterns can you use to group the leaves?

3. **Identify** What types of patterns can be used to classify other organisms?

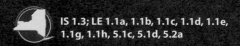

Chapter 10

IS 1.3; LE 1.1a, 1.1b, 1.1c, 1.1d, 1.1e, 1.1g, 1.1h, 5.1c, 5.1d, 5.2a

Life's Classification and Structure

THE BIG IDEA

How is the classification of living things related to the structure of their cells?

Inquiry Why All the Hooks?

This color-enhanced scanning electron micrograph shows the hooked fruit of the goosegrass plant. The hooks attach to the fur of passing animals. This enables the plant's seeds, which are in the fruit, to spread.

- What characteristics would you use to classify this plant?

- How is the classification of living things related to the structure of their cells?

Andrew Syred/Photo Researchers

Get Ready to Read

What do you think?

Before you read, decide if you agree or disagree with each of these statements. As you read this chapter, see if you change your mind about any of the statements.

1 All living things are made of cells.

2 A group of organs that work together and perform a function is called a tissue.

3 Living things are classified based on similar characteristics.

4 *Cell wall* is a term used to describe the cell membrane.

5 Prokaryotic cells contain a nucleus.

6 Plants use chloroplasts to process energy.

Connect ED Your one-stop online resource

MHEonline.com

Video	WebQuest
Audio	Assessment
Review	Concepts in Motion
Inquiry	Multilingual eGlossary

Lesson 1

Reading Guide

Key Concepts

ESSENTIAL QUESTIONS

- What are living things?
- What do living things need?
- How are living things classified?

Vocabulary

autotroph

heterotroph

habitat

binomial nomenclature

taxon

 Multilingual eGlossary

IS 1.3; LE 1.1a, 1.1b, 1.1d, 1.1e, 1.1g, 1.1h, 5.1c, 5.1d, 5.2a

Classifying Living Things

Inquiry Living or Not?

This tide pool contains sea anemones, barnacles, and sea stars that are living and rocks that are not living. How can you tell whether something is alive? Do all living things move? All living things have certain characteristics that you will read about in this lesson.

How can you tell whether it is alive?

Living things share several basic characteristics. Think about what you have in common with other living things such as a bug or a tree. Do other things have some of those same characteristics?

1. Read and complete a lab safety form.

2. Observe a **lit candle** for 1–2 min. Pay attention to both the candle and the flame.

3. Write what you observe in your Science Journal.

4. Write what you think you would observe if you were to observe the candle for several hours.

Think About This

1. What characteristics does the flame have that would lead some people to think the flame is alive?

2. What qualities did you think of earlier (that you share with other living things) that the candle does not possess?

3. 🔑 **Key Concept** What characteristics do you think something must have to be considered alive?

What are living things?

It might be easy to tell whether a bird, a tree, or a person is alive. But for some organisms, it is harder to tell whether they are living things. Look at the moldy bread shown in **Figure 1**. Is the bread a living thing? What about the green mold and white mold on the bread? All living things have six characteristics in common:

- Living things are made of cells.

- Living things are organized.

- Living things grow and develop.

- Living things respond to their environment.

- Living things reproduce.

- Living things use energy.

The bread shown in **Figure 1** is not living, but the molds growing on the bread are living things. Mold is a type of fungus. If you looked at the mold using a microscope, you would see that it is made of cells. Mold cells respond to their environment by growing and reproducing. The molds obtain energy, which they need to grow, from the bread.

🔑 **Key Concept Check** What are living things?

Figure 1 🔑 Mold is a living thing.

Living things are organized.

Marching bands are made up of rows of people playing different instruments. Some rows are made up of people playing flutes, and other rows are filled with drummers. Although marching bands are organized into different rows, all band members work together to play a song. Like marching bands, living things also are organized. Some living things are more complex than others, but all organisms are made of cells. In all cells, **macromolecules** are organized into different structures that help cells function. You might recall that there are four macromolecules in cells—nucleic acids, lipids, proteins, and carbohydrates. Nucleic acids, such as DNA, store information. Lipids are the main component of cell membranes and provide structure. Some proteins are enzymes, and others provide structure. Carbohydrates are used for energy.

 Reading Check Name the four macromolecules in cells.

Unicellular Organisms Some living things are unicellular, which means they are made up of only one cell. In fact, most living things on Earth are unicellular organisms. Unicellular organisms are the oldest forms of life. There are many groups of unicellular organisms, each with **unique** characteristics. Bacteria, amoebas (uh MEE buhz), and paramecia (per uh MEE see ah) are examples of unicellular organisms. Unicellular organisms have everything needed to obtain and use energy, reproduce, and grow inside one cell. Some unicellular organisms are tiny and cannot be seen without a microscope. Other unicellular organisms, such as the plasmodial (plaz MOH dee ul) slime mold shown in **Figure 2,** can be large.

Figure 2 A plasmodial slime mold is a huge cell formed by many cells that join together and form one cell.

Multicellular Organisms Soccer teams are made up of many types of players, including goalkeepers, forwards, and fullbacks. Each team member has a specific job, but they all work together when playing a game. Many living things are made of more than one cell and are called multicellular organisms. Like the different types of players on a soccer team, multicellular organisms have different types of cells that carry out specialized functions. The ladybug shown in **Figure 3** has cells that form wings and other cells that form eyes.

Multicellular organisms have different levels of organization. Groups of cells that work together and perform a specific function are called tissues. Tissues that work together and carry out a specific function are called organs. Organs that work together and perform a specific function are called organ systems. Organ systems work together and perform all the functions an organism needs to survive.

Living things grow, develop, and reproduce.

During their lifetimes, living things grow, or increase in size. For a unicellular organism, the size of its cell increases. For a multicellular organism, the number of its cells increases. Living things also develop, or change, during their lifetimes. For some organisms, it is easy to see the changes that happen as they grow and develop. As shown in **Figure 4,** ladybug larva grow into pupae (PYEW pee; singular, pupa), an intermediate stage, before developing into adults.

Once an organism is an adult, it can reproduce either asexually or sexually and form new organisms. Unicellular organisms, such as bacteria, reproduce asexually when one cell divides and forms two new organisms. Some multicellular organisms also can reproduce asexually; one parent organism produces offspring when body cells replicate and divide. Sexual reproduction occurs when the reproductive cells of one or two parent organisms join and form a new organism. Multicellular organisms such as humans and other mammals reproduce sexually. Some organisms such as yeast can reproduce both asexually and sexually.

▲ **Figure 3** 🔑
Multicellular organisms, such as this ladybug, contain groups of cells that carry out special functions.

☑ **Visual Check** What structures can you identify in the ladybug?

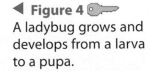

Larva   Pupa

◀ **Figure 4** 🔑
A ladybug grows and develops from a larva to a pupa.

☑ **Visual Check** What differences do you see between the two stages?

Andre Skonieczny/F1online/Getty Images

▲ **Figure 5** 🔑 Algae are autotrophic because they use sunlight to produce energy.

Living things use energy.

All living things need energy to survive. Some organisms are able to convert light energy to chemical energy that is used for many cellular processes. *Organisms that convert energy from light or inorganic substances to usable energy are called* **autotrophs** (AW tuh trohfs).

Many autotrophs use energy from light and convert carbon dioxide and water into carbohydrates, or sugars. Autotrophs use the carbohydrates for energy. Plants and the algae shown growing on the pond in **Figure 5** are autotrophs.

Other autotrophs, called chemoautotrophs (kee moh AW tuh trohfs), grow on energy released by chemical reactions of inorganic substances such as sulfur and ammonia. Many chemoautotrophs are bacteria that live in extreme environments such as deep in the ocean or in hot sulfur springs.

✓ **Reading Check** How do some autotrophs use energy from sunlight?

Heterotrophs (HE tuh roh trohfs) *are organisms that obtain energy from other organisms.* Heterotrophs eat autotrophs or other heterotrophs to obtain energy. Animals and fungi are examples of heterotrophs.

Living things respond to stimuli.

All living things sense their environments. If an organism detects a change in its external environment, it will respond to that change. A change in an organism's environment is called a stimulus (STIHM yuh lus; plural, stimuli). Responding to a stimulus might help an organism protect itself. For example, the octopus in **Figure 6** responds to predators by releasing ink, a black liquid. In many organisms, nerve cells detect the environment, process the information, and coordinate a response.

Figure 6 🔑 An octopus responds to potential harm by secreting ink. The ink hides the octopus while it escapes. ▼

What do living things need?

You just read that all living things need energy in order to survive. Some organisms obtain energy from food. What else do living things need to survive? Living things also need water and a place to live. Organisms live in environments specific to their needs where they are protected, can obtain food and water, and can get shelter.

A Place to Live

Living things are everywhere. Organisms live in the soil, in lakes, and in caves. Some living things live on or in other organisms. For example, bacteria live in your intestines and on other body surfaces. *A specific environment where an organism lives is its* **habitat.** Most organisms can survive in only a few habitats. The land iguana shown in **Figure 7** lives in warm, tropical environments and would not survive in cold places such as the Arctic.

Food and Water

Living things also need food and water. Food is used for energy. Water is essential for survival. You will read about how water is in all cells and helps them function in Lesson 2. The type of food that an organism eats depends on the habitat in which it lives. Marine iguanas live near the ocean and eat algae. Land iguanas, such as the one in **Figure 7,** live in hot, dry areas and eat cactus fruits and leaves. The food is processed to obtain energy. Plants and some bacteria use energy from sunlight and produce chemical energy for use in cells.

 Key Concept Check What do living things need?

WORD ORIGIN

habitat
from Latin *habitare*, means "to live or dwell"

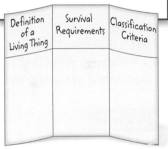

FOLDABLES®

Make a vertical three-column chart book. Label it as shown. Use it to organize your notes about living things, their needs, and classification criteria.

Definition of a Living Thing	Survival Requirements	Classification Criteria

Figure 7 This Galápagos land iguana is eating the fruit of a prickly pear cactus.

Needs of Living Things 🗝

Carolyn Jenkins/Alamy

Use Ratios

A ratio expresses the relationship between two or more things. Ratios can be written

3 to 5, 3:5, or $\frac{3}{5}$.

Reduce ratios to their simplest form. For example, of about 3 million species in the animal kingdom, about 50,000 are mammals. What is the ratio of mammals to animals?

Write the ratio as a fraction.

$$\frac{50,000}{3,000,000}$$

Reduce the fraction to the simplest form.

$$\frac{50,000}{3,000,000} = \frac{5}{300} = \frac{1}{60}$$

(or 1:60 or 1 to 60)

Practice

Of the 5,000 species of mammals, 250 species are carnivores. What is the ratio of carnivores to mammals? Write the ratio in all three ways.

 Review

- **Math Practice**
- **Personal Tutor**

How are living things classified?

You might have a notebook with different sections. Each section might contain notes from a different class. This organizes information and makes it easy to find notes on different subjects. Scientists use a classification system to group organisms with similar traits. Classifying living things makes it easier to organize organisms and to recall how they are similar and how they differ.

Naming Living Things

Scientists name living things using a system called binomial nomenclature (bi NOH mee ul • NOH mun klay chur). **Binomial nomenclature** *is a naming system that gives each living thing a two-word scientific name.*

More than 300 years ago a scientist named Carolus Linnaeus created the binomial nomenclature system. All scientific names are in Latin. *Homo sapiens* is the scientific name for humans. As shown in **Table 1,** the scientific name for an Eastern chipmunk is *Tamias striatus.*

Table 1 Classification of the Eastern Chipmunk   **Review** Personal Tutor

Taxonomic Group	Number of Species	Examples
Domain Eukarya	about 4–10 million	
Kingdom Animalia	about 2 million	
Phylum Chordata	about 50,000	
Class Mammalia	about 5,000	
Order Rodentia	about 2,300	
Family Sciuridae	299	
Genus *Tamias*	25	
Species *Tamias striatus*	1	

Frank Cezus/ Getty Images

Classification Systems

Linnaeus also classified organisms based on their behavior and appearance. Today, the branch of science that classifies living things is called taxonomy. *A group of organisms is called a* **taxon** *(plural, taxa).* There are many taxa, as shown in **Table 1.** Recall that all living things share similar traits. However, not all living things are exactly the same.

Taxonomy

Using taxonomy, scientists divide all living things on Earth into three groups called domains. Domains are divided into kingdoms, and then phyla (FI luh; singular, phylum), classes, orders, families, genera (singular, genus), and species. A species is made of all organisms that can mate with one another and produce offspring that can reproduce. The first word in an organism's scientific name is the organism's genus (JEE nus), and the second word might describe a distinguishing characteristic of the organism. For example, dogs belong to the genus *Canis.* The *Canis* genus also includes wolves, coyotes, and jackals.

Recall that Linnaeus used similar physical traits to group organisms. Today, scientists also look for other similarities, such as how an organism reproduces, how it processes energy, and the types of genes it has.

Dichotomous Keys

A dichotomous (di KAH tah mus) **key** is a tool used to identify an organism based on its characteristics. Dichotomous keys contain descriptions of traits that are compared when classifying an organism. Dichotomous keys are organized in steps. Each step might ask a yes or a no question and have two answer choices. Which question is answered next depends on the answer to the previous question. Based on the features, a choice is made that best describes the organism.

Key Concept Check How are living things classified?

Inquiry MiniLab   20 minutes

Whose shoe is it?

A dichotomous key is a tool to help identify an unknown object or organism.

1. Read and complete a lab safety form.

2. Have each person in your group place one of his or her **shoes** in a pile.

3. Observe the shoes, looking for similarities and differences among them.

4. In your Science Journal, write a question that can be used to separate the shoes into two groups.

5. Divide the shoes into the two groups.

6. Continue asking questions for each subgroup until all of the shoes are identified.

7. Number the questions from the top of the key down, and create your key this way:

   1. Question 1?
   Yes . . . . go to question _____
   No . . . . go to question _____

Analyze and Conclude

1. **Classify** What characteristics probably should not be used when creating a dichotomous key?

2. **Key Concept** Describe how a doctor and a pest exterminator could use a dichotomous key.

SCIENCE USE v. COMMON USE

key

Science Use an aid to identification

Common Use a device to open a lock

Visual Summary

All living things grow, develop, and reproduce.

All living things are organized, respond to their environment, and use energy.

Scientists use a classification system to group organisms with similar traits and genetic makeup.

FOLDABLES®

Use your lesson Foldable to review the lesson. Save your Foldable for the project at the end of the chapter.

What do you think NOW?

You first read the statements below at the beginning of the chapter.

1. All living things are made of cells.

2. A group of organs that work together and perform a function is called a tissue.

3. Living things are classified based on similar characteristics.

Did you change your mind about whether you agree or disagree with the statements? Rewrite any false statements to make them true.

Use Vocabulary

1 **Use the term** *taxon* in a sentence.

2 **Distinguish** between the terms *autotroph* and *heterotroph*.

3 Linnaeus created a two-word naming system for organisms called _____.

Understand Key Concepts

4 An environment where specific organisms live is called a(n)
   A. autotroph.   **C.** heterotrophy.
   B. habitat.   **D.** taxon.

5 **Explain** how binomial nomenclature helps scientists classify organisms.

6 **Relate** the number of cells an organism has to the way it reproduces.

Interpret Graphics

7 **Summarize** Copy and fill in the graphic organizer below to summarize the characteristics of living things.

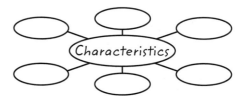

Critical Thinking

8 **Differentiate** between living and nonliving things in the picture at right.

Math Skills

— Math Practice —

9 There are 3 million species in the animal kingdom. Of those, about 270 species are carnivores. What is the ratio of carnivores to animals? Write the ratio all three ways.

On a Quest for Leeches

How do you catch a leech? Let it bite you!

Mark Siddall travels the world searching for creatures that make most people cringe—leeches. He collects leeches to understand how they are related and how they evolved. This is a huge job since there are more than 600 known species of leeches!

Siddall is a scientist at the American Museum of Natural History. He travels to remote places, such as the jungles of Rwanda and the swamps of Argentina, to collect leeches. Once he's there, he lets the leeches find him. Barefoot, he treks through damp forests or wades in streams. Leeches attach to his skin, draw blood until they're full, and then fall off. That's when Mark adds them to the museum's collection.

Siddall identifies the leeches by their body parts. Some have jaws and teeth. Others have thin tubes for sucking in liquid. They use these parts to draw blood or fluids from animals, such as frogs, humans, snails, and other worms. Some even swallow their prey whole!

Through his research, Siddall is helping build a family tree for leeches to learn how they evolved. For example, leeches today live on land, in freshwater, and in the ocean. Siddall's research shows that leeches first appeared in freshwater and then moved onto land and into the ocean. Many species of leeches are being threatened by habitat destruction. Siddall hopes his research will help protect leeches and their habitats.

▲ **Mark Siddall uses himself as bait to catch leeches. When a leech is done feeding, it falls off into a collection bag.**

In just 30 minutes, a leech can swallow more than five times its weight in blood. It might not need to feed again for a few months.

It's Your Turn

DIAGRAM Leeches are classified according to how they feed. Choose a jawed leech (*Hirudinidae*), a jawless leech (*Erpobdellidae*), or a leech that uses a proboscis (*Glossiphoniidae*). Research how it feeds. Draw a diagram and present your findings.

Lesson 2

Cells

Reading Guide

Key Concepts

ESSENTIAL QUESTIONS

- What is a cell made of?
- How do the parts of a cell enable it to survive?

Vocabulary

prokaryotic cell

eukaryotic cell

cytoplasm

mitochondrion

 Multilingual eGlossary

Video BrainPOP®

 IS 1.3; LE 1.1a, 1.1b, 1.1c, 1.1d, 5.1c

Inquiry Weird Web?

This isn't a spider's strange web. These are nerve cells shown in a color-enhanced electron micrograph. The larger green parts are the cell bodies. The threadlike parts carry electrical signals from one nerve cell to another. How do these parts help the cells?

SPL/Science Source

Are all cells alive?

There are many bacteria that live on and in people. These unicellular organisms have all the characteristics of life and are alive. Are human cells, which the bacteria live on and in, also alive?

1. In your Science Journal, draw a circle that takes up half of the page. The circle represents a human cell.

2. Draw and label the following things in your cell:

    A power plant to represent the need for and use of energy; label it *energy production*.

    A garbage truck to represent waste removal; label it *waste removal*.

    A city hall with a mayor to represent the organization and processes of the cell; label it *organization*.

    A road system to represent the transportation that occurs in the cell; label it *transportation*.

A cement truck to represent the construction of new structures in the cell; label it *growth*.

A fire truck to represent a cell's ability to respond to changes in its surroundings; label it *response to environment*.

A copy machine in city hall to represent the cell's ability to follow instructions and make more cells; label it *reproduction*.

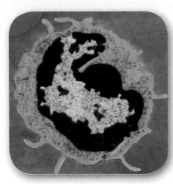

Think About This

1. Does the human cell you drew have all the characteristics of life? Explain your answer.

2. 🔑 **Key Concept** Do you think each of the trillions of cells that are part of you are either alive or once-living? Why?

What are cells?

What is one thing all living things have in common? All living things have cells, the basic unit of an organism. As you read in Lesson 1, most organisms have only one cell. Other organisms have many cells. Humans have about 100 trillion cells! Most cells are so small that they cannot be seen without a microscope. Microscopes, such as the one shown in **Figure 8,** are used to view details of small objects or to view things that are too small to be seen by the unaided eye.

Scientists first used microscopes to look at cells over 300 years ago. Cells come in different shapes and sizes. Nerve cells are long and slender. Many female reproductive cells, or eggs, are large and round.

✓ **Reading Check** Why is a microscope needed to view most cells?

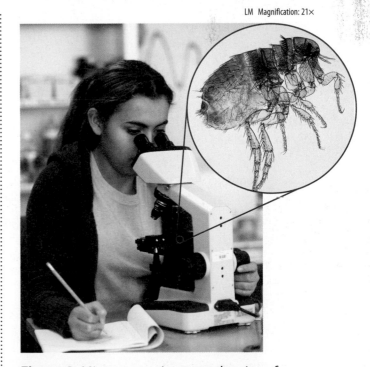

LM Magnification: 21×

Figure 8 Microscopes increase the size of an image so that a small thing, such as the flea shown here, can be observed.

What are cells made of?

Recall that all cells are made of four macromolecules—nucleic acids, lipids, proteins, and carbohydrates. Cells also have many other characteristics. For example, all cells are surrounded by an outer structure called a cell membrane. The cell membrane keeps substances such as macromolecules inside the cell. It also helps protect cells by keeping harmful substances from entering. About 70 percent of the inside of a cell is water. Because many of the substances inside a cell are dissolved in water, they move easily within the cell.

Key Concept Check What is a cell made of?

Types of Cells

There are two main types of cells, as shown in **Figure 9.** **Prokaryotic** (pro kayr ee AH tihk) **cells** *do not have a nucleus or other membrane-bound organelles.* Organelles are structures in cells that carry out specific functions. The few organelles in prokaryotic cells are not surrounded by membranes. Organisms with prokaryotic cells are called prokaryotes. Most prokaryotes are unicellular organisms, such as bacteria.

Eukaryotic (yew ker ee AH tihk) **cells** *have a nucleus and other membrane-bound organelles.* Most multicellular organisms and some unicellular organisms are eukaryotes. The eukaryotic cell shown in **Figure 9** contains many structures that are not in a prokaryotic cell. In eukaryotes, membranes surround most of the organelles, including the nucleus.

Concepts in Motion

Animation

Figure 9 Prokaryotic cells do not have a nucleus. Eukaryotic cells have a nucleus and many other organelles.

Visual Check What structures are in both prokaryotic cells and eukaryotic cells?

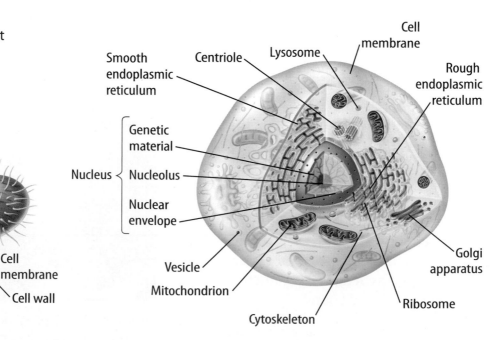

Prokaryotic Cell

Ribosome
DNA
Cytoplasm
Cell membrane
Cell wall
Flagellum
Capsule

Eukaryotic Cell

Smooth endoplasmic reticulum
Centriole
Lysosome
Cell membrane
Rough endoplasmic reticulum
Genetic material
Nucleus
Nucleolus
Nuclear envelope
Vesicle
Mitochondrion
Cytoskeleton
Ribosome
Golgi apparatus

The Outside of a Cell

As you have just read, the cell membrane surrounds a cell. Much like a fence surrounds a school, the cell membrane helps keep the substances inside a cell separate from the substances outside a cell. Some cells also are surrounded by a more rigid layer called a cell wall.

Cell Membrane

The cell membrane is made of lipids and proteins. Recall that lipids and proteins are macromolecules that help cells function. Lipids in the cell membrane protect the inside of a cell from the external environment. Proteins in the cell membrane transport substances between a cell's environment and the inside of the cell. Proteins in the cell membrane also communicate with other cells and organisms and sense changes in the cell's environment.

 Reading Check Summarize the major components of cell membranes.

Cell Wall

In addition to a cell membrane, some cells also have a cell wall, as shown in **Figure 10.** The cell wall is a strong, rigid layer outside the cell membrane. Cells in plants, fungi, and many types of bacteria have cell walls. Cell walls provide structure and help protect the cell from the outside environment. Most cell walls are made from different types of carbohydrates.

Animation

Figure 10 This plant cell has a cell membrane and a cell wall.

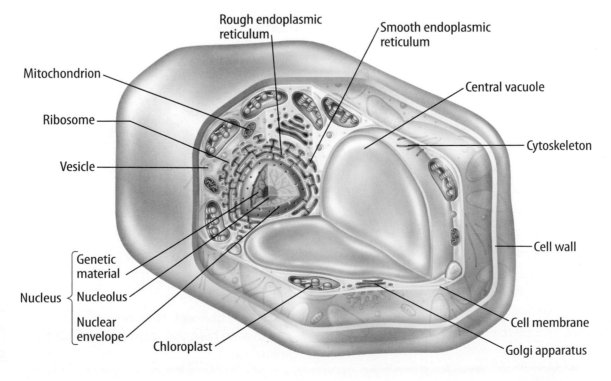

Rough endoplasmic reticulum
Smooth endoplasmic reticulum
Mitochondrion
Ribosome
Vesicle
Central vacuole
Cytoskeleton
Genetic material
Nucleus
Nucleolus
Nuclear envelope
Chloroplast
Cell wall
Cell membrane
Golgi apparatus

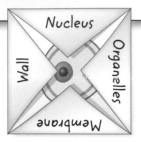
The Inside of a Cell

Recall that the inside of a cell is mainly water. Many substances used for communication, energy, and growth dissolve in water. This makes it easier for the substances to move around inside a cell. Water also gives cells their shapes and helps keep the structures inside a cell organized. The organelles inside a cell perform specific functions. They control cell activities, provide energy, transport materials, and store materials.

Cytoplasm

The liquid part of a cell inside the cell membrane is called the **cytoplasm.** It contains water, macromolecules, and other substances. The organelles in eukaryotic cells are located in the cytoplasm. Proteins in the cytoplasm provide structure and help organelles and other substances move around.

Controlling Cell Activities

The information that controls all of a cell's activities is stored in its genetic material, called DNA. DNA is a type of macromolecule called a nucleic acid. The information in DNA is transferred to another nucleic acid called RNA. RNA gives cells instructions about which proteins need to be made. In prokaryotic cells, DNA is in the cytoplasm. In eukaryotic cells, DNA is stored in an organelle called the nucleus. A membrane, called the nuclear membrane, surrounds the nucleus. Tiny holes in the nuclear membrane let certain substances move between the nucleus and the cytoplasm.

Inquiry MiniLab

20–30 minutes

What can you see in a cell?

When people developed microscopes, they were able to see things that they could not see with their eyes alone.

1. Read and complete a lab safety form.
2. Carefully remove a thin layer of membrane from a piece of **onion.**
3. Place the membrane on the center of a dry **microscope slide.**
4. Add a drop of **iodine** on top of the sample.
5. Place a **cover slip** on top of the sample.
6. Use a **microscope** to focus on the slide using low power. Sketch what you see in your Science Journal.
7. View and sketch the sample on medium and high powers.

Analyze and Conclude

1. **Observe** What structures did you see at low, medium, and high powers?

2. **Infer** How might your view of the cells change if you view them at an even higher power?

3. 🔑 **Key Concept** How does a microscope help you learn more about the onion plant?

Hutchings Photography/Digital Light Source

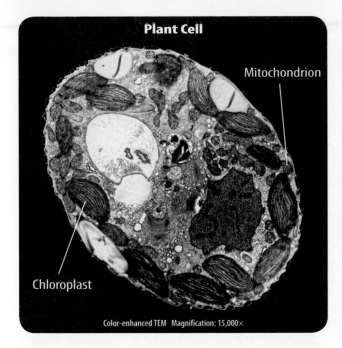

Plant Cell

Mitochondrion

Chloroplast

Color-enhanced TEM   Magnification: 15,000×

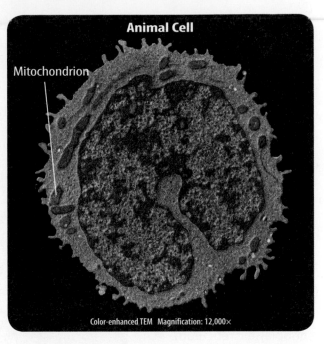

Animal Cell

Mitochondrion

Color-enhanced TEM   Magnification: 12,000×

Figure 11 Plant cells have mitochondria and chloroplasts. Animal cells only contain mitochondria.

 Visual Check Where are the mitochondria located in a cell?

Energy for the Cell

You read in Lesson 1 that all living things use energy. Proteins in the cytoplasm process energy in prokaryotes. Eukaryotes have special organelles, the chloroplasts and mitochondria (mi tuh KAHN dree uh; singular, mitochondrion) shown in **Figure 11,** that process energy.

Mitochondria Most eukaryotes contain hundreds of mitochondria. **Mitochondria** *are organelles that break down food and release energy.* This energy is stored in molecules called ATP—adenosine triphosphate (uh DEN uh seen • tri FAHS fayt). ATP provides a cell with energy to perform many functions, such as making proteins, storing information, and communicating with other cells.

WORD ORIGIN

mitochondrion
from Greek *mitos*, means "thread"; and *khondrion*, means "little granule"

Reading Check What energy molecule is made in a mitochondrion?

Chloroplasts Energy also can be processed in organelles called chloroplasts, shown in **Figure 11.** Plants and many other autotrophs have chloroplasts and mitochondria. Chloroplasts capture light energy and convert it into chemical energy in a process called photosynthesis. Chloroplasts contain many structures that capture light energy. Like the reactions that occur in mitochondria, ATP molecules are produced during photosynthesis. However, photosynthesis also produces carbohydrates such as glucose that also are used to store energy.

Protein Production

You just read that cells use protein for many functions. These proteins are made on the surface of ribosomes that are in the cytoplasm of both prokaryotic and eukaryotic cells. In eukaryotic cells, some ribosomes are attached to an organelle called the endoplasmic reticulum (en duh PLAZ mihk • rih TIHK yuh lum), as shown in **Figure 12.** It is made of folded membranes. The proteins can be processed and can move inside the cell through the endoplasmic reticulum.

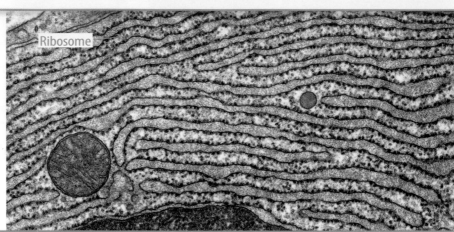

Color-enhanced TEM Magnification: Unavailable

Ribosome

Figure 12 Ribosomes are attached to the rough endoplasmic reticulum. ▶

Cell Storage

What happens to the molecules that are made in a cell? An organelle called the Golgi (GAWL jee) apparatus packages proteins into tiny organelles called vesicles. Vesicles transport proteins around a cell. Other molecules are stored in organelles called vacuoles. A vacuole is usually the largest organelle in a plant cell, as shown in **Figure 13.** In plant cells, vacuoles store water and provide support. In contrast to all plant cells, only some animal and bacterial cells contain vacuoles. The vacuoles in animal and bacterial cells are smaller than the ones in plant cells.

 Key Concept Check How do the parts of a cell enable it to survive?

Figure 13 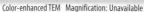 Vacuoles are used by plant cells for storage and to provide structure. ▶

Color-enhanced TEM Magnification: 2,000×

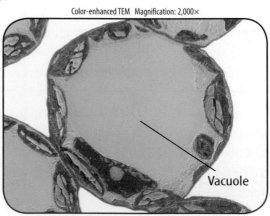

Vacuole

(t)MedImage/Science Source; (b)Dr. Jeremy Burgess/Science Source

Lesson 2 Review

✓ **Assessment**   Online Quiz

? **Inquiry**   Virtual Lab

Visual Summary

Prokaryotic cells are surrounded by a cell membrane but have no internal organelles with membranes.

Eukaryotic cells contain a nucleus and many other organelles.

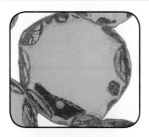

Plant cells have cell walls, chloroplasts, and a large vacuole.

FOLDABLES®

Use your lesson Foldable to review the lesson. Save your Foldable for the project at the end of the chapter.

What do you think NOW?

You first read the statements below at the beginning of the chapter.

4. *Cell wall* is a term used to describe the cell membrane.

5. Prokaryotic cells contain a nucleus.

6. Plants use chloroplasts to process energy.

Did you change your mind about whether you agree or disagree with the statements? Rewrite any false statements to make them true.

Use Vocabulary

1 **Distinguish** between prokaryotic cells and eukaryotic cells.

2 Water, proteins, and other substances are found in the _____ of a cell.

3 **Define** *mitochondrion* in your own words.

Understand Key Concepts

4 Which organelles store water, carbohydrates, and wastes in plants?
- **A.** chloroplasts
- **C.** nuclei
- **B.** mitochondria
- **D.** vacuoles

5 **Compare** how energy is processed in animal and plant cells.

6 **Distinguish** between a cell membrane and a cell wall.

Interpret Graphics

7 **Summarize** Use the table below to identify organelles and their functions.

Organelle	Function
Nucleus	
	energy processing
Vacuole	

8 **Compare and contrast** the structures of the two cells shown below.

Critical Thinking

9 **Assess** the role of water in cell function.

10 **Relate** the cell wall to protection in bacteria.

Materials

compound microscope

dissecting microscope

magnifying lens

ruler

Also needed:
specimens

Safety

How can living things be classified?

Thousands of new organisms are discovered each year. Today, an organism's DNA can be used to determine how closely a newly discovered organism is related to living things that are already known. A long time ago, taxonomists had to rely on what they could observe with their senses to determine the relationships between organisms. They looked at characteristics such as an organism's parts, behaviors, or the environments in which they lived to help them determine relationships among organisms. The father of taxonomy, Carolus Linnaeus, developed a system in the 1700s by which he classified over 9,000 organisms, primarily based on their external features.

Question

What characteristics can be used to distinguish among different types of organisms?

Procedure

1. Read and complete a lab safety form.

2. Use your background knowledge of the specimens provided and the available tools to identify distinguishing characteristics of the specimens. Be sure to observe each of the specimens thoroughly and completely.

3. In your Science Journal, record as much information as possible about each of the organisms. This information can include your observations and any knowledge you have of the organism.

(t to b, 2-4)Hutchings Photography/Digital Light Source; (tr)Image Source/Getty Images; (cr)©IT Stock/age fotostock; (b)Getty Images

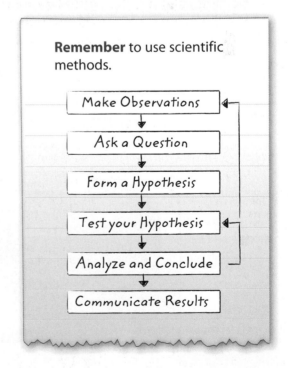

4 Using the information you have recorded, create a dichotomous key that can be used to identify all of the specimens.

5 Trade your key with another student.

6 Verify that the key you received works by trying to identify all ten of the organisms, one at a time.

7 If your key did not work, repeat steps 2–5. If your key did work, move on to the **Analyze and Conclude** section.

Analyze and Conclude

8 **Compare and Contrast** How are the questions in the key you made similar to and different from the questions in the key that you checked?

9 **Classify** How would an elephant, bread mold, and a rose be identified if the key you created were used to identify them? Are these identifications accurate? Why did this happen?

10 **The Big Idea** How would the questions in your key be different if all ten organisms were more closely related, such as ten different plants?

Communicate Your Results

Share your key and questions with a small group of students. After everyone shares, make a group key that combines the most objective questions that were asked among the various keys.

Inquiry Extension

Research the scientific names of the specimens that you observed, and find the meanings of the species name of each organism. Research the characteristics by which bacteria are classified. Design a key to be used by younger students to help identify different polygons (triangles, pentagons, octagons, and so on) using correct mathematical terms.

Lab Tips

☑ Recall from earlier in the chapter the types of characteristics that are good to use in creating a dichotomous key.

Remember to use scientific methods.

Make Observations
↓
Ask a Question
↓
Form a Hypothesis
↓
Test your Hypothesis
↓
Analyze and Conclude
↓
Communicate Results

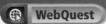
 Organisms are classified based on similar characteristics, including cell structure and function.

Key Concepts Summary 🔑 | Vocabulary

Lesson 1: Classifying Living Things

- Living things are organized, process energy, grow, reproduce, respond to stimuli, and contain cells.
- Living things need food, water, and a **habitat.**
- Organisms are classified based on similar characteristics.

Vocabulary

autotroph

heterotroph

habitat

binomial nomenclature

taxon

Lesson 2: Cells

- Cells are made of water and macromolecules.
- Different parts of a cell enable it to perform special functions.

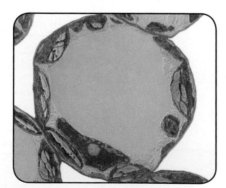

prokaryotic cell

eukaryotic cell

cytoplasm

mitochondrion

FOLDABLES® Chapter Project

Assemble your lesson Foldables as shown to make a Chapter Project. Use the project to review what you have learned in this chapter.

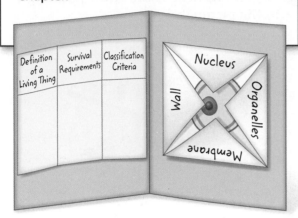

Use Vocabulary

1 The Latin term *Homo sapiens* is an example of _____.

2 Organisms that obtain energy by eating other organisms are called _____.

3 Use the term *habitat* in a sentence.

4 Define the term *cytoplasm* in your own words.

5 Animal cells obtain energy by breaking down food in _____.

6 Use the term *prokaryotic cell* in a sentence.

Link Vocabulary and Key Concepts

Concepts in Motion Interactive Concept Map

Copy this concept map, and then use vocabulary terms from the previous page to complete the concept map.

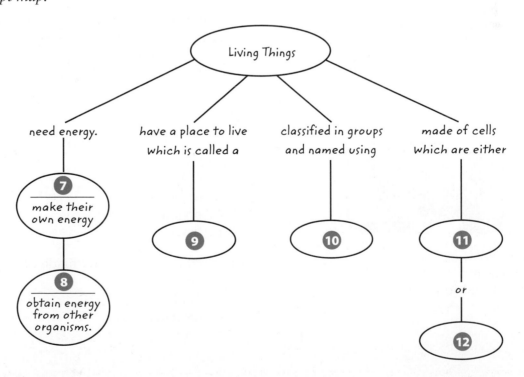

Understand Key Concepts 🔑

1 What is a rigid structure that provides support and protection to plants and some types of bacteria?

A. chloroplast
B. nucleus
C. cell membrane
D. cell wall

2 What type of reproduction occurs when a cell divides to form two new cells?

A. autotrophic
B. heterotrophic
C. asexual reproduction
D. sexual reproduction

3 Which is the binomial nomenclature for humans?

A. *Canis lupos*
B. *Felis catus*
C. *Homo sapiens*
D. *Tamias striatus*

4 What is a group of organisms called?

A. taxon
B. tissue
C. dichotomous key
D. organ system

5 Which organelle is the arrow pointing to in the picture below?

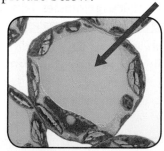

A. chloroplast
B. cytoplasm
C. mitochondrion
D. vacuole

6 Which is NOT a characteristic of all living things?

A. grow
B. reproduce
C. have organelles
D. use energy

7 Which organelle is the arrow pointing to in the picture below?

A. chloroplast
B. cytoplasm
C. mitochondrion
D. nucleus

8 What is the name used to describe the specific place where an organism lives?

A. autotroph
B. habitat
C. heterotroph
D. taxon

9 What is the smallest unit of all living things?

A. cell
B. organ
C. organelle
D. tissue

10 What are cells mostly made of?

A. DNA
B. lipids
C. proteins
D. water

Dr. Jeremy Burgess/Science Source

Critical Thinking

⓫ **Summarize** the characteristics of all living things.

⓬ **Describe** how the organization of a multicellular organism helps it function. Diagram the relationships.

⓭ **Assess** how taxonomy relates to the diversity of species.

⓮ **Explain** why different organisms live in different habitats.

⓯ **Assess** the role of organelles in the functions of eukaryotic cells.

⓰ **Relate** the structure in the plant cell shown at the pointer in the picture below to how it obtains energy.

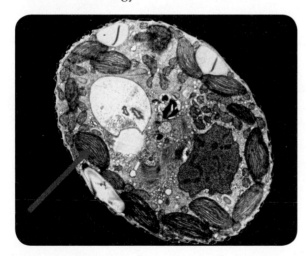

⓱ **Summarize** the role of nucleic acids in controlling cell functions.

⓲ **Discuss** how heterotrophs process energy.

Writing in Science

⓳ **Write** a five-sentence paragraph that describes the characteristics that all living things share.

REVIEW THE BIG IDEA

⓴ **Assess** how the classification of prokaryotes and eukaryotes relates to the structure of their cells.

㉑ How is the classification of living things related to the structure of their cells? Use the plant in the photo below as an example.

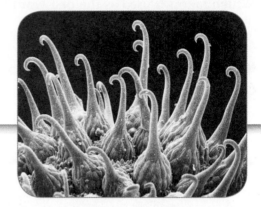

Math Skills ×÷

📖 **Review**

Math Practice

Use Ratios

㉒ There are about 300,000 species of plants. Of those, 12,000 are mosses. What is the ratio of mosses to plants? Express the answer all three ways.

㉓ Out of 300,000 plant species, 260,000 are flowering plants. What is the ratio of flowering plants to all plant species? Express the ratio in all three ways.

㉔ Out of 12,000 species of mosses, only about 400 are club mosses. What is the ratio of club mosses to all mosses? Express the ratio in all three ways.

Record your answers on the answer sheet provided by your teacher or on a sheet of paper.

Multiple Choice

1 Which would a chemoautotroph use to produce energy?

A sulfur

B sunlight

C carbon dioxide

D other organisms

2 Which taxon is used as the first word in an organism's scientific name?

A class

B genus

C kingdom

D order

Use the diagram below to answer question 3.

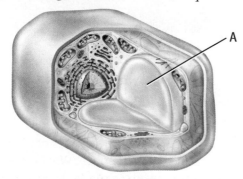

3 The diagram shows the parts of a plant cell. What is the name and function of structure A?

A chloroplast, making carbohydrates

B chloroplast, producing energy

C vacuole, storing water

D vacuole, transporting proteins

4 Which molecule stores energy for cells?

A ATP

B DNA

C proteins

D ribosomes

5 What do scientists call the largest taxonomic level of organization for organisms?

A domains

B genera

C kingdoms

D phyla

Use the image below to answer question 6.

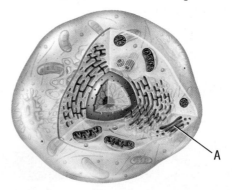

6 In the diagram, the organelle labeled *A* packages proteins into vesicles. What is this organelle called?

A central vacuole

B endoplasmic reticulum

C Golgi apparatus

D nuclear envelope

7 Which cell structures break down food and release energy?

A chloroplasts

B mitochrondria

C ribosomes

D vacuoles

8 Carl Linnaeus grouped organisms into categories based on which characteristic?

   A energy production

   B gene type

   C physical traits

   D reproduction habits

9 Which term defines a group of cells that work together and perform a function?

   A organ

   B taxon

   C tissue

   D phylum

Use the diagram to answer question 10.

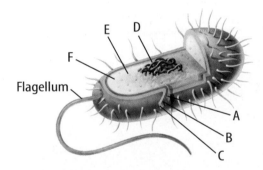

10 In the cell shown, what is the letter for the structure that provides much of the cell's support and helps protect it from the outside environment?

   A A

   B B

   C C

   D D

Constructed Response

Use the figure to answer questions 11 and 12.

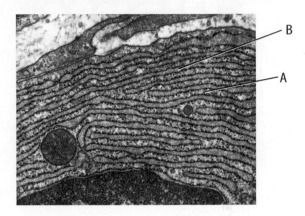

11 Identify the structure labeled *A* in the diagram. What is its function?

12 How are the organelles labeled *A* and *B* related? Are they found in prokaryotic cells, eukaryotic cells, or both?

13 Explain the relationship between cells, tissues, organs, and organ systems in a multicellular organism.

14 Cell membranes are made up mainly of proteins and carbohydrates. How do these molecules function in the cell membrane?

NEED EXTRA HELP?														
If You Missed Question...	1	2	3	4	5	6	7	8	9	10	11	12	13	14
Go to Lesson...	1	1	2	2	1	2	2	1	1	2	2	2	1	2

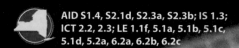

Chapter 11

AID S1.4, S2.1d, S2.3a, S2.3b; IS 1.3;
ICT 2.2, 2.3; LE 1.1f, 5.1a, 5.1b, 5.1c,
5.1d, 5.2a, 6.2a, 6.2b, 6.2c

Introduction to Plants

What structures help ensure the survival of plants, and what is the function of each?

Inquiry **What Type of Tree?**

This is a magnified cross section of a needle from a Scotch pine tree.

- How do the needles help the pine tree stay alive?

- What plant structures can you name that are common to plants? What function does each of these structures carry out to enable a plant's survival?

P. Dayanandan/Science Source

Get Ready to Read

What do you think?

Before you read, decide if you agree or disagree with each of these statements. As you read this chapter, see if you change your mind about any of the statements.

1 Humans could survive without plants.

2 Plant cells contain the same organelles as animal cells.

3 Plants can reproduce both sexually and asexually.

4 All plants have a two-stage life cycle.

5 Plants respond to their environments.

6 Because plants make their own food, they do not carry on cellular respiration.

 Your one-stop online resource

MHEonline.com

 Video   WebQuest

 Audio   Assessment

Review   Concepts in Motion

 Inquiry   Multilingual eGlossary

Plant Diversity

Reading Guide

Key Concepts
ESSENTIAL QUESTIONS

- How do a plant's structures ensure its survival?

- How are the different plant types alike and different?

Vocabulary

rhizoids

stomata

nonvascular plant

vascular plant

gymnosperm

angiosperm

 Multilingual eGlossary

 Video BrainPOP®

AID S2.3a, S2.3b; IS 1.3; LE 1.1f, 5.1a, 5.1b

Inquiry Why Such Diversity?

There are a wide variety of plant species shown in this photo. Some of the plants are growing directly in the pond, while other plants are growing outside the pond. What similarities do all of these plants share? What differences do you observe?

joel-t/Getty images

What does a plant need to grow?

Plants grow in many different environments. What sorts of things do plants need to survive?

1. Read and complete a lab safety form.

2. Brainstorm things a plant needs to survive. List the items on a large sheet of **poster board** and **tape** it to a wall of your classroom.

3. Obtain several **radish seeds.** Select the materials you will need to grow the seeds from the materials provided.

4. Plant the radish seeds in a **petri dish.** Place the petri dish in an appropriate environment.

5. Write a brief plan in your Science Journal describing how to grow and care for your radish plants. Include information about what your seeds need and how you will meet these needs. Follow this plan for the next several days.

Think About This

1. What things do plants require to survive? Which of these requirements are similar to the things humans need to survive?

2. What did you use to grow your radish seeds? Explain your reasoning for each.

3. **Key Concept** What types of structures do you think plants have in order to obtain the things they need to survive?

What is a plant?

Humans depend on plants for food, oxygen, building materials, and many other things. Even the pages of this book are made from plant material! Plants are a vital part of the world.

Plant Cells

Did you know that your cells and all animal cells are similar to plant cells in many ways? They have many of the same organelles such as a nucleus, mitochondria, and ribosomes. However, a plant cell also contains chloroplasts, which are organelles that make food. Unlike an animal cell, a rigid cell wall surrounds a plant cell and helps protect and support it. As shown in **Figure 1,** a plant cell also contains a large central vacuole.

Reading Check What are some structures in plant cells that are not in animal cells?

Concepts in Motion **Animation**

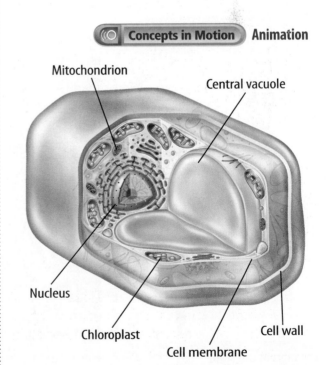

Figure 1 A plant cell has chloroplasts, a cell wall, and a large central vacuole.

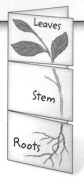

Leaves

Stem

Roots

Figure 2 Roots take many forms, each suited to the plant's needs.

✔ **Visual Check** Why are fibrous roots better at absorbing water but prop roots are better at supporting a plant?

Plant Structures and Functions

Most plants have roots, stems, and leaves. These structures have functions that help plants survive. Root, stems, and leaves have specialized transport tissues. Some plants, such as the mosses you will read about later, don't have specialized transport tissues. However, they do have root-, stem-, and leaflike structures that perform similar functions.

Roots There are many different types of roots, as shown in **Figure 2.** Some plants have a large main root, called a taproot, with smaller roots growing from it. Some plants have additional small roots above ground, called prop roots, that help support the plant. Other plants have fibrous root systems that consist of many small branching roots. Roots anchor a plant in the soil and enable it to grow upright and not be blown away by wind or carried away by water.

Roots also absorb water and minerals from the soil, which plants require for cellular processes. Some roots store food such as sugar and starch. Plants that survive from one growing season to the next use this stored food for growing leaves at the beginning of the next season.

Some plants, such as mosses and hornworts, have rootlike structures called rhizoids. **Rhizoids** *are structures that anchor a plant without transport tissue to a surface.* Scientists do not consider rhizoids roots because they do not have the transport tissues that roots have.

Plant Roots 🔑

The taproot can store food for the plant.

Prop roots can provide additional support for the corn plant.

Fibrous roots spread out and can absorb large amounts of water for the plant.

Stems Have you ever leaned against a tree? If so, you were leaning on a plant stem. Stems help support the leaves, and in some cases flowers, of a plant. There are two main types of stems, as shown in **Figure 3.** A woody stem is like the one you might have leaned against, and an herbaceous (hur BAY shus) stem is flexible and green, such as the stem of a vine.

Stems have tissues that help carry water and the minerals absorbed by the roots to a plant's leaves. These tissues also transport the sugar produced in chloroplasts during photosynthesis (the process by which cells convert light energy into food energy) to the roots. In some plants such as cacti, stems store water that the plants use during dry periods. Other plants such as potatoes have underground stems that store food.

Leaves In most plants, leaves are the major sites for photosynthesis. Some cells in a leaf contain many chloroplasts where light energy is converted into the chemical energy stored in sugar during photosynthesis. There are many different sizes and shapes of leaves, as shown in **Figure 4.**

In addition to making food, leaves also are involved in the exchange of gases with the environment. *The* **stomata** *(singular, stoma) are small openings in the surfaces of most plant leaves.* Water vapor, carbon dioxide, and oxygen can pass into and out of a leaf through stomata.

 Key Concept Check How do plant structures such as roots, stems, and leaves ensure a plant's survival?

▲ **Figure 3** 🔑 The tree has a woody stem, while the vine has an herbaceous stem.

ACADEMIC VOCABULARY

major
(adjective) greater in number, quantity, or extent

Figure 4 🔑 No matter the size or shape, all leaves have vascular tissue. ▼

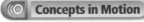 **Concepts in Motion** **Animation**

Beech

Yew

Oak

Conifer

Ginkgo

Palm

Buckeye

Tulip

Cycad

Monkey puzzle

Maple

How can you compare and contrast plant groups?

Plants can be organized into different groups according to their characteristics using a dichotomous key.

1 List characteristics of nonvascular plants, vascular seedless plants, and vascular seed plants in your Science Journal.

2 Using these characteristics, create a dichotomous key to separate the three groups of plants. Write a yes/no question about the plants' characteristics that can separate the plants into two groups. For example, your first question might be about vascular tissue. Use the format below:

1. Does the plant group have vascular tissue?
Yes . . . . go to question _____
No . . . . go to question _____

3 Repeat this process by splitting each group repeatedly until they can no longer be divided. Use more-specific questions with each split of the group.

Analyze and Conclude

1. **Infer** which characteristics are helpful in creating a key.

2. **Explain** how you could use a dichotomous key to determine which plant group an unknown plant belongs to.

3. 🔑 **Key Concept** Compare and contrast the plant groups to determine which group has the fewest specialized structures and which group has the most specialized structures.

Nonvascular Plants

Have you ever noticed the tiny green plants that grow on the bark of a tree? These plants might be one of several types of non-vascular plants. *Plants that lack specialized tissues for transporting water and nutrients are* **nonvascular plants.**

You might recall that animals are grouped into phyla, and plants are grouped into divisions. The divisions of nonvascular plants include mosses, liverworts, and hornworts.

Mosses

One type of plant that lacks specialized transport tissues is mosses. Most mosses are less than 5 cm tall. As shown in **Figure 5,** mosses have tiny green leaflike structures. Scientists do not call these structures leaves because they do not have transport tissues. Recall that rootlike structures called rhizoids help anchor a moss and absorb water.

Liverworts and Hornworts

There are two types of liverworts. The thallose (THA lohs) form is flat and lobed, as shown in **Figure 5.** A leafy liverwort has small, leaflike structures attached to a central stalk.

Hornworts appear similar to liverworts. However, a hornwort's reproductive structure resembles a small horn. That's why it has the name *hornwort.*

Figure 5 🔑 Mosses and liverworts lack vascular tissue.

Mosses grow in a variety of habitats.

Liverworts tend to grow in damp environments.

Ferns grow in a variety of habitats, including forests and gardens.

The name *horsetail* came from the bushy form of this plant.

Some club mosses are called ground pines.

Vascular Seedless Plants

Vascular plants *have specialized tissues, called vascular tissues, that transport water and nutrients throughout the plant.* Vascular plants are divided into two groups—those that produce seeds and those that do not. Ferns, horsetails, and club mosses do not produce seeds.

Ferns

Fossil evidence indicates that millions of years ago ferns grew as large as trees. Present-day ferns are much smaller, many growing to only 50 cm or less. A fern leaf is called a frond. It can have an intricate shape, as shown in **Figure 6.** A fern's fronds grow from an underground stem called a rhizome (RI zohm). Ferns usually grow in shady locations.

Horsetails

Horsetails get their name from a stage of their life cycle that looks like a horse's tail, as shown in **Figure 6.** Horsetails also are called scouring rushes due to an abrasive mineral called silica in the stems. This abrasiveness made the horsetail plant useful to early settlers and to campers for cleaning pots and pans.

 Reading Check How did horsetails get their name?

Club Mosses

This group of plants gets its name from its reproductive structure that resembles a club. They often look like small pine trees, as shown in **Figure 6.** These plants once were abundant in ancient forests. Much of the fossil fuels we use today come from the remains of these forests. Present-day club mosses grow in diverse locations that include tropical and arctic habitats.

Figure 6 Ferns, horsetails, and club mosses have vascular tissue that transports water and nutrients.

New York FYI

Plant Life Processes Plants around the world have a huge variety of shapes and sizes. Each organism's body plan is related to the type of environment it lives in. The way that a huge redwood in California carries out its life processes is different from that of a tiny moss in Alaska.

Vascular Seed Plants

Probably most of the plants you are familiar with are vascular seed plants. They are the most common type of plants. Grasses, flowering shrubs, and trees are all examples of vascular seed plants. From tiny aquatic plants that are less than 1 mm across to towering redwood trees, all vascular plants share one important characteristic—they produce seeds. Scientists further organize vascular seed plants into two groups—those that produce flowers and those that do not.

Nonflowering Seed Plants

For many plants, seeds are inside or on the surface of fruits. However, some plants produce seeds without fruits. **Gymnosperms** *are plants that produce seeds that are not part of a fruit.* As shown in **Figure 7,** gymnosperms are a diverse group. The most common gymnosperms are conifers. Conifers are usually evergreen, meaning they stay green all year. They have needlelike or scalelike leaves and most produce **cones.** The seeds are part of the cones. Conifers can grow in diverse habitats from near-arctic regions to tropical areas. Conifers also have many commercial uses. Lumber, paper products, and turpentine are products made from conifers.

WORD ORIGIN ···········

gymnosperm
From French *gymnosperme,*
means "naked seed"

SCIENCE USE v. COMMON USE ··

cone
Science Use a structure in most conifers or in cycads that contains reproductive structures

Common Use a crisp, usually cone-shaped wafer for holding ice cream

Gymnosperms 🔑

Figure 7 There are many different types of gymnosperms. What is one characteristic they all share?

✔**Visual Check** How do conifer leaves differ from ginkgo leaves?

Cycad

Ginkgo

Conifer

Gnetophyte

(t)Photograph by Jan Smith; (tr)Michael Pettigrew/Getty Images; (bl)©D. Hurst/Alamy; (br)Bear Dancer Studios/Mark Dierker

Flowering Seed Plants

How many flowering plants can you name? There are more than 260,000 species of flowering plants! **Angiosperms** *are plants that produce flowers and develop fruits.* Some of the different varieties of flowering seed plants are shown in **Figure 8.**

Flowering plants have many adaptations that enable them to survive in most habitats on Earth. Their specialized vascular tissues carry water and nutrients throughout the plants. Plants that live in dry areas have special adaptations that help prevent water loss. Perhaps the most amazing characteristic is the incredible diversity of their flowers. There are flowers that attract insects and birds of all kinds. Other flowers are specialized so wind or water can aid in reproduction. As you will read in the next lesson, flowers play a key role in plant reproduction.

 Key Concept Check How do the different plant types compare and contrast?

Figure 8 No group of plants is more diverse than flowering plants.

Squash

Rosemary

Wisteria vine

Poppies

Pear tree

Palm tree

Grass

Cactus

Lily pads

Visual Summary

Unlike animal cells, a plant cell has a rigid cell wall, chloroplasts, and a large central vacuole.

Plants have structures that help ensure their survival.

Vascular plants have specialized tissues for transporting water and nutrients.

FOLDABLES

Use your lesson Foldable to review the lesson. Save your Foldable for the project at the end of the chapter.

What do you think NOW?

You first read the statements below at the beginning of the chapter.

1. Humans could survive without plants.

2. Plant cells contain the same organelles as animal cells.

Did you change your mind about whether you agree or disagree with the statements? Rewrite any false statements to make them true.

Use Vocabulary

1 **Distinguish** between vascular and nonvascular plants.

2 **Define** *stomata* in your own words.

3 **Write** a sentence using the terms *angiosperm* and *gymnosperm*.

Understand Key Concepts 🔑

4 Which are NOT vascular plants?
- **A.** angiosperms
- **B.** ferns
- **C.** gymnosperms
- **D.** mosses

5 **Give an example** of a vascular seed plant.

6 **Compare** roots and rhizoids.

7 **Differentiate** between woody and herbaceous stems.

Interpret Graphics

8 **Describe** the function of the structure below.

9 **Summarize** Copy and fill in the table below to describe the function of roots, stems, and leaves.

Structure	Function

Critical Thinking

10 **Assess** the importance of vascular tissue in larger plants.

11 **Evaluate** the advantage to a plant of flower production.

A Life-Saving Plant

How can a plant protect you from disease?

Nobody likes a mosquito bite—especially the itchy, red bump it leaves behind. But in some parts of the world, mosquito bites can be deadly. In many tropical countries, female *Anopheles* mosquitoes transmit a serious disease called malaria. Every year, hundreds of millions of people become sick with malaria, and more than 1 million die from the infection.

The real cause of malaria isn't the mosquito—it's a tiny parasite called *Plasmodium* that lives in the mosquito. Mosquitoes get infected with the parasite after biting a person who has malarial fever. When an infected mosquito then bites someone else, it transfers the parasite into that person's blood.

One of the most effective treatments for malaria comes from a plant—the sweet wormwood tree (*Artemisia annua*). The drug, called artemisinin (ar tah MIH sih nin), is a natural substance taken from the tree's leaves. Like many medicinal plants, the sweet wormwood tree has been used since ancient times. Around 2,000 years ago, the Chinese treated malaria with tea made from the tree's dried leaves. However, artemisinin was not scientifically studied until 1972 and has only become widely available since 2001.

Today, artemisinin is available in pill or shot form and is proving to be the critical weapon in the fight against malaria. Treatment with artemisinin has cured more than a million patients so far. Recently, however, scientists working in Cambodia discovered that artemisinin is becoming less effective. This could be a sign that the parasite is becoming resistant to the drug. Now more than ever, it's important that researchers keep investigating other plants for possible treatments.

▲ Sweet wormwood tree leaves are the source of artemisinin.

AMERICAN MUSEUM Ö NATURAL HISTORY

It's Your Turn

RESEARCH The spices cinnamon, cayenne pepper, garlic, thyme, and ginger come from plants and can be used to cure ailments. Select one and research how it can be used medicinally. Report your findings to your class.

(t)Scott Bauer/USDA; (bkgd)Ira Block/National Geographic/Getty Images

Lesson 2

Reading Guide

Key Concepts 🗝
ESSENTIAL QUESTIONS

- How do asexual and sexual reproduction in plants compare and contrast?

- What are the differences between the life cycles of seedless and seed plants?

Vocabulary

pollination

dormancy

pistil

stamen

 Multilingual eGlossary

 Video **BrainPOP®**

 LE 1.1f

Plant Reproduction

Inquiry A Plant Sneeze?

It might look as if this plant has just sneezed, but what is being released from the plant might make you sneeze! These grass flowers are releasing pollen, which causes itchy noses in many people. However, pollen is important in the reproduction of this species.

Do you need seeds to grow a plant?

You grew radish plants from seeds in Lesson 1. Can you grow a plant without using seeds?

1 Read and complete a lab safety form.

2 Pour water into a **glass** until it is half full. Place several **toothpicks** around the middle of a **potato.** Place the potato in the glass so that the bottom of it touches the water and the toothpicks hold the rest of the potato above the rim of the glass.

3 Place the glass and potato in a sunny area.

4 Using a **dissecting knife,** carefully cut a stem approximately 8 cm long from a **coleus plant.** Place the stem cutting in a glass of water so that only the cut portion of the stem is immersed in the water.

5 Place the coleus cutting in a sunny area.

6 Observe the potato and the coleus cutting after one week.

Think About This

1. How did the potato and the coleus plant change after one week?

2. How do you think the traits of the plantlets will compare with those of the parent plants?

3. 🔑 **Key Concept** Compare and contrast the growth of the potato and the coleus plant with that of the radish plants from Lesson 1.

Asexual Reproduction

Some plants don't need seeds to make new plants. Some plants can be grown from a leaf, a stem, or another plant part, as shown in **Figure 9.** Asexual reproduction occurs when only one parent organism or part of that organism produces a new organism. The new organism is genetically identical to the parent. Farmers and florists often use asexual reproduction to produce multiple plants with desired traits.

Sexual Reproduction

The process of sexual reproduction involves male sex cells and female sex cells. Each sex cell contributes genetic material to the offspring. Like animals, plants produce sperm, which are the male sex cells, and eggs, which are the female sex cells. Fertilization occurs when a sperm and an egg join, combining their genetic material. Sexual reproduction produces individuals that have a different genetic makeup than the parent organism or organisms. Both seedless plants and seed plants can reproduce sexually.

🔑 **Key Concept Check** How do asexual and sexual reproduction in plants compare and contrast?

REVIEW VOCABULARY

trait
a distinguishing characteristic of an organism

Figure 9 🔑 These plants have grown at the edges of a leaf from a single parent plant.

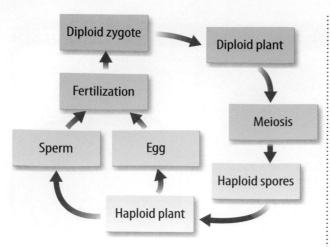

▲ Figure 10 🔑 All plants have a life cycle that includes two stages.

✓ **Visual Check** Identify the gametophyte and the sporophyte stages in this diagram.

🔘 **Concepts in Motion** Animation

Figure 11 🔑 The life cycle of a fern alternates between a gametophyte and a sporophyte stage. ▼

Plant Life Cycles

There are two stages in the life cycle of every plant—the gametophyte (guh MEE tuh fite) stage and the sporophyte (SPO ruh fite) stage. The gametophyte stage begins with a spore, or haploid cell. Through mitosis and cell division, the spore produces a plant structure or an entire plant called a gametophyte. The gametophyte produces male and female sex cells through meiosis.

During sexual reproduction, a male sex cell and a female sex cell combine. If fertilization occurs, a diploid cell forms, as shown in **Figure 10.** That diploid cell is the beginning of the sporophyte stage. This cell divides through mitosis and cell division and forms the sporophyte. In some plants, the sporophyte is a small structure, but in others such as an apple tree, the sporophyte is the tree.

Seedless Plants

Plants that do not produce seeds are called seedless plants. They can reproduce either by asexual reproduction or by producing spores. Spores are produced by the sporophyte. Recall that the sporophyte results from sexual reproduction. Mosses, liverworts, and ferns are examples of seedless plants. The life cycle of a fern is shown in **Figure 11.**

✓ **Reading Check** Name the two stages in the life cycle of a plant.

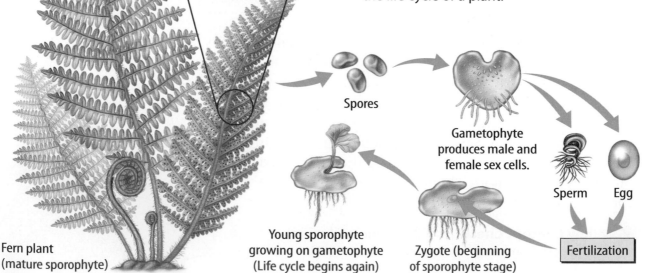

Spores

Gametophyte produces male and female sex cells.

Sperm   Egg

Fertilization

Young sporophyte growing on gametophyte (Life cycle begins again)

Zygote (beginning of sporophyte stage)

Fern plant (mature sporophyte)

Seed Plants

Most plants produce seeds that result from sexual reproduction. The plants produce pollen grains, which contain sperm. They also produce female structures, which contain one or more eggs. *The process that occurs when pollen grains land on a female plant structure of a plant in the same species is* **pollination.** If a sperm from a pollen grain joins with an egg, this is called fertilization. Once fertilization occurs, the diploid cell undergoes many cell divisions, forming an embryo. The embryo is the beginning of the sporophyte stage of seed plants. The embryo and its food supply are enclosed within a protective coat. This is the seed, as shown in **Figure 12.**

In most seed plants, the seed will go through **dormancy,** *which is a period of no growth.* Dormancy might last days, weeks, or even years. Once environmental conditions are favorable, the seed will become active again. The process of a seed beginning to grow is called germination.

Gymnosperm Reproduction The life cycle shown in **Figure 12** is typical of a gymnosperm. Notice that pollen is produced by the male cone, while the eggs, and eventually the seeds, are contained within the female cone.

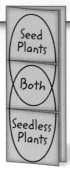
Gymnosperm Life Cycle 🔑

Concepts in Motion Animation

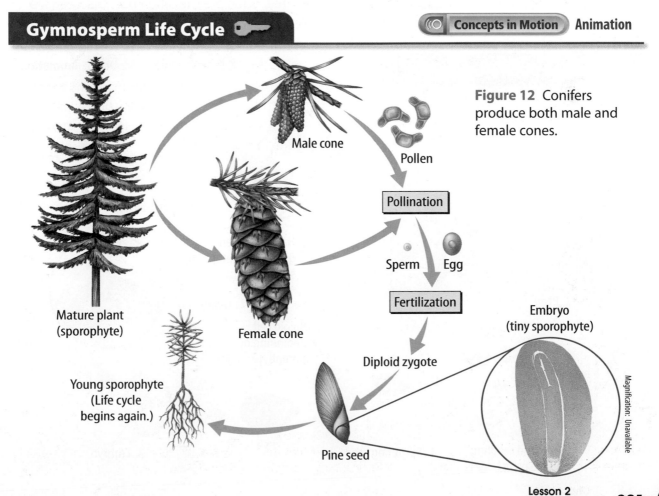

Figure 12 Conifers produce both male and female cones.

Male cone

Pollen

Pollination

Sperm   Egg

Fertilization

Embryo (tiny sporophyte)

Diploid zygote

Mature plant (sporophyte)

Female cone

Young sporophyte (Life cycle begins again.)

Pine seed

Magnification: Unavailable

©Steven P. Lynch

Angiosperm Reproduction Flowering plants often are seen in parks and around houses. You might not know that some plants, such as grasses and maple trees, produce flowers. Some aquatic flowering plants are less than 1 mm in length!

Most flowers have four main structures. The petals, which attract insect or animal pollinators, might be brightly colored. The sepals are usually located beneath the petals and help protect the flower when it is a bud. *The female reproductive organ of a flower is the* **pistil.** It contains the ovary, where the seed develops. *The* **stamen** *is the male reproductive organ of a flower.* The anthers of the stamen produce pollen. Examine **Figure 13** to see all the parts of a flower. Some plants have flowers that have only the male or only the female structures. These are called male flowers or female flowers.

As shown in **Figure 13,** the life cycle of a flowering plant includes both gametophyte and sporophyte stages. The gametophyte stage lasts a short time and includes the production of eggs and sperm by a flower. When a sperm fertilizes an egg, the resulting diploid cell is the beginning of the sporophyte stage. In flowering plants, the sporophyte stage lasts much longer than the gametophyte stage.

 Key Concept Check What are the differences between life cycles of seedless and seed plants?

WORD ORIGIN ···········

pistil
from French *pistil,* means "female organ of a flower"

Figure 13 The life cycle of an angiosperm involves several steps.

Visual Check Describe what happens following fertilization.

Angiosperm Life Cycle

Concepts in Motion Animation

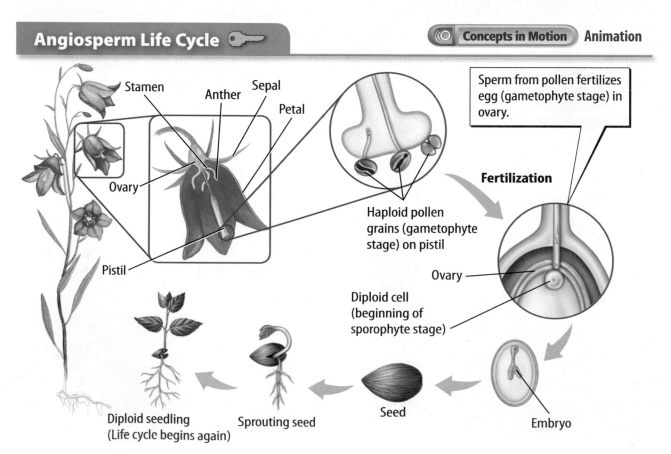

Stamen · Anther · Sepal · Petal · Ovary · Pistil

Sperm from pollen fertilizes egg (gametophyte stage) in ovary.

Haploid pollen grains (gametophyte stage) on pistil

Fertilization

Ovary

Diploid cell (beginning of sporophyte stage)

Diploid seedling (Life cycle begins again) · Sprouting seed · Seed · Embryo

Growth Cycles Plants that grow from a seed and produce flowers in one growing season are called annuals. They must be planted every year.

Some plants take two growing seasons to produce flowers, such as the mullein (MUH lun) in **Figure 14.** These are known as biennials and include carrots and beets. Biennials go through a period of dormancy between growing seasons. Many biennials have large roots that store food between growing seasons.

Perennials are plants that grow and bud for many years. Some perennials, such as trees, can grow for hundreds of years. In cold climates, some perennials lose their leaves and become dormant for several months. Once warmer temperatures return, the plant produces new leaves and begins capturing sunlight for photosynthesis.

First-year growth   Second-year growth

Figure 14 Plants that take two growing seasons to flower and produce seeds are biennials.

✅ **Visual Check** Describe the differences between the plants in **Figure 14.** Why are there differences?

Inquiry MiniLab   **15 minutes**

How do seeds differ?

Flowering plants and nonflowering plants both use seeds to reproduce. How are the seeds different?

1. Read and complete a lab safety form.

2. Examine a **pine cone** and find the seeds. Draw a sketch of a pine cone seed, and record the location of the seeds in your Science Journal.

3. Examine an **apple.** Using a **knife,** carefully cut the apple in half to locate the seeds. Draw a sketch of an apple seed that shows the location of the seeds.

Analyze and Conclude

1. **Analyze** the location of the seeds in the pine cone. Is a pine tree a flowering or a nonflowering plant?

2. **Describe** the location of the seeds in the apple. Is an apple tree a flowering or a nonflowering plant?

3. 🔑 **Key Concept** Compare and contrast the seeds of flowering and nonflowering plants.

Visual Summary

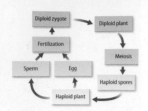

There are two stages in the life cycle of every plant—the gametophyte stage and the sporophyte stage.

Annuals, biennials, and perennials are the different growth cycles of plants.

Most seed plants produce flowers.

FOLDABLES®

Use your lesson Foldable to review the lesson. Save your Foldable for the project at the end of the chapter.

What do you think NOW?

You first read the statements below at the beginning of the chapter.

3. Plants can reproduce both sexually and asexually.

4. All plants have a two-stage life cycle.

Did you change your mind about whether you agree or disagree with the statements? Rewrite any false statements to make them true.

Use Vocabulary

1. A period of no growth is called _____.

2. **Define** *pollination* in your own words.

3. **Write** a sentence using the terms *pistil* and *stamen*.

Understand Key Concepts

4. Which has a cone for its reproductive structure?
   A. angiosperm   C. hornwort
   B. gymnosperm   D. horsetail

5. **Compare** the life cycles of seedless plants and seed plants.

6. **Illustrate** and label the four parts of a flower.

7. **Contrast** sexual and asexual reproduction.

Interpret Graphics

8. **Compare** the traits of the new plants produced above to those of the parent plant.

9. **Classify Information** Copy and fill in the table below to list differences between gymnosperms and angiosperms.

Division	Description

Critical Thinking

10. **Assess** the value of fruit production.

11. **Analyze** the difference between a fern's life cycle and that of a gymnosperm.

How can you learn about plant structures?

Scientists learn more about plants by dissecting and observing their internal structures. A longitudinal section is made by cutting an object in half along its longest plane. A cross section is made by cutting an object in half at a right angle with its shortest plane.

Materials

dissecting
microscope

dissecting knife

flowering plant

Safety

Learn It

Comparing and contrasting structures and functions enables scientists to learn by analyzing similarities and differences.

Try It

1. Read and complete a lab safety form.

2. Cut off a 5-cm to 7-cm section of stem from a flowering plant.

3. Cut a cross section from the remaining stem.

4. Observe the cross section under a dissecting microscope. Draw what you observe in a table like the one below, listing *stem* under the Structure column.

5. Make a longitudinal cut of your stem by cutting the stem in half lengthwise. Observe the inside of one half of your longitudinal cut under the dissecting microscope. Draw what you observe in the Longitudinal View column of your table.

6. Repeat these procedures using the roots, leaves, and flowers of the plant. List each type of structure on your table and then make sketches of your observations in the table.

Apply It

7. **Create a diagram** that represents a three-dimensional view of each of the structures you observed using the information from both the cross-section and the longitudinal cuts.

8. **Analyze** the information from each view. Describe which types of measurements could be obtained from each one—for the entire section of the plant, as well as the details of any internal structures seen within the section.

9. 🔑 **Key Concept** Evaluate how cross-sections and longitudinal sections provide information about a structure. Describe how sometimes one view might be more helpful than the other.

Structure	Cross-section View	Longitudinal View

Reading Guide

Key Concepts 🔑
ESSENTIAL QUESTIONS

- What is the relationship between photosynthesis and cellular respiration?

- How do water and minerals move in vascular and nonvascular plants?

- How do plants respond to environmental changes?

Vocabulary

transpiration

stimulus

tropism

 Multilingual eGlossary

🌐 AID S1.4, S2.1d; ICT 2.2, 2.3; LE 5.1c, 5.1d, 5.2a, 6.2a, 6.2b, 6.2c

Plant Processes

Inquiry Alien Life-Form?

This might look like a space creature with green skin and black eyes, but it is a color-enhanced magnification of openings on the surface of a leaf. These openings enable carbon dioxide, oxygen, and water vapor to pass into and out of a leaf. Why do you think this is important to a plant?

Biophoto Associates/Science Source

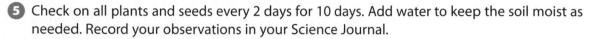
How important is light to the growth of plants?

All plants require light to grow, but just how important is it?

1 Read and complete a lab safety form.

2 Plant several **bean seeds** in two identical **cups** filled with **potting soil.** Add water to moisten the soil in both cups.

3 Place one cup in a sunny place, such as a windowsill. Place the other cup in a dark place, such as a cabinet.

4 Place a **two-week-old bean plant** in the dark location alongside the seeds you planted. Place another **two-week-old bean plant** in the sunny location alongside the other seeds you planted.

5 Check on all plants and seeds every 2 days for 10 days. Add water to keep the soil moist as needed. Record your observations in your Science Journal.

Think About This

1. How does the growth of the seeds exposed to light compare with those kept in the dark?

2. How does the appearance of the plant that was exposed to light compare with the plant that was kept in the dark?

3.  **Key Concept** How do you think the presence or absence of light in the environment affects plant growth?

Photosynthesis and Cellular Respiration

Without plants, all animal life, including human beings, would not exist! Some of the many foods and products that are provided by plants are shown in **Figure 15.** Recall that plants absorb light energy from the Sun and convert it into chemical energy in a process called photosynthesis. During photosynthesis, a plant produces sugar that it uses as food. Even organisms that don't eat plants directly depend on plants because they eat other organisms that do eat plants.

Organisms need energy for growth, repair, movement, and other life processes. Where does this energy come from? Cellular respiration is the process of releasing energy by breaking down food.

 **Key Concept Check** What is the relationship between photosynthesis and cellular respiration?

Figure 15 People consume many different foods from plants. People use many products made from plant materials such as paper, wood, and cotton cloth.

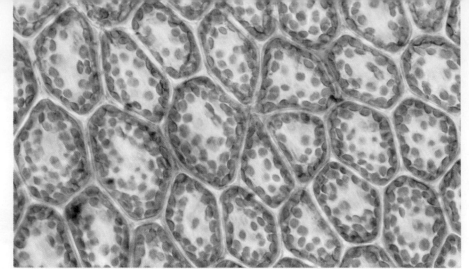

LM Magnification: 250×

Figure 16 The chlorophyll within chloroplasts is what gives most plants their green color.

 Visual Check Where are the chloroplasts located in these plant cells?

REVIEW VOCABULARY ⸱⸱⸱⸱⸱

organelle
a structure in a eukaryotic cell that performs a specific function for the cell
⸱⸱⸱⸱⸱⸱⸱⸱⸱⸱⸱⸱⸱⸱⸱

New York FYI

Sugar Storage When a plant performs photosynthesis, it forms sugar molecules to use as an energy source. Sugar that is not immediately used is stored. Potatoes and carrots are examples of plant structures where excess sugar is stored.

Making Sugars By Using Light Energy

For most plants, photosynthesis occurs in the leaves. Some leaf cells contain chloroplasts. Photosynthesis occurs inside these organelles. As shown in **Figure 16**, chloroplasts contain chlorophyll, a green pigment that absorbs light energy. That energy splits apart water molecules into hydrogen atoms and oxygen atoms. Some of the oxygen leaves the plant through the stomata. Carbon dioxide, which entered the leaf through the stomata, combines with the hydrogen atoms and forms glucose, a type of sugar. Photosynthesis can be shown by the following equation:

$$6CO_2 + 6H_2O \xrightarrow[\text{Chlorophyll}]{\text{Light energy}} C_6H_{12}O_6 + 6O_2$$

A plant can store sugars, and it uses some of the oxygen in another process called cellular respiration.

✓ **Reading Check** Write the equation for photosynthesis using words.

Breaking Down Sugars

The process of cellular respiration breaks down the glucose produced during photosynthesis and releases the sugar's energy. This process occurs in the cytoplasm and the mitochondria. As shown below, oxygen also is used during cellular respiration. The equation for cellular respiration is as follows:

$$C_6H_{12}O_6 + 6O_2 \longrightarrow 6CO_2 + 6H_2O + ATP \text{ (Energy)}$$

During cellular respiration, glucose molecules release more energy than cells can use at one time. That energy is stored in a molecule called adenosine triphosphate (uh DEN uh seen • tri FAHS fayt), or ATP. It is used later for other cell processes.

John Durham/Photo Researchers

The Importance of Photosynthesis and Cellular Respiration

Do you know why plants are so important to life on Earth? One answer can be found in the equations on the previous page. Organisms, such as humans, need oxygen. Each time you inhale, your lungs fill with air that contains oxygen. Your body uses that oxygen for cellular respiration. In your body's cells, cellular respiration breaks down food and stores the energy from food in ATP. Cellular processes such as growth, repair, and reproduction all use ATP. During cellular respiration, carbon dioxide and water are given off as waste products. Plants use these two compounds for photosynthesis.

Most organisms, including humans, use the products of photosynthesis—sugars and oxygen—during cellular respiration. Plants and some other organisms can use the waste products of cellular respiration—carbon dioxide and water—during photosynthesis, as shown in **Figure 17.** It is important to remember that plants also carry on cellular respiration, so they will use some of the oxygen released during photosynthesis.

Math Skills

Use Proportions

A proportion is an equation with two ratios that are equivalent. The cross products of the ratios are equal. Proportions can be used to solve problems such as the following: In a cell, when one molecule of glucose breaks down completely to carbon dioxide and water, 36 ATP molecules are produced. How many ATP molecules are produced when 30 glucose molecules break down?

Set up the proportion.

$$\frac{1 \text{ molecule glucose}}{36 \text{ molecules ATP}} = \frac{30 \text{ molecules glucose}}{x \text{ molecule ATP}}$$

Cross multiply.

$$x = 30 \times 36$$

$$x = 1{,}080 \text{ molecules ATP}$$

Practice

During photosynthesis, 18 ATP molecules are required to produce 1 glucose molecule. How many ATP molecules would be required to produce 2,500 glucose molecules?

Review

- **Math Practice**
- **Personal Tutor**

Making and Using Energy 🔑

Light energy
$$6CO_2 + 6H_2O \longrightarrow C_6H_{12}O_6 + 6O_2$$
Chlorophyll

Photosynthesis

$$C_6H_{12}O_6 + 6O_2 \longrightarrow 6CO_2 + 6H_2O + \underset{\text{(Energy)}}{ATP}$$

Cellular respiration

Review

Personal Tutor

Figure 17 The products of photosynthesis are used during cellular respiration. The products of cellular respiration are used during photosynthesis.

✓ **Visual Check**
Compare the equations for photosynthesis and cellular respiration.

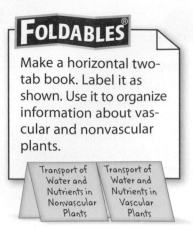

FOLDABLES®

Make a horizontal two-tab book. Label it as shown. Use it to organize information about vascular and nonvascular plants.

| Transport of Water and Nutrients in Nonvascular Plants | Transport of Water and Nutrients in Vascular Plants |

REVIEW VOCABULARY

diffusion
the movement of substances from an area of higher concentration to an area of lower concentration

osmosis
the diffusion of water molecules through a membrane

Figure 18 Water is absorbed into the roots and travels to the leaves, where it is used for plant processes or released.

Movement of Nutrients and Water

In order for plants to carry on processes such as photosynthesis and cellular respiration, water and nutrients must move inside them. This movement or transport of materials occurs through **diffusion** and **osmosis** in nonvascular plants. In vascular plants, water and nutrients move inside specialized vascular tissues. Osmosis and diffusion also move materials once they are outside the vascular tissues.

Absorption

Roots and rhizoids of plants absorb water and nutrients from the soil. Once inside a plant, water and nutrients move to cells, where they are used in cellular processes. As you just read, water is used for photosynthesis. It also is part of many other chemical reactions inside cells. Nutrients from the soil, such as minerals, are used for making many of the compounds needed for cell growth and maintenance.

Transpiration

Recall that water is a waste product of cellular respiration. Plants release excess water as water vapor in a process called transpiration. **Transpiration** *is the release of water vapor from stomata in leaves.* This process helps move water from the roots, up through the vascular tissue, and to the leaves. This movement provides water for photosynthesis and helps cool a plant on hot days. Examine **Figure 18** and follow the path of water from the soil, up through the plant, and out of the leaves.

🔑 **Key Concept Check** How do water and nutrients move in a nonvascular plant? In a vascular plant?

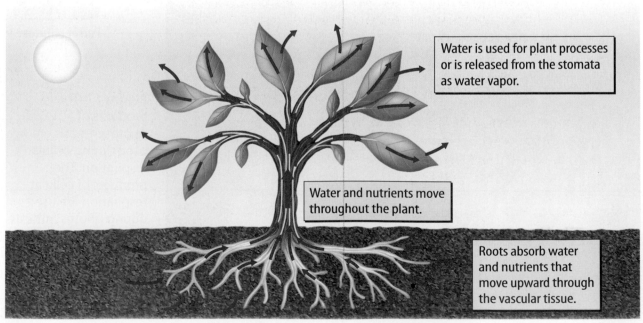

Water is used for plant processes or is released from the stomata as water vapor.

Water and nutrients move throughout the plant.

Roots absorb water and nutrients that move upward through the vascular tissue.

Plant Responses

Can you remember the last time a loud noise startled you? You might have jumped and turned around to see what made the noise. **Stimuli** (singular, stimulus) *are any changes in an organism's environment that cause a response.* Although a plant might not jump or turn around like a person would, a plant can respond to stimuli in a number of ways, one of which is shown in **Figure 19.**

Types of Stimuli

Plants respond to both external and internal stimuli. External stimuli include light, touch, and gravity. Internal stimuli occur inside a plant. These internal stimuli are chemicals, called hormones, that the plant produces. Plants produce many different hormones. These hormones can affect growth, seed germination, or fruit ripening. The hormones that promote growth increase the rate of mitosis and cell divisions. Some hormones slow growth and can be used to help control weeds. One type of hormone can cause seeds to germinate, or begin to grow, by starting the breakdown of the stored food in a seed. This releases energy needed for new growth. Another plant hormone often is used to speed up the ripening of fruit to be sold in grocery stores.

Figure 19 The mimosa plant responds to the stimulus of being touched by collapsing its leaves.

Inquiry MiniLab

10 minutes

How does an external stimulus affect the growth of a plant?

A plant can grow toward or away from an external stimulus. You can observe the responses to a stimulus by changing the environment of a growing plant.

1 Read and complete a lab safety form.

2 Obtain the **petri dish** with the growing **radish plant** from Lesson 1. Turn the dish vertically so that the roots and the top of the plant are now both facing sideways in opposite directions. Make sure the dish is oriented so that the source of light comes from a different direction as well.

3 Place the dish on a shelf or windowsill in this new position.

4 Observe the radish plant over several days. Record your observations in your Science Journal.

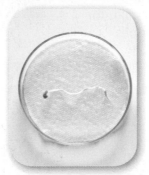

Analyze and Conclude

1. **Analyze** how the change in position affected the growth of the top of the radish plant.

2. **Infer** from your observations how the force of gravity affects the growth of plant roots.

3. **Key Concept** Infer how both responses to light and gravity are important to the survival of plants in a changing environment.

WORD ORIGIN ···········

tropism
from Greek *tropos*, means "a turn, change"

Tropisms

Any external environmental stimulus affects plants. This includes light, gravity, and touch. *Plant growth toward or away from an external stimulus is called* **tropism.**

Phototropism When a plant grows toward a light source, it is called positive phototropism. As shown in **Figure 20,** growing toward a light source enables leaves and stems to receive the maximum amount of light for photosynthesis. The roots of a plant generally exhibit negative phototropism by growing into the soil away from light. By growing into the soil, the roots are able to anchor the plant.

Gravitropism A plant's response to gravity is called gravitropism. The first root produced by a germinating seed grows downward. This is positive gravitropism. It enables the new plant to be anchored in soil, where it can absorb water. A plant's stems and leaves grow upward and away from gravity, as shown in **Figure 20.** This is negative gravitropism. This response enables leaves to be exposed to light, making photosynthesis possible.

Thigmotropism Did you know plants have a sense of touch? A plant's response to touch is called thigmotropism. The coiling of a vine's tendrils around another plant, as shown in **Figure 20,** is an example of positive thigmotropism. A plant's roots exhibit negative thigmotropism when they grow around a rock in the soil.

Figure 20 Plants respond to stimuli in a variety of ways. See if you can determine the stimulus for each of these pictures.

 Key Concept Check How do plants respond to environmental changes?

Plant Responses to External Stimuli

Positive phototropism

Negative gravitropism

Positive thigmotropism

Lesson 3 Review

Visual Summary

Plants make sugar through the process of photosynthesis. Plants break down sugar into usable energy through the process of cellular respiration.

All plants must be able to transport water and nutrients in order to survive.

Plants respond to internal and external stimuli.

FOLDABLES

Use your lesson Foldable to review the lesson. Save your Foldable for the project at the end of the chapter.

What do you think NOW?

You first read the statements below at the beginning of the chapter.

5. Plants respond to their environments.

6. Because plants make their own food, they do not carry on cellular respiration.

Did you change your mind about whether you agree or disagree with the statements? Rewrite any false statements to make them true.

Use Vocabulary

1 Plant growth toward or away from a stimulus is called _____.

2 **Define** *transpiration* in your own words.

Understand Key Concepts

3 A plant that is growing toward a window most likely is exhibiting _____.
- **A.** gravitropism
- **C.** phototropism
- **B.** hydrotropism
- **D.** thigmotropism

4 **Explain** how water and nutrients move in nonvascular plants.

5 **Compare** cellular respiration and photosynthesis.

Interpret Graphics

6 **Sequence** Draw a graphic organizer like the one below to illustrate important transpiration events, beginning with the absorption of water by roots.

7 **Identify** Where are the cells at right likely to be located in a plant? Justify your answer.

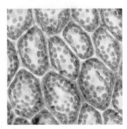

Critical Thinking

8 **Invent** a new type of tropism, and explain why it would be beneficial to plants.

9 **Reflect** on the relationship between photosynthesis and cellular respiration.

Math Skills

— Math Practice —

10 During one step in a cellular process, 9 molecules of ATP are produced from 2 starting molecules. How many molecules of ATP would be produced from 100 starting molecules?

(tl)Pixtal/age fotostock; (bl)©Nigel Cattlin/Alamy; (br)John Durham/Photo Researchers

Model the Form and Function of Plant Structures

Plants use different structures to perform specialized functions and obtain materials for survival. Use your knowledge of plant structures to design a model of a plant using common materials to represent both form and function.

Question

What types of materials could be used to represent both the appearance and the function of the different parts of a plant?

Procedure

1. Read and complete a lab safety form.

2. Make a list of all the plant structures you will need to model in a vascular seed-producing plant and a vascular seedless plant.

3. Expand your list into a table by adding a column with the heading *Function*. In this column, write a brief, general description of the function of each plant structure. Use as many descriptive words as you can think of that fit the structure or function.

4. Add another column with the heading *Materials*.

5. Complete the Materials column of your table by writing down any materials that fit the descriptions in the previous columns.

6. Select the most appropriate materials from your table to create three-dimensional models of a vascular seedless plant and a vascular seed-producing plant. Use the materials to construct models that show form and function. For example, you might use drinking straws to represent the vascular tissues of the stem of your plant model.

Hutchings Photography/Digital Light Source

6

Lab Tips

☑ Take your time filling out the first two columns of the table before beginning to brainstorm materials. Use as many descriptive terms as you can to describe the functions. Then think of as many different materials as you can that might model the functions you've listed.

☑ Discuss the possible materials with your lab partners. Remember that the materials should represent functions yet still be usable for construction.

☑ Don't limit yourself to obvious materials. You do not have to use objects that resemble plant structures or typical craft construction materials. Try to use some objects that will be unique, yet remind observers about different functions.

Analyze and Conclude

7 **Analyze** Was there a structure that was difficult to model using an appropriate material? Describe which structures were easy and which ones were a challenge.

8 **Contrast** How were some of the materials you chose for each of your models different from each other? How did these materials reflect differences in their functions?

9 **The Big Idea** How do the structures you modeled help ensure the survival of plants? Cite some examples in your answer.

Communicate Your Results

Share your results with the class. Discuss your choice of materials. Compare and contrast your choice of materials with those chosen by other students. Which materials were most common? Which choices were unique?

Inquiry **Extension**

Think about how you would use appropriate materials to design a model of some nonvascular plants. As a class, design and build some models of nonvascular plants using materials that represent both function and structure.

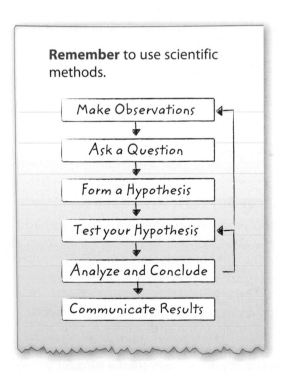

Remember to use scientific methods.

Make Observations

Ask a Question

Form a Hypothesis

Test your Hypothesis

Analyze and Conclude

Communicate Results

Hutchings Photography/Digital Light Source

THE BIG IDEA

There are many different types of plants, but they all have structures and functions that help ensure survival.

Key Concepts Summary

	Vocabulary

Lesson 1: Plant Diversity

- Roots and **rhizoids** anchor a plant and absorb water and nutrients. Stems help support the leaves, and in some cases flowers, of a plant. Stems help carry water and nutrients throughout the plant. In most plants, leaves are the major sites for photosynthesis. In addition to making food, leaves also are involved in the exchange of gases with the environment through the **stomata**.

- Plants are classified into groups called divisions. The main divisions are **nonvascular plants** and **vascular plants**.

Vocabulary

rhizoid

stoma

nonvascular plant

vascular plant

gymnosperm

angiosperm

Lesson 2: Plant Reproduction

- Asexual reproduction does not involve sex cells. Offspring are genetically identical to the parent. Sexual reproduction involves sex cells and produces offspring that are not genetically identical to each other or the parent plant(s).

- The life cycles of seedless and seed plants both contain a gametophyte and a sporophyte stage. Seed plants produce seeds, and seedless plants produce spores.

pollination

dormancy

pistil

stamen

Lesson 3: Plant Processes

- Plants produce sugar through photosynthesis. Cellular respiration is the process by which organisms break down the sugar and release energy. This energy is stored in ATP. ATP is used for life processes.

- Water and nutrients move by osmosis and diffusion in nonvascular plants. These substances are transported through vascular tissue in vascular plants.

- Plants respond to **stimuli** in their environment. Growth toward or away from a stimulus is called a **tropism**.

transpiration

stimulus

tropism

FOLDABLES® Chapter Project

Assemble your lesson Foldables as shown to make a Chapter Project. Use the project to review what you have learned in this chapter.

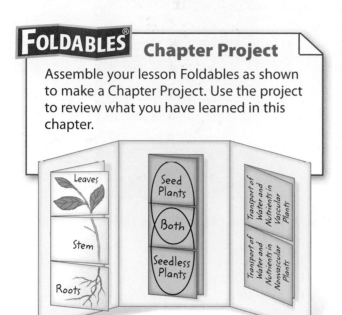

Use Vocabulary

1. The release of water vapor from stomata in leaves is called _____.

2. Pollen is produced in the male reproductive structure of a plant, or the _____.

3. Distinguish between angiosperms and gymnosperms.

4. Changes in an organism's environment that cause a response are called _____.

5. Use the term *dormancy* in a sentence.

Link Vocabulary and Key Concepts

 **Concepts in Motion** Interactive Concept Map

Copy this concept map, and then use vocabulary terms from the previous page to complete the concept map.

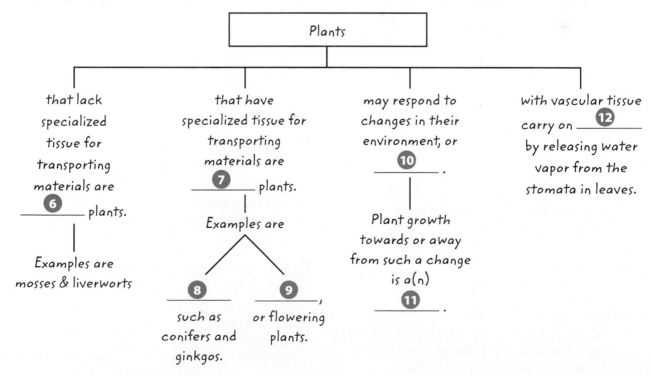

Understand Key Concepts

1 During which process are carbon dioxide, water, and ATP produced?
A. cellular respiration
B. photosynthesis
C. thigmotropism
D. transpiration

2 Which is the cause of the green color in plant leaves?
A. chlorophyll
B. flowers
C. glucose
D. oxygen

3 What do angiosperms produce?
A. cones
B. flowers
C. needles
D. rhizoids

Use the diagram below to answer questions 4 and 5.

4 In which flower part is an egg produced?
A. A
B. B
C. C
D. D

5 Which flower part is often brightly colored and helps attract insects?
A. A
B. B
C. C
D. D

6 The stomata on a leaf
A. allow gases to enter and leave the leaf.
B. allow water and energy into the leaf.
C. perform cellular respiration.
D. produce sugar and water vapor.

7 What is the plant shown above?
A. fern
B. horsetail
C. moss
D. pine tree

8 Which do ferns produce in order to reproduce?
A. cones
B. flowers
C. seeds
D. spores

9 All plants have a life cycle that includes a _____
A. cone and gametophyte.
B. cone and seed.
C. seed and sporophyte.
D. sporophyte and gametophyte.

10 Which is an organelle in plant cells but not in animal cells?
A. chlorophyll
B. chloroplast
C. mitochondria
D. nucleus

11 What is the major site of photosynthesis in plants?
A. flowers
B. leaves
C. stems
D. roots

Critical Thinking

12 **Suggest** an environment where you might find succulents, or plants that store water in their leaves.

13 **Reflect** on the importance of flowers in plant reproduction.

14 **Assess** the advantages of sexual and asexual reproduction.

15 **Predict** the effect of germinating a seed without any light.

16 **Hypothesize** why natural selection has favored flowers with colorful petals.

17 **Analyze** the need for woody stems in some plants that live many years through many different seasons and weather conditions, such as some perennials.

18 **Hypothesize** why the type of plant shown below often grows in moist areas.

19 **Evaluate** the differences between the life cycles of a moss and a gymnosperm.

20 **Suggest** a reason for the great abundance and diversity of flowering plants.

Writing in Science

21 **Choose** a habitat near your home, and write a description of the plants in that habitat. Be sure to include a physical description of the plants, as well as how many of each kind of plant are present. See if you can identify the division and name of each plant.

REVIEW THE BIG IDEA

22 Make a list to summarize the different structures and functions of plants that you have learned about in this chapter. How does each structure and function from your list help plants survive?

23 The photo below shows a magnified cross section of a pine needle. How do pine needles help conifers live in their environment?

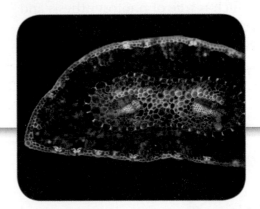

Math Skills

Review

Math Practice

Use Proportions

24 If each ATP molecule in the body takes part in about three reactions every minute, how many reactions would this molecule take part in during one hour?

25 The human body contains about 0.05 kg of ATP. During each 24-hour period, the body's ATP is recycled about 3,600 times. How many kilograms of ATP would the body need in order to provide separate ATP molecules for each reaction?

Standardized Test Practice

Record your answers on the answer sheet provided by your teacher or on a sheet of paper.

Multiple Choice

1 Which structures enable a plant to exchange water vapor and gases such as carbon dioxide and oxygen with its environment?

  A rhizoids

  B roots

  C seeds

  D stomata

2 Which is true of photosynthesis and cellular respiration?

  A They both occur in plants.

  B They both occur in animals.

  C They both produce sugars.

  D They both require sunlight.

Use the image below to answer question 3.

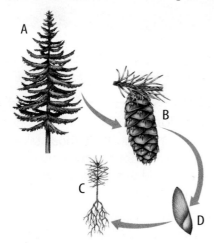

3 For the life cycle shown, which structures are part of the sporophyte stage?

  A A and B

  B A and C

  C B and C

  D B and D

4 Which is NOT a product of cellular respiration?

  A energy

  B glucose

  C oxygen

  D water

5 Which two divisions are used to classify vascular seed plants?

  A conifers and nonconifers

  B flowering and nonflowering

  C mosses and liverworts

  D sporophytes and gametophytes

Use the image below to answer question 6.

6 What term describes the plant response shown above?

  A gravitropism

  B hydrotropism

  C phototropism

  D thigmotropism

7 Which structures anchor nonvascular plants to surfaces?

  A rhizoids

  B roots

  C stems

  D xylem

8 Which processes do nonvascular plants use to transport water and nutrients through their tissues?

   A absorption and photosynthesis

   B cellular respiration and pollination

   C diffusion and osmosis

   D transpiration and reproduction

Use the diagram below to answer questions 9 and 10.

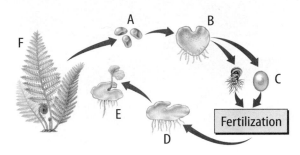

9 Which structures in the diagram are haploid?

   A A, B, and F

   B C, D, and E

   C A, B, and C

   D D, E, and F

10 Which structures in the diagram are diploid?

   A A, B, and F

   B C, D, and E

   C A, B, and C

   D D, E, and F

Constructed Response

Use the diagram below to answer question 11.

11 The diagram shows the path water takes in moving through a plant. Describe what happens to CO_2 in the plant. Use the terms *sunlight, sugar, leaves,* and *cellular respiration* in your answer.

12 Which structures in a plant contain vascular tissue? What is their function?

13 How are the life cycles of a fern and a pine similar? How are they different?

14 How do offspring produced by asexual reproduction differ from offspring produced by sexual reproduction?

NEED EXTRA HELP?														
If You Missed Question...	1	2	3	4	5	6	7	8	9	10	11	12	13	14
Go to Lesson...	1	3	2	3	1	3	1	1	2	2	3	1	2	2

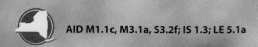
Introduction to Animals

THE BIG IDEA

What are animals, and how are they classified?

Inquiry What's the same?

This American robin is eating an earthworm. The earthworm provides energy for the robin's use.

- What animal characteristics do the robin and the worm have?

- What makes the robin and the worm different kinds of animals?

- What are animals, and how are they classified?

Abdolhamid Ebrahimi-e/Getty Images

Get Ready to Read

What do you think?

Before you read, decide if you agree or disagree with each of these statements. As you read this chapter, see if you change your mind about any of the statements.

1. Animals must eat plants or other animals to live.

2. All animals have a left side and a right side that are similar.

3. A sponge is not an animal because it cannot move.

4. There are more arthropods on Earth than all other kinds of animals combined.

5. All young mammals take in milk from their mothers.

6. Birds are the only animals that lay shelled eggs.

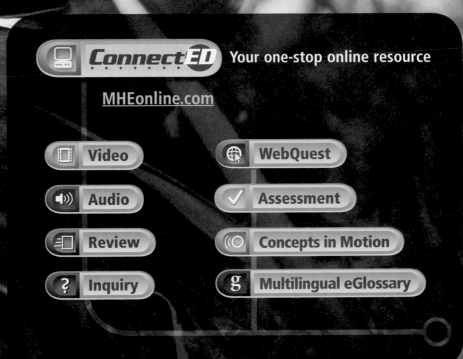

ConnectED Your one-stop online resource

MHEonline.com

- Video
- WebQuest
- Audio
- Assessment
- Review
- Concepts in Motion
- Inquiry
- Multilingual eGlossary

Reading Guide

Key Concepts
ESSENTIAL QUESTIONS

- What characteristics are common to all animals?
- How do scientists group animals?
- How are animal species adapted to their environments?

Vocabulary

bilateral symmetry

radial symmetry

asymmetry

adaptation

hydrostatic skeleton

exoskeleton

endoskeleton

 Multilingual eGlossary

Video

- **BrainPOP®**
- **Science Video**

AID S3.2f; LE 5.1a

What are animals?

inquiry Plant or Animal?

When ancient Greeks first classified living things, they thought sponges, such as the ones in this picture, were plants. What animal characteristics do you think sponges have? Why was the sponge thought to be a plant? How can we make similar mistakes in identifying living things today?

Michael Stubblefield/iStock/Getty Images

What are animals?

The animal kingdom is diverse. Its members live everywhere from the depths of the ocean to the heights of the upper atmosphere. Though there are many differences among animals, they all have some of the same characteristics.

1. Examine the pictures of sea squirts, a bird, a crab, and a human.

2. In your Science Journal, make two lists. Title one *Similarities* and the other *Differences*.

3. Using what you know about the animals and what you can see in the pictures, list traits, behaviors, and processes the animals share or do not share under the appropriate heading.

Think About This

1. Which list was easier to create? Why?

2. 🔑 **Key Concept** What are some characteristics that you think are common to all animals?

Animal Characteristics

Zoos are interesting to people of all ages. Why do people keep coming back to the zoo year after year? To see the animals of course! In fact, *zoo* comes from the Greek word *zoion*, which means "living being" or "animal."

All animals, like plants, are multicellular. Like plant cells, each animal cell has a nucleus at some point during its life. While cell walls support plant cells, a protein called collagen holds animal cells together. Animals are the only living things that have nerve cells. Nerve cells conduct nerve impulses. Most animals also have muscle cells that help them move.

Animals cannot transform light energy into food energy as most plants can. All animals get energy from the food they take into their bodies. In most animals, food passes through their stomachs, and then their intestines absorb nutrients from it.

All animals begin as a fertilized egg cell called a zygote. Recall that fertilization is the joining of an egg cell with a sperm cell. The zygote divides into more cells and forms an embryo. After many more cell divisions, the body of the animal is recognizable.

🔑 **Key Concept Check** What characteristics are common to all animals?

FOLDABLES

Make a vertical two-column chart. Label it as shown. Use it to organize your notes on animal characteristics and identification.

Symmetry | Adaptations

How do scientists group animals?

When you first learned to talk, you probably grouped things by what they looked like. For example, you might have called any round object "ball." As you developed, however, you came to know the differences between things, such as trees and cats. You knew that dogs were not birds. This was your first experience with classification. Scientists classify animals in many different ways.

Symmetry

One way to group animals is by looking at their symmetry, or how body parts are arranged. The three types of symmetry are shown in **Figure 1.**

Some animals have **bilateral symmetry,** *a body plan in which an organism can be divided into two parts that are nearly mirror images of each other.* Humans, frogs, and the gecko in **Figure 1** are examples of organisms with bilateral symmetry.

An animal with **radial symmetry** *has a body plan which can be divided into two parts that are nearly mirror images of each other anywhere through its central axis.* The sand dollar in **Figure 1** has radial symmetry.

Some animals, such as the sponges in **Figure 1** and in the photo at the beginning of this lesson, do not have bilateral symmetry or radial symmetry. They have **asymmetry,** *meaning they have body plans which cannot be divided into any two parts that are nearly mirror images.*

WORD ORIGIN

asymmetry
from Greek *asymmetros*, means "not having a common measure"

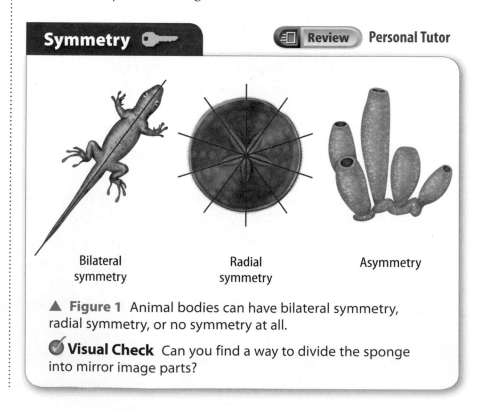

Symmetry 🔑   🖽 Review   **Personal Tutor**

Bilateral symmetry   Radial symmetry   Asymmetry

▲ **Figure 1** Animal bodies can have bilateral symmetry, radial symmetry, or no symmetry at all.

☑ **Visual Check** Can you find a way to divide the sponge into mirror image parts?

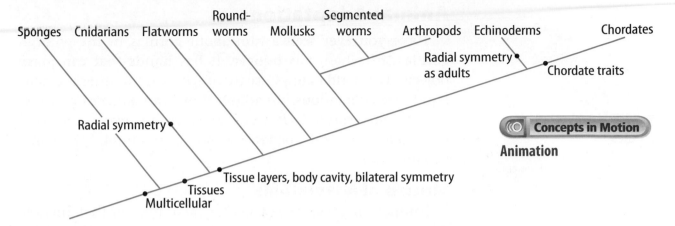

Sponges Cnidarians Flatworms Round-worms Mollusks Segmented worms Arthropods Echinoderms Chordates

Radial symmetry as adults

Chordate traits

Radial symmetry

Tissue layers, body cavity, bilateral symmetry

Tissues

Multicellular

Concepts in Motion
Animation

Figure 2 Scientists organize animals into groups based on characteristics they have in common. This tree diagram shows the relationships among animal groups based on common characteristics.

☑ **Visual Check** Which animals are multicellular?

Groups of Animals

Scientists use a system called taxonomy to organize living things. This system groups living things into levels called taxons. Taxons are groups of living things that have certain traits in common.

Taxonomy The biggest groups in taxonomy are called domains. Because each animal cell has a nucleus at some point in its life, animals are in the Domain Eukarya. The next level consists of the kingdom taxons. Scientists use the traits you read about earlier to determine whether an organism belongs in the Kingdom Animalia. Animals then are classified into phyla (singular, phylum), genera (singular, genus), and species. Lessons 2 and 3 cover the nine most common animal phyla shown in **Figure 2**.

Family Tree A family tree shows the relationships among and within generations of a family. Animal phyla also are organized by how they are related through time. A tree of phyla shows the relationships among animals. As each new feature evolved over time, it was placed on a new branch of the tree, as shown in **Figure 2**. For example, all animals above sponges have tissues.

 Key Concept Check How do scientists group animals?

Animal Adaptations

Have you ever seen a film about gorillas in the wild? A gorilla eats when it is hungry. It has hands that can grasp objects. The gorilla's response to hunger and the structure of its hands are adaptations. *An* **adaptation** *is an inherited trait that increases an organism's chances of surviving and reproducing in its environment.* Animal adaptations can be structural, behavioral, or functional.

Structural Adaptations

Animal **species** have structural adaptations that include their senses, skeletons, and circulation. For example, snakes can detect infrared light, and some insects can sense ultraviolet light. These adaptations can help them detect the presence of food or an enemy. Other animals have complex eyes that work like a camera. These eyes help the animals form accurate images of their environments.

Animals' skeletons have evolved into different types to support their bodies. An earthworm has a **hydrostatic skeleton,** *a fluid-filled internal cavity surrounded by muscle tissue.* A crab has soft internal structures. They are protected by *a thick, hard outer covering called an* **exoskeleton.** You probably are most familiar with *the internal rigid framework that supports you and other animals called an* **endoskeleton.** Your endoskeleton is made of bone. Your muscles attach to your bones and help you move.

Animal species also have structural adaptations for circulating blood. For example, ants have an open circulatory system. An ant's heart pumps blood into open spaces around its organs. However, an earthworm has a closed circulatory system. Many hearts pump blood through a system of vessels. Other animals with closed circulation have only one heart. More animal structural adaptations are shown in **Figure 3.**

REVIEW VOCABULARY

species
a group of organisms that have similar traits and are able to produce fertile offspring

Figure 3 🔑 Many animal species have evolved special tongue and teeth adaptations to help them obtain food and break it down.

A fly uses its tongue to lap liquid.

A chameleon's tongue is long and sticky for catching insects.

A piranha has razor-sharp teeth for catching prey.

The sharp edge of a beaver's teeth can cut through tree trunks.

How are adaptations useful?

Materials

rice

plastic cup (2)

forceps

tape

stopwatch

Safety

A physical adaptation is a feature an organism has that makes it better able to live in its environment. Some adaptations help an organism gather food. Others help an animal build a shelter or hide from a predator.

Learn It

A **prediction** makes a statement in advance, based on prior observation, experience, or scientific reasoning. In science, predictions are tested. Sometimes the predictions are supported after testing, but other times they are not.

Try It

1. Read and complete a lab safety form.

2. Count out 100 grains of rice and place them in a plastic cup. The rice is your food. The cup represents where you found your food.

3. Place an empty cup 15 cm away from the cup containing rice. The empty cup represents your shelter.

4. You will transfer rice from the first cup to the second cup two times—once using your fingers, and once using forceps. The forceps represent longer, pointier fingers or beaks that some animals have. You only can move one grain of rice at a time and only use one hand. The cups must remain standing up.

5. Based on your experiences and knowledge of forceps and rice, predict if using forceps or not using forceps will be more efficient in moving the rice. Write your prediction in your Science Journal and explain your reasoning.

6. Have your partner use the stopwatch to time you as you transfer the rice with your fingers. Record the time in your Science Journal.

7. Tape the forceps inside your thumb and index finger, as shown below.

8. Have your partner time you again as you transfer the rice with forceps. Record the time.

Apply It

9. What were the independent and dependent variables and the controls in this activity?

10. Was your prediction accurate? What data supports your answer?

11. **Key Concept** Would the adaptation of longer, pointier fingers or beaks be an advantage or disadvantage for obtaining food if the food source were peanuts? What if the food were alive, such as a wiggling worm? Explain your reasoning.

Lesson 2

Reading Guide

Key Concepts 🔑
ESSENTIAL QUESTIONS

- What characteristics do invertebrates have in common?

- How do the groups of invertebrates differ?

Vocabulary

parasite

mantle

molting

metamorphosis

 Multilingual eGlossary

 Video **BrainPOP®**

 IS 1.3; LE 5.1a

Invertebrates

Inquiry Pretty Flowers?

No, these are animals called sea anemones. Would you believe that these sea anemones can paralyze and eat many other animals that swim or float by them? How do you think the animals in this picture support their bodies? How do they move?

Joebelanger/iStock/Getty Images

Who lives here?

The number of animals living in a small patch of soil can outnumber the human population of a large city. Some of these animals do not have a backbone; others might have a backbone. What types of animals can you find on a patch of ground?

1. Read and complete a lab safety form.
2. Throw a large **plastic hoop** on a **patch of ground.**
3. Search your patch of ground for animals and evidence of animal life. You may need to use a **magnifying lens.**
4. In your Science Journal, record your observations. Make a list of any animals or evidence of animals that you find.

Think About This

1. Which animals did you observe? What evidence did you find that suggests other animals had been in your sample area?

2. Did most of the animals you found have backbones or not have backbones?

3. **Key Concept** Describe three differences among the animals without backbones that you identified.

What is an invertebrate?

What was your first thought when you saw the picture on the facing page? Maybe you wondered why there was a picture of flowers in a chapter about animals. What you saw are strawberry anemones, which are animals. They trap food in fingerlike tentacles. Anemones lack a backbone.

Recall how animals support their bodies. Most animals with an endoskeleton have a backbone for support. These animals are called vertebrates. Animals without backbones are called invertebrates. Most invertebrates support their bodies with either a hydrostatic skeleton—a fluid-filled internal cavity—or an exoskeleton—a hard outer covering. Some invertebrates have endoskeletons.

Invertebrates are about 95 percent of all known animal species. In this lesson, you will read about eight of the most common invertebrate phyla. Recall phyla are one of the taxons.

Invertebrates have many adaptations for survival. Some invertebrates are **parasites,** *animals that survive by living inside or on another organism, get food from the organism, and do not help in the organism's survival.* Other invertebrates hunt their food. Some invertebrates can even change the color of their skin to match their environments.

Key Concept Check What characteristics do invertebrates have in common?

FOLDABLES

Make a horizontal two-tab book with an extended tab. Label it as shown. Use it to identify similarities and differences in invertebrates.

Invertebrates

Common Characteristics | Differences

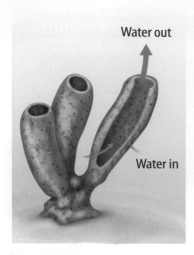

▲ **Figure 5** Water passes through sponges, and food particles are filtered out.

ACADEMIC VOCABULARY

attach
(verb) to fasten

Figure 6 Cnidarians can inject paralyzing poison into their prey. ▼

 Visual Check Where are the nematocysts on this cnidarian?

Sponges

The oldest branch of the animal family tree, phylum Porifera (puh RIH fuh ruh), includes the sponges. Sponges are often called simple animals because they have only a few types of cells and no true tissues. Sponges live in water and cannot move as adults. Instead, they **attach** to rocks and other underwater structures. Sponges take in food when water passes through their bodies, as shown in **Figure 5.** Special cells inside the sponge filter out food particles in the water.

Sponges have tiny, stiff fibers that support their bodies. Scientists group sponges by the kinds of materials that make up these fibers. The fibers in the most common group of sponges are made of the protein spongin or silica, or both. These sponges are sold as natural sponges. They are used to scrub surfaces, but the fibers can scratch shiny surfaces.

Cnidarians

Corals, anemones, jellyfish, hydras, and Portuguese man-of-wars are members of phylum Cnidaria (nih DAYR ee uh). The name *Cnidaria* comes from special cells these animals use to catch their prey. The cells—called nematocysts (NE mah toh sihsts) and shown in **Figure 6**—can inject poison into animals that come in contact with them. Cnidarians also have radial symmetry.

Cnidarians are different from sponges because they have true tissues. Some cnidarians, such as corals and anemones, spend their adult lives attached to underwater surfaces. Others, such as jellyfish, can swim.

Reading Check Identify how cnidarians are different from sponges.

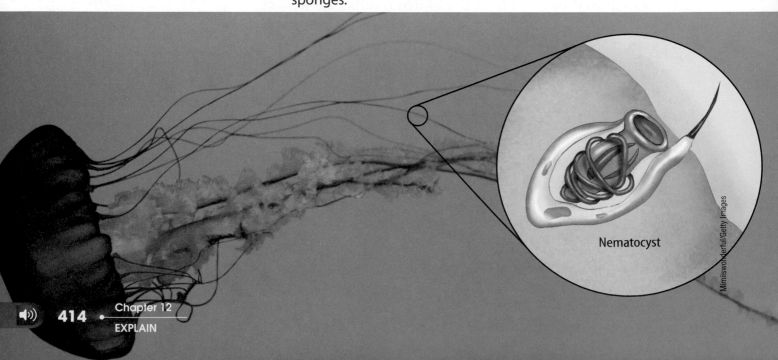

Nematocyst

Mimiswonderful/Getty Images

Flatworms

The common name for an animal in the phylum Platyhelminthes (pla tih hel MIHN theez), flatworm, describes it accurately. Its body shape is flat. Flatworms also have bilateral symmetry; each worm has a left side and a right side that are similar.

Most flatworms live in freshwater or salt water. Some flatworms are free-living. A planarian, for example, swims freely in water and ingests food through a tube on the underside of its body. Other flatworms, such as the liver fluke shown in **Figure 7,** are parasites and can infect humans.

Segmented Worms

Have you ever handled an earthworm? Did you notice that its body was like a tube of tiny rings? The name for the phylum that includes earthworms, *Annelida* (ah NEL ud uh), means "little rings." These rings, shown in **Figure 8,** are called segments. Each segment is a fluid-filled compartment. Therefore, a segmented worm has a hydrostatic skeleton.

You also might have noticed that the sides of the earthworm's body felt prickly. The prickles are tiny, stiff hairs called setae (SEE tee). Setae help earthworms grip surfaces.

Earthworms tunnel through soil and take it into their bodies to absorb nutrients from the soil. Their tunnels help break up soil. Segmented worms also can be parasites. Leeches attach their mouths to other animals and suck blood.

 Reading Check Why are Annelida called segmented worms?

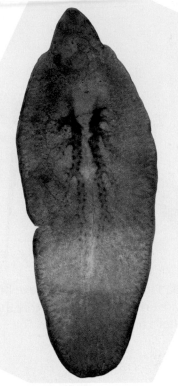

▲ **Figure 7** The liver fluke is a parasite that sometimes infects humans.

Figure 8 ⊙══ Segmented worms have bilateral symmetry. Each segment is a compartment filled with fluid. The fluid helps give the worm internal support.
▼

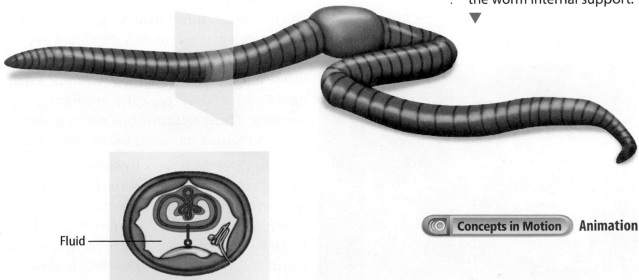

Fluid ——

《○》 **Concepts in Motion** Animation

▲ **Figure 9** Mollusks have bilateral symmetry. Most mollusks, such as this snail, have external shells for protection.

Mollusks

On summer mornings, you might notice thin, slimy trails across a sidewalk. These trails were likely made by snails or slugs searching for food during the night. Snails, such as the one shown in **Figure 9,** and slugs are mollusks in phylum Mollusca (mah LUS kuh). Most mollusks have a footlike muscle that generally is used for movement. A mollusk also has a mass of tissue called a mantle. A **mantle** *is a thin layer of tissue that covers a mollusk's internal organs.* It also is involved in making the shell of most mollusks. A mollusk's shell supports and protects its soft body. Some mollusks, such as slugs, do not have shells. Other mollusks, such as squids, have internal shells.

Reading Check Name one type of mollusk that does not have a shell.

The eating methods of mollusks vary. Some mollusks, such as clams, oysters, and scallops, eat by filtering food particles from the water in which they live. Other mollusks, such as octopuses, are predators and catch their prey in long, strong tentacles.

Roundworms

Animals in phylum Nematoda (ne muh TOH duh) are called nematodes or roundworms. Some roundworms can infect humans, and others can infect plant roots. Others, such as the vinegar eel shown in **Figure 10,** are harmless to humans. Most roundworms live in soil and are too small to see without a magnifying lens. They typically are harmless to humans. These roundworms eat dead organisms and return nutrients to the soil.

Roundworms have a hydrostatic skeleton for movement. They also have a hard outer covering, called a cuticle, for protection. The cuticle does not grow. It must be shed and replaced with a larger cuticle for the roundworm to grow. *An outer covering is shed and replaced in a process called* **molting**.

Figure 10 The vinegar eel is a roundworm that feeds on organisms used in making vinegar. It is harmless but is removed from vinegar by the manufacturer. All roundworms have bilateral symmetry. ▼

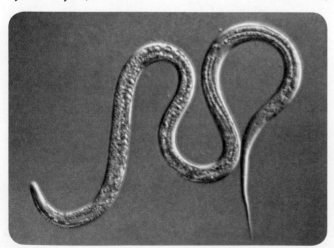

Arthropods

Can you imagine a billion billion of something? Scientists estimate that is how many individual arthropods there are on Earth. There are more animals in phylum Arthropoda (ar THRAH puh duh) than in all other animal phyla combined. Arthropods have bilateral symmetry.

Like a roundworm, an arthropod has a hard outer covering, so it must molt in order to grow. An arthropod has an exoskeleton for both movement and protection. Its muscles attach to the exoskeleton. An arthropod uses its muscles when moving its jointed appendages. An appendage is a structure, such as a leg or an arm, that extends from the central part of the body.

Arthropod bodies have three parts: a head, a thorax, and an abdomen. The head contains sense organs that can see, feel, and taste the environment. The thorax is where legs are attached. The abdomen contains intestines and reproductive organs. Arthropods have open circulation. This means their blood is not in vessels. Instead, it washes over internal organs.

Insects Most arthropods are insects, such as the one shown in **Figure 11.** Scientists call them hexapods because they have six legs. Insects are the only arthropods that have the ability to fly. Another trait of insects is metamorphosis. In **metamorphosis,** *the body form of an animal changes as it grows from an egg to an adult.* For example, a caterpillar eventually changes into a moth or a butterfly.

Figure 11 The Colorado potato beetle is a pest of potato crops.

WORD ORIGIN

metamorphosis
from Greek *metamorphoun,*
means "to transform"

Inquiry MiniLab

10 minutes

Bigger on Land or in Water?

Invertebrates come in many sizes. A fruit fly is about 3 mm long. The Chilean rose hair tarantula is a large spider. It can have a leg span of 12.5 cm as an adult. It gets its name from its rose-colored hair.

1. In your Science Journal, write the following list of invertebrates in order from smallest in size to largest in size: anemone, ant, bee, butterfly, earthworm, fly, jellyfish, lobster, octopus, spider, sponge, and sea star.

2. Identify each of the organisms as either an aquatic invertebrate (lives in water) or a terrestrial invertebrate (lives on land).

Analyze and Conclude

1. **Interpret Data** Based on your list of invertebrates, which tend to be larger—aquatic or terrestrial invertebrates?

2. **Infer** Why do you think the group you chose in question 1 is able to be larger?

3. **Key Concept** How does the relationship between invertebrate animal size and habitat compare to vertebrate animal size and habitat?

(t)Scott Bauer/USDA, (b)Jeffrey Coolidge/Getty Images

Other Arthropod Groups There are three other major groups of arthropods. Spiders and scorpions are one group. They have eight legs used for walking and grasping. Crabs and lobsters make up another group. Members of this group mostly live in water. They have chewing mouthparts and three or more pairs of legs. Some lobsters have as many as 19 pairs of appendages! Centipedes and millipedes are in another group. They have the most appendages of all. Generally, a centipede has one pair of legs per segment and a millipede has two pairs per segment. Millipedes eat dead plants, but centipedes are predators.

Echinoderms

Do the animals in **Figure 12** appear fuzzy and soft? Touch an echinoderm (ih KI nuh durm), from the phylum Echinodermata (ih kin uh DUR muh tuh), and you will find it is the opposite. *Echinoderm* means "spiny skin." An echinoderm feels spiny due to the hard endoskeleton just beneath its thin outer skin.

Sea star

Sea cucumber

Sea urchin

Figure 12 Echinoderms have hard, spiny skin. They move slowly using tube feet.

 Visual Check For which echinoderm is it hard to identify radial symmetry?

All echinoderms live in salt water. They move slowly with tiny suction-cuplike feet, called tube feet. Their tube feet are connected to larger tubes called canals. These canals connect to a central ring that controls water movement within the animal. Water moves back and forth through the canals and tube feet. This movement enables echinoderms to grab onto or let go of any surface they are moving across. Echinoderms have bilateral symmetry when they are young, and radial symmetry as adults.

Echinoderms are more closely related to humans than all other invertebrates. Both echinoderm embryos and human embryos have similar early growth patterns.

Key Concept Check How do the invertebrate groups differ?

Visual Summary

Invertebrates do not have a backbone; they support their bodies with an exo-skeleton, an endo-skeleton, or a hydrostatic skeleton.

Sponges and cnidari-ans are the oldest branches on the ani-mal family tree.

Insects have three body parts—the head, the thorax, and the abdomen.

FOLDABLES

Use your lesson Foldable to review the lesson. Save your Foldable for the project at the end of the chapter.

What do you think NOW?

You first read the statements below at the beginning of the chapter.

3. A sponge is not an animal because it cannot move.

4. There are more arthropods on Earth than all other kinds of animals combined.

Did you change your mind about whether you agree or disagree with the statements? Rewrite any false statements to make them true.

Use Vocabulary

1. The tissue involved in making the shell of most mollusks is called the _____.

2. **Use the term** *metamorphosis* in a complete sentence.

3. **Define** *parasite* in your own words.

Understand Key Concepts 🔑

4. Which characteristic is common to all invertebrates?
   A. backbone   C. cell walls
   B. mantle   D. no backbone

5. **Explain** how a scientist might determine that a grasshopper is an arthropod.

6. **Describe** how an echinoderm is different from a cnidarian.

Interpret Graphics

7. **Summarize** Use the graphic organizer below to identify which invertebrate phyla have bilateral symmetry.

8. **Classify** the animal shown below as a mollusk, an arthropod, or a cnidarian. Explain your choice.

Critical Thinking

9. **Diagram** an ant, and label the three body parts that are common to all arthropods.

10. **Analyze** why some invertebrates that live in the sea grow to be larger than invertebrates that live on land.

(l)Scott Bauer/USDA, (r)age fotostock/SuperStock

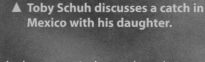
Investigating True Bugs

Toby Schuh discusses a catch in Mexico with his daughter.

True Bugs Close-Up

Here's a look at a few remarkable true bugs:

This sea skater (*Gerris lacustris*) spends its entire life on the ocean surface.

The southern green stink bug (*Nezara viridula*) gives off a strong odor when disturbed.

Meet Toby Schuh, a scientist who studies bugs.

Many of the amazing creatures people call bugs aren't really bugs at all. Bees, flies, butterflies, ground beetles, and ladybugs are examples of insects. However, scientists classify some insects into a group called "true bugs." This group includes assassin bugs that shoot poison into their prey, water striders that "skate" on water, and stink bugs that ooze smelly fluid.

How are true bugs different from other insects? Just ask Dr. Toby Schuh. He's an entomologist, a scientist who studies insects, at the American Museum of Natural History. He specializes in true bugs.

All insects have six legs, three body sections, and usually two pairs of wings. Bugs are a group of insects that share certain characteristics. They use slender, tubelike mouthparts to suck fluids from plants and sometimes from animals. Their saliva, or spit, has chemicals that break down food into liquid. They also have "stink glands" that release scents for finding mates, defending themselves, and communicating with each other. True bugs hatch from their eggs looking like small versions of adults. They don't go through a gradual metamorphosis as many insects, such as butterflies, do. During metamorphosis, an animal changes from one form to another as it develops from an egg to an adult.

Scientists have identified more than 40,000 species of true bugs, and they discover new ones all the time. Schuh is in charge of a worldwide database called the Plant Bug Planetary Biodiversity Inventory. It tracks information about true bugs. He also adds to this collection by searching for new species in places such as Africa, Australia, and South America. So far, Schuh and his colleagues have discovered over 1,200 new species of true bugs. Their search continues.

It's Your Turn

DIAGRAM Choose a true bug to research. Draw a picture of it. Label the features that make it an insect and the features that make it a true bug. Share your labeled diagram with your class.

Chordates

Reading Guide

Key Concepts 🔑
ESSENTIAL QUESTIONS

- What characteristics do chordates have in common?
- What is the difference between vertebrate and invertebrate chordates?
- How do the groups of vertebrate chordates differ?

Vocabulary

notochord

pharyngeal pouch

gill

amnion

ectotherm

endotherm

mammary gland

 Multilingual eGlossary

 Video Science Video

 AID M1.1c, M3.1a; IS 1.3; LE 5.1a

Inquiry **Are they related?**

The two animals in this photo appear different. The fish has a backbone. The purple tunicate does not. However, both belong to the phylum Chordata. What similar traits do these animals display?

Mathieu Meur/Stocktrek Images/Getty Images

What animals are around you?

Have you ever noticed all the animals around you in the park or in your neighborhood?

1 In your Science Journal, make a list of all the animals you have seen in your neighborhood or at a park.

2 Classify each of the animals you listed as either a vertebrate or an invertebrate.

3 Tally the number of vertebrates on your list. Do the same for the invertebrates.

Think About This

1. How do your totals compare with those of your classmates?

2. Did you think of more vertebrates or invertebrates? Why?

3. 🔑 **Key Concept** What do you think are two main differences between land vertebrates and invertebrates?

FOLDABLES

Make a horizontal three-tab Venn book. Label it as shown. Use it to compare and contrast the different types of chordates.

WORD ORIGIN

notochord
from Greek *notos*, means "back"; and Latin *chorda*, means "cord"

What is a chordate?

Think of the zoo you read about at the beginning of this chapter. It's likely that most of the animals at the zoo were chordates. It also is likely that most of the animals at the zoo were mammals, like you. Chordates are animals that are grouped in the phylum Chordata. Mammals are chordates.

There are two types of chordates—vertebrate chordates and invertebrate chordates. Recall that a vertebrate is an animal with a backbone. An invertebrate chordate shares many traits with vertebrates, but it has no backbone. All chordates have four traits in common: a notochord, a tail, a nerve cord, and pharyngeal pouches. These four traits exist at some time during the life of a chordate.

You are a chordate. When you were developing in the womb, you had a notochord. *A* **notochord** *is a flexible rod-shaped structure that supports the body of a developing chordate.* It was replaced by your backbone. You also had a tail. What is left of your tail is your tailbone. Before you had a brain and a spinal cord, you had a nerve cord. You also had pharyngeal (fuh run JEE uhl) pouches. **Pharyngeal pouches** *are grooves along the side of a developing chordate.* Your pharyngeal pouches developed into parts of your ears, head, and neck. Fish have pharyngeal slits that provide support for gills. That you had these characteristics at one time is evidence that you and other chordates have ancestors in common.

🔑 **Key Concept Check** Name characteristics all chordates share.

John Giustina/Getty Images

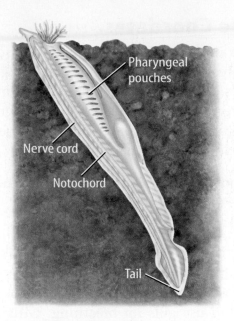

Figure 13 🔑 Lancelets live today, but they probably resemble the ancestor to all chordates.

Pharyngeal pouches

Nerve cord

Notochord

Tail

Invertebrate Chordates

As you have read, some chordates never develop backbones. These animals are called invertebrate chordates. The tunicate in the picture at the beginning of this lesson is an invertebrate chordate. You will read about tunicates later. But first, what did the ancestor of chordates look like?

Lancelets

The earliest chordates probably looked similar to the lancelet in **Figure 13.** Lancelets are small animals found burrowed in the sand just off ocean shores. Lancelets grow only 5 cm in length. Lancelets can swim, but they often sit in the sand and catch food particles floating by. Lancelets have all four chordate traits, as shown in **Figure 13.**

Tunicates

Adult tunicates, shown in the photo at the beginning of this lesson, look like sponges. Like sponges, adult tunicates live in the sea attached to rocks or other stationary objects. However, adult tunicates have organized tissues and internal structures such as organs. They also have all the characteristics of chordates at some time in their lives. If you study a tunicate before it becomes an adult, you will see an animal that looks and acts like a tadpole. Young tunicates can swim and have all four chordate traits.

Lancelets look more like fish than tunicates. Therefore, scientists once thought lancelets were more closely related to vertebrates than tunicates were. But when scientists studied the DNA of all three groups, they discovered the opposite to be true. Vertebrate and tunicate DNA is more similar than vertebrate and lancelet DNA.

Vertebrate Chordates

Most of the animals you are familiar with are probably vertebrate chordates. This group includes cats, dogs, fish, snakes, frogs, and birds. Recall that vertebrates are animals with backbones. Most vertebrates also have jaws. As vertebrate bodies and skeletons continued to adapt, vertebrates became better at catching food and avoiding being eaten.

 Key Concept Check What is the difference between invertebrate and vertebrate chordates?

Fish

When you think of a fish, you might think of a goldfish. You even might think of a shark. But would you think of a sea horse? All are fish and have traits that make them fish. All fish live in water and use gills for breathing. **Gills** *are organs that exchange carbon dioxide for oxygen in the water.* All fish have powerful tails, and most fish have paired fins. There are three major groups of fish, as shown in **Table 1.**

Table 1  Fish are classified into three different groups.

Visual Check Which group of fish does not have paired fins?

Table 1 Groups of Fish

Jawless Fish Lampreys are jawless fish. The skeleton of jawless fish is made of cartilage. The tip of your nose and the flaps of your ears are made of cartilage. Some jawless fish get their nutrition from other fish. They have a circle of teeth that attach to the sides of other fish and make a wound. They then slowly suck out blood and other body fluid from the fish.

Sharks and Rays Most of the skeleton of sharks and rays is made of cartilage. However, shark skulls are made of bone. Sharks have paired fins. They are fast swimmers and also have powerful jaws. Their jaws make them dangerous predators of other animals, especially other fish.

Bony Fish All other fish have a bony skeleton, as well as paired fins and jaws. Bony fish, such as goldfish, also have a special sac called a swim bladder that the fish can fill with gas. This helps the fish move up and down in the water. Sea horses are unique bony fish because the males carry the young in their bodies as they develop.

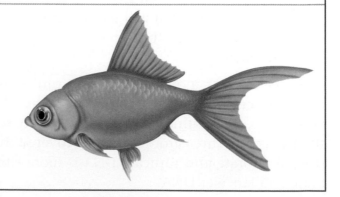

Amphibians

In Canada in 2004, scientists discovered the fossil of an animal that lived long ago in shallow water. The animal had both gills and lungs, a flexible neck, and fins with arm and hand bones. The fins could help the animal move in the water and on land. The scientists think they discovered one of the first tetrapods. A tetrapod is a vertebrate animal with four limbs.

Amphibians are a group of tetrapods that live on land. But like the fossil described above, amphibians still depend on water to survive and reproduce. The word *amphibian* means "both ways of life." Most amphibians must lay their eggs in water. In addition, young amphibians, such as tadpoles, have gills and must spend most of their time in water. Most adult amphibians have lungs for breathing on land. However, amphibian skin is thin and moist. On land, amphibians must live in moist habitats to keep their bodies from drying out.

 Reading Check Summarize the characteristics of amphibians.

There are three types of amphibians, as shown in **Figure 14.** Salamanders and newts have tails and move by bending their bodies side-to-side. Frogs and toads do not have tails as adults. They have long legs that enable them to jump. Some frogs can jump several meters in one bound! Caecilians (sih SIHL yuhnz) are a group of amphibians that do not have legs. They look similar to earthworms and move by twisting their bodies back and forth like a snake.

Scientists are concerned about the survival of amphibians. Many amphibian populations have become smaller since 1980. Some types of amphibians have not been seen for years. Scientists think the amphibian population is decreasing because of disease, climate change, herbicides, and the destruction of amphibian habitat.

Some adult salamanders live on land.

Frog legs are longer and more powerful than toad legs.

Caecilians burrow in the soil.

Figure 14 ⌐ The three types of amphibians look different, but all have similar characteristics.

Figure 15 Reptiles, birds, and mammals do not require water for reproduction. The amniotic egg protects the developing embryo.

✓ Visual Check What surrounds the developing embryo?

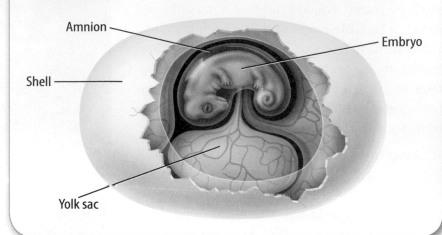

Amnion

Embryo

Shell

Yolk sac

Math Skills

Use a Formula

The size of two organisms might be the same, but one floats while the other sinks. This is because the organisms have different densities. The formula for density is

$$\text{density} = \frac{\text{mass}}{\text{volume}}$$

For example, what is the density of a chicken's leg bone that has a mass of 5.5 g and a volume of 5.0 cm³?

Replace the terms in the formula with the given values.

$$\text{density} = \frac{5.5 \text{ g}}{5.0 \text{ cm}^3}$$

Solve the problem.

$$\frac{5.5 \text{ g}}{5.0 \text{ cm}^3} = \frac{1.1 \text{ g}}{\text{cm}^3}$$

Practice

A piece of a cow's leg bone with a volume of 10 cm³ has a mass of 18 g. What is the density of the bone?

▣ Review

- **Math Practice**
- **Personal Tutor**

Reptiles

Lizards and snakes, turtles, and alligators and crocodiles are the three most common groups of reptiles. Most reptiles live on land, and all have lungs for breathing. **Scales** on their skin prevent reptiles from drying out. Reptiles also do not need water to lay their eggs. Most reptiles lay shelled eggs that don't dry out. Inside the egg is **amnion**, *a protective membrane that surrounds the embryo.* An egg with an amnion is called an amniotic egg, as shown in **Figure 15.** Reptiles, birds, and mammals all have amniotic eggs.

One group of reptiles includes both lizards and snakes. Most lizards are small and can fit in your hand. However, one lizard, the Komodo dragon, can grow up to 3 m. Snakes are legless reptiles. Many snakes also are small, but some can be several meters long. All snakes eat other animals. When snakes catch their prey, they can crush them or bite and poison them. Either way, most snakes swallow their prey whole!

Turtles are best known for their protective shells. Some turtles can live in the desert. Others, such as snapping turtles and sea turtles, live mostly in water.

Alligators and crocodiles are found in warm parts of the world. They live in or near water but lay their eggs in nests on the shore. They are fierce hunters and can move quickly for short distances.

Reptiles are **ectotherms**, *animals that heat their bodies from heat in their environments.* Warming, or basking, in sunlight is a behavioral adaptation of ectotherms. A reptile with a warm body can move faster and catch prey more easily. Reptiles move to cool, dark places to conserve energy when food is scarce.

Birds

Can you name a unique trait of birds? Did you think of flight? Many insects fly, and so do certain mammals. Some birds, such as penguins and emus, don't fly. Maybe you thought of wings. But most insects and some mammals also have wings. The one trait that makes birds different from all other animals is their feathers.

Birds have many adaptations that enable them to fly. A bird does not have a urinary bladder to weigh the bird down when the bladder is full. Instead, birds concentrate their urine into crystals. The crystals are the white part of bird droppings. Birds have bones that are nearly hollow and filled with air. This makes the bones lighter than the bones of other vertebrates.

Wings and feathers are birds' major adaptations for flight. A bird's wings are connected to powerful chest muscles. Bird wings come in different shapes. Long, narrow wings enable a seagull to soar on long flights. The short, broad wings of a sparrow, shown in **Figure 16,** enable quick changes of direction to catch food or escape an enemy.

✓ Reading Check Describe the different shapes of bird wings, and explain how the shapes help the birds survive.

Feathers also keep birds warm. Unlike reptiles, birds are **endotherms,** *animals that generate their body heat from the inside.* This enables birds to live in cold habitats. However, keeping their body temperatures high requires much energy. Like you, birds shiver when they get cold. Shivering muscles help produce more body heat.

Figure 16 Short, broad wings help a sparrow survive.

Inquiry MiniLab **30 minutes**

Which bone is less dense?

The number of bones in a vertebrate varies from one species to another. Many birds have about 120 bones in their bodies. Humans have just over 200. Dogs have over 300! How do the bones of animals compare?

1. Read and complete a lab safety form.

2. Copy the table below into your Science Journal.

Bone Type	Mass (g)	Volume (mL)	Density (g/mL)
Chicken bone			
Mammal bone			

3. Use a **triple-beam balance** to find the mass of a **dry chicken bone.** Record the mass in your table.

4. Find the volume of the chicken bone using water displacement. Place 50 mL of water in a 100-mL **graduated cylinder.** Place the chicken bone in the water, and record the combined volume of water and chicken bone. Calculate the volume of the chicken bone by subtracting the volume of water from the combined volume of the water and the chicken bone. Record the volume in your table.

5. Repeat steps 3 and 4 for the **mammal bone.**

Analyze and Conclude

1. **Make and Use Tables** Complete the table by calculating the density for each of the bones. Recall that density = mass/volume. Be sure to include units. How do the densities of the chicken and mammal bones compare?

2. 🔑 **Key Concept** Evaluate how the difference in densities might be considered a physical adaptation for birds.

An echidna is a monotreme.

This opossum raises its young in a pouch.

Like most mammals, this coyote is a placental mammal.

Figure 17 There are three different groups of mammals, but all have hair and nourish their young with milk.

Mammals

Maybe the main reason to go to the zoo is to see the mammals. Lemurs, lions, alpacas, and apes all are mammals. You are a mammal, too. All mammals have hair and **mammary glands,** *special tissues that produce milk for young mammals.* Like birds, mammals are endotherms. The hair of mammals is an adaptation that helps keep them warm. Milk production also is an adaptation. The milk helps the young grow and survive when they are too young to find their own food. There are three groups of mammals: monotremes, marsupials, and placental mammals, as shown in **Figure 17.**

Monotremes A few types of mammals lay eggs. When their young hatch, they are nourished by their mother's milk. These mammals include the platypus and the echidna.

Marsupials Mammals that raise their young in pouches are called marsupials. The young are not fully developed when born. After birth, they crawl through their mother's hair into a pouch. Here they can drink their mother's milk and continue to grow. Most marsupials are native to, or live in, Australia. Many marsupials resemble mammals that live in North America. There are marsupial squirrels, marsupial mice, and marsupial moles! The only marsupial native to North America is the opossum, shown in **Figure 17.**

Placental Mammals The last group of mammals is called placental mammals. They have a structure called a placenta that the young are attached to as they grow inside the mother. You are probably most familiar with different kinds of placental mammals, such as dogs, cats, horses, cows, and humans.

 Key Concept Check How do the groups of vertebrate chordates differ?

Lesson 3 Review

Visual Summary

There are two types of chordates—vertebrate chordates and invertebrate chordates.

Invertebrate chordates do not have a backbone and include lancelets and tunicates.

Vertebrate chordates have a backbone and include fish, amphibians, reptiles, birds, and mammals.

FOLDABLES®

Use your lesson Foldable to review the lesson. Save your Foldable for the project at the end of the chapter.

What do you think NOW?

You first read the statements below at the beginning of the chapter.

5. All young mammals take in milk from their mothers.

6. Birds are the only animals that lay shelled eggs.

Did you change your mind about whether you agree or disagree with the statements? Rewrite any false statements to make them true.

Use Vocabulary

1. **Contrast** ectotherms and endotherms.

2. **Define** *pharyngeal pouches* and *gills*.

3. **Use the term** *amnion* in a sentence.

Understand Key Concepts

4. Which is a characteristic all chordates have in common?

   A. amnion   **C.** mammary glands
   B. notochord   **D.** paired fins

5. **Summarize** the difference between invertebrate and vertebrate chordates.

6. **Explain** how amphibians are different from reptiles.

Interpret Graphics

7. **Summarize** Copy and fill in the graphic organizer below to summarize the four characteristics of all chordates.

Chordate characteristics

Critical Thinking

8. **Assess** the benefits of the structure shown in the figure below.

Math Skills

Review
Math Practice

9. A wing bone from a flying bird has a mass of 1.8 g. The volume of the bone is 3.0 cm³. What is the density of the bone?

Animal Adaptations

Materials

number die

coin

drawing supplies

Safety

Did you know that some breeds of chickens are well-suited for living in warm environments, while others are better suited for living in cool environments? Chickens accustomed to a warmer climate tend to have few feathers near their legs and feet to help them stay cool. They also have large combs. These chickens are able to lose heat through their combs, much like we lose heat through our heads. Chickens accustomed to cooler climates have the opposite characteristics, feathery legs and feet and small combs. Most animals are well-suited for their environments. If you knew about a species' habitat and needs, what adaptations would help ensure the survival of the species?

Question

What adaptations would help your animal survive in its environment?

Procedure

1. Read and complete a lab safety form.

2. Flip a coin to determine whether your animal is an invertebrate or a vertebrate. If you get heads, your animal will be an invertebrate. If you get tails, it will be a vertebrate. Record the result in your Science Journal.

3. Roll the die to determine your animal's habitat. If you roll a 1, your animal is aquatic. If you roll a 2, your animal is terrestrial. If you roll a 3, your animal lives in trees. If you roll a 4, your animal is primarily aerial and is able to fly. If you roll a 5 or a 6, roll again. Record the result.

4. Roll the die to determine what your animal eats. If you roll a 1 or a 2, your animal is an herbivore and eats only plants. If you roll a 3 or a 4, your animal is a carnivore and eats only other animals. If you roll a 5 or a 6, your animal is an omnivore and can eat both plants and other animals. Record the result.

5. Roll the die to determine your animal's body plan. If you roll a 1 or a 2, your animal has no appendages. If you roll a 3 or a 4, your animal can have 1–4 appendages. If you roll a 5 or a 6, your animal can have 5 or more appendages. Record the result.

(t to b)©Ingram Publishing/Fotosearch; (2)McGraw-Hill Education; (3)Jacques Cornell/McGraw-Hill Education; (cr)Mikael Nordin/iStock/Getty Images; (br)©Wayne Hutchinson/AgStock Images/Corbis

6. Flip a coin to determine your animal's sleep pattern. If you get heads, your animal will be diurnal and is awake during the day. If you get tails, your animal will be nocturnal and is awake during the night. Record the result.

7. Review the list of restrictions/parameters that you have for your animal. Identify and write down physical features that you can give your animal to help them better survive where and how they live.

8. Using the materials provided, sketch a model of your animal and its adaptations. Write a paragraph explaining the adaptations your animal has and their usefulness.

Analyze and Conclude

9. **Predict** Choose a different habitat than the one you were assigned. Identify two things you would change about your animal's adaptations. Explain how the changes would make your animal better suited for its new habitat.

10. **Compare and Contrast** Choose an animal with adaptations designed by another classmate. Does it have any similar adaptations to your animal? Why do you think this is so?

11. **The Big Idea** How can adaptations be used to classify animals?

Communicate Your Results

Share your animal sketch with your classmates. Identify and explain the special adaptations that your animal has and why it has them.

Extension

Perform some additional research into periods of mass extinctions. Explore the adaptations, physical and behavioral, of the animals that survived during those periods, or create a three-dimensional model of your animal.

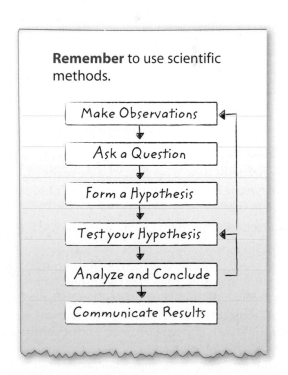

Remember to use scientific methods.

Make Observations
↓
Ask a Question
↓
Form a Hypothesis
↓
Test your Hypothesis
↓
Analyze and Conclude
↓
Communicate Results

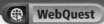
 THE BIG IDEA

Animals are multicellular, have muscle cells and nerve cells, cannot make their own food, and ingest their food. Animals are grouped by how they develop and by what type of symmetry they display.

Key Concepts Summary 🔑	Vocabulary
Lesson 1: What are animals? • All animals are multicellular, have collagen protein to hold their cells together, have muscle and nerve cells, and cannot make their own food. • Animals are grouped by what kinds of symmetry they have and by how they develop. • Animal species are adapted to their environments by having unique structures, exhibiting specialized behaviors, and reproducing by certain methods. 	**bilateral symmetry** **radial symmetry** **asymmetry** **adaptation** **hydrostatic skeleton** **exoskeleton** **endoskeleton**
Lesson 2: Invertebrates 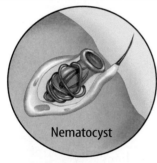 Nematocyst • Invertebrates do not have backbones, and instead they have hydrostatic skeletons, endoskeletons, or exoskeletons. • Invertebrates differ in how they develop as embryos, how they support their soft bodies, how they live and obtain food, and in their symmetry.	**parasite** **mantle** **molting** **metamorphosis**
Lesson 3: Chordates • All chordates have a nerve cord, a **notochord, pharyngeal pouches** or slits, and a tail at some time in their lives. • Invertebrate chordates never develop a backbone. • Vertebrate chordates can be fish, fully aquatic with fins and **gills**. They may be amphibians with four limbs and aquatic fertilization; or reptiles, **ectotherms** with scaly skin and an **amnion**. They also may be birds, **endotherms** with feathers and an amnion; or mammals, endotherms with an amnion, hair, and mammary glands.	**notochord** **pharyngeal pouch** **gill** **amnion** **ectotherm** **endotherm** **mammary gland**

FOLDABLES® Chapter Project

Assemble your lesson Foldables as shown to make a Chapter Project. Use the project to review what you have learned in this chapter.

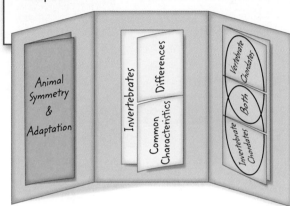

Use Vocabulary

1 Use *molting* in a sentence.

2 Define the term *adaptation* in your own words.

3 Use *hydrostatic skeleton* in a sentence.

4 Animals that heat their bodies from heat in their environments are called _____ .

5 An animal that lives inside another animal, gets food from the other animal, and does not help it survive is called a(n) _____ .

6 Special tissue that produces milk for young animals is called _____ .

Link Vocabulary and Key Concepts

Concepts in Motion Interactive Concept Map

Copy this concept map, and then use vocabulary terms from the previous page to complete the concept map.

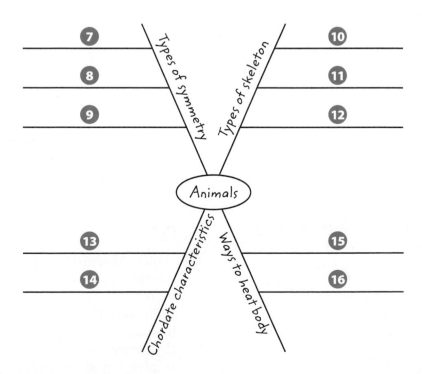

Understand Key Concepts 🗝️

1 Which is a characteristic common to all animals?

A. asymmetry
B. collagen
C. endothermy
D. exoskeleton

2 Which is NOT a type of body plan in animals?

A. asymmetry
B. ectothermy
C. bilateral symmetry
D. radial symmetry

3 Which best describes an adaptation?

A. A trait that has no effect on the survival of an individual.
B. A trait that makes it difficult for an individual to survive.
C. A trait that makes a population a better match for its environment and helps it survive.
D. A trait that shows up in an individual but is not passed on to its offspring.

4 Examine the branching tree diagram below.

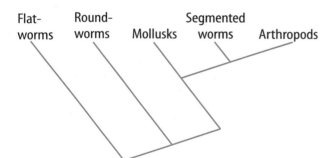

Which group of animals is most closely related to segmented worms?

A. arthropods
B. flatworms
C. mollusks
D. roundworms

5 Which is true of invertebrates?

A. They have no backbones.
B. They have no muscle tissue.
C. They have no nervous tissue.
D. They have no skeletons.

6 In which group would you place the animal pictured below?

A. arthropods
B. echinoderms
C. flatworms
D. sponges

7 Which is NOT a typical chordate characteristic?

A. nerve cord
B. notochord
C. scales
D. tail

8 Which chordate might be confused with an invertebrate?

A. marsupial
B. sea horse
C. snake
D. tunicate

9 Which structural adaptation made it possible for vertebrates to reproduce on land?

A. exoskeleton
B. spiracles
C. amniotic egg
D. pharyngeal pouches

Critical Thinking

10 **Evaluate** the importance of the amnion to life on land.

11 **Compare** ectotherms and endotherms.

12 **Summarize** the characteristics that are common to all chordates.

13 **Evaluate** why so many vertebrate animals have jaws.

14 **Infer** how you, a human, can be classified as a chordate when you have no tail.

15 **Justify** why the organism shown below is considered an animal.

16 **Assess** the role of endothermy in an animal's ability to survive and reproduce.

17 **Formulate** a theory of why mammals are able to live in so many different kinds of environments.

Writing in Science

18 **Write** a five-sentence paragraph comparing the adaptation of feathers in birds to the adaptation of hair in mammals. Be sure to include a topic sentence and a concluding sentence in your paragraph.

REVIEW THE **BIG** IDEA

19 **Assess** how you would determine whether a new organism you found was an animal, and how you would decide what kind of animal it was.

20 What are animals and how are they classified? Use the animals in the photo below as examples.

Math Skills

📖 **Review**
— Math Practice —

Use a Formula

The table below shows the mass and the volume of several sample leg bones. Use the table to answer questions 21 and 22.

Animal	Mass (g)	Volume (cm³)
Giraffe	76.8	40
Human	46.25	25

21 What is the density of the giraffe's leg bone?

22 What is the density of the human's leg bone?

23 A chicken's leg bone has a density of about 1.11 g/cm³.

   a. Would you expect the density of a buffalo's leg bone to be greater or less than a chicken's leg bone? Explain.

   b. A buffalo's leg bone with a volume of 35 cm³ has a mass of 68.6 g. What is the density of the buffalo's leg bone?

Record your answers on the answer sheet provided by your teacher or on a sheet of paper.

Multiple Choice

1 Which is a similarity between plants and animals?

 A Both have cells with cell walls.

 B Both have cells with nuclei.

 C Both have nerve cells.

 D Both use light to make energy.

2 Which is the main difference between vertebrates and invertebrates?

 A Invertebrates have backbones, and vertebrates do not.

 B Invertebrates only live in water, and vertebrates live in many environments.

 C There are many more vertebrate species than invertebrates.

 D Vertebrates have backbones, and invertebrates do not.

3 The human brain and spinal cord develop from which structure?

 A nerve cord

 B notochord

 C pharyngeal pouch

 D tail

Use the diagram to answer question 4.

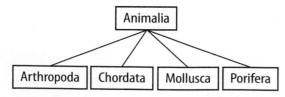

4 What taxon level is Porifera?

 A genus

 B kingdom

 C phylum

 D species

5 Which characteristic is found only in mammals?

 A Mammals are endotherms and generate body heat.

 B Mammals have lungs for respiration on land.

 C Mammals produce milk for their young.

 D Mammals use amniotic eggs for reproduction.

Use the diagram to answer question 6.

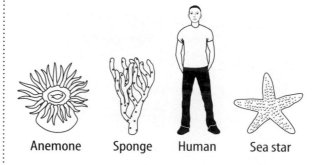

Anemone   Sponge   Human   Sea star

6 Which animal is an example of bilateral symmetry?

 A anemone

 B human

 C sea star

 D sponge

7 Which is NOT a characteristic of arthropods?

 A Arthropods have hard exoskeletons.

 B Arthropods have blood vessels.

 C Arthropods are a very large group of species.

 D Arthropods have a head, a thorax, and an abdomen.

8 Which is an example of a behavioral adaptation?

   A a hydrostatic skeleton

   B an open circulatory system

   C external fertilization in water

   D waving wings to attract a mate

Use the diagram to answer question 9.

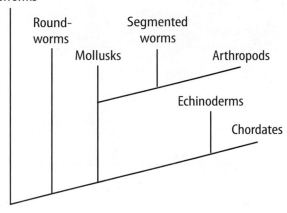

Flatworms

9 Which invertebrate phylum is most closely related to chordates?

   A arthropods

   B echinoderms

   C mollusks

   D sponges

10 Why is a lancelet classified as an invertebrate chordate?

   A It can swim.

   B It does not have a backbone.

   C It lives near the ocean.

   D It lives under the ground.

Constructed Response

11 What type of habitat do amphibians need to survive? What change in that habitat would cause amphibian populations to decline?

12 An explorer discovers a new species on the sea floor. The explorer isn't sure if this discovery is an animal. What would he or she look for to classify this discovery as an animal?

Use the diagram to answer question 13.

13 Based on the physical characteristics of this organism, what phylum could it belong to? Explain why you made this choice.

14 Name an adaptation of an animal you are familiar with. How does this adaptation help the animal survive or reproduce? Is the adaptation structural, behavioral, or functional? Explain why.

NEED EXTRA HELP?													
If You Missed Question...	1	2	3	4	5	6	7	8	9	10	11	12	13	14
Go to Lesson...	1	2	3	1	3	1	2	1	1	3	3	1	2	1

Digestion and Excretion

THE BIG IDEA

How do the digestive and excretory systems help maintain the body's homeostasis?

Inquiry **Why So Long?**

This image shows parts of the digestive system. The small intestine is the structure that looks like a tangled-up rope. The small intestine can be up to 6 m long.

- Why do you think the small intestine is so long?

- What do you think the function of the small intestine is?

- How might the digestive system help your body maintain homeostasis?

MedicalRF.com/Getty Images

Get Ready to Read

What do you think?

Before you read, decide if you agree or disagree with each of these statements. As you read this chapter, see if you change your mind about any of the statements.

1. An activity such as sleeping does not require energy.
2. All fats in food should be avoided.
3. Digestion begins in the mouth.
4. Energy from food stays in the digestive system.
5. Several human body systems work together to eliminate wastes.
6. Blood contains waste products that must be removed from the body.

 **ConnectED** Your one-stop online resource

MHEonline.com

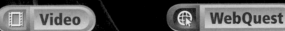 Video

 WebQuest

Audio

Assessment

Review

Concepts in Motion

Inquiry

Multilingual eGlossary

Lesson 1

Nutrition

Reading Guide

Key Concepts
ESSENTIAL QUESTIONS

- Why do you eat?
- Why does your body need each of the six groups of nutrients?
- Why is eating a balanced diet important?

Vocabulary

Calorie

protein

carbohydrate

fat

vitamin

mineral

 Multilingual eGlossary

Video **Science Video**

AID S3.1a; LE 5.2a, 5.2b, 5.2c, 5.2d, 5.2e

 **Time for Lunch?**

This photo shows fried moth larvae. It might not look appetizing, but it contains nutrients your body needs for energy and growth. Nutrients are in many different foods, from a cheeseburger to a fried insect.

Svetliana/Getty Images

How much energy is in an almond?

Food contains energy. Is there enough energy in an almond to boil water?

1 Read and complete a lab safety form.

2 Place a small amount of **clay** in a **shallow baking dish.** Straighten a **metal paper clip.** Insert one end into an unshelled **almond.** Anchor the other end in the clay.

3 Place a **25-mL test tube** in a **test-tube clamp.** Add 10 mL of **water** to the test tube.

4 Have your partner light the almond with a **long wooden match** until the almond starts burning on its own.

5 Gently swirl the test tube at an angle over the flame until the almond completely burns. Record your observations in your Science Journal.

⚠ *Point the test tube away from fellow students.*

Think About This

1. What happened to the water? Why did this happen?

2.  **Key Concept** What do you think happens to your body when you eat an almond?

Why do you eat?

How do you decide what to eat or when to eat? Although you can survive for weeks without food, you might become hungry within hours of your last meal. Hunger is your body's way of telling you that it needs food. Why does your body need food? Food provides your body with the energy and nutrients it needs to survive.

Energy

Every activity you do, such as riding a bike or even sleeping, requires energy. Your digestive system processes food and releases energy that is used for cellular processes and all activities that you do.

The amount of energy in food is measured in Calories. *A* **Calorie** *(Cal) is the amount of energy it takes to raise the temperature of 1 kg of water by 1°C.* How much energy do foods contain? Each food is different. One grape contains 2 Cal, but a slice of cheese pizza has 220 Cal. All foods give your body energy to use.

The amount of energy a person needs depends on several factors, such as weight, age, activity level, and gender. For example, a person with a mass of 68 kg usually burns more Calories than a person with a mass of 45 kg. Playing soccer requires more energy than playing a video game. How does the food you eat supply you with energy? The energy comes from nutrients.

Nutrients

Food is made of nutrients—substances that provide energy and materials for cell development, growth, and repair. The types and amounts of nutrients a person needs depend on age, gender, and activity level. Toddlers need more fat in their diets than older children do. Women need more calcium and iron than men do. Active people need more protein. Next, you'll read about the six groups of nutrients and their roles in maintaining your health.

✔ **Key Concept Check** Why do you eat?

Nutrient Imbalance Humans, like all other organisms, need to take in a certain amount of each type of nutrient every day to maintain a balanced state. If an organism takes in too much or too little of any type of nutrient, it could gain weight, lose weight, or be more likely to contract a disease.

Metabolism The sum of all chemical reactions in an organism is called its metabolism. Go online to learn more about metabolism and how it is influenced by hormones, exercise, diet, and aging.

Figure 1 Good sources of protein include red meat, eggs, beans, and peanuts. Good sources of carbohydrates include red beans, fruits, and vegetables.

Proteins

Carbohydrates

Visual Check Describe a lunch that is high in proteins and carbohydrates.

Groups of Nutrients

The six groups of nutrients are proteins, carbohydrates, fats, vitamins, minerals, and water. Each nutrient has a different function in the body. To be healthy, you need foods from each group every day.

Proteins

Most of the tissues in your body are made of proteins. *A* **protein** *is a large molecule that is made of amino acids and contains carbon, hydrogen, oxygen, nitrogen, and sometimes sulfur.* Proteins have many functions, such as relaying signals between cells, protecting against disease, providing support to cells, and speeding up chemical reactions. All of these functions are needed to maintain homeostasis, or the regulation of an organism's internal condition regardless of changes in its environment.

Combinations of 20 different amino acids make up the proteins in your body. Your cells can make more than half of these amino acids. The remaining amino acids must come from the foods that you eat. Some foods that are good sources of protein are shown in **Figure 1.**

Reading Check How does your body obtain amino acids that cannot be made in cells?

Carbohydrates

What do pasta, bread, and potatoes have in common? They are all foods that have high levels of carbohydrates (kar boh HI drayts). **Carbohydrates** *are molecules made of carbon, hydrogen, and oxygen atoms and are usually the body's major source of energy.* They are commonly in one of three forms—starches, sugars, or fibers. All of them are made of sugar molecules that are linked together like a chain. It is best to eat foods that contain carbohydrates from whole grains because they are easier to digest. Also shown in **Figure 1** are some foods that are high in carbohydrates.

Fats

You might think that fats in food are bad for you. But, you need a certain amount of fat in your diet and on your body to stay healthy. **Fats,** *also called lipids, provide energy and help your body absorb vitamins.* They are a major part of cell membranes. Body fat helps to insulate against cold temperatures. Most people get plenty of fat in their diet, so deficiencies in fats are rare. But too much fat in your diet can lead to health problems. Only about 25–35 percent of the Calories you consume should be fats.

Fats are often classified as either saturated or unsaturated. A diet high in saturated fats can increase levels of cholesterol, which can increase the risk of heart disease. Most of the fat in your diet should come from unsaturated fats, such as those shown in **Figure 2.**

Vitamins

Has anyone ever told you to eat certain foods because you need vitamins? **Vitamins** *are nutrients that are needed in small amounts for growth, regulation of body functions, and prevention of some diseases.* You can obtain most of the vitamins you need by eating a well-balanced diet. If you do not consume enough of one or more vitamins, then you might develop symptoms of vitamin deficiency. The symptoms depend on which vitamin you are lacking. **Table 1** lists some vitamins people need in their diet.

Reading Check Why do you need vitamins in your diet?

Minerals

In addition to vitamins, you also need other nutrients called minerals. **Minerals** *are inorganic nutrients—nutrients that do not contain carbon—that help the body regulate many chemical reactions.* Similar to vitamins, if you do not consume enough of certain minerals, you might develop a mineral deficiency. **Table 1** also lists some minerals that you need in your diet.

Figure 2 Fish, nuts, and liquid vegetable oils contain unsaturated fats.

Fats

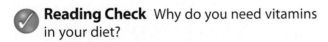
Concepts in Motion   Interactive Table

Table 1 Vitamins and Minerals

Vitamin	Good Sources	Health Benefit
Vitamin B₂ (riboflavin)	milk, meats, vegetables	helps release energy from nutrients
Vitamin C	oranges, broccoli, tomatoes, cabbage	growth and repair of body tissues
Vitamin A	carrots, milk, sweet potatoes, broccoli	enhances night vision, helps maintain skin and bones
Mineral	**Good Sources**	**Health Benefit**
Calcium	milk, spinach, green beans	builds strong bones and teeth
Iron	meat, eggs, green beans	helps carry oxygen throughout the body
Zinc	meat, fish, wheat/grains	aids protein formation

Table 1 Vitamins and minerals are essential for maintaining a healthy body.

Visual Check What foods are good sources of vitamin A?

Water

You might recall that your body is mostly water. You need water for chemical reactions to occur in your body. Your body takes in water when you eat or drink. However, you lose water when you sweat, urinate, and breathe. To stay healthy, it is important to replace the water that your body loses. If you exercise, live in a warm area, or become sick, your body loses more water. When lost water is not replaced, you might become dehydrated. Symptoms of dehydration include thirst, headache, weakness, dizziness, and little or no urination.

Key Concept Check Why does your body need nutrients?

Healthful Eating

Imagine walking through a grocery store. Each aisle in the store contains hundreds of different foods. With so many choices, it's difficult to choose foods that are part of a healthful diet. Healthful eaters need to be smart shoppers. They make grocery lists beforehand and buy products that are high in nutrients. Nutritious foods come from the major food groups, which include grains, vegetables, fruits, oils, milk products, and meats and beans.

Inquiry MiniLab

25 minutes

What nutrients are in foods?

Food provides your body with nutrients and Calories. Each nutrient is important and has its own function in the body.

1. Using the materials provided by your teacher, search for foods that contain a high amount of your assigned nutrient.

2. Find the number of items for your nutrient that your teacher has assigned.

3. Once you have found the appropriate number of items, form a group with other students who were assigned the same nutrient.

4. As a group, make a chart listing your food items. Show the amount of your assigned nutrient present in each item. Share your chart with the class.

Analyze and Conclude

1. **Classify** the foods studied by all groups according to their nutrient value. Which foods were high in proteins? Fats? Carbohydrates?

2. **Explain** the function each nutrient has in the body.

3. **Key Concept** Describe what might happen if your body did not get enough of a particular nutrient.

Table 2 Daily Recommended Amounts of Each Food Group for 9–13-Year-Olds

Food Group	Daily Amount males, 9–13 years old	Daily Amount females, 9–13 years old	Examples of Foods
Grains	6-ounce equivalents	5-ounce equivalents	whole-wheat flour, rye bread, brown rice
Vegetables	2 1/2 cups	2 cups	broccoli, spinach, carrots
Fruits	1 1/2 cups	1 1/2 cups	apples, strawberries, oranges
Fats	5 teaspoons or less	5 teaspoons or less	canola oil, olive oil, avocados
Milk	3 cups	3 cups	milk, cheese, yogurt
Meat and beans	5 ounces or less	5 ounces or less	fish, beans, lean beef, lean chicken

A Balanced Diet

A healthful diet includes carbohydrates, proteins, fats, vitamins, minerals, and water. But how do you know how much of each food group you should eat? **Table 2** lists the daily recommended amounts of each food group for 9–13-year-olds.

The nutrient-rich foods that you choose might be different from the nutrient-rich foods eaten by people in China, Kenya, or Mexico. People usually eat foods that are grown and produced regionally. Regardless of where you live, eating a balanced diet ensures that your body has the nutrients it needs to function.

Key Concept Check Why is eating a balanced diet important?

Food Labels

What foods would you buy to follow the recommended guidelines in **Table 2?** Most grocery stores sell many varieties of bread, milk, meat, and other types of food. How would you know what nutrients these foods contain? You can look at food labels, such as the one in **Figure 3.** Food labels help you determine the amount of protein, carbohydrates, fats, and other substances in food.

Review **Personal Tutor**

Figure 3 A food label lists a food's nutrients per serving, not per container.

Visual Check List the nutrients in this food product.

(l)Ken Karp/McGraw-Hill Education; (r)McGraw-Hill Education

Lesson 1 Review

Visual Summary

People eat food to obtain the energy their bodies need to function.

Proteins are one of the six groups of nutrients.

Evaluating food labels can help you eat a balanced diet.

FOLDABLES®

Use your lesson Foldable to review the lesson. Save your Foldable for the project at the end of the chapter.

What do you think NOW?

You first read the statements below at the beginning of the chapter.

1. An activity such as sleeping does not require energy.

2. All fats in food should be avoided.

Did you change your mind about whether you agree or disagree with the statements? Rewrite any false statements to make them true.

Use Vocabulary

1 Nutrients made of long chains of amino acids are _____.

2 The major source of energy in your diet comes from _____.

3 The amount of energy in food is measured in _____.

Understand Key Concepts 🔑

4 **Explain** why it is important to consume vitamins.

5 Which nutrient helps your body absorb vitamins?
  A. carbohydrate   **C.** mineral
  B. fat   **D.** protein

6 **Give an example** of when you might need to drink more water than usual.

Interpret Graphics

7 **Calculate** How many grams of carbohydrates are in three servings of this food?

Sodium 220mg	9%
Total Carbohydrate 5g	2%
Dietary Fiber 1g	4%
Sugars 3g	
Protein 1g	

8 **Summarize** Copy and fill in the graphic organizer below to identify the six groups of nutrients.

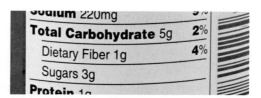

Critical Thinking

9 **Plan** a meal that contains a food from each of the six food groups.

10 **Analyze** One serving of a certain food contains 370 Cal, 170 Cal from fat, and 12 g of saturated fat (60% of the daily value). Is this food a good choice for a healthful lifestyle? Why or why not?

How do foods compare?

Materials

brown paper grocery bag

permanent marker

food samples

small plastic cup

metric ruler

Safety

As you have learned, not all foods are alike. Knowing about different types of nutrients will help you make good food choices. Foods with a lot of fat often taste good but might not be healthful for you in large amounts. It is important to be able to identify foods with different fat contents in order to have a balanced diet. How do these different foods compare?

Learn It

Observations can be analyzed by noting the similarities and differences between two or more objects or events that you observe. You **compare** objects or events by seeing how they are similar. You **contrast** objects or events by looking for differences.

Try It

1. Read and complete a lab safety form.

2. Create a data table like the one below in your Science Journal.

3. Use a permanent marker and a plastic cup to draw seven circles on a large piece of a brown paper grocery bag.

4. Obtain one each of the seven food items your teacher has provided. Label each circle with the name of the food to be tested.

5. Place one piece of the labeled food in each circle.

6. Allow the foods to sit for 30 minutes.

7. Remove the foods and properly dispose of them. Record in the table whether the food left a greasy mark, a wet mark, or no mark. Also record the diameter of the mark.

8. Dispose of the used grocery bag as directed by your teacher.

Apply It

9. **Compare and contrast** the marks produced by the foods. Describe both their appearances and their sizes.

10. **Infer** Which items left a greasy mark on the paper bag? How are these foods alike?

11. **Key Concept** Why is it important to eat a variety of foods every day?

Product	Type of Mark	Diameter (cm)

The Digestive System

Reading Guide

Key Concepts 🔑
ESSENTIAL QUESTIONS

- What does the digestive system do?
- How do the parts of the digestive system work together?
- How does the digestive system interact with other systems?

Vocabulary

digestion
mechanical digestion
chemical digestion
enzyme
esophagus
peristalsis
chyme
villi

g Multilingual eGlossary

▢ Video **BrainPOP**®

🌐 IS 1.3

Inquiry Under the Sea?

These colorful projections look like something you might see on the ocean floor, but they are found in your body. They line the walls of the small intestine, which is part of your digestive system. What do you think these projections do?

Which dissolves faster?

Has anyone ever told you to take small bites and chew your food thoroughly? The size of chewed food particles can affect how quickly food is digested. Similarly, the size of a sugar particle can affect how fast it dissolves in water.

1. Read and complete a lab safety form.

2. Add the contents of one serving package of **granulated sugar** to a **500-mL beaker** containing 300 mL of **warm water.**

3. Gently stir the contents of the beaker with a **plastic spoon.** Have your partner use a **stopwatch** to time how long it takes the sugar to dissolve. Record the time in your Science Journal.

4. Add a **sugar cube** to another **500-mL beaker** containing 300 mL of warm water.

5. Repeat step 3.

Think About This

1. Which dissolved faster—the granulated sugar or the sugar cube?

2. Why do you think particle size affects the rate at which sugar dissolves?

3. 🔑 **Key Concept** How might food particle size affect how quickly food is digested?

Functions of the Digestive System

Suppose you ate a cheeseburger and a pear for lunch. What happens to the food after it is eaten?

As soon as the food enters your mouth, it begins its journey through your digestive system. No matter what you eat, your food goes through four steps—ingestion, digestion, absorption, and elimination. All four steps happen in the organs and tissues of the digestive system in the following order:

- Food is ingested. Ingestion is the act of eating, or putting food in your mouth.

- Food is digested. **Digestion** *is the mechanical and chemical breakdown of food into small particles and molecules that your body can absorb and use.*

- Nutrients and water in the food are absorbed, or taken in, by cells. Absorption occurs when the cells of the digestive system take in small molecules of digested food.

- Undigested food is eliminated. Elimination is the removal of undigested food and other wastes from your body.

🔑 **Key Concept Check** What does the digestive system do?

WORD ORIGIN · · · · · · · · · · · ·

digestion
from Latin *digestus*, means "to separate, divide" · · · · · · · · · · · · ·

Types of Digestion

Before your body can absorb nutrients from food, the food must be broken down into small molecules by digestion. There are two types of digestion—mechanical and chemical. *In **mechanical digestion**, food is physically broken into smaller pieces.* Mechanical digestion happens when you chew, mash, and grind food with your teeth and tongue. Smaller pieces of food are easier to swallow and have more surface area, which helps with chemical digestion. *In **chemical digestion**, chemical reactions break down pieces of food into small molecules.*

Enzymes

Chemical digestion cannot occur without substances called enzymes (EN zimez). ***Enzymes** are proteins that help break down larger molecules into smaller molecules.* Enzymes also speed up, or catalyze, the rate of chemical reactions. Without enzymes, some chemical reactions would be too slow or would not occur at all.

There are many kinds of enzymes. Each one is specialized to help break down a specific molecule at a specific location.

REVIEW VOCABULARY

chemical reaction
process in which a compound is formed or broken down

✓ **Reading Check** What are enzymes?

 MiniLab **20 minutes**

How can you model digestion?

Your saliva contains enzymes to help with digestion. You can use radishes to model the effect saliva has on food. Radishes and saliva contain the same enzyme.

1. Read and complete a lab safety form.
2. Place a small amount of **cooked rice** into two **100-mL beakers.**
3. Add a small amount of **grated radish** to one beaker and stir well with a **plastic spoon.**
4. Let the rice sit for 5 minutes.
5. Use a **dropper** to add three drops of **iodine tincture solution** to the rice in each beaker. Record the color of the rice in your Science Journal.

Analyze and Conclude

1. **Compare** the colors of the rice in the two beakers after the iodine was added.
2. **Infer** Iodine reacts with starches. Starches are made up of sugar molecules. Infer what happened to the starches in the rice when an enzyme was added.
3. 🔑 **Key Concept** Summarize the role enzymes play in digestion.

Hutchings Photography/Digital Light Source

The Role of Enzymes in Digestion

Nutrients in food are made of different molecules, such as carbohydrates, proteins, and fats. Many of these molecules are too large for your body to use. But, because these molecules are made of long chains of smaller molecules joined together, they can be broken down into smaller pieces.

The digestive system produces enzymes that are specialized to help break down each type of food molecule. For example, the enzyme amylase helps break down carbohydrates. The enzymes pepsin and papain help break down proteins. Fats are broken down with the help of the enzyme lipase. **Figure 4** illustrates how an enzyme helps break down food molecules into smaller pieces.

Notice in **Figure 4** that the food molecule breaks apart, but the enzyme itself does not change. Therefore, the enzyme can immediately be used to break down another food molecule.

 Reading Check What happens to an enzyme after it helps break down a food molecule?

Organs of the Digestive System

In order for your body to use the nutrients in the foods you eat, the nutrients must pass through your digestive system. Your digestive system has two parts: the digestive tract and the other organs that help the body break down and absorb food. These organs include the tongue, salivary glands, liver, gallbladder, and pancreas.

The digestive tract extends from the mouth to the anus. It has different organs connected by tubelike structures. Each of these organs is specialized for a certain function.

Recall the cheeseburger and pear mentioned at the beginning of this lesson. Where do you think digestion of this food begins?

Figure 4 An enzyme helps break down food molecules into smaller pieces.

Step 1
An enzyme attaches to a food particle.

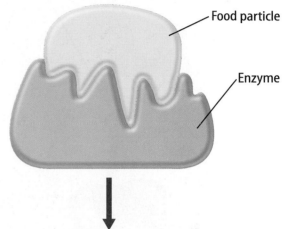

Food particle

Enzyme

Step 2
The enzyme speeds up a chemical reaction that breaks down the food particle.

Step 3
The enzyme releases the broken-down food particle.

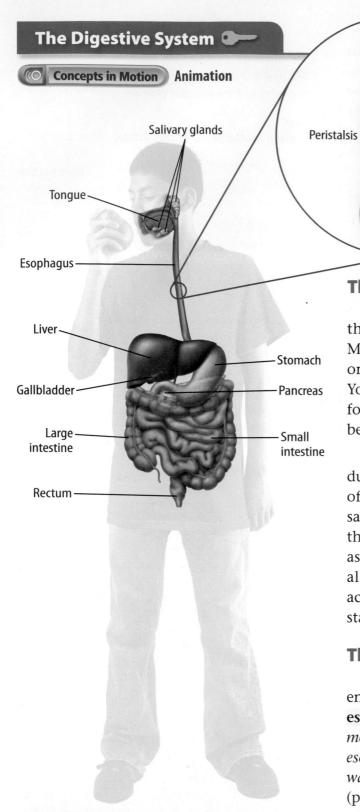

Figure 5 The digestive system includes the organs of the digestive tract, as well as other organs such as the tongue, salivary glands, liver, gallbladder, and pancreas.

✓ **Visual Check** Which organ connects the mouth to the stomach?

The Mouth

You can follow the path food takes through your digestive tract in **Figure 5.** Mechanical digestion of food, such as a pear or a cheeseburger, begins in your mouth. Your teeth and tongue mechanically digest food as you chew. But even before chewing begins, your mouth prepares for digestion.

Your salivary (SA luh ver ee) glands produce saliva (suh LI vuh) at the very thought of food. They produce more than 1 L of saliva every day. Saliva contains an enzyme that helps break down carbohydrates, such as those found in a hamburger bun. Saliva also contains substances that neutralize acidic foods. It also contains a slippery substance that makes food easier to swallow.

The Esophagus

After you swallow a bite of your food, it enters your esophagus (ih SAH fuh gus). *The* **esophagus** *is a muscular tube that connects the mouth to the stomach. Food moves through the esophagus and the rest of the digestive tract by waves of muscle contractions, called* **peristalsis** (per uh STAHL sus).

Peristalsis is similar to squeezing a tube of toothpaste. When you squeeze the bottom of the tube, toothpaste is forced toward the top of the tube. As muscles in the esophagus contract and relax, partially digested food is pushed down the esophagus and into the stomach.

Hutchings Photography/Digital Light Source

The Stomach

Once your partially digested food leaves the esophagus, it enters the stomach. The stomach is a large, hollow organ. One function of the stomach is to temporarily store food. This allows you to go many hours between meals. The stomach is like a balloon that can stretch when filled. An adult stomach can hold about 2 L of food and liquids.

 Reading Check Why is the stomach's ability to store food beneficial?

Another function of the stomach is to aid in chemical digestion. As shown in **Figure 6,** the walls of the stomach are folded. These folds enable the stomach to expand and hold large amounts of food. In addition, the cells in these folds produce chemicals that help break down proteins. For example, the stomach contains an acidic fluid called gastric juice. Gastric juice makes the stomach acidic. Acid helps break down some of the structures that hold plant and animal cells together, like the cells in hamburger meat, lettuce, tomatoes, and pears. Gastric juice also contains pepsin, an enzyme that helps break down proteins in foods into amino acids. Food and gastric juices mix as muscles in the stomach contract through peristalsis. As food mixes with gastric juice in the stomach, it forms *a thin, watery liquid called* **chyme** (KIME).

FOLDABLES®

Make a shutterfold book to illustrate the organs of the digestive system. Use it to record information about their functions.

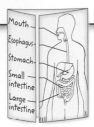

Figure 6 The stomach temporarily stores food and aids in chemical digestion.

Visual Check Where does food go after it leaves the stomach?

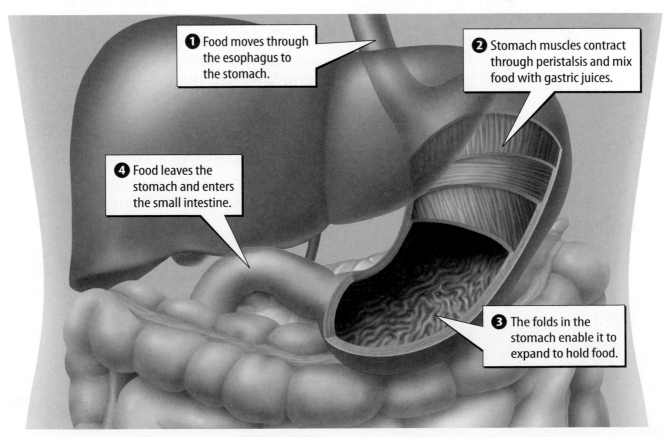

❶ Food moves through the esophagus to the stomach.

❷ Stomach muscles contract through peristalsis and mix food with gastric juices.

❹ Food leaves the stomach and enters the small intestine.

❸ The folds in the stomach enable it to expand to hold food.

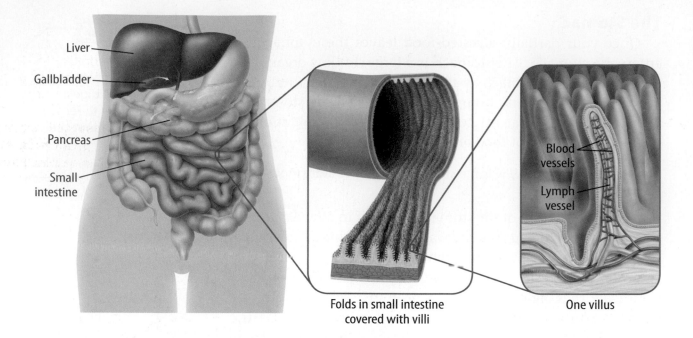

Blood vessels

Lymph vessel

Folds in small intestine covered with villi

One villus

Figure 7 The walls of the small intestine are covered with villi that help move nutrients into the blood.

The Small Intestine

Chemical digestion of your cheeseburger and pear begins in the mouth and stomach. But most chemical digestion occurs in the small intestine. The small intestine is a long tube connected to the stomach. It is where chemical digestion and nutrient absorption occur. The small intestine is named for its small diameter—about 2.5 cm. It is about 7 m long.

Chemical digestion of proteins, carbohydrates, nucleic acids, and fats takes place in the first part of the small intestine, called the duodenum (doo uh DEE num). The remainder of the small intestine absorbs nutrients from food. Notice in **Figure 8** that, like the stomach, the wall of the intestine is folded. *The folds of the small intestine are covered with fingerlike projections called* **villi** *(VIH li) (singular, villus).* Notice also that each villus contains small blood vessels. Nutrients in the small intestine diffuse into the blood through these blood vessels. You might recall that diffusion is the movement of particles from an area of higher concentration to an area of lower concentration.

The pancreas and the liver, shown in **Figure 7,** produce **substances** that enter the small intestine and help with chemical digestion. The pancreas produces an enzyme called amylase that helps break down carbohydrates and a substance that neutralizes stomach acid. The liver produces a substance called bile. Bile makes it easier to digest fats. The gallbladder stores bile until it is needed in the small intestine.

Key Concept Check What organs work together to help with chemical digestion?

Figure 8 The bacteria shown here live in the large intestine. Without them, your food would not be digested well.

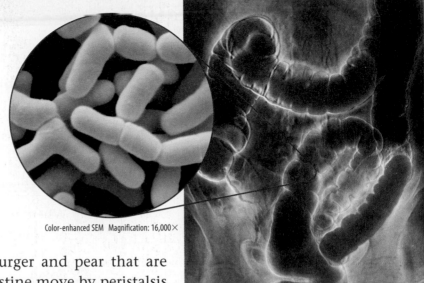

Color-enhanced SEM Magnification: 16,000×

✓ **Visual Check** Cocci bacteria are spherical, bacilli bacteria are rod-shaped, and spirilla bacteria are spiral-shaped. Which type of bacteria is shown in the photo?

The Large Intestine

The parts of your cheeseburger and pear that are not absorbed in the small intestine move by peristalsis into the large intestine, also called the colon. The large intestine, shown in **Figure 8**, has a larger diameter (about 5 cm) than the small intestine. However, at about 1.5 m long, it is much shorter than the small intestine.

Most of the water in ingested foods and liquids is absorbed in the small intestine. As food travels through the large intestine, even more water is absorbed. Materials that pass through the large intestine are the waste products of digestion. The waste products become more solid as excess water is absorbed. Peristalsis continues to force the remaining semisolid waste material into the last section of the large intestine, called the rectum. Muscles in the rectum and anus control the release of this semisolid waste, called feces (FEE seez).

Bacteria and Digestion

You might think that all bacteria are harmful. However, some bacteria have an important role in the digestive system. Bacteria, such as the ones shown in **Figure 8**, digest food and produce important vitamins and amino acids. Bacteria in the intestines are essential for proper digestion.

The Digestive System and Homeostasis

Recall that nutrients from food are absorbed in the small intestine. The digestive system must be functioning properly for this absorption to occur. These nutrients are necessary for other body systems to maintain homeostasis. For example, the blood in the circulatory system absorbs the products of digestion. The blood carries the nutrients to all other body systems, providing them with materials that contain energy.

🔑 **Key Concept Check** What might happen to other body systems if the digestive system did not function properly?

Math Skills ✕ ➗ ➕

Use Percentages

A percentage is a ratio that compares a number to 100. For example, the total length of the intestines is about 8.5 m. That value represents 100%. If the rectum is 0.12 m long, what percentage of the intestines is made up of the rectum?

The ratio is $\frac{0.12 \text{ m}}{8.5 \text{ m}}$.

Find the equivalent decimal for the ratio.

$$\frac{0.12 \text{ m}}{8.5 \text{ m}} = 0.014$$

Multiply by 100.

$$0.014 \times 100 = 1.4\%$$

Practice

The total length of the intestines is about 8.5 m. If the small intestine is 7.0 m long, what percentage of the intestines is made up of the small intestine?

 Review

- Math Practice
- Personal Tutor

Visual Summary

Enzymes in the digestive system break down food so nutrients can be absorbed by your body.

Food moves through the digestive tract by waves of peristalsis.

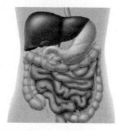

The liver and the pancreas produce substances that help with chemical digestion.

FOLDABLES

Use your lesson Foldable to review the lesson. Save your Foldable for the project at the end of the chapter.

What do you think NOW?

You first read the statements below at the beginning of the chapter.

3. Digestion begins in the mouth.

4. Energy from food stays in the digestive system.

Did you change your mind about whether you agree or disagree with the statements? Rewrite any false statements to make them true.

Use Vocabulary

1 **Define** *enzyme* in your own words.

2 **Distinguish** between absorption and digestion.

Understand Key Concepts

3 Where is the first place digestion occurs?
  A. mouth   C. large intestine
  B. stomach   D. small intestine

4 **Compare** the functions of the stomach and the small intestine.

5 **Give an example** of how the digestive system affects other body systems.

Interpret Graphics

6 **Explain** How do structures like the one to the right affect digestion?

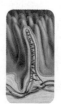

7 **Organize Information** Copy and fill in the graphic organizer below to show how food moves through the digestive tract.

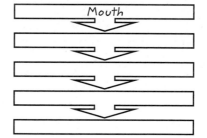

Mouth

Critical Thinking

8 **Infer** what would happen if food passed more quickly than normal through the digestive system.

Math Skills

Review
— Math Practice —

9 If the total length of the intestines is 8.5 m and the large intestine is 1.5 m long, what percentage of the intestines is made up of the small intestine?

Are digestive bacteria related to obesity?

Bacteria percentages might affect your health.

The worldwide rate of obesity greatly concerns medical and health professionals. New research reveals a possible link between bacteria in the human digestive tract and the risk of being overweight.

Your digestive system is home to between 10 and 100 trillion bacteria. That's ten times the number of cells in your body! Certain bacteria are necessary, however, for the digestion of food. Without "friendly" bacteria, you could eat all you wanted, but the food would pass through your intestines mostly undigested.

Recent studies suggest there might be a link between the bacteria in the human digestive tract and obesity. Some people have a type of bacteria that causes them to absorb more calories than normal from their food. They gain more weight than people with a different type of bacteria. In general, obese humans have a lower percentage of a group of bacteria called Bacteroidetes (BAK-tear-oid-dee-teez) and more of a group of bacteria called Firmicutes (fir-MIC-cu-teez). It is not clear whether Firmicutes bacteria make people obese, or whether obese people have more of this type of bacteria. But evidence supports the idea that changing the bacteria in someone's intestines and stomach—by means of diet or medications—might be an important weapon in the fight against obesity.

Additional research is needed to understand any link between digestive bacteria and obesity. But it is an exciting possibility that managing the bacteria in the digestive tract could be a new way to improve human health.

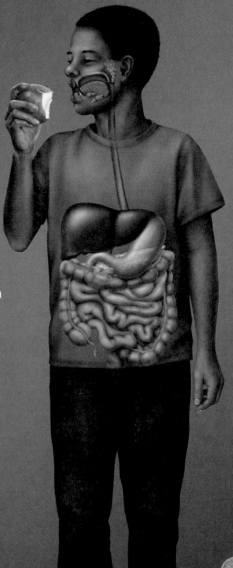

CNRI/Science Source

It's Your Turn

RESEARCH Find out more about the role of bacteria in human health. Research how the bacteria in your digestive tract help to regulate your immune system.

Lesson 3

Reading Guide

Key Concepts
ESSENTIAL QUESTIONS

- What does the excretory system do?
- How do the parts of the excretory system work together?
- How does the excretory system interact with other body systems?

Vocabulary

excretory system
kidney
nephron
urine
ureter
bladder
urethra

 Multilingual eGlossary

 ICT 2.1, 2.2; LE 1.2e

The Excretory System

Inquiry A Sweaty Job?

Did you know that these are the ridges on a fingertip? The circular openings along the ridges are sweat glands. The sweat from these glands can leave a mark, or fingerprint, on objects that you touch. Why does sweat, or any material, leave your body?

What happens when you breathe out?

Look again at the photo of the fingertip on the previous page. The sweat glands in your skin are one way substances leave your body. Do substances also leave your body when you breathe out?

1. Read and complete a lab safety form.
2. Take a deep breath and hold it.
3. Breathe out through your mouth into a **plastic bag.** Leave a small opening to allow some of the air to leave the bag as you blow into it.
4. Remove the bag from around your mouth. Let the air escape from the bag, but do not push the sides of the bag together.
5. Using the same plastic bag, repeat steps 2–4 three more times.
6. Observe the contents of the bag. Record your observations in your Science Journal.

Think About This

1. Did the plastic bag look different after you breathed into it? Explain.
2. What do you think was in the plastic bag at the end of the activity?
3. **Key Concept** Based on your observations, do you think the respiratory system is part of the excretory system? Explain.

Functions of the Excretory System

You have read about the nutrients in food that are necessary to maintain health. You have also read how the digestive system processes that food. However, your body doesn't use all the food that you ingest. The unused food parts are waste products. What happens to the wastes? They are processed by the excretory system. *The* **excretory system** *collects and eliminates wastes from the body and regulates the level of fluid in the body.*

Collection and Elimination

Your home probably has several places where waste is collected. You might have a trash can in the kitchen and another one in the bathroom. The furnace has an air filter that removes and collects dust from the air. Similarly, your body also collects wastes. The digestive system collects waste products in the intestines. The circulatory system collects waste products in the blood.

When the trash cans in your home fill up, you must take the trash outside. The same is true of the waste in your body. If waste is not removed, or eliminated, from your body, it could become toxic and damage your organs. You'll read about the different body systems that eliminate waste later in this lesson.

Regulation of Liquids

Another function of the excretory system is to regulate the level of fluids in the body. You might recall that water is an essential nutrient for your body. Some of the water in your body is lost when waste is eliminated. The excretory system controls how much water leaves the body through elimination. This ensures that neither too little nor too much water is lost.

Key Concept Check What does the excretory system do?

Figure 9 Several body systems make up the excretory system.

✔ **Visual Check** What substances are eliminated by the body systems shown below?

Types of Excretion

Your body excretes, or eliminates, different substances from different body systems. The excretory system is made of four body systems.

- The digestive system collects and removes undigested solids from the foods you eat.

- The urinary system processes, transports, collects, and removes liquid waste from the body.

- The respiratory system removes carbon dioxide and water vapor from the body.

- The integumentary system, which includes the skin, secretes excess salt and water through sweat glands.

Figure 9 illustrates the body systems that make up the excretory system and identifies the substances they excrete. You read previously about how the organs of the digestive system, the respiratory system, and the integumentary system eliminate waste products from the body. In this lesson, you will read about the organs of the urinary system and their roles in eliminating waste from the body.

✔ **Reading Check** What body systems make up the excretory system?

The Excretory System 🔑

Urinary system
Removes liquid wastes

Integumentary system
Removes excess salt and water

Digestive system
Removes undigested food

Respiratory system
Removes carbon dioxide and water

Organs of the Urinary System

The urinary system produces, stores, and removes liquid waste from the body and helps maintain homeostasis. The organs of the urinary system are shown in **Figure 10.** They include two kidneys, two ureters, the bladder, and the urethra. These organs work together to process, transport, collect, and excrete liquid waste.

 Reading Check What is the function of the urinary system?

The Kidneys

The bean-shaped organ that filters, or removes, wastes from blood is the **kidney.** You have two kidneys, one on each side of your body. They are near the back wall of your abdomen, above your waist, and below your rib cage. Each kidney is about the size of your fist. Kidneys are dark red in color because of the large volume of blood that passes through them.

The kidneys have several functions. This lesson will focus on the role of the kidneys in the urinary system. However, the kidneys also produce hormones that stimulate the production of red blood cells. In addition, they control blood pressure and help control calcium levels in the body.

The kidneys contain blood vessels and nephrons (NEH frahnz). **Nephrons** *are networks of capillaries and small tubes, or tubules, where filtration of blood occurs.* Each kidney contains about one million nephrons.

Blood contains waste products, salts, and sometimes toxins from cells that need to be removed from the body. These products are filtered from the blood as it passes through the kidneys. *When blood is filtered, a fluid called* **urine** *is produced.* The kidneys filter the blood and produce urine in two stages. You will read about this two-stage filtration process on the next page.

The Urinary System

Figure 10 Most functions of the urinary system occur in the kidneys. The kidneys connect to the ureters, then the bladder, and finally the urethra.

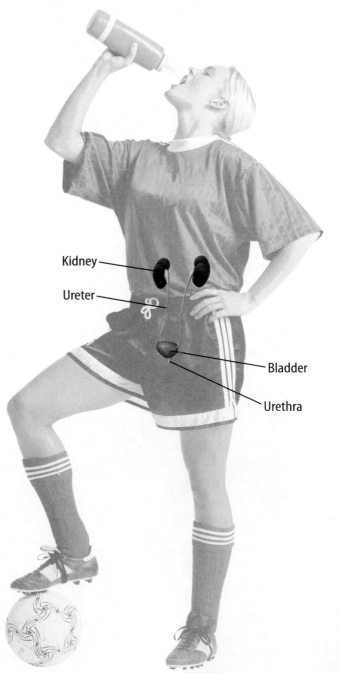

Kidney

Ureter

Bladder

Urethra

WORD ORIGIN ··········

nephron
from Greek *nephros,* means
"kidney"

First Filtration Blood is constantly circulating and filtering through the kidneys. In one day, the kidneys filter about 180 L of blood plasma, or the liquid part of blood. That's enough liquid to fill 90 2-L bottles. Your body contains about 3 L of blood plasma. This means your entire blood supply is filtered by your kidneys about 60 times each day. As shown in **Figure 11,** the first filtration occurs in clusters of capillaries in the nephrons. These clusters of capillaries filter water, sugar, salt, and wastes out of the blood.

Second Filtration If all of the liquid from the first filtration were excreted, your body would quickly dehydrate and important nutrients would be lost. To regain some of this water, the kidneys filter the liquid collected in the first filtration again. As shown in **Figure 11,** the second filtration occurs in small tubes in the nephrons. During the second filtration, up to 99 percent of the water and nutrients from the first filtration are separated out and reabsorbed into the blood. The remaining liquid and waste products form urine. On average, an adult excretes about 1.5 L of urine per day.

Figure 11 The kidneys produce urine in two stages.

✓ **Visual Check** Urine passes through which structure before entering the ureter?

Filtration in the Kidneys

(((O))) **Concepts in Motion** Animation

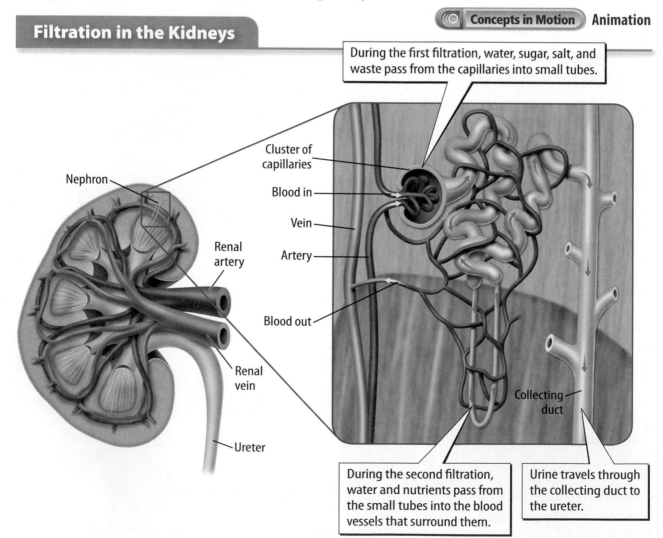

During the first filtration, water, sugar, salt, and waste pass from the capillaries into small tubes.

Nephron

Cluster of capillaries

Blood in

Vein

Artery

Renal artery

Blood out

Renal vein

Ureter

Collecting duct

During the second filtration, water and nutrients pass from the small tubes into the blood vessels that surround them.

Urine travels through the collecting duct to the ureter.

The Ureters, Bladder, and Urethra

Do you remember the trash can you read about earlier in this lesson? What would happen if you put garbage in the trash can but never emptied the trash can? The garbage would pile up. After a while, there would be too much garbage for the trash can to hold. To keep this from happening, you must empty the trash from the trash can. In a similar way, the urine produced by your body cannot stay in the kidney. *Urine leaves each kidney through a tube called the* **ureter** (YOO ruh tur). Refer back to **Figure 10** to see the locations of the ureter and other organs of the urinary system.

Both ureters drain into the bladder. *The* **bladder** *is a muscular sac that holds urine until the urine is excreted.* The bladder expands and contracts like a balloon when filled or emptied. An adult bladder can hold about 0.5 L of urine.

Urine leaves the bladder through a tube called the **urethra** (yoo REE thruh). The urethra contains circular muscles called sphincters (SFINGK turz) that control the release of urine.

Key Concept Check How do the ureters, bladder, and urethra work together to excrete urine?

WORD ORIGIN ·············

ureter
from Greek *ourethra*, means "passage for urine"

Inquiry **MiniLab**

30 minutes

How can you model the function of a kidney?

The kidneys filter substances from blood plasma. How can you use everyday materials to model the function of the kidneys?

1. Read and complete a lab safety form.
2. Label three **plastic cups** *1, 2,* and *3.*
3. Mix a small amount of **fine gravel** and **sand** with **water** in cup 1.
4. Place a small piece of **wire screen** in a **funnel,** and place the funnel in cup 2.
5. Carefully pour the sand-water-gravel mixture into the funnel. Let it drain. Record your observations in your Science Journal.
6. Remove the screen. Replace it with a piece of **filter paper.** Place the funnel in cup 3.
7. Carefully pour the contents of cup 2 into the funnel. Let it drain. Record your observations.

Analyze and Conclude

1. **Describe** what happened during each filtration.

2. **Key Concept** Summarize how your filtration systems model the function of the kidneys.

Table 3 Urinary Disorders

Concepts in Motion   Interactive Table

Urinary Disorder	Description	Possible Causes
Kidney disease	The nephrons are damaged and the ability of the kidneys to filter blood is reduced. However, a person can have the beginning stages of kidney disease and experience no symptoms.	diabetes, high blood pressure, poisons, trauma
Urinary tract infection	Infections usually occur in the bladder or urethra, but infections can also occur in the kidney and ureters. Symptoms can include burning during urination, small and frequent urination, and blood in urine.	bacteria in the urinary system
Kidney stones	Kidney stones are solid substances that form in the kidney. The most common type is made of calcium. Stones that pass through the urinary system can be very painful.	calcium buildup in the kidney
Bladder control problems	The bladder releases urine involuntarily. Occurs in women more often than men.	urinary tract infections, muscle weakness, prostate enlargement

Urinary Disorders

A urinary disorder is an illness that affects one or more organs of the urinary system. Some urinary disorders are described in **Table 3.** Several of these disorders are relatively common. Urinary tract infections, for example, are a leading cause of doctor visits, second only to respiratory infections.

The Excretory System and Homeostasis

You have already read about some of the ways the excretory system helps to maintain homeostasis. For example, the excretory system filters wastes from the blood. The blood is part of the circulatory system. If wastes were allowed to build up in the circulatory system, they would become toxic.

Another example of maintaining homeostasis is the removal of wastes from the digestive system. Similar to the circulatory system, wastes would damage your body if they were not removed from the digestive system by the excretory system.

The excretory system also interacts with the nervous system. The hypothalamus is an **area** of the brain that helps to maintain homeostasis. One function of the hypothalamus is to control the secretion of some hormones. One such hormone causes the tubules in the kidney to absorb more water from the blood. This helps the body to regulate fluid levels. Water is retained in the blood instead of being excreted in the urine.

ACADEMIC VOCABULARY

area

(noun) a part of something that has a particular function

 Key Concept Check How does the excretory system interact with the nervous system?

Visual Summary

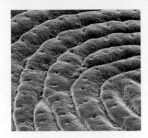

The excretory system collects and eliminates wastes from the body and regulates the level of fluid in the body.

The respiratory system is one of the body systems that make up the excretory system.

The organs of the urinary system process, transport, collect, and excrete waste.

FOLDABLES

Use your lesson Foldable to review the lesson. Save your Foldable for the project at the end of the chapter.

What do you think NOW?

You first read the statements below at the beginning of the chapter.

5. Several human body systems work together to eliminate wastes.

6. Blood contains waste products that must be removed from the body.

Did you change your mind about whether you agree or disagree with the statements? Rewrite any false statements to make them true.

Use Vocabulary

1. **Define** the word *nephron* in your own words.

2. **Distinguish** between ureter and urethra.

3. **Use the term** *bladder* in a sentence.

Understand Key Concepts

4. The kidneys filter wastes from the
   - **A.** blood.
   - **B.** intestine.
   - **C.** lungs.
   - **D.** skin.

5. **Construct** a diagram of the urinary system showing the production and flow of urine.

6. **Distinguish** between the excretory functions of the respiratory system and the integumentary system.

Interpret Graphics

7. **Identify** the function of the highlighted portion of the diagram to the right.

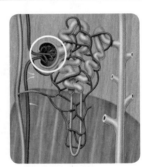

8. **Organize Information** Copy and fill in the table below with details about each organ of the urinary system.

Organ	Structure and Function

Critical Thinking

9. **Hypothesize** What might happen if urine did not go through a second filtration?

10. **Evaluate** the role of the hypothalamus in maintaining the level of fluid in the body.

Model Digestion from Start to Finish

graham crackers

banana

resealable plastic bag (1 quart size)

nylon hose

nylon netting

funnel

Also needed:
scissors, water, paper towel, paper cup, newspaper

Safety

Recall from Lesson 2 that all food goes through four steps: ingestion, digestion, absorption, and elimination. These steps happen in the digestive system. Your task is to model the four steps with the materials provided by your teacher. Before you create your model, think about all the digestive processes and plan each step. Will you model mechanical or chemical digestion or both?

Question

How does food change during the process of digestion? What are the steps in digestion?

Procedure

1 Read and complete a lab safety form.

2 In your Science Journal, make a chart like the one shown here that includes the parts of the digestive system. Record the functions of each part.

3 Using the materials provided by your teacher, design a model to show the steps in digestion. Begin with chewing and end with excretion.

4 Your teacher must approve your design before you test your model.

5 Pass food through your model.

6 Compare the food at the beginning and the end of digestion.

7 Dispose of the materials as directed by your teacher.

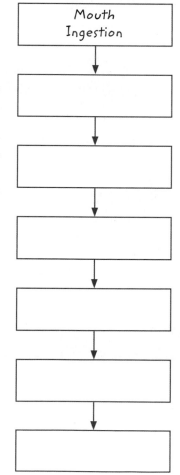

Mouth
Ingestion

(t to b, 4, br)Hutchings Photography/Digital Light Source; (2)McGraw-Hill Education; (3, 5-6)Jacques Cornell/McGraw-Hill Education

8 Copy and complete the chart at right. Then, compare your model to the four steps as outlined in the text. Does your model include everything? Is there another way to model some of the steps?

9 Make modifications to your model. Record your revisions in your Science Journal.

Part of the Digestive System	Function	Part of the Model	Comparison
Mouth	Ingestion		

Analyze and Conclude

10 **Analyze** Is there a structure or function in digestion that was not included in your model? Did you model mechanical or chemical digestion or both?

11 **Contrast** How did the food change in your model? How does food change in the digestive process?

12 **The Big Idea** How does the digestive system maintain homeostasis in a healthy body?

Communicate Your Results

Share your results with the class. Discuss your chart with those of other groups. Demonstrate to the class how you modeled the digestive system.

 **Extension**

How might your model change if you were modeling a disease of the digestive system, such as an inability to produce saliva?

Lab Tips

☑ This lab might be messy, so work on several layers of newspaper.

☑ Be careful not to cut large holes in bags or cups; small holes work better.

☑ Never eat anything during a lab exercise.

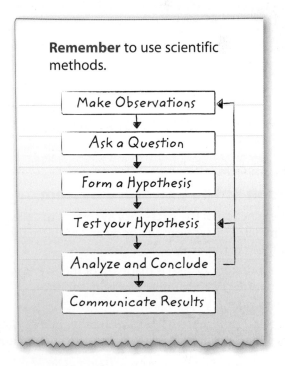

Remember to use scientific methods.

Make Observations

↓

Ask a Question

↓

Form a Hypothesis

↓

Test your Hypothesis

↓

Analyze and Conclude

↓

Communicate Results

Chapter 13 Study Guide

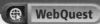

 THE BIG IDEA The digestive and excretory systems move materials through the body and remove waste. The digestive system also absorbs nutrients.

Key Concepts Summary 🔑	Vocabulary
Lesson 1: Nutrition • People eat food to obtain the energy their bodies need to function. The amount of energy in food is measured in **Calories.** • The types and amounts of nutrients a person needs depend on age, gender, and activity level. • The six groups of nutrients are **proteins, carbohydrates, fats, vitamins, minerals,** and water. • A balanced diet provides nutrients and energy for a healthful lifestyle. 	**Calorie** **protein** **carbohydrate** **fat** **vitamin** **mineral**
Lesson 2: The Digestive System  • The function of the digestive system is to break down food and absorb nutrients for the body. • Organs of the digestive system include the mouth, **esophagus,** stomach, small intestine, and large intestine. • The digestive system interacts with other body systems to maintain the body's internal balance.	**digestion** **mechanical digestion** **chemical digestion** **enzyme** **esophagus** **peristalsis** **chyme** **villi**
Lesson 3: The Excretory System • The function of the **excretory system** is to collect and eliminate wastes from the body and regulate the level of fluids in the body. • The excretory system is made up of the digestive system, respiratory system, urinary system, and the integumentary system. • The excretory system works with other body systems, including the nervous system, to maintain homeostasis.	**excretory system** **kidney** **nephron** **urine** **ureter** **bladder** **urethra**

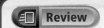
FOLDABLES® Chapter Project

Assemble your lesson Foldables as shown to make a Chapter Project. Use the project to review what you have learned in this chapter.

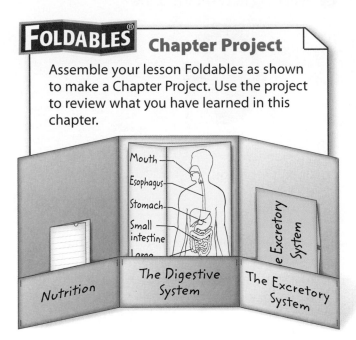

Mouth
Esophagus
Stomach
Small intestine
Large

The Excretory System

Nutrition   The Digestive System   The Excretory System

Use Vocabulary

1 About 25–35 percent of your total daily _____ should be from fats.

2 One type of nutrient, _____, is made of long chains of sugars.

3 Food moves down the esophagus by _____.

4 The breakdown of food into small particles and molecules is called _____.

5 A tube that connects a kidney to the bladder is called a(n) _____.

6 Urine is stored in the _____.

Link Vocabulary and Key Concepts

 **Concepts in Motion** Interactive Concept Map

Copy this concept map, and then use vocabulary terms from the previous page to complete the concept map.

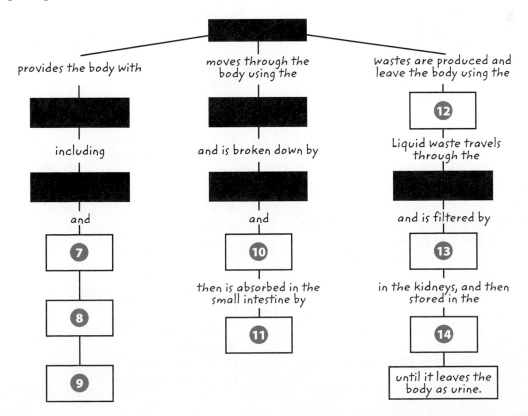

provides the body with

including

and

7

8

9

moves through the body using the

and is broken down by

and

10

then is absorbed in the small intestine by

11

wastes are produced and leave the body using the

12

Liquid waste travels through the

and is filtered by

13

in the kidneys, and then stored in the

14

until it leaves the body as urine.

Understand Key Concepts

1 What are proteins made of?
A. amino acids
B. minerals
C. sugars
D. vitamins

2 Which would be considered a grain?
A. black beans
B. brown rice
C. canola oil
D. lean chicken

3 What is the main source of energy for your body?
A. carbohydrates
B. minerals
C. proteins
D. water

4 Look at the diagram below. Where does most absorption of nutrients occur?

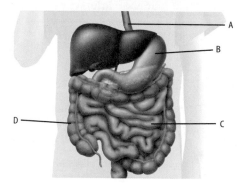

A. A
B. B
C. C
D. D

5 What is the correct order for how food is processed in the digestive system?
A. absorption, digestion, ingestion, elimination
B. elimination, ingestion, absorption, digestion
C. ingestion, absorption, digestion, elimination
D. ingestion, digestion, absorption, elimination

6 What organ is shown below?

A. bladder
B. hypothalamus
C. kidney
D. ureter

7 What organ produces a substance that neutralizes acid from the stomach?
A. esophagus
B. gallbladder
C. liver
D. pancreas

8 What fluid produced in the mouth contains digestive enzymes?
A. bile
B. blood
C. chyme
D. saliva

9 Carbon dioxide is eliminated by which body system?
A. digestive system
B. integumentary system
C. respiratory system
D. urinary system

10 What is produced by the urinary system?
A. blood
B. feces
C. perspiration
D. urine

11 The bladder is most similar to which object?
A. a balloon
B. a tube
C. a folded paper
D. a rigid container

Critical Thinking

12 **Distinguish** between minerals and vitamins.

13 **Hypothesize** why a child might have different nutritional needs than an adult over the age of 60.

14 **Select** Study the nutrient information below. Select the snack that would be a better choice as part of a healthful lifestyle. Explain your choice.

Nutrient Information	Tortilla Chips	
	Fried	Baked
Calories	150	110
Calories from fat	60	5
Total fat (g)	7	1
Saturated fat (g)	1	0
Sodium (mg)	135	200
Total carbohydrate (g)	22	24
Sugars	3	0
Protein	3	2

15 **Differentiate** Suppose your teacher showed you a diagram of a small intestine and a diagram of a large intestine. How might you distinguish between them?

16 **Hypothesize** How might digestion be affected if a person swallowed his or her food without first chewing it?

17 **Critique** the following statement: "Bacteria are harmful and should not be in the digestive system."

18 **Compare** the excretions of the urinary system and the digestive system.

Writing in Science

19 **Create** a commercial to encourage people to eat a healthful amount from each food group. Include a setting and dialogue for your commercial.

REVIEW THE **BIG IDEA**

20 Give examples of how the digestive system and excretory system help to maintain homeostasis.

21 What is the function of the small intestine?

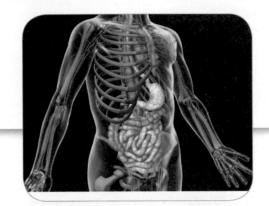

Math Skills ×÷

 Review

Math Practice

Use Percentages

Use the table below to answer questions 22–24.

Location of food	Time in location (hrs)
Stomach	4
Small intestine	6
Large intestine	24

22 What percentage of the total digestive time does food spend in the stomach?

23 What percentage of the total digestive time does food spend in the large intestine?

24 What percentage of the total digestive time does food spend in the stomach and the small intestine combined?

Record your answers on the answer sheet provided by your teacher or on a sheet of paper.

Multiple Choice

1 Which process depends on enzymes?

A chemical digestion

B elimination

C mechanical digestion

D respiration

Use the diagram below to answer question 2.

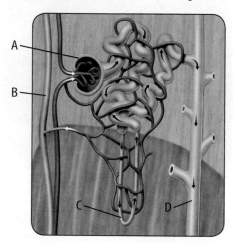

2 Where does the first filtration process occur in the nephron shown above?

A A

B B

C C

D D

3 Which factor does NOT influence how much energy a person needs?

A age

B gender

C height

D weight

Use the diagram below to answer questions 4 and 5.

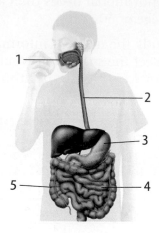

4 In which part of the system pictured above does chemical digestion begin?

A 1

B 2

C 3

D 4

5 In the diagram above, from which organ are nutrients absorbed into the bloodstream?

A 2

B 3

C 4

D 5

6 What is a main function of the excretory system?

A fight diseases

B move limbs

C pump blood

D remove wastes

Hutchings Photography/Digital Light Source

7 Which part of the brain works with the urinary system to help maintain homeostasis?

   A cerebellum

   B cerebrum

   C hypothalamus

   D medulla

Use the diagram below to answer question 8.

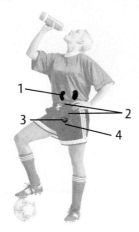

8 In the diagram above, where is urine produced?

   A 1

   B 2

   C 3

   D 4

9 Which system works with the digestive system to carry nutrients to the cells of the body?

   A circulatory

   B excretory

   C lymphatic

   D respiratory

Constructed Response

Use the table below to answer questions 10 and 11.

Nutrient	Example of Food
Carbohydrates	
Fats	
Minerals	
Proteins	
Vitamins	
Water	

10 In the table above, the six main groups of nutrients are provided. What is an example of a food that contains each nutrient? What is the function of each nutrient in the body?

11 Explain how the nutrients in the table above are related to eating a balanced diet.

Use the table below to answer question 12.

Process	Description
Ingestion	
Digestion	
Absorption	
Elimination	

12 When a person eats food, the food undergoes four processes in the digestive system. Briefly describe each process provided in the table above.

NEED EXTRA HELP?												
If You Missed Question...	1	2	3	4	5	6	7	8	9	10	11	12
Go to Lesson...	2	3	1	2	2	3	3	3	2	1	1	2

AID M1.1c; IS 1.3;
ICT 2.2; PS 2.2r

Animal Structure and Function

THE BIG IDEA

Why do animals have different structures that perform similar functions?

Inquiry Feathers for Hearing?

The feathers around this great gray owl's eyes enable it to hear better. The feathers form discs around the eyes that funnel sounds toward the owl's ears.

- What other functions do you think feathers have for an owl?

- What other structures might enable the owl to survive?

- Why do animals have different structures that perform similar functions?

Get Ready to Read

What do you think?

Before you read, decide if you agree or disagree with each of these statements. As you read this chapter, see if you change your mind about any of the statements.

1 All animals on Earth have internal skeletons.

2 All animals that live in the water move using fins.

3 Earthworms have an open circulatory system that transports blood and other substances throughout the body.

4 Gills and lungs are different structures that perform the same function.

5 The shape of an animal's teeth depends on its diet.

6 Excretion is used only by animals that live on land.

ConnectED Your one-stop online resource

MHEonline.com

- Video
- Audio
- Review
- Inquiry
- WebQuest
- Assessment
- Concepts in Motion
- Multilingual eGlossary

Lesson 1

Reading Guide

Key Concepts
ESSENTIAL QUESTIONS

- How are the types of support alike, and how are they different?

- How do the types of control compare and contrast?

- How do the types of movement compare and contrast?

Vocabulary

hydrostatic skeleton

coelom

nerve net

undulation

 Multilingual eGlossary

 Video **Science Video**

IS 1.3

Support, Control, and Movement

Inquiry How does it move?

The animal shown above moves through its environment using a unique motion. The structures in its body enable it to move. How does an animal's movement depend on the environment it lives in? What structures in its body enable it to move?

©Yvette Cardozo/Alamy

How does an earthworm move?

You move by using your muscles and skeleton. However, an earthworm does not have a skeleton. How is an earthworm able to move?

1 Read and complete a lab safety form.

2 Place a **paper towel** in the bottom of a **plastic container.** Add water to the paper towel until it is damp, but not dripping wet.

3 Place an **earthworm** on the surface of the paper towel and observe the earthworm for several minutes.

4 Pay particular attention to what happens when the earthworm moves. Note the changes in the earthworm's body and the motion that enables it to move.

Think About This

1. How do you think the body of an earthworm has structure even though it has no skeleton?

2. Describe how the shape and length of the different segments of the earthworm change to cause it to move.

3. 🔑 **Key Concept** How do you think the structure and movement of an earthworm is different from that of animals with skeletons?

The Importance of Support, Control, and Movement

Think about the different environments where animals live. Some animals live their entire lives in water. Others live only on land. Regardless of their environments, all animals have the same basic needs: food, water, and oxygen. However, in order to survive in different habitats, animals have different structures with similar functions.

Fish and birds live in dramatically different environments. However, both use structures to obtain oxygen from their environments. In a similar way, animals have different structures for support, control, and movement. Without these, animals, such as the goats in **Figure 1,** could not obtain the things they need to survive. In this lesson you will read about how animals in different habitats use different structures to provide support and control for their bodies and to move around.

Figure 1 These goats have pads between their hooves that enable them to climb trees and reach food.

Structures for Support

As you have just read, organisms have structures to provide support, control, and movement. What structures provide support? Most animals are invertebrates, or animals without backbones. Animals with backbones, such as humans, are called vertebrates. Vertebrate and invertebrate animals have different types of structures that provide support.

Hydrostatic Skeletons

Filling a balloon with water gives it shape. This is because the force of the water against the surface of the balloon gives the balloon structure. Just as the water in a balloon provides structure, many organisms use internal fluids to provide support. *A* **hydrostatic skeleton** *is a fluid-filled internal cavity surrounded by muscle tissue. The fluid-filled cavity is called the* **coelom** (SEE lum). Muscles that surround the coelom help some organisms move by pushing the fluid in different directions. Earthworms, such as the one shown in **Figure 2,** jellyfish, and sea anemones (uh NE muh neez) are organisms that have hydrostatic skeletons. Organisms with hydrostatic skeletons do not have bones or other hard structures that provide support.

Reading Check What type of skeleton do jellyfish have?

FOLDABLES

Make a vertical three-tab book. Label it as shown. Use it to organize your notes about support structures.

Characteristics of Hydrostatic Skeletons

Characteristics of Exoskeletons

Characteristics of Endoskeletons

Hydrostatic Skeletons

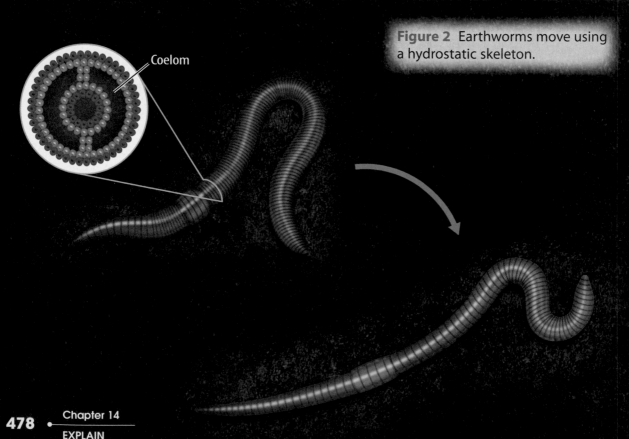

Coelom

Figure 2 Earthworms move using a hydrostatic skeleton.

Exoskeletons and Endoskeletons 🔑

Exoskeletons

Some organisms get support from structures on the outside of the body. Hard outer coverings, called exoskeletons, provide support and protection for many invertebrates. A hard exoskeleton protects internal tissues from predators or damage. Exoskeletons are sometimes called shells in species such as crabs and snails. In some species, such as the lobster shown in **Figure 3,** the exoskeleton does not grow as the animal grows. It must be shed when it gets too small, leaving the animal defenseless until the new exoskeleton forms and hardens.

Endoskeletons

Peaches have a soft, fleshy exterior that covers a hard seed. The bodies of many animals are similar in that they also have a covering over hard internal structures. These internal support structures in animals such as fish, birds, and mammals are called endoskeletons. Most endoskeletons, such as the one shown in **Figure 3,** are made of bone. Some, for example the endoskeletons of sharks, are made of cartilage. An endoskeleton protects internal organs and provides the organism with structure and support. Tortoises and turtles are unique because they have both endoskeletons and exoskeletons. The endoskeleton protects the organs and the hard exoskeleton shell protects the animal from predators.

Key Concept Check How are the types of support alike, and how are they different?

Figure 3 Most organisms get support from either exoskeletons or endoskeletons.

✓ **Visual Check** How do the support structures of the squirrel and the lobster differ?

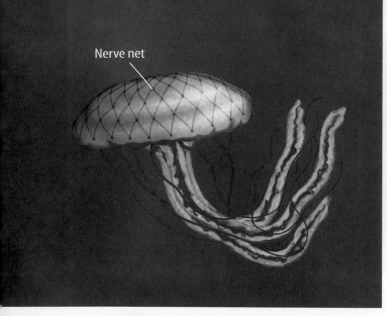

Nerve net

Figure 4 🔑 The nerve net of this jellyfish enables it to respond to its environment.

Structures for Control

All animals react to changes in their environments. Just as different animals have different structures for support, they also have different control systems. These control systems, called nervous systems, help protect animals from harm and help animals move and find food.

Nerve Nets

Animals with radial symmetry and no brain have nerve nets with a central ring that control their bodies. *A **nerve net** is a netlike control system that sends signals to and from all parts of the body.* Signals sent through the nerve net and ring cause an organism's muscle cells to contract. These contractions help the animal move. Cnidarians (nih DAYR ee unz) such as jellyfish and sea anemones have nerve nets that sense physical contact and detect food. Nerve nets and rings help the jellyfish shown in **Figure 4** move and capture prey.

Inquiry MiniLab

10 minutes

How do nerve nets and nerve cords function? 📖

Animals use different types of systems to sense the environment and react. Animals that do not have a brain use nerve nets to send signals throughout their bodies. Animals with brains use a nerve cord.

1. Read and complete a lab safety form.
2. One of your classmates will use a **stopwatch** to time the procedure.
3. Use **segments of string** to connect to your classmates in the shape of a nerve net. When you have formed the structure, close your eyes and bow your head.
4. When you receive the signal, gently tug on the next student's nerve-cell string. When you feel a tug on your string, raise your head, open your eyes, and tug the ends of the string connected to the people next to you.
5. Form a nerve-cord structure and repeat the activity. Record the results of your activities in your Science Journal.

Analyze and Conclude

1. **Assess** which nerve structure took longer to reach the final student.
2. 🔑 **Key Concept** Describe one advantage and one disadvantage of using each type of structure to convey information.

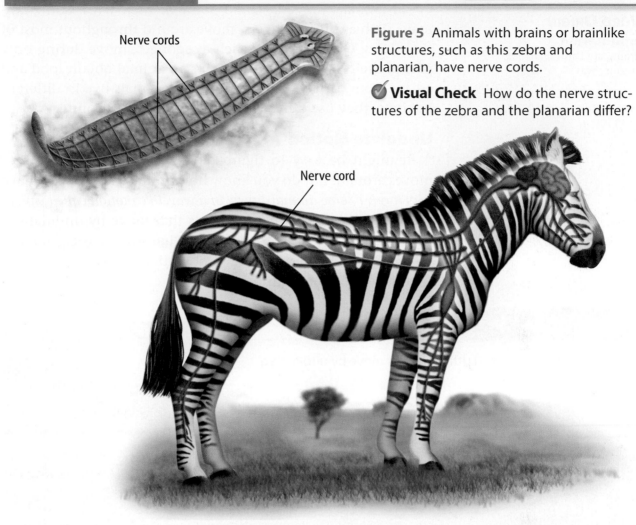

Nerve cords

Nerve cord

Figure 5 Animals with brains or brainlike structures, such as this zebra and planarian, have nerve cords.

✔ **Visual Check** How do the nerve structures of the zebra and the planarian differ?

Nerve Cords

Animals with bilateral symmetry have brains or brainlike structures to detect and respond to their environments. An animal with a brain or a brainlike structure has a nerve cord, as shown in **Figure 5.** An animal with a nerve cord usually has many neurons that detect changes in its external environment. Signals detected by neurons are sent to the nerve cord, which might initiate a reflex response, and then to the brain for processing. Just as a telephone wire transmits signals between two buildings, the nerve cord enables signals to move between neurons and the brain. In vertebrates, nerve cords are also called spinal cords.

 Key Concept Check How do the types of control compare and contrast?

REVIEW VOCABULARY ·············

neuron
basic functioning unit of the nervous system

Types of Movement

All animals move at some point in their lives. Some animals, such as birds or tigers, move around throughout most of their lives. Other animals, such as sponges, move during only part of their lives. Movement helps an animal obtain food and escape from danger. Because different animals live in different habitats, they use different structures to move around.

Undulate Motion

It might be easy to figure out how an animal with legs moves around. But do you know how animals that do not have legs move? *Some animals move in a wavelike motion called* **undulation** (un juh LAY shun). Animals that move by undulation, such as snakes, fishes, and the eel in **Figure 6,** use their muscles to push their bodies forward. Undulation is used by animals that live on land and in the water.

Undulation 🔑

Figure 6 Snakes, eels, and other animals move by undulating their bodies.

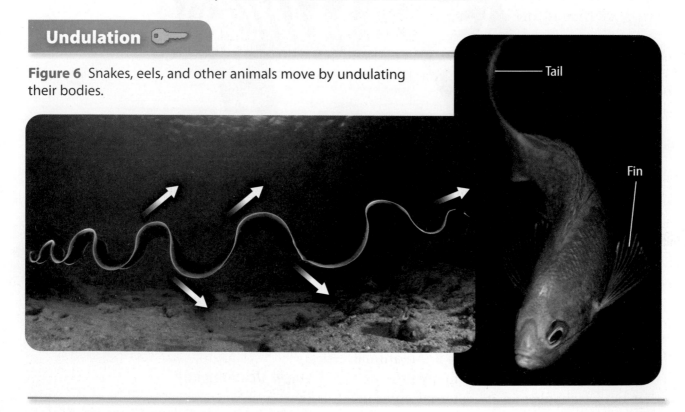

Tail

Fin

Swimming

Many animals that live in water move by swimming. Some animals, such as the fish shown in **Figure 6,** use their fins and tails to move through water. Other animals, such as octopuses, take in water and then push the water out forcefully to move forward in a process called jet propulsion. You might already know that many organisms, such as humans and dogs, also can swim by moving their arms and legs, even though they do not live in water.

(bl)rrrr/Moment/Getty Images; (br)Ken Usami/Getty Images

Walking

Most animals that live on land move by walking. The body's weight rests on two, four, six, or eight legs and shifts when the legs move. Some animals, such as rabbits and frogs, also are capable of jumping using their limbs.

Flying

Many animals move through the air by flying. Birds, some insects, and bats all use wings to move around. Wings, such as those shown in **Figure 7,** are a type of limb. By moving their wings, animals can lift their bodies and keep them in the air. Animals that have wings also have legs that are used to move around on land.

Wings are not the only structures that enable animals to move through the air. Some animals can glide or move through the air without flapping their limbs. Some species of fish have large fins that are used to glide short distances to escape predators. Some squirrels, marsupials, and even snakes can glide. They launch themselves from a high point and glide down by flattening their bodies or stretching out tissues to form a structure similar to a parachute.

 Key Concept Check How do the types of movement compare and contrast?

Figure 7 Many birds move by flying, while a flying squirrel has the ability to glide.

Lesson 1 Review

Visual Summary

Animals have different structures for support, control, and movement.

Some animals have hydrostatic skeletons.

Most animals with wings move by flying.

FOLDABLES

Use your lesson Foldable to review the lesson. Save your Foldable for the project at the end of the chapter.

What do you think NOW?

You first read the statements below at the beginning of the chapter.

1. All animals on Earth have internal skeletons.

2. All animals that live in the water move using fins.

Did you change your mind about whether you agree or disagree with the statements? Rewrite any false statements to make them true.

Use Vocabulary

1 **Use the terms** *hydrostatic skeleton* and *coelom* in a sentence.

2 **Define** *endoskeleton* in your own words.

3 Eels contract their muscles and move forward by a process called _____.

Understand Key Concepts

4 Which is used by a jellyfish to sense and respond to changes in the environment?
   A. coelom   **C.** nerve cord
   B. undulation   **D.** nerve net

5 **Explain** how a turtle's support system enables it to survive.

Interpret Graphics

6 **Analyze** how the control system shown below helps cnidarians respond to changes and capture prey.

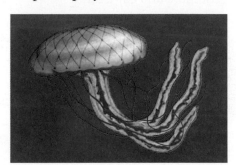

7 **Organize Information** Copy and fill in the table below to describe how animals move in their habitats.

Type of Movement	Type of Limb	Habitat
Undulation		
Swimming	fins	
Walking		land
Flying		

Critical Thinking

8 **Relate** a bird's limbs to its ability to walk and fly.

9 **Assess** the role of the coelom in providing earthworms with support.

Jet Propulsion

The Secret of a Squid's Speed

A squid swims slowly along the ocean floor, flapping its delicate fins. Suddenly, it spots a shark approaching. In a flash, the squid darts away and is gone. When a squid has to move fast, its fins can't get the job done. It uses jet propulsion.

Think of what happens when you let go of a balloon as you're blowing it up. Air rushes out of the balloon in one direction, launching it in the opposite direction. This movement is an example of jet propulsion. Cephalopods (SE fuh luh podz) , animals such as squids, jellyfishes, and octopuses, use jet propulsion to move quickly through the ocean. However, they shoot water out of their bodies instead of air.

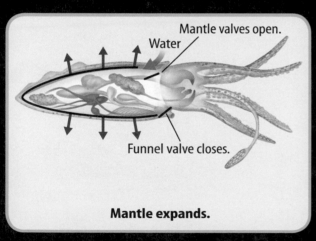

Mantle valves open.
Water
Funnel valve closes.

Mantle expands.

A A squid opens its mantle valves, drawing in water. Then the mantle valves close so the water can't escape.

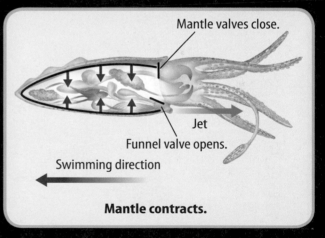

Mantle valves close.

Jet
Funnel valve opens.
Swimming direction

Mantle contracts.

B The squid contracts its mantle, opens its funnel valve, and shoots out water through the funnel. This propels the squid through the water in the opposite direction. A squid can change directions by bending its funnel the other way.

AMERICAN MUSEUM ᴼ̆ NATURAL HISTORY

 It's Your Turn

DIAGRAM Work with a partner to research another animal that uses jet propulsion. Then draw and label a diagram that you can use to explain your findings to the class.

Prisma/SuperStock

Circulation and Gas Exchange

Reading Guide

Key Concepts 🔑

ESSENTIAL QUESTIONS

- How do the types of gas exchange differ?
- What are the differences between open and closed circulatory systems?

Vocabulary

diffusion

spiracle

gills

open circulatory system

closed circulatory system

 Multilingual eGlossary

 AID M1.1c

Inquiry Underground Tunnels?

The large, orange structure might look like the entrance to an underground system of tunnels, but it is part of an insect! Tiny holes such as this enable some organisms to exchange gases directly with the environment.

Mansfield Scientific Ltd/Photo Researchers

Which system is faster?

In some animals, blood surrounds organs. In other animals, blood is carried through vessels. Which system can transport oxygen and nutrients more efficiently?

1. Read and complete a lab safety form.

2. Fill a **large plastic bowl** with water. Center a **coin** on the bottom of the bowl as a target. Place three **marbles** around the inside bottom of the bowl.

3. Have your partner time you with a **stopwatch.** Use a **turkey baster** to move each of the marbles onto the target by pushing water behind each marble. Do not touch any of the marbles directly. Stop timing when all marbles have touched the target.

4. Remove water from the bowl until it is 1/3 full. Center the coin on the bottom of the bowl. Place the three marbles in a small **beaker** of water.

5. Take a length of **plastic tubing** and aim one end at the target in the water. Have your partner start timing you. Pour the marbles and water from the beaker into the other end of the tube so that the marbles flow through the tube and strike the target in the bowl. Stop timing when the third marble touches the target.

Think About This

1. Which system was able to deliver the marbles to the target faster? Why do you think one system is faster than the other?

2. What materials are represented by the marbles? What is represented by the target?

3. 🔑 **Key Concept** Which system do you think might work best for slow-moving animals? For fast-moving animals? Explain your reasoning.

The Importance of Gas Exchange and Circulation

All cells need nutrients and oxygen to survive. Recall that animals obtain nutrients and oxygen from their environment. Organisms must take in these substances and get them to each cell. Structures in animal bodies transport the substances to all cells. They also help remove wastes such as carbon dioxide from the body. You might recall that most of an animal cell is made of water. In addition to nutrients, oxygen, and wastes, water also is transported throughout the body.

As with support, control, and movement, different animals use different structures to exchange gases and move substances throughout the body. The type of system used depends on the animal's habitat. In this lesson, you will read about the different structures that animals have that help cells exchange gases and get nutrients and oxygen.

FOLDABLES

Make a vertical book. Label it as shown. Use it to organize your notes about gas exchange and circulatory systems.

Gas Exchange Systems | Circulatory Systems

How do the surface areas of different respiratory systems compare?

The respiratory systems of animals need a large surface area to perform gas exchange. Which system has the most surface area?

1. Read and complete a lab safety form.

2. Use **paper** and **scissors** to create a model of gills and a model of book lungs. Calculate the surface areas of the completed models. Record the data in your Science Journal.

3. Create a model of the alveoli in a lung. Wrap paper around **marbles** to model alveoli. Use **rubber bands** or **string** to hold the paper around the marbles. Calculate the surface area of the model.

4. When your models are completed, unfold each of them and measure the surface area of each model. Record the data in your Science Journal.

Analyze and Conclude

1. **Compare and contrast** the surface area of each model before and after you unfolded it. How does it differ?

2. **Analyze** how folding affects the structures of the respiratory system in terms of size and surface area.

3. 🔑 **Key Concept** Infer why the amount of surface area might be important in determining the respiratory rates of organisms.

Gas Exchange

All animals must take in oxygen and eliminate carbon dioxide to survive. Oxygen must enter the body so the cells and tissues are able to use it for life processes. However, different animals use various structures to perform gas exchange.

Diffusion

The basic process of gas exchange requires no structures at all and is called diffusion. **Diffusion** *is the movement of substances from an area of higher concentration to an area of lower concentration.* In simple animals such as sponges, whose bodies are only a few cell layers thick, no special gas exchange structures are needed. Diffusion occurs through all parts of the body. Oxygen passes directly into cells from the environment. In a similar manner, waste gases leave cells and enter the environment. Other animals use specialized structures in addition to diffusion.

✓ **Reading Check** What is diffusion?

Spiracles

Some organisms exchange gases through the sides of their bodies. **Spiracles** *are tiny holes on the surface of an organism where oxygen enters the body and carbon dioxide leaves the body.* Insects such as beetles and arachnids such as spiders have spiracles. Although beetles and spiders both have spiracles, they use different tissues to transport oxygen throughout the body. Beetles have structures called tracheal (TRAY kee ul) tubes, and spiders have folded structures called book lungs to take in oxygen.

Tracheal tubes, such as the ones shown in **Figure 8,** are hoselike structures that branch into smaller tubes. Much as a river branches off into smaller streams, smaller branches of tracheal tubes help oxygen get to more places in the body. In contrast, book lungs are stacks of folded wall-like structures. Although tracheal tubes and book lungs look different, they are both used for gas exchange.

Structures for Gas Exchange 🗝️

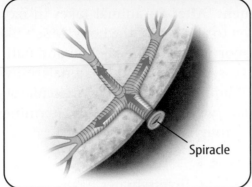

Tracheal tubes

Gills

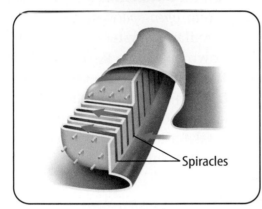

Book lungs

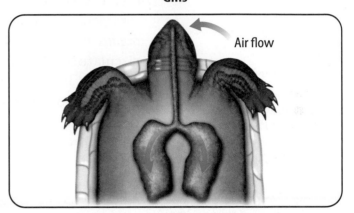

Lungs

Gills

Most animals that live in the water have gills for gas exchange. **Gills** *are organs that enable oxygen to diffuse into an animal's body and carbon dioxide to diffuse out.* In aquatic animals such as the fish shown in **Figure 8,** water enters the mouth to get to the gills. Oxygen in the water is taken in by gill filaments and then transported to the rest of the body. Gills also remove carbon dioxide from the body. Like other organs in the body, gills are surrounded by capillaries that help transport oxygen and carbon dioxide to and from cells.

Lungs

Many animals that live on land, including the turtle in **Figure 8,** and some types of fish and snails have lungs for gas exchange. Lungs are baglike organs that can be filled with air. Once the lungs fill with air, oxygen diffuses into the capillaries within the lungs' tissues and carbon dioxide diffuses out of the animal's body. Recall that capillaries transport oxygen to other cells in the body through the circulatory system.

🗝️ **Key Concept Check** How do the organs used for gas exchange differ?

Figure 8 Spiracles, tracheal tubes, gills, and lungs are all used for gas exchange.

✅ **Visual Check** What structures for gas exchange involve spiracles?

WORD ORIGIN · · · · · · · · · ·
diffusion
from Latin *diffundere*, means "to scatter"

Circulation

You have just read about how gases are **exchanged** between animals and the environment. After an animal takes in oxygen, the oxygen has to travel to all parts of the body. Much like pipes in a house help transport water to the kitchen and bathrooms, an animal's circulatory system helps materials move through the body. Different animals have different circulatory systems. The type of circulatory system used often determines how quickly blood moves through the animal.

Open Circulatory Systems

Snails, insects, and many other invertebrates have open circulatory systems. *An* **open circulatory system** *is a system that transports blood and other fluids into open spaces that surround organs in the body.* In an open circulatory system, such as the circulatory system of a bee shown in **Figure 9,** oxygen and nutrients in blood can enter all tissues and cells directly. Carbon dioxide and other wastes are taken up by blood surrounding the organs and removed from the body. Muscles help move blood through the body. It can take a long time for blood to move through an open circulatory system.

Figure 9 Open circulatory systems transport blood into open spaces in the body. Closed circulatory systems transport blood through vessels.

Open and Closed Circulatory Systems 🔑

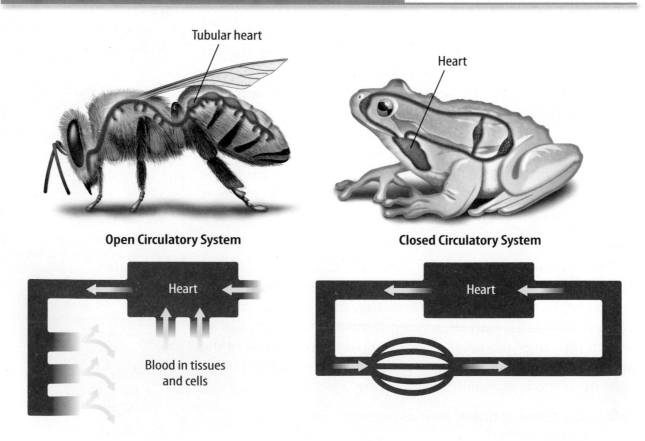

Tubular heart

Heart

Open Circulatory System

Closed Circulatory System

Heart

Blood in tissues and cells

Heart

Closed Circulatory Systems

Some animals, such as the tree frog shown in **Figure 9,** transport materials through another system called a closed circulatory system. *A* **closed circulatory system** *is a system that transports materials through blood using vessels.* Vessels help animals with closed circulatory systems move blood and other substances through the body faster than an open circulatory system.

As in an open circulatory system, muscles help blood move in a closed circulatory system. However, in a closed circulatory system, the muscles surround the blood vessels. These muscles contract and push blood through the vessels. They also can change the amount of blood flow. A closed circulatory system keeps plasma and red blood cells that carry oxygen separated from other fluids and structures in the body. Small blood vessels called capillaries surround organs and help oxygen and nutrients move from the circulatory system to cells in organs.

 Key Concept Check What are the differences between open and closed circulatory systems?

Chambered Hearts

Different animals have hearts with different numbers of compartments called chambers, as shown in **Figure 10.** Fish have hearts with two chambers, whereas amphibian hearts consist of three chambers. Birds and mammals such as cats, dogs, and humans have hearts with four chambers. Almost all animals with three- or four-chambered hearts have lungs.

Figure 10 Animals can have hearts with two, three, or four chambers.

 Visual Check How would you describe an amphibian's circulatory system?

Math Skills

Use Proportions

A proportion is an equation with two ratios that are equivalent. Use proportions to solve problems such as the following: Veins hold about 55 percent of the body's blood. What is an organism's blood volume if the veins hold 2.6 L?

Set up the proportion.

$$\frac{55\%}{2.6\ L} = \frac{100\%}{x\ L}$$

Cross multiply.

$$55x = 260$$

Divide both sides by 55.

$$\frac{55x}{55} = \frac{260}{55} = 4.7\ L$$

$$x = 4.7\ L$$

Practice

If a normal, complete heart cycle takes 0.8 s, how many cycles would the heart make in one day?

Review

- **Math Practice**
- **Personal Tutor**

Concepts in Motion **Animation**

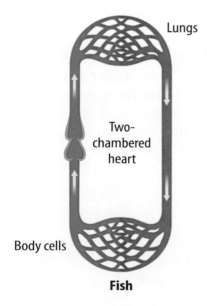

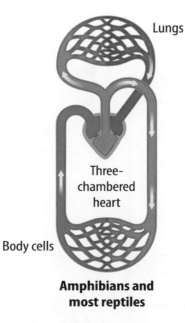

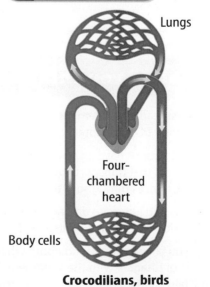

Lungs — Two-chambered heart — Body cells — **Fish**

Lungs — Three-chambered heart — Body cells — **Amphibians and most reptiles**

Lungs — Four-chambered heart — Body cells — **Crocodilians, birds and mammals**

Lesson 2 Review

Visual Summary

Animals have different structures for gas exchange and circulation.

Animals can have open or closed circulatory systems.

Different animals have a different number of chambers in their hearts.

Use your lesson Foldable to review the lesson. Save your Foldable for the project at the end of the chapter.

What do you think NOW?

You first read the statements below at the beginning of the chapter.

3. Earthworms have an open circulatory system that transports blood and other substances throughout the body.

4. Gills and lungs are different structures that perform the same function.

Did you change your mind about whether you agree or disagree with the statements? Rewrite any false statements to make them true.

Use Vocabulary

1. **Use the term** *spiracles* in a sentence.

2. **Distinguish** between an open circulatory system and a closed circulatory system.

3. Aquatic animals use _____ to obtain oxygen from their environment.

Understand Key Concepts

4. Which process helps oxygen move from the outside to the inside of cells?
   - A. absorption
   - C. diffusion
   - B. circulation
   - D. undulation

5. **Compare** the roles of book lungs and tracheal tubes in gas exchange.

6. **Infer** how the number of chambers in an animal's heart relates to its habitat.

Interpret Graphics

7. **Identify** Copy and fill in the graphic organizer below with the ways animals exchange gases with their environment.

Critical Thinking

8. **Hypothesize** how blood moves faster in a closed circulatory system when compared to an open circulatory system.

9. **Relate** the structures of gills and lungs to their roles in gas exchange.

Math Skills

— Math Practice —

10. In one experiment, the heart rate of a mollusk at rest was measured at 0.3 cycles/s. How many times did the mollusk's heart beat in 1 min?

How do you determine what environment an animal lives in?

Materials

index cards

Safety

Animals have different structures and functions in order to survive in their environments. The combination of these different structures and functions makes animals unique from each other. How can you recognize the characteristics that determine the environments in which animals live and survive?

Learn It

Classifying is the process of grouping objects or living organisms based on common features. Scientists classify animals according to the structures and functions they share.

Try It

1. Label one blank index card for each of the characteristics listed in the categories below.

2. Shuffle the cards and spread them facedown on top of your desk.

3. Label four more index cards as follows: *Earthworm, Spider, Wolf,* and *Fish*. Shuffle these cards and place them facedown in a pile next to the cards you spread out.

4. Taking turns with your partner, choose one of the cards from the animal deck. Next, choose one of the cards spread out on the table and turn it over. If the characteristic you turned over applies to your animal, turn over another card and see if the second characteristic applies to your animal. If the characteristic does not apply to your animal, turn the card over, return it to the deck, and end your turn.

5. The object of the game is to select two cards in a row that apply to your animal. Each time you select a card, you must decide if it applies to your animal. If it does, select another card.

6. Score 1 point each time you can successfully select and turn over two cards that apply to the animal card you selected. Continue playing until all of the cards have been used.

Apply It

7. **Record** the matches you made between characteristics and animals. Which matches did you complete?

8. **Describe** how some characteristics help animals compete better to find food or shelter.

9. 🔑 **Key Concept** Analyze the types of physical characteristics that make an animal best suited for a terrestrial or an aquatic environment. Explain how the different methods of gas exchange might be linked to these environments or other characteristics.

Support Systems	Gas Exchange Systems	Circulatory Systems	Environments
Hydrostatic skeleton	book lungs	open circulatory system	aquatic environment
Exoskeleton	gills	closed circulatory system	terrestrial environment
Endoskeleton	lungs		
	diffusion		

Reading Guide

Key Concepts
ESSENTIAL QUESTIONS

- How are an animal's structures for feeding and digestion related to its diet?

- How do the excretory structures of aquatic and terrestrial animals differ?

Vocabulary

crop

gizzard

absorption

g **Multilingual eGlossary**

ICT 2.2

Digestion and Excretion

Martin Shields/Alamy

Inquiry **What is it doing?**

This caterpillar is chewing food—one step in the processes of digestion and excretion. Animals these processes to get the energy they need to live.

What does it eat?

Humans and animals use several types of teeth to eat. Can you tell what an animal eats by looking at its teeth?

1 Incisors are teeth with a sharp edge in the shape of a wedge. Canines are pointy teeth. Molars have a large rough surface. Look at the photo of these teeth and answer the questions below.

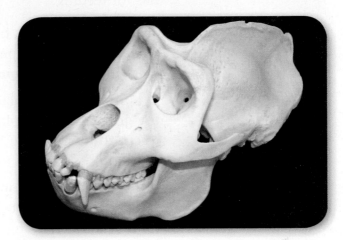

Think About This

1. Which tooth do you think would be useful for cutting off the stem of a plant?

2. Which tooth might be helpful for tearing into flesh?

3. Which tooth might be used to grind up plants and meat?

4. 🔑 **Key Concept** Which type of teeth do you think is used by humans? Why?

The Importance of Digestion and Excretion

You read in the first lesson that animals need nutrients to survive. Nutrients are obtained from food through digestion—the process of breaking down food into molecules that cells can absorb and use. After all nutrients are taken in, waste products not used by the body are removed by excretion. Excretion is important for survival because it removes harmful substances from the body. Just as different animals have different structures for gas exchange, they also have different structures to obtain and process nutrients and to remove wastes.

Digestion

Animals have different structures for digestion, depending on what type of food they eat. For example, an animal that eats only seeds has a different set of structures from an animal that eats only meat. The first step of digestion usually happens when food is chewed, as shown in **Figure 11.** The food is further broken down by the digestive system in various ways, depending on the animal's diet. As you will read in this lesson, different animals use different structures to obtain and break down food.

✓ **Reading Check** How do animals obtain nutrients?

Figure 11 The structures that this cow uses for digestion are good at breaking down grass and other plant matter.

Structures for Feeding

For many animals, the first step in feeding is obtaining food. As with other functions of the body, animals use different structures to find and chew their food. You often can tell what type of diet an animal eats by looking at the structures that it has for feeding.

Teeth Many animals have teeth, one type of structure used for feeding. Different types of teeth are used to process different diets, as shown in **Figure 12.**

Animals that eat plants often have wide teeth used for chewing grass and other plants. Some have a few sharp teeth used to cut through twigs. Animals that eat insects have teeth with sharp points that are used for chewing.

Animals that eat only meat have several types of teeth. As shown in **Figure 12,** teeth in the front of the mouth are used for biting and holding food. Teeth in the rear of the mouth are pointed and used to cut up food. Animals that eat both plants and meat have sharp teeth that are used for cutting up food and wide, flat teeth that are used for grinding up food.

Figure 12 🔑 The shape of an animal's teeth depends on its diet.

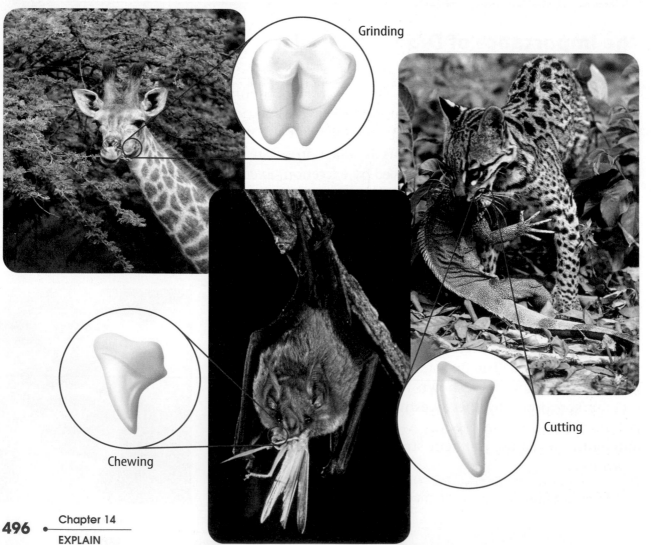

Grinding

Chewing

Cutting

Whale Shark mouthparts

Ant mouthparts

Moth mouthparts

Filter Feeding Animals that take in food suspended in water have structures for filter feeding. They take in the water with the food, push the water out through a filtering structure, then eat the organisms that remain.

Some animals, such as certain whales, take a mouthful of water and push it out through baleen (bay LEEN). Baleen is a material similar to the bristles of a broom that filter out tiny organisms in the water. Certain types of sharks and fish filter food through their gills, such as the whale shark shown in **Figure 13.** Some animals, such as clams, filter feed without moving. They filter food from the water that moves around them. However, many filter feeders move around to find food. When flamingoes filter feed, they eat shrimp that is filtered through their beak from the water they take in.

Mouthparts Some animals, particularly insects, have specialized mouthparts for eating. Butterflies and moths use a long, tubelike mouthpart, shown in **Figure 13,** to get nectar from flowers. Ants and certain beetles have crushing jaws for ripping plant and animal matter.

🔑 **Key Concept Check** How are an animal's feeding structures related to its diet?

Figure 13 🔑 Whale sharks and some insects have specialized mouthparts for feeding.

✓ **Visual Check** *How do mouthparts differ among the shark, the ant, and the moth?*

Structures for Digestion

After food is broken down into smaller parts by chewing, it breaks into even smaller components during digestion. Most animals have organs that form a specialized system for digestion. For example, many animals have stomachs and intestines that are used to digest food. The structures of the stomach and the intestine depend on the animal's diet. For example, animals such as cows and sheep that eat a lot of plant material have stomachs with several chambers. In each of these chambers, the tough plant material is processed so the animal can digest it.

Crops Some animals store their food in a crop before digesting it. *A* **crop** *is a specialized structure in the digestive system where ingested material is stored.* Many birds and insects have crops. Leeches, snails, and earthworms also have crops where they store undigested food. The crop in a leech can store blood and expands up to five times its body size.

Gizzards Animals without teeth that eat hard foods such as seeds sometimes have structures called gizzards. *A* **gizzard** *is a muscular pouch similar to a stomach that is used to grind food.* Some animals with gizzards, including certain birds, swallow rocks with their food. The rocks help break up the food.

SCIENCE USE V. COMMON USE

crop
Science Use a digestive system structure where material is stored

Common Use a plant or animal product that can be grown or harvested

---

Inquiry MiniLab

10 minutes

How do gizzards help birds eat?

Some birds use gizzards to grind food into smaller pieces. Gizzards are small pouches that store food. The bird fills its gizzard with small stones that create the grinding action.

1. Read and complete a lab safety form.
2. Place 20 **sunflower seeds in the shell** in a **small, self-sealing plastic freezer bag.**
3. Fill another freezer bag about one-quarter full with **small stones.** Add 20 sunflower seeds in the shell.
4. Seal both bags and knead the contents of each bag for several minutes with your hands.
5. Open the bags and observe the condition of the seeds. Record your observations in your Science Journal.

Analyze and Conclude

1. **Compare and contrast** the condition of the sunflower seeds in the bag with stones to the sunflower seeds in the bag without stones.

2. **Analyze** how you think having a gizzard could be an advantage to a bird.

3. **Key Concept** Infer how the structure and function of the gizzard relates to the type of food that a bird can eat.

McGraw-Hill Education

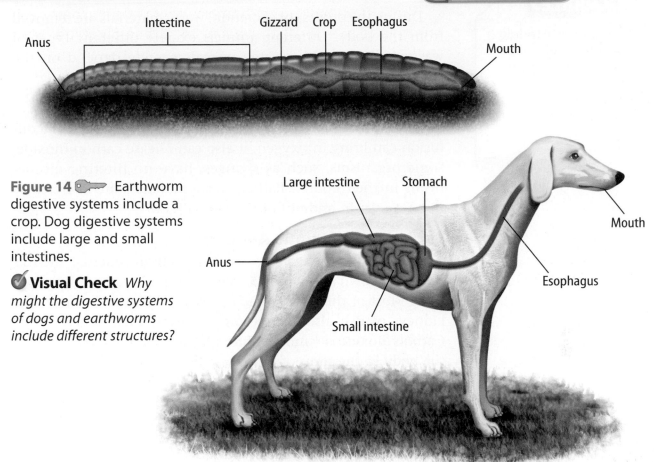

Anus Intestine Gizzard Crop Esophagus Mouth

Large intestine Stomach Mouth

Anus Esophagus

Small intestine

Figure 14 Earthworm digestive systems include a crop. Dog digestive systems include large and small intestines.

Visual Check *Why might the digestive systems of dogs and earthworms include different structures?*

Absorption

Whether an animal stores food before digestion or not, it must take the nutrients into the body in order to use them. **Absorption** *is the process in which nutrients from digested food are taken into the body.* Absorption happens as food moves through the digestive system, such as the ones shown in **Figure 14.** Many animals have digestive systems that contain enzymes. Enzymes are chemicals that help break food into small parts so that cells can absorb the nutrients.

In addition to enzymes, many organisms have structures that enable absorption. For example, many animals absorb nutrients in the intestine. After absorption, the structures used to move the nutrients throughout the animal's body also differ. In animals with a closed circulatory system, the capillaries that surround the intestine transport nutrients throughout the body. Recall that blood surrounds the organs of animals with open circulatory systems. In this case, nutrients enter the blood directly after absorption.

WORD ORIGIN

absorption
from Latin *absorbere,* means "to swallow up"

 Key Concept Check How are an animal's structures for digestion related to its diet?

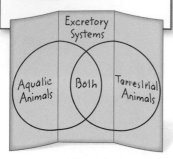

FOLDABLES®

Make a vertical tri-fold Venn book. Label it as shown. Use it to compare and contrast the excretion process in animals from different habitats.

Excretion

During the process of excretion, waste materials are removed from the body. Different animals excrete different types of wastes. The types of wastes animals excrete depend on the environments where they live.

Diffusion

Recall that gas exchange occurs due to diffusion. While diffusion can bring in oxygen, it also can release carbon dioxide. Some organisms, such as sponges, have no filtering mechanisms in their bodies. Rather, waste materials are excreted as water moves in and out of the animal's pores.

Excretion in Aquatic Animals

Many animals that live in aquatic environments, such as the fish shown in **Figure 15,** remove liquid wastes using kidneys. Most of the waste removed by the kidneys is water. The kidneys of fish also excrete other wastes, such as ammonia. Carbon dioxide is removed through the gills. Solid waste leaves the body in the form of feces.

Excretion in Terrestrial Animals

Like aquatic animals, terrestrial animals also have kidneys. However, they excrete less water when removing wastes. Instead of excreting ammonia, most animals that live on land excrete urea as a waste product. Birds also excrete wastes, but they conserve water by excreting uric acid instead of ammonia or urea. Land animals excrete carbon dioxide through the lungs. They also excrete solid waste as feces.

 Key Concept Check How do the excretory structures of aquatic and terrestrial animals differ?

Figure 15 Aquatic animals, such as this fish, use kidneys and gills to excrete wastes.

Kidney

Gills

Urinary bladder

Anus

©Juniors Bildarchiv GmbH/Alamy

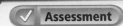
Visual Summary

Animals have different structures for digestion and excretion.

Some organisms have structures that enable them to store food.

The type of waste an animal excretes depends on its environment.

FOLDABLES

Use your lesson Foldable to review the lesson. Save your Foldable for the project at the end of the chapter.

What do you think NOW?

You first read the statements below at the beginning of the chapter.

5. The shape of an animal's teeth depends on its diet.

6. Excretion is used only by animals that live on land.

Did you change your mind about whether you agree or disagree with the statements? Rewrite any false statements to make them true.

Use Vocabulary

1 Nutrients are taken into the body by the process of _____.

2 **Define** *gizzard* in your own words.

3 Flamingoes and leeches have storage compartments for food called _____.

Understand Key Concepts

4 Which process moves nutrients from the digestive system into the circulatory system?
   A. absorption   C. excretion
   B. diffusion   D. undulation

5 **Compare** the roles of gills and lungs in excreting carbon dioxide.

6 **Explain** the role of gizzards in digestion.

Interpret Graphics

7 **Explain** the function of the system of structures shown below.

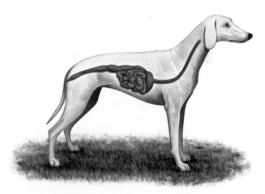

8 **Summarize** Copy and fill in the graphic organizer below with the names of materials that animals excrete.

Wastes

Critical Thinking

9 **Relate** the shape of an animal's teeth to its diet.

10 **Assess** the role of kidneys in aquatic and terrestrial animals.

(t)Merlin Tuttle/BCI/Science Source; (b)©Juniors Bildarchiv GmbH/Alamy

Materials

craft materials

Safety

Design an Alien Animal

You have read that animals have a variety of structures and functions in order to survive. The type of structures that a particular animal has depends on the environment where it lives. Your task is to imagine a unique environment on another planet. Be creative and describe the alien planet in detail. Then use what you know about animal structures and functions to imagine what life-forms live on the planet. The life-forms you design must be able to survive in the unique environmental conditions of the planet you described.

Question

How do specialized structures and abilities help animals survive in specific environments? What animal characteristics would you expect to find in different environments?

Procedure

1 Read and complete a lab safety form.

2 In your Science Journal, write a description of an imaginary alien planet. Be creative in describing your planet. Write down as many details as you can think of, including:

- Is the planet dry, or covered with water?

- What temperatures are experienced on your planet?

- What sources of food are present?

3 Include drawings along with your descriptions. Use labels to add detailed information to the environments you create.

4 Think about how the different animal species you studied have changed over time to live in different environments. Write a statement about the relationship between a species' characteristics and its environment. Predict how the environments you have created will affect organisms on your planet.

Alien Structure and Function	
Structure	Function in Environment
Fins	
Claws	

5 Design several animals that will inhabit your alien planet. Create a data card for each animal that includes a picture of the animal. Add a chart like the one on the previous page to each data card that describes the structures of the animal and the functions of the structures. Include detailed drawings and/or descriptions of the body systems of each animal.

6 Use the information you've gathered to create a three-dimensional model, or diorama, that illustrates your environment and the animals you have described.

Analyze and Conclude

7 **Explain** For what environmental conditions has your organism developed structures?

8 **Analyze** How have some organisms gained an advantage over other organisms on the planet?

9 **Compare and Contrast** How are the animals on your planet similar to and different from each other in terms of control, support, movement, gas exchange, feeding, digestion, and excretion? How do these characteristics help them maintain homeostasis?

10 **The Big Idea** Why do the animals on your alien planet have different structures, even though they all live on the same planet?

Lab Tips

☑ Consider your animal's environment when determining its diet.

Communicate Your Results

Share your diorama with the rest of the class. Compare your planet's environment and life-forms with the ones your classmates created. What similarities and differences do you notice?

 **Extension**

Pair up with another student. Choose an organism from your partner's planet to bring to your planet. Write a prediction of what would happen. Would the new organism survive? How would the species adapt to the new environment? What organisms would it compete with? Would it threaten the survival of other organisms upon its arrival?

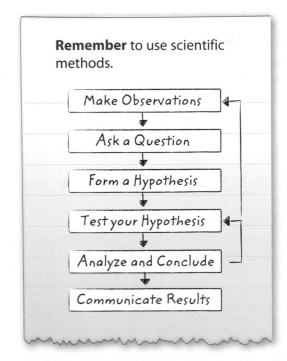

Remember to use scientific methods.

> Make Observations
> Ask a Question
> Form a Hypothesis
> Test your Hypothesis
> Analyze and Conclude
> Communicate Results

Chapter 14 Study Guide

Animals have different structures that perform similar functions which enable them to survive in different environments.

Key Concepts Summary 🔑	Vocabulary
Lesson 1: Support, Control, and Movement • Support structures give internal organs protection. Endoskeletons are made of bone or cartilage. Exoskeletons form shells made of minerals. 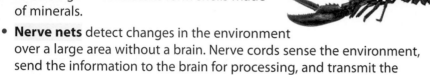 • **Nerve nets** detect changes in the environment over a large area without a brain. Nerve cords sense the environment, send the information to the brain for processing, and transmit the response to neurons. • Animals have different structures that enable them to move through their habitats.	hydrostatic skeleton coelum nerve net undulation
Lesson 2: Circulation and Gas Exchange • Gas exchange occurs through **gills** in aquatic animals and through lungs or **spiracles** in terrestrial animals.    • In **open circulatory systems**, blood surrounds all organs in the body. **Closed circulatory systems** use blood vessels to transport substances throughout the body.	diffusion spiracle gills open circulatory system closed circulatory system
Lesson 3: Digestion and Excretion • An animal's feeding structures depend on its diet. Animals that eat meat have sharp teeth that cut and tear, and animals that eat plants have wide, flat teeth for grinding.    • Aquatic animals use kidneys to excrete large amounts of water and ammonia. Terrestrial animals use kidneys to excrete smaller amounts of water and either urea or uric acid. Aquatic animals excrete carbon dioxide through gills, and terrestrial animals excrete carbon dioxide through the lungs or spiracles.	crop gizzard absorption

Dorling Kindersley/Getty Images

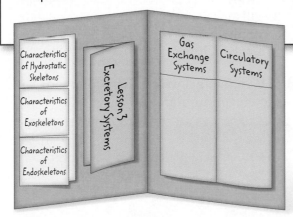

FOLDABLES® Chapter Project

Assemble your lesson Foldables as shown to make a Chapter Project. Use the project to review what you have learned in this chapter.

Characteristics of Hydrostatic Skeletons

Characteristics of Exoskeletons

Characteristics of Endoskeletons

Lesson 3 Excretory Systems

Gas Exchange Systems

Circulatory Systems

Use Vocabulary

1 Use the term *coelom* in a sentence.

2 Some animals store food in structures called _____.

3 Tiny openings on the surface of some animals that are used to take in oxygen are _____.

4 Define the term *crop* in your own words.

5 Snakes and eels move by _____.

6 Define the term *diffusion* in your own words.

Link Vocabulary and Key Concepts

Concepts in Motion Interactive Concept Map

Copy this concept map, and then use vocabulary terms from the previous page to complete the concept map.

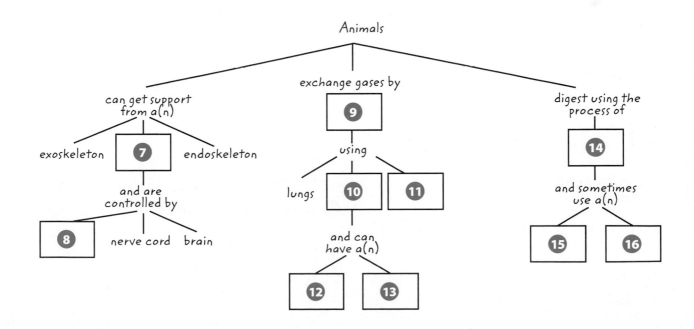

Chapter 14 Review

Understand Key Concepts 🔑

1. Which is NOT used to provide an animal with structural support?
   A. endoskeleton
   B. exoskeleton
   C. hydrostatic skeleton
   D. nerve net

2. The fluid-filled sac in an earthworm is called a(n)
   A. coelom.
   B. endoskeleton.
   C. nerve cord.
   D. nerve net.

3. The animal pictured below has which type of support system?

   A. endoskeleton
   B. exoskeleton
   C. hydrostatic skeleton
   D. no skeleton

4. Animals with _____ do not have brains.
   A. endoskeletons
   B. gills
   C. nerve cords
   D. nerve nets

5. Which structure is used for food storage?
   A. crop
   B. gizzard
   C. kidney
   D. stomach

6. Capillaries are found in animals with
   A. coeloms.
   B. spiracles.
   C. closed circulatory systems.
   D. open circulatory systems.

7. Which is NOT used for gas exchange?
   A. crops
   B. gills
   C. book lungs
   D. tracheal tubes

8. The animal below uses which organs to excrete ammonia?

   A. gills
   B. intestines
   C. kidneys
   D. lungs

9. Which is NOT used by aquatic animals to move through the water?
   A. fin
   B. gill
   C. tail
   D. wing

10. What is the basic process of gas exchange?
    A. absorption
    B. circulation
    C. diffusion
    D. excretion

Critical Thinking

11 **Describe** how the structure of cnidarians helps them respond to stimuli from all directions.

12 **Compare** the roles of endoskeletons and exoskeletons in providing animals with protection.

13 **Assess** the role of undulation in helping animals without appendages move.

14 **Relate** the structure of an animal's circulatory system to the rate at which blood moves throughout its body.

15 **Relate** the structure an organism uses for gas exchange to its habitat.

16 **Describe** how diffusion helps animals exchange gases.

17 **Relate** an animal's habitat to the amount of water it excretes.

18 **Hypothesize** how the structure pictured below helps an animal obtain nutrients without having to eat more food.

19 **Compare** the structure of teeth in animals that eat plants and animals that eat other animals.

Writing in Science

20 **Write** a five-sentence paragraph that describes how spiracles work together with book lungs and tracheal tubes to obtain oxygen. Be sure to include a topic sentence and a concluding sentence in your paragraph.

REVIEW **THE BIG IDEA**

21 Why do animals have different structures that perform similar functions? Compare and contrast some structures that appear different but perform the same function.

22 The owl shown below has various structures that enable it to survive. Compare these structures with an animal that lives in a different environment. List the similarities and differences.

Math Skills

 Review

— Math Practice —

Use Proportions

23 Birds and mammals have four-chambered hearts. Out of a sample with 52,750 species of animals, 9,600 are birds and 5,500 are mammals. What percentage of animals in the sample have four-chambered hearts?

24 The average human heart beats about 3 billion times during a lifetime. If the average heart rate is 70 beats/min, what is the average life span, in years, for the human heart? [Hint: 525,600 min = 1 y]

Standardized Test Practice

Record your answers on the answer sheet provided by your teacher or on a sheet of paper.

Multiple Choice

1 Which term describes a protective support structure found on the outside of certain organisms?

   A endoskeleton

   B exoskeleton

   C cartilage skeleton

   D hydrostatic skeleton

Use the figure below to answer question 2.

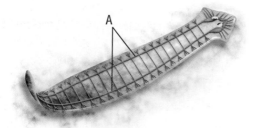

2 What parts are labeled with the letter *A* in the figure?

   A bones

   B intestines

   C nerve cords

   D nerve nets

3 How do the excretory structures of fish compare with those of birds?

   A Birds excrete feces and fish do not.

   B Birds have gizzards and fish have crops.

   C Fish have gills and birds have lungs.

   D Fish have kidneys and birds do not.

4 Which animal moves by undulation?

   A a seagull

   B a snake

   C a squid

   D a squirrel

5 What is the function of a crop?

   A exchange gases

   B protect organs

   C store food

   D transport material

Use the figure below to answer question 6.

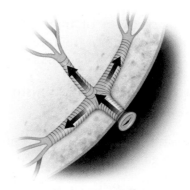

6 Which gas exchange structure is shown?

   A a gill

   B a lung

   C a book lung

   D a tracheal tube

7 How do terrestrial animals excrete carbon dioxide?

   A through gills

   B through inhalation

   C through lungs

   D through undulation

8 Which animal has a nerve net that controls its body?

   A a dog

   B a python

   C a flying squirrel

   D a sea anemone

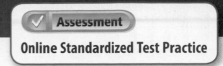
Use the figure below to answer question 9.

9 A biologist in the field finds a large animal tooth like the one shown. Which describes how a tooth of this shape and size was most likely used?

  A to bite into large prey

  B to chew insects

  C to eat grass

  D to eat leaves from trees

10 What gives a hydrostatic skeleton support?

  A bones

  B cartilage

  C coelom

  D shell

Constructed Response

Use the diagrams below to answer questions 11 and 12.

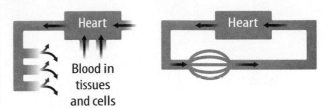

11 Which type of circulatory system would be more efficient in moving blood through the body? Explain your answer.

12 An open circulatory system allows oxygen and nutrients to enter all tissues and cells directly. A closed circulatory system allows blood to be moved through the body faster. Which system would enable an animal to process energy faster? Explain your answer.

13 Explain how a book lung differs from the lung of a turtle.

14 Give an example of an animal that has the ability to move by two different means.

NEED EXTRA HELP?													
If You Missed Question...	1	2	3	4	5	6	7	8	9	10	11	12	13	14
Go to Lesson...	1	1	3	1	3	2	3	1	3	1	2	2	2	1

Unit 4

INTERDEPENDENCE

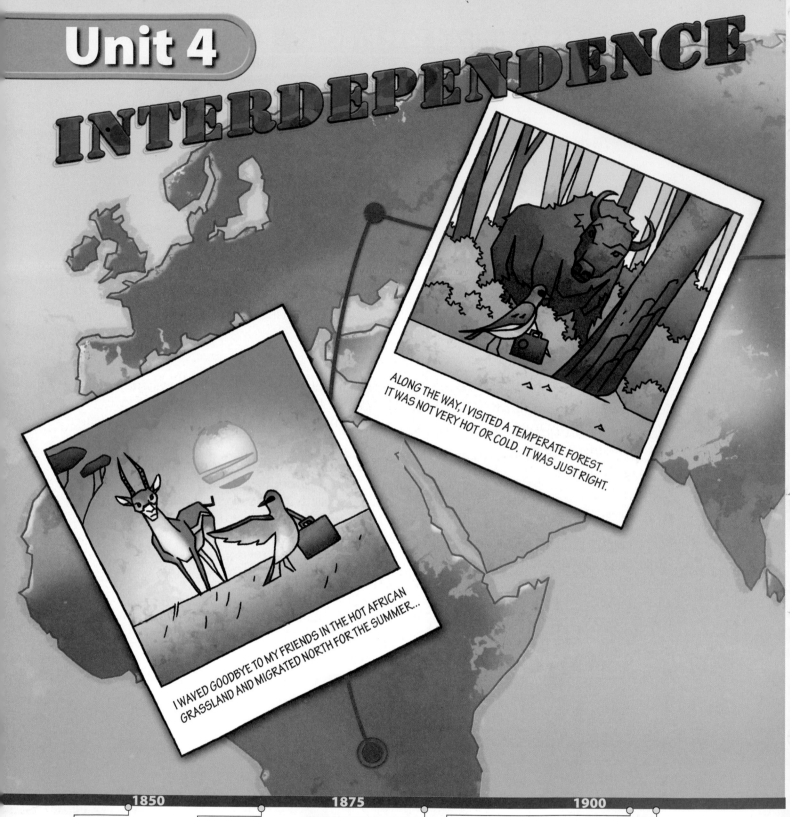

ALONG THE WAY, I VISITED A TEMPERATE FOREST. IT WAS NOT VERY HOT OR COLD. IT WAS JUST RIGHT.

I WAVED GOODBYE TO MY FRIENDS IN THE HOT AFRICAN GRASSLAND AND MIGRATED NORTH FOR THE SUMMER...

1850   **1875**   **1900**

1849
The U.S. Department of Interior is established and is responsible for the management and conservation of most federal land.

1872
The world's first national park, Yellowstone, is created.

1892
The Sierra Club is founded in San Francisco by John Muir. It goes on to be the oldest and largest grassroots environmental organization in the United States.

1915
Congress passes a bill establishing Rocky Mountain National Park in Colorado.

1920
Congress passes the Federal Water Power Act. This act creates a Federal Power Commission with authority over waterways, and the construction and use of water-power projects.

THEN, I RESTED FOR A FEW DAYS IN A COLD, RAINY, MOUNTAIN FOREST IN ASIA. I SAW BEAUTIFUL BAMBOO TREES AND GIANT PANDAS.

I SAID "HI" TO MY FRIENDS IN THE ARCTIC CIRCLE BEFORE HEADING HOME TO THE ALASKAN TUNDRA. NEXT FALL IT'S BACK TO AFRICA FOR THE WINTER.

1950

2000

1955
The Air Pollution Control Act is the first of several United States Clean Air Acts to control air pollution on a national level.

1990
The Clean Air Act Amendments propose emissions trading and add provisions for reducing acid rain, ozone depletion, and toxic air pollution. They also establish a national permits program.

2006
The documentary *An Inconvenient Truth* is released to educate about global warming. The film's popularity raises international awareness of the cause.

? **Inquiry**

Visit ConnectED for this unit's **STEM** activity.

Graphs

 AID S3.2h

Polar bears are one of the largest land mammals. They hunt for food on ice packs that stretch across the Arctic Ocean. Recently, ice in the Arctic has not been as thick as it has been in the past. In addition, the ice does not cover as much area as it used to, making it difficult for polar bears to hunt. Scientists collect data about how these changes in the ice affect polar bear populations. One well-studied population of polar bears is on Wrangel Island, Russia, shown in **Figure 1.** Scientists collect and study data on polar bears to draw conclusions and make predictions about a possible polar bear extinction. Scientists often use graphs to better understand data. A **graph** is a type of chart that shows relationships between variables. Scientists use graphs to visually organize and summarize data. You can use different types of graphs to present different kinds of data.

Figure 1 Scientists collect data about polar bears on Wrangel Island, Russia.

Types of Graphs

Bar Graphs

The horizontal *x*-axis on a bar graph often contains categories rather than measurements. The heights of the bars show the measured quantity. For example, the *x*-axis on this bar graph contains different locations on Wrangel Island. The heights of the bars show how many bears researchers observed. The different colors show the age categories of polar bears. Where were ten adult polar bears observed?

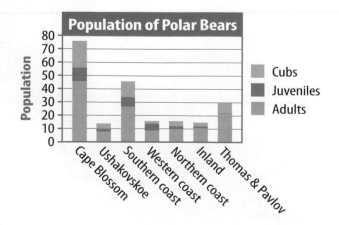

Circle Graphs

A circle graph usually illustrates the percentage of each category of data as it relates to the whole. This circle graph shows the percentage of different age categories of polar bears on Wrangel Island. Adults, shown by the blue color, make up the largest percentage of the total population. This circle graph contains similar data to the bar graph but presents it in a different way. What percentage of the total polar bear population are cubs?

Age Distribution of Polar Bears

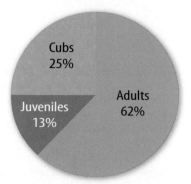

What can graphs tell you about polar bears?

A colleague gives you some data she collected about polar bears on Wrangel Island. She observed the condition of bears near Cape Blossom and classified the bears as starving, average, or healthy. She also recorded the age category of each bear. What can you learn by graphing these data?

1️⃣ Make a bar graph of the number of bears in each category that are starving, in average condition, or healthy.

2️⃣ Add the numbers of starving bears. Add the total number of bears. Divide the number of starving bears by the total number of bears and multiply by 100 to calculate the percentage of starving bears. Repeat the calculations to find the percentages of average-condition and healthy bears. Make a circle graph showing the different conditions of the bears. For more information on how to make circle graphs, go to the Science Skill Handbook in the back of your book.

	Starving	Average	Healthy
Adult	3	11	14
Juvenile	4	33	13
Cub	3	12	6

Analyze and Conclude

1. **Analyze** On your bar graph, indicate how you can tell which age category of bears is the healthiest.

2. **Determine** What group of bears do you think left the most walrus carcasses? Explain.

Line Graphs

A line graph helps you analyze how a change in one variable affects another variable. Scientists on Wrangel Island counted all the polar bears on the island each year for 10 years. They plotted each year of the survey on the horizontal *x*-axis and the bear population on the vertical *y*-axis. The population decreased between years 2 and 4. It increased between years 6 and 8. How did the population change during the last three years of the survey?

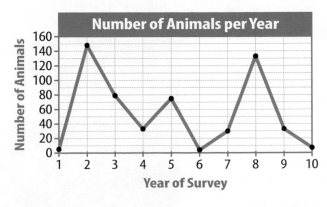

Double Line Graphs

You can use a double line graph to compare relationships of two sets of data. The blue line represents the population of polar bears. The orange line represents the number of walrus carcasses found on Wrangel Island. You can see that the blue and orange lines follow a similar pattern. This tells scientists that these two sets of data are related. Walruses are an important food source for polar bears on the island.

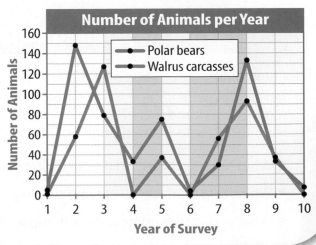

AID M1.1b, M1.1c, M2.1b, M3.1a, S1.2a,
S1.2b, S2.1a, S2.1b, S2.1d, S2.2a, S2.2b,
S2.2c, S2.2d, S2.2e, S2.3a, S2.3b, S3.1a,
S3.2a, S3.2d, S3.2e, S3.2f, S3.2g, S3.2h,
S3.3; IS 1.3; ICT 2.2, 4.2, 5.1; IPS 1.2, 1.4;
PS 1.1i, 2.2j, 2.2r

Climate

THE BIG IDEA

What is climate and how does it impact life on Earth?

Inquiry **What happened to this tree?**

Climate differs from one area of Earth to another. Some areas have little rain and high temperatures. Other areas have low temperatures and lots of snow. Where this tree grows—on Humphrey Head Point in England—there is constant wind.

- What are the characteristics of different climates?

- What factors affect the climate of a region?

- What is climate and how does it impact life on Earth?

©Ashley Cooper/Corbis

Get Ready to Read

What do you think?

Before you read, decide if you agree or disagree with each of these statements. As you read this chapter, see if you change your mind about any of the statements.

1 Locations at the center of large continents usually have the same climate as locations along the coast.

2 Latitude does not affect climate.

3 Climate on Earth today is the same as it has been in the past.

4 Climate change occurs in short-term cycles.

5 Human activities can impact climate.

6 You can help reduce the amount of greenhouse gases released into the atmosphere.

ConnectED Your one-stop online resource

MHEonline.com

- Video
- WebQuest
- Audio
- Assessment
- Review
- Concepts in Motion
- Inquiry
- Multilingual eGlossary

Lesson 1

Climates of Earth

Reading Guide

Key Concepts 🔑
ESSENTIAL QUESTIONS

- What is climate?
- Why is one climate different from another?
- How are climates classified?

Vocabulary

climate

rain shadow

specific heat

microclimate

 Multilingual eGlossary

 AID M1.1b, S1.2c, S3.1a, S3.1b, S3.2h; ICT 2.2; PS 2.2j

Inquiry **What makes a desert a desert?**

How much precipitation do deserts get? Are deserts always hot? What types of plants grow in the desert? Scientists look at the answers to all these questions to determine if an area is a desert.

How do climates compare?

Climate describes long-term weather patterns for an area. Temperature and precipitation are two factors that help determine climate.

1. Read and complete a lab safety form.

2. Select a location on a **globe.**

3. Research the average monthly temperatures and levels of precipitation for this location.

4. Record your data in a chart like the one shown here in your Science Journal.

Think About This

1. Describe the climate of your selected location in terms of temperature and precipitation.

2. Compare your data to Omsk, Russia. How do the climates differ?

3. **Key Concept** Mountains, oceans, and latitude can affect climates. Do any of these factors account for the differences you observed? Explain.

Omsk, Russia 73.5° E, 55° N		
Month	Average Monthly Temperature	Average Monthly Level of Precipitation
January	−14°C	13 mm
February	−12°C	9 mm
March	−5°C	9 mm
April	8°C	18 mm
May	18°C	31 mm
June	24°C	52 mm
July	25°C	61 mm
August	22°C	50 mm
September	17°C	32 mm
October	7°C	26 mm
November	−4°C	19 mm
December	−12°C	15 mm

What is climate?

You probably already know that the term *weather* describes the atmospheric conditions and short term changes of a certain place at a certain time. The weather changes from day to day in many places on Earth. Other places on Earth have more constant weather. For example, temperatures in Antarctica rarely are above 0°C, even in the summer. Areas in Africa's Sahara, shown in the photo on the previous page, have temperatures above 20°C year-round.

Climate *is the long-term average weather conditions that occur in a particular region.* A region's climate depends on average temperature and precipitation, as well as how these variables change throughout the year.

What affects climate?

Several factors determine a region's climate. The latitude of a location affects climate. For example, areas close to the equator have the warmest climates. Large bodies of water, including lakes and oceans, also influence the climate of a region. Along coastlines, weather is more constant throughout the year. Hot summers and cold winters typically happen in the center of continents. The altitude of an area affects climate. Mountainous areas are often rainy or snowy. Buildings and concrete, which retain solar energy, cause temperatures to be higher in urban areas. This creates a special climate in a small area.

Key Concept Check What is climate?

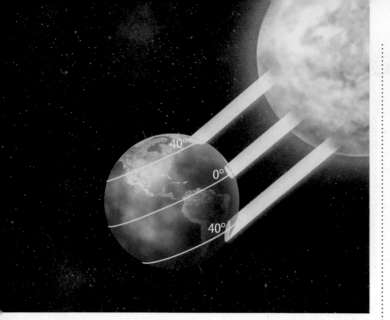

Figure 1 Latitudes near the poles receive less solar energy and have lower average temperatures.

Latitude

Recall that, starting at the equator, latitude increases from 0° to 90° as you move toward the North Pole or the South Pole. The amount of solar energy per unit of Earth's surface area depends on latitude. **Figure 1** shows that locations close to the equator receive more solar energy per unit of surface area annually than locations located farther north or south. This is due mainly to the fact that Earth's curved surface causes the angle of the Sun's rays to spread out over a larger area. Locations near the equator also tend to have warmer climates than locations at higher latitudes. Polar regions are colder because annually they receive less solar energy per unit of surface area. In the middle latitudes, between 30° and 60°, summers are generally hot and winters are usually cold.

Altitude

Climate is also influenced by altitude. Recall that temperature decreases as altitude increases in the troposphere. So, as you climb a tall mountain you might experience the same cold, snowy climate that is near the poles. **Figure 2** shows the difference in average temperatures between two cities in Colorado at different altitudes.

Altitude and Climate 🔑

Figure 2 As altitude increases, temperature decreases.

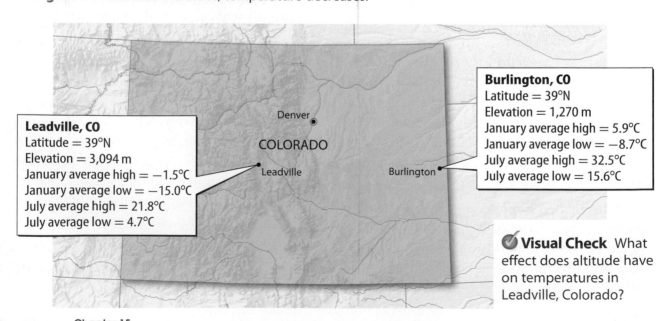

Burlington, CO
Latitude = 39°N
Elevation = 1,270 m
January average high = 5.9°C
January average low = −8.7°C
July average high = 32.5°C
July average low = 15.6°C

Leadville, CO
Latitude = 39°N
Elevation = 3,094 m
January average high = −1.5°C
January average low = −15.0°C
July average high = 21.8°C
July average low = 4.7°C

✅ **Visual Check** What effect does altitude have on temperatures in Leadville, Colorado?

Rain Shadow 🔑

1. Prevailing winds carry moist, warm air over Earth's surface.

2. As the air approaches mountains, it rises and cools. Water vapor in the air condenses. Precipitation falls as rain or snow on the upwind slope of the mountains.

3. The now-dry air passes over the mountains. As it sinks, it warms.

4. Dry weather exists on the downwind slope of the mountains.

Rain Shadows

Mountains influence climate because they are barriers to prevailing winds. This leads to unique **precipitation** patterns called rain shadows. *An area of low rainfall on the downwind slope of a mountain is called a* **rain shadow**, as shown in **Figure 3.** Different amounts of precipitation on either side of a mountain range influence the types of vegetation that grow. Abundant amounts of vegetation grow on the side of the mountain exposed to the precipitation. The amount of vegetation on the downwind slope is sparse due to the dry weather.

Large Bodies of Water

On a sunny day at the beach, why does the sand feel warmer than the water? It is because water has a high specific heat. **Specific heat** *is the amount (joules) of thermal energy needed to raise the temperature of 1 kg of a material by 1°C.* The specific heat of water is about six times higher than the specific heat of sand. This means the ocean water would have to absorb six times as much thermal energy to be the same temperature as the sand.

The high specific heat of water causes the climates along coastlines to remain more constant than those in the middle of a continent. For example, the West Coast of the United States has moderate temperatures year-round.

Ocean currents can also modify climate. The Gulf Stream is a warm current flowing northward along the coast of eastern North America. It brings warmer temperatures to portions of the East Coast of the United States and parts of Europe.

✓ **Reading Check** How do large bodies of water influence climate?

Figure 3 Rain shadows form on the downwind slope of a mountain.

✓ **Visual Check** Why don't rain shadows form on the upwind slope of mountains?

REVIEW VOCABULARY · · · · ·

precipitation
water, in liquid or solid form, that falls from the atmosphere

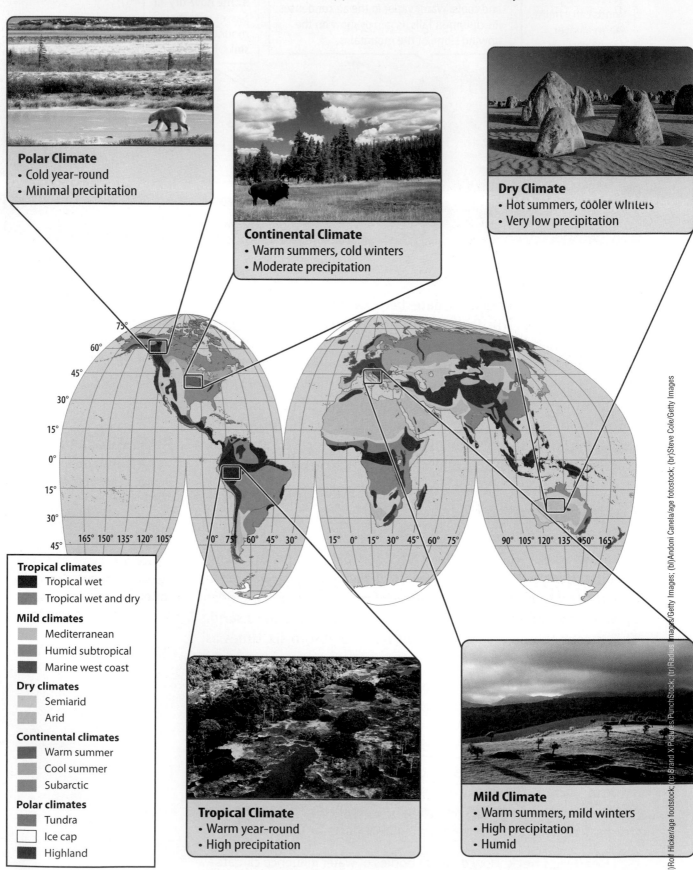
Figure 4 The map shows a modified version of Köppen's climate classification system.

Polar Climate
- Cold year-round
- Minimal precipitation

Continental Climate
- Warm summers, cold winters
- Moderate precipitation

Dry Climate
- Hot summers, cooler winters
- Very low precipitation

Tropical climates
- Tropical wet
- Tropical wet and dry

Mild climates
- Mediterranean
- Humid subtropical
- Marine west coast

Dry climates
- Semiarid
- Arid

Continental climates
- Warm summer
- Cool summer
- Subarctic

Polar climates
- Tundra
- Ice cap
- Highland

Tropical Climate
- Warm year-round
- High precipitation

Mild Climate
- Warm summers, mild winters
- High precipitation
- Humid

(tl)Rolf Hicker/age fotostock; (tc)Brand X Pictures/PunchStock; (tr)Radius Images/Getty Images; (bl)Andoni Canela/age fotostock; (br)Steve Cole/Getty Images

Classifying Climates

What is the climate of any particular region on Earth? This can be a difficult question to answer because many factors affect climate. In 1918 German scientist Wladimir Köppen (vlah DEE mihr • KAWP pehn) developed a system for classifying the world's many climates. Köppen classified a region's climate by studying its temperature, precipitation, and native vegetation. Native vegetation is often limited to particular climate conditions. For example, you would not expect to find a warm-desert cactus growing in the cold, snowy arctic. Köppen identified five climate types. A modified version of Köppen's classification system is shown in **Figure 4.**

 Key Concept Check How are climates classified?

Microclimates

Roads and buildings in cities have more concrete than surrounding rural areas. The concrete absorbs solar radiation, causing warmer temperatures than in the surrounding countryside. The result is a common microclimate called the urban heat island, as shown in **Figure 5.** A **microclimate** is a localized climate that is different from the climate of the larger area surrounding it. Other examples of microclimates include forests, which are often cooler and less windy than the surrounding countryside, and hilltops, which are windier than nearby lower land.

 Key Concept Check Why is one climate different from another?

FOLDABLES

Use three sheets of notebook paper to make a layered book. Label it as shown. Use it to organize your notes on the factors that determine a region's climate.

Factors that Determine Climate
Latitude
Rain Shadows
Altitude
Water
Local Effects (microclimates)

WORD ORIGIN ············

microclimate
from Greek *mikros*, means "small"; and *klima*, means "region, zone"

Microclimate

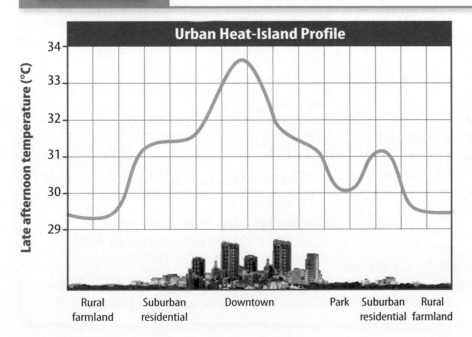

Urban Heat-Island Profile

Late afternoon temperature (°C)

34 — 33 — 32 — 31 — 30 — 29

Rural farmland | Suburban residential | Downtown | Park | Suburban residential | Rural farmland

Figure 5 The temperature is often warmer in urban areas when compared to temperatures in the surrounding countryside.

Visual Check What is the temperature difference between downtown and rural farmland?

Figure 6 Camels are adapted to dry climates and can survive up to three weeks without drinking water.

How Climate Affects Living Organisms

Organisms have adaptations for the climates where they live. For example, polar bears have thick fur and a layer of fat that helps keep them warm in the Arctic. Many animals that live in deserts, such as the camels in **Figure 6,** have adaptations for surviving in hot, dry conditions. Some desert plants have extensive shallow root systems that collect rainwater. Deciduous trees, found in continental climates, lose their leaves during the winter, which reduces water loss when soils are frozen.

Climate also influences humans in many ways. Average temperature and rainfall in a location help determine the type of crops humans grow there. Thousands of orange trees grow in Florida, where the climate is mild. Wisconsin's continental climate is ideal for growing cranberries.

Climate also influences the way humans design buildings. In polar climates, the soil is frozen year-round—a condition called permafrost. Humans build houses and other buildings in these climates on stilts. This is done so that thermal energy from the building does not melt the permafrost.

Reading Check How are organisms adapted to different climates?

Inquiry MiniLab 40 minutes

Where are microclimates found?

Microclimates differ from climates in the larger region around them. In this lab, you will identify a microclimate.

1 Read and complete a lab safety form.

2 Select two areas near your school. One area should be in an open location. The other area should be near the school building.

3 Make a data table like the one at the right in your Science Journal.

4 Measure and record data at the first area. Find wind direction using a **wind sock,** temperature using a **thermometer,** and relative humidity using a **psychrometer** and a **relative humidity chart.**

5 Repeat step 4 at the second area.

	Sidewalk	Soccer Fields
Temperature		
Wind direction		
Relative humidity		

Analyze and Conclude

1. **Graph Data** Make a bar graph showing the temperature and relative humidity at both sites.

2. **Use** the data in your table to compare wind direction.

3. **Interpret Data** How did weather conditions at the two sites differ? What might account for these differences?

4. **Key Concept** How might you decide which site is a microclimate? Explain.

imagebroker/Alamy

Visual Summary

Climate is influenced by several factors including latitude, altitude, and an area's location relative to a large body of water or mountains.

Rain shadows occur on the downwind slope of mountains.

Microclimates can occur in urban areas, forests, and hilltops.

FOLDABLES

Use your lesson Foldable to review the lesson. Save your Foldable for the project at the end of the chapter.

What do you think NOW?

You first read the statements below at the beginning of the chapter.

1. Locations at the center of large continents usually have the same climate as locations along the coast.

2. Latitude does not affect climate.

Did you change your mind about whether you agree or disagree with the statements? Rewrite any false statements to make them true.

Use Vocabulary

1. The amount of thermal energy needed to raise the temperature of 1 kg of a material by 1°C is called _____.

2. **Distinguish** between climate and microclimate.

3. **Use the term** *rain shadow* in a sentence.

Understand Key Concepts 🔑

4. How are climates classified?
   A. by cold- and warm-water ocean currents
   B. by latitude and longitude
   C. by measurements of temperature and humidity
   D. by temperature, precipitation, and vegetation

5. **Describe** the climate of an island in the tropical Pacific Ocean.

6. **Compare** the climates on either side of a large mountain range.

7. **Distinguish** between weather and climate.

Interpret Graphics

8. **Summarize** Copy and fill in the graphic organizer below to summarize information about the different types of climate worldwide.

Climate Type	Description
Tropical	
Dry	
Mild	
Continental	
Polar	

Critical Thinking

9. **Distinguish** between the climates of a coastal location and a location in the center of a large continent.

10. **Infer** how you might snow ski on the island of Hawaii.

(t)Rolf Hicker/age fotostock; (b)rabbit75_ist/Getty Images

Can reflection of the Sun's rays change the climate?

Materials

bowl

polyester film

transparent tape

stopwatch

light source

thermometer

Safety

Albedo is the term used to refer to the percent of solar energy that is reflected back into space. Clouds, for example, reflect about 50 percent of the solar energy they receive, whereas dark surfaces on Earth might reflect as little as 5 percent. Snow has a very high albedo and reflects 75 to 90 percent of the solar energy it receives. The differences in how much solar energy is reflected back into the atmosphere from different regions of Earth can cause differences in climate. Also, changes in albedo can affect the climate of that region.

Learn It

When an observation cannot be made directly, a simulation can be used to draw reasonable conclusions. This strategy is known as **inferring.** Simulating natural occurrences on a small scale can provide indirect observations so realistic outcomes can be inferred.

Try It

1 Read and complete a lab safety form.

2 Make a data table for recording temperatures in your Science Journal.

3 Cover the bottom of a bowl with a sheet of polyester film. Place a thermometer on top of the sheet. Record the temperature in the bottom of the bowl.

4 Put the bowl under the light source and set the timer for 5 minutes. After 5 minutes, record the temperature. Remove the thermometer and allow it to return to its original temperature. Repeat two more times.

5 Repeat the experiment, but this time tape the sheet of polyester film over the top of the bowl and the thermometer.

Apply It

6 **Analyze** the data you collected. What difference did you find when the polyester film covered the bowl?

7 **Conclude** What can you conclude about the Sun's rays reaching the bottom of the bowl when it was covered by the polyester film?

8 **Infer** what happens to the Sun's rays when they reach clouds in the atmosphere. Explain.

9 **Describe** how the high albedo of the ice and snow in the polar regions contribute to the climate there.

10 🔑 **Key Concept** If a region of Earth were to be covered most of the time by smog or clouds, would the climate of that region change? Explain your answer.

Reading Guide

Key Concepts 🔑
ESSENTIAL QUESTIONS

- How has climate varied over time?
- What causes seasons?
- How does the ocean affect climate?

Vocabulary
ice age

interglacial

El Niño/Southern Oscillation

monsoon

drought

g Multilingual eGlossary

 AID M2.1b, M3.1a, S3.2e; IS 1.3; ICT 4.2, 5.1; PS 1.1i

Climate Cycles

Inquiry How did this lake form?

A melting glacier formed this lake. How long ago did this happen? What type of climate change occurred to cause a glacier to melt? Will it happen again?

Quasarphoto/Getty Images

How does Earth's tilted axis affect climate?

Earth's axis is tilted at an angle of 23.5°. This tilt influences climate by affecting the amount of sunlight that reaches Earth's surface.

1. Read and complete a lab safety form.

2. Hold a **penlight** about 25 cm above a sheet of paper at a 90° angle. Use a **protractor** to check the angle.

3. Turn off the overhead lights and turn on the penlight. Your partner should trace the circle of light cast by the penlight onto the paper.

4. Repeat steps 2 and 3, but this time hold the penlight at an angle of 23.5° from perpendicular.

Think About This

1. How did the circles of light change during each trial?

2. Which trial represented the tilt of Earth's axis?

3. 🔑 **Key Concept** How might changes in the tilt of Earth's axis affect climate? Explain.

Figure 7 Scientists study the different layers in an ice core to learn more about climate changes in the past.

Long-Term Cycles

Weather and climate have many cycles. In most areas on Earth, temperatures increase during the day and decrease at night. Each year, the air is warmer during summer and colder during winter. But climate also changes in cycles that take much longer than a lifetime to complete.

Much of our knowledge about past climates comes from natural records of climate. Scientists study ice cores, shown in **Figure 7,** drilled from ice layers in glaciers and ice sheets. Fossilized pollen, ocean sediments, and the growth rings of trees also are used to gain information about climate changes in the past. Scientists use the information to compare present-day climates to those that occurred many thousands of years ago.

✓ **Reading Check** How do scientists find information about past climates on Earth?

Ice Ages and Interglacials

Earth has experienced many major atmospheric and climate changes in its history. **Ice ages** *are cold periods lasting from hundreds to millions of years when glaciers cover much of Earth.* Glaciers and ice sheets advance during cold periods and retreat during **interglacials**—*the warm periods that occur during ice ages or between ice ages.*

Major Ice Ages and Warm Periods

The most recent ice age began about 2 million years ago. The ice sheets reached maximum size about 20,000 years ago. At that time, about half the northern hemisphere was covered by ice. About 10,000 years ago, Earth entered its current interglacial period, called the Holocene Epoch.

Temperatures on Earth have fluctuated during the Holocene. For example, the period between 950 and 1100 was one of the warmest in Europe. The Little Ice Age, which lasted from 1250 to about 1850, was a period of bitterly cold temperatures.

 Key Concept Check How has climate varied over time?

Causes of Long-Term Climate Cycles

As the amount of solar energy reaching Earth changes, Earth's climate also changes. One factor that affects how much energy Earth receives is the shape of its orbit. The shape of Earth's orbit appears to vary between elliptical and circular over the course of about 100,000 years. As shown in **Figure 8,** when Earth's orbit is more circular, Earth averages a greater distance from the Sun. This results in below-average temperatures on Earth.

Another factor that scientists suspect influences climate change on Earth is changes in the tilt of Earth's axis. The tilt of Earth's axis changes in 41,000-year cycles. Changes in the angle of Earth's tilt affect the range of temperatures throughout the year. For example, a decrease in the angle of Earth's tilt, as shown in **Figure 8,** could result in a decrease in temperature differences between summer and winter. Long-term climate cycles are also influenced by the slow movement of Earth's continents, as well as changes in ocean circulation.

WORD ORIGIN ············

interglacial
from Latin *inter–*, means "among, between"; and *glacialis*, means "icy, frozen"

Figure 8 This exaggerated image shows how the shape of Earth's orbit varies between elliptical and circular. The angle of the tilt varies from 22° to 24.5° about every 41,000 years. Earth's current tilt is 23.5°.

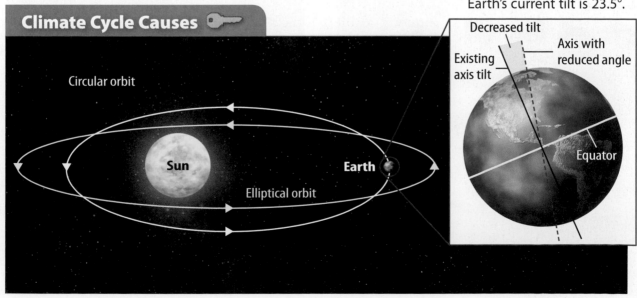

Climate Cycle Causes

Circular orbit

Sun

Earth

Elliptical orbit

Decreased tilt

Axis with reduced angle

Existing axis tilt

Equator

Short-Term Cycles

In addition to its long-term cycles, climate also changes in short-term cycles. Seasonal changes and changes that result from the interaction between the ocean and the atmosphere are some examples of short-term climate change.

Seasons

Changes in the amount of solar energy received at different latitudes during different times of the year give rise to the seasons. Seasonal changes include regular changes in temperature and the number of hours of day and night.

Recall from Lesson 1 that the amount of solar energy per unit of Earth's surface is related to latitude. Another factor that affects the amount of solar energy received by an area is the tilt of Earth's axis. **Figure 9** shows that when the northern hemisphere is tilted toward the Sun, the angle at which the Sun's rays strike Earth's surface is higher. There are more daylight hours than dark hours. During this time, temperatures are warmer, and the northern hemisphere experiences summer. At the same time, the southern hemisphere is tilted away from the Sun and the angle at which the Sun's rays strike Earth's surface is lower. There are fewer hours of daylight, and the southern hemisphere experiences winter.

Figure 9 shows that the opposite occurs when six months later the northern hemisphere is tilted away from the Sun. The angle at which Sun's rays strike Earth's surface is lower, and temperatures are colder. During this time, the northern hemisphere experiences winter. The southern hemisphere is tilted toward the Sun and the angle between the Sun's rays and Earth's surface is higher. The southern hemisphere experiences summer.

Figure 9 The solar energy rays reaching a given area of Earth's surface is more intense when tilted toward the Sun.

🖥 **Review** **Personal Tutor**

🔑 **Key Concept Check** What causes seasons?

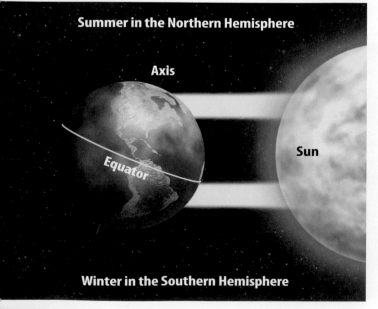

Summer in the Northern Hemisphere

Axis

Equator

Sun

Winter in the Southern Hemisphere

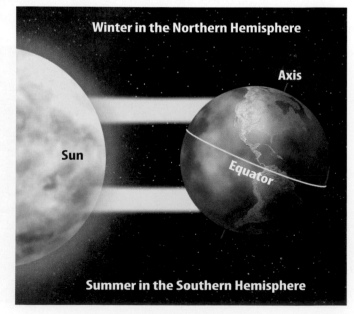

Winter in the Northern Hemisphere

Axis

Sun

Equator

Summer in the Southern Hemisphere

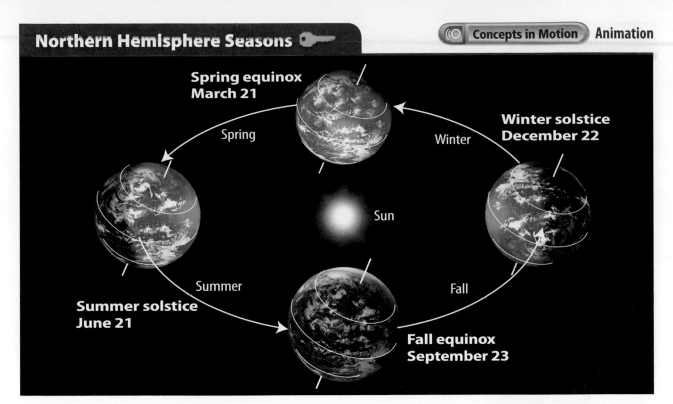

Spring equinox
March 21

Spring

Winter

Winter solstice
December 22

Sun

Summer

Fall

Summer solstice
June 21

Fall equinox
September 23

Solstices and Equinoxes

Earth revolves around the Sun once about every 365 days. During Earth's **revolution,** there are four days that mark the beginning of each of the seasons. These days are a summer solstice, a fall equinox, a winter solstice, and a spring equinox.

As shown in **Figure 10,** the solstices mark the beginnings of summer and winter. In the northern hemisphere, the summer solstice occurs on June 21 or 22. On this day, the northern hemisphere is tilted toward the Sun. In the southern hemisphere, this day marks the beginning of winter. The winter solstice begins on December 21 or 22 in the northern hemisphere. On this day, the northern hemisphere is tilted away from the Sun. In the southern hemisphere, this day marks the beginning of summer.

Equinoxes, also shown in **Figure 10,** are days when Earth is positioned so that neither the northern hemisphere nor the southern hemisphere is tilted toward or away from the Sun. The equinoxes are the beginning of spring and fall. On equinox days, the number of daylight hours almost equals the number of nighttime hours everywhere on Earth. In the northern hemisphere, the spring equinox occurs on March 21 or 22. This is the beginning of fall in the southern hemisphere. On September 22 or 23, fall begins in the northern hemisphere and spring begins in the southern hemisphere.

✓ **Reading Check** Compare and contrast solstices and equinoxes.

Figure 10 Seasons change as Earth completes its yearly revolution around the Sun.

✓ **Visual Check** How does the amount of sunlight striking the North Pole change from summer to winter?

SCIENCE USE V. COMMON USE ··

revolution
Science Use the action by a celestial body of going around in an orbit or an elliptical course

Common Use a sudden, radical, or complete change

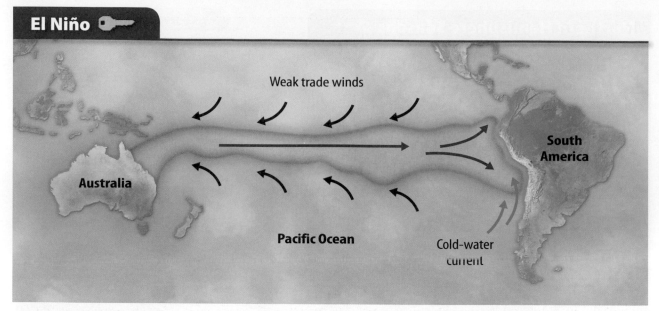

Weak trade winds

Australia

Pacific Ocean

Cold-water current

South America

Figure 11 During El Niño, the trade winds weaken and warm water surges toward South America.

Visual Check Where is the warm water during normal conditions?

El Niño and the Southern Oscillation

Close to the equator, the trade winds blow from east to west. These steady winds push warm surface water in the Pacific Ocean away from the western coast of South America. This allows cold water to rush upward from below—a process called upwelling. The air above the cold, upwelling water cools and sinks, creating a high-pressure area. On the other side of the Pacific Ocean, air rises over warm, equatorial waters, creating a low-pressure area. This difference in air pressures across the Pacific Ocean helps keep the trade winds blowing.

As **Figure 11** shows, sometimes the trade winds weaken, reversing the normal pattern of high and low pressures across the Pacific Ocean. Warm water surges back toward South America, preventing cold water from upwelling. This **phenomenon**, called El Niño, shows the connection between the atmosphere and the ocean. During El Niño, the normally dry, cool western coast of South America warms and receives lots of precipitation. Climate changes can be seen around the world. Droughts occur in areas that are normally wet. The number of violent storms in California and the southern United States increases.

Reading Check How do conditions in the Pacific Ocean differ from normal during El Niño?

The combined ocean and atmospheric cycle that results in weakened trade winds across the Pacific Ocean is called **El Niño/ Southern Oscillation**, *or ENSO. A complete ENSO cycle occurs every 3–8 years. The North Atlantic Oscillation (NAO) is another cycle that can change the climate for decades at a time. The NAO affects the strength of storms throughout North America and Europe by changing the position of the jet stream.*

Monsoons

Another climate cycle involving both the atmosphere and the ocean is a monsoon. A **monsoon** *is a wind circulation pattern that changes direction with the seasons.* Temperature differences between the ocean and the land cause winds, as shown in **Figure 12.** During summer, warm air over land rises and creates low pressure. Cooler, heavier air sinks over the water, creating high pressure. The winds blow from the water toward the land, bringing heavy rainfall. During winter, the pattern reverses and winds blow from the land toward the water.

The world's largest monsoon is found in Asia. Cherrapunji, India, is one of the world's wettest locations—receiving an average of 10 m of monsoon rainfall each year. Precipitation is even greater during El Niño events. A smaller monsoon occurs in southern Arizona. As a result, weather is dry during spring and early summer with thunderstorms occurring more often from July to September.

 Key Concept Check How does the ocean affect climate?

Droughts, Heat Waves, and Cold Waves

A **drought** *is a period with below-average precipitation.* A drought can cause crop damage and water shortages.

Droughts are often accompanied by heat waves—periods of unusually high temperatures. Droughts and heat waves occur when large hot-air masses remain in one place for weeks or months. Cold waves are long periods of unusually cold temperatures. These events occur when a large continental polar air mass stays over a region for days or weeks. Severe weather of these kinds can be the result of climatic changes on Earth or just extremes in the average weather of a climate.

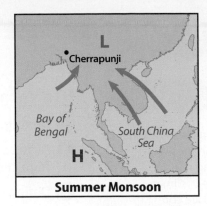
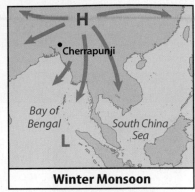

Summer Monsoon **Winter Monsoon**

Figure 12 Monsoon winds reverse with the change of seasons.

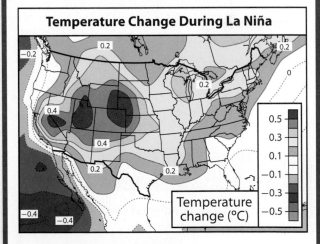

Inquiry MiniLab **20 minutes**

How do climates vary?
Unlike El Niño, La Niña is associated with cold ocean temperatures in the Pacific Ocean.

1. As the map shows, average temperatures change during a La Niña winter.

2. The color key shows the range of temperature variation from normal.

3. Find a location on the map. How much did temperatures during La Niña depart from average temperatures?

Temperature Change During La Niña

Analyze and Conclude

1. **Recognize Cause and Effect** Did La Niña affect the climate in your chosen area?

2. **Key Concept** Describe any patterns you see. How did La Niña affect climate in your chosen area? Use data from the map to support your answer.

Lesson 2 Review

Visual Summary

Scientists learn about past climates by studying natural records of climate, such as ice cores, fossilized pollen, and growth rings of trees.

Long-term climate changes, such as ice ages and interglacials, can be caused by changes in the shape of Earth's orbit and the tilt of its axis.

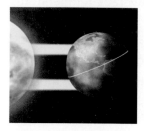

Short-term climate changes include seasons, El Niño/Southern Oscillation, and monsoons.

FOLDABLES®

Use your lesson Foldable to review the lesson. Save your Foldable for the project at the end of the chapter.

What do you think NOW?

You first read the statements below at the beginning of the chapter.

3. Climate on Earth today is the same as it has been in the past.

4. Climate change occurs in short-term cycles.

Did you change your mind about whether you agree or disagree with the statements? Rewrite any false statements to make them true.

Use Vocabulary

1. **Distinguish** an ice age from an interglacial.

2. A(n) _____ is a period of unusually high temperatures.

3. **Define** *drought* in your own words.

Understand Key Concepts

4. What happens during El Niño/Southern Oscillation?
   - **A.** An interglacial climate shift occurs.
   - **B.** The Pacific pressure pattern reverses.
   - **C.** The tilt of Earth's axis changes.
   - **D.** The trade winds stop blowing.

5. **Identify** causes of long-term climate change.

6. **Describe** how upwelling can affect climate.

Interpret Graphics

7. **Sequence** Copy and fill in the graphic organizer below to describe the sequence of events during El Niño/Southern Oscillation.

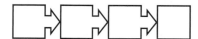

Critical Thinking

8. **Assess** the possibility that Earth will soon enter another ice age.

9. **Evaluate** the relationship between heat waves and drought.

10. **Identify** and explain the climate cycle shown below. Illustrate how conditions change during the summer.

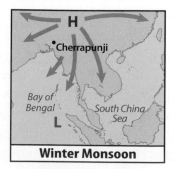

Winter Monsoon

©Ragnar Th Sigurdsson/ARCTIC IMAGES/Alamy

Frozen in Time

Looking for clues to past climates, Lonnie Thompson races against the clock to collect ancient ice from melting glaciers.

◀ **Thompson has led expeditions to 15 countries and Antarctica.**

Earth's climate is changing. To understand why, scientists investigate how climates have changed throughout Earth's history by looking at ancient ice that contains clues from past climates. Scientists collected these ice samples only from glaciers at the North Pole and the South Pole. Then, in the 1970s, geologist Lonnie Thompson began collecting ice from a new location—the tropics.

Thompson, a geologist from the Ohio State University, and his team scale glaciers atop mountains in tropical regions. On the Quelccaya ice cap in Peru, they collect ice cores—columns of ice layers that built up over hundreds to thousands of years. Each layer is a capsule of a past climate, holding dust, chemicals, and gas that were trapped in the ice and snow during that period.

To collect ice cores, they drill hundreds of feet into the ice. The deeper they drill, the further back in time they go. One core is nearly 12,000 years old!

Collecting ice cores is not easy. The team hauls heavy equipment up rocky slopes in dangerous conditions—icy windstorms, thin air, and avalanche threats. Thompson's greatest challenge is the warming climate. The Quelccaya ice cap is melting. It has shrunk by 30 percent since Thompson's first visit in 1974. It's a race against time to collect ice cores before the ice disappears. When the ice is gone, so are the secrets it holds about climate change.

Thousands of ice core samples are stored in deep freeze at Thompson's lab. One core from Antarctica is over 700,000 years old, which is well before the existence of humans. ▶

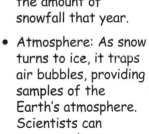

Secrets in the Ice

In the lab, Thompson and his team analyze the ice cores to determine

- **Age of ice:** Every year, snow accumulations form a new layer. Layers help scientists date the ice and specific climate events.

- **Precipitation:** Each layer's thickness and composition help scientists determine the amount of snowfall that year.

- **Atmosphere:** As snow turns to ice, it traps air bubbles, providing samples of the Earth's atmosphere. Scientists can measure the trace gases from past climates.

- **Climate events:** The concentration of dust particles helps scientists determine periods of increased wind, volcanic activity, dust storms, and fires.

It's Your Turn

WRITE AN INTRODUCTION Imagine Lonnie Thompson is giving a speech at your school. You have been chosen to introduce him. Write an introduction highlighting his work and achievements.

(t,b)American Museum of Natural History

Lesson 3

Reading Guide

Key Concepts 🗝
ESSENTIAL QUESTIONS

- How can human activities affect climate?
- How are predictions for future climate change made?

Vocabulary

global warming

greenhouse gas

deforestation

global climate model

 Multilingual eGlossary

 Video **BrainPOP®**

 AID M1.1c, S1.2a, S1.2b, S2.1a, S2.1b, S2.1d, S2.2a, S2.2b, S2.2c, S2.2d, S2.2e, S2.3a, S2.3b, S3.1a, S3.2a, S3.2d, S3.2f, S3.2g, S3.3; ICT 4.2; IPS 1.2, 1.4; PS 2.2r

Recent Climate Change

Inquiry Will Tuvalu sink or swim?

This small island sits in the middle of the Pacific Ocean. What might happen to this island if the sea level rose? What type of climate change might cause sea level to rise?

What changes climates?

Natural events such as volcanic eruptions spew dust and gas into the atmosphere. These events can cause climate change.

1. Read and complete a lab safety form.

2. Place a **thermometer** on a sheet of **paper.**

3. Hold a **flashlight** 10 cm above the paper. Shine the light on the thermometer bulb for 5 minutes. Observe the light intensity. Record the temperature in your Science Journal.

4. Use a **rubber band** to secure 3–4 layers of **cheesecloth or gauze** over the bulb end of the flashlight. Repeat step 3.

Think About This

1. Describe the effect of the cheesecloth on the flashlight in terms of brightness and temperature.

2. 🔑 **Key Concept** Would a volcanic eruption cause temperatures to increase or decrease? Explain.

Regional and Global Climate Change

Average temperatures on Earth have been increasing for the past 100 years. As the graph in **Figure 13** shows, the warming has not been steady. Globally, average temperatures were fairly steady from 1880 to 1900. From 1900 to 1945, they increased by about 0.5°C. A cooling period followed, ending in 1975. Since then, average temperatures have steadily increased. The greatest warming has been in the northern hemisphere. However, temperatures have been steady in some areas of the southern hemisphere. Parts of Antarctica have cooled.

✓ **Reading Check** How have temperatures changed over the last 100 years?

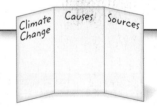

FOLDABLES®

Make a tri-fold book from a sheet of paper. Label it as shown. Use it to organize your notes about climate change and the possible causes.

Climate Change	Causes	Sources

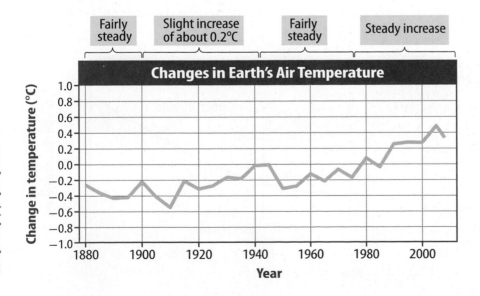

Fairly steady | Slight increase of about 0.2°C | Fairly steady | Steady increase

Changes in Earth's Air Temperature

Change in temperature (°C)

1.0
0.8
0.6
0.4
0.2
0.0
−0.2
−0.4
−0.6
−0.8
−1.0

1880   1900   1920   1940   1960   1980   2000

Year

Figure 13 Temperature change has not been constant throughout the past 100 years.

✓ **Visual Check** What 20-year period has seen the most change?

Hutchings Photography/Digital Light Source

Human Impact on Climate Change

The rise in Earth's average surface temperature during the past 100 years is often referred to as **global warming.** Scientists have been studying this change and the possible causes of it. In 2007, the Intergovernmental Panel on Climate Change (IPCC), an international organization created to study global warming, concluded that most of this temperature increase is due to human activities. These activities include the release of increasing amounts of greenhouse gases into the atmosphere through burning fossil fuels and large-scale cutting and burning of forests. Although many scientists agree with the IPCC, some scientists propose that global warming is due to natural climate cycles.

WORD ORIGIN

deforestation
from Latin *de–*, means "down from, concerning"; and *forestum silvam*, means "the outside woods"

Greenhouse Gases

Gases in the atmosphere that absorb Earth's outgoing infrared radiation are **greenhouse gases.** Greenhouse gases help keep temperatures on Earth warm enough for living things to survive. Recall that this phenomenon is referred to as the greenhouse effect. Without greenhouse gases, the average temperature on Earth would be much colder, about −18°C. Carbon dioxide (CO_2), methane, and water vapor are all greenhouse gases.

Study the graph in **Figure 14.** What has happened to the levels of CO_2 in the atmosphere over the last 120 years? Levels of CO_2 have been increasing. Higher levels of greenhouse gases create a greater greenhouse effect. Most scientists suggest that global warming is due to the greater greenhouse effect. What are some sources of the excess CO_2?

 Reading Check How do greenhouse gases affect temperatures on Earth?

Climate Change 🔑

Figure 14 Over the recent past, globally averaged temperatures and carbon dioxide concentration in the atmosphere have both increased.

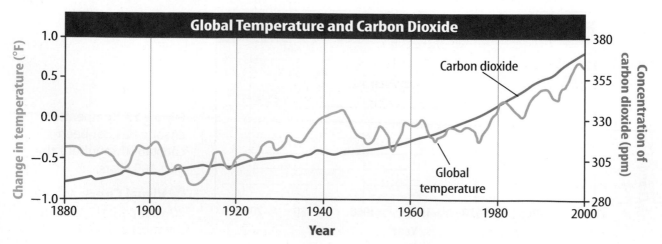

Human-Caused Sources Carbon dioxide enters the atmosphere when fossil fuels, such as coal, oil, and natural gas, burn. Burning fossil fuels releases energy that provides electricity, heats homes and buildings, and powers automobiles.

Deforestation *is the large-scale cutting and/or burning of forests.* Forest land is often cleared for agricultural and development purposes. Deforestation, shown in **Figure 15,** affects global climate by increasing carbon dioxide in the atmosphere in two ways. Living trees remove carbon dioxide from the air during photosynthesis. Cut trees, however, do not. Sometimes cut trees are burned to clear a field, adding carbon dioxide to the atmosphere as the trees burn. According to the Food and Agriculture Organization of the United Nations, deforestation makes up about 25 percent of the carbon dioxide released from human activities.

Natural Sources Carbon dioxide occurs naturally in the atmosphere. Its sources include volcanic eruptions and forest fires. Cellular respiration in organisms contributes additional CO_2.

Aerosols

The burning of fossil fuels releases more than just greenhouse gases into the atmosphere. Aerosols, tiny liquid or solid particles, are also released. Most aerosols reflect sunlight back into space. This prevents some of the Sun's energy from reaching Earth, potentially cooling the climate over time.

Aerosols also cool the climate in another way. When clouds form in areas with large amounts of aerosols, the cloud droplets are smaller. Clouds with small droplets, as shown in **Figure 16,** reflect more sunlight than clouds with larger droplets. By preventing sunlight from reaching Earth's surface, small-droplet clouds help cool the climate.

 Key Concept Check How can human activities affect climate?

▲ **Figure 15** When forests are cut down, trees can no longer use carbon dioxide from the atmosphere. In addition, any wood left rots and releases more carbon dioxide into the atmosphere.

Figure 16 Clouds made up of small droplets reflect more sunlight than clouds made up of larger droplets. ▼

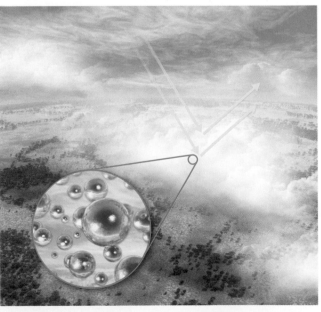

Chris Cheadle/Getty Images

Math Skills

Use Percents

If Earth's population increases from 6 billion to 9 billion, what percent is this increase?

1. Subtract the initial value from the final value:

   9 billion − 6 billion = 3 billion

2. Divide the difference by the starting value:

   $\frac{3\ \text{billion}}{6\ \text{billion}} = 0.50$

3. Multiply by 100 and add a % sign: $0.50 \times 100 = 50\%$

Practice

If a climate's mean temperature changes from 18.2°C to 18.6°C, what is the percentage of increase?

 Review

- **Math Practice**
- **Personal Tutor**

Climate and Society

A changing climate can present serious problems for society. Heat waves and droughts can cause food and water shortages. Excessive rainfall can cause flooding and mudslides. However, climate change can also benefit society. Warmer temperatures can mean longer growing seasons. Farmers can grow crops in areas that were previously too cold. Governments throughout the world are responding to the problems and opportunities created by climate change.

Environmental Impacts of Climate Change

Recall that ENSO cycles can change the amount of precipitation in some areas. Warmer ocean surface temperatures can cause more water to evaporate from the ocean surface. The increased water vapor in the atmosphere can result in heavy rainfall and frequent storms in North and South America. Increased precipitation in these areas can lead to decreased precipitation in other areas, such as parts of southern Africa, the Mediterranean, and southern Asia.

Increasing temperatures can also impact the environment in other ways. Melting glaciers and polar ice sheets can cause the sea level to rise. Ecosystems can be disrupted as coastal areas flood. Coastal flooding is a serious concern for the one billion people living in low-lying areas on Earth.

Extreme weather events are also becoming more common. What effect will heat waves, droughts, and heavy rainfall have on infectious disease, existing plants and animals, and other systems of nature? Will increased CO_2 levels work similarly?

The annual thawing of frozen ground has caused the building shown in **Figure 17** to slowly sink as the ground becomes soft and muddy. Permanently higher temperatures would create similar events worldwide. This and other ecosystem changes can affect migration patterns of insects, birds, fish, and mammals.

Figure 17 Buildings in the Arctic that were built on frozen soil are now being damaged by the constant freezing and thawing of the soil.

©Pete Ryan/National Geographic Image Collection/Alamy

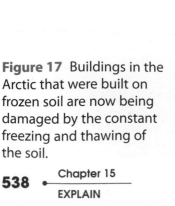

Predicting Climate Change

Weather forecasts help people make daily choices about their clothing and activities. In a similar way, climate forecasts help governments decide how to respond to future climate changes.

A **global climate model**, *or GCM, is a set of complex equations used to predict future climates.* GCMs are similar to models used to forecast the weather. GCMs and weather forecast models are different. GCMs make long-term, global predictions, but weather forecasts are short-term and can be only regional predictions. GCMs combine mathematics and physics to predict temperature, amount of precipitation, wind speeds, and other characteristics of climate. Powerful supercomputers solve mathematical equations and the results are displayed as maps. GCMs include the effects of greenhouse gases and oceans in their calculations. In order to test climate models, past records of climate change can and have been used.

 Reading Check What is a GCM?

One drawback of GCMs is that the forecasts and predictions cannot be immediately compared to real data. A weather forecast model can be analyzed by comparing its predictions with meteorological measurements made the next day. GCMs predict climate conditions for several decades in the future. For this reason, it is difficult to evaluate the accuracy of climate models.

Most GCMs predict further global warming as a result of greenhouse gas emissions. By the year 2100, temperatures are expected to rise by between 1°C and 4°C. The polar regions are expected to warm more than the tropics. Summer arctic sea ice is expected to completely disappear by the end of the twenty-first century. Global warming and sea-level rise are predicted to continue for several centuries.

 Key Concept Check How are predictions for future climate change made?

Inquiry **MiniLab**   **30 minutes**

How much CO_2 do vehicles emit?

Much of the carbon dioxide emitted into the atmosphere by households comes from gasoline-powered vehicles. Different vehicles emit different amounts of CO_2.

1 To calculate the amount of CO_2 given off by a vehicle, you must know how many miles per gallon of gasoline the vehicle gets. This information is shown in the chart below.

2 Assume that each vehicle is driven about 15,000 miles annually. Calculate how many gallons each vehicle uses per year. Record your data in your Science Journal in a chart like the one below.

3 One gallon of gasoline emits about 20 lbs of CO_2. Calculate and record how many pounds of CO_2 are emitted by each vehicle annually.

	Estimated MPG	Gallons of Gas Used Annually	Amount of CO_2 Emitted Annually (lbs)
SUV	15		
Hybrid	45		
Compact car	25		

Analyze and Conclude

1. **Compare and contrast** the amount of CO_2 emitted by each vehicle.

2. 🔑 **Key Concept** Write a letter to a person who is planning to buy a vehicle. Explain which vehicle would have the least impact on global warming and why.

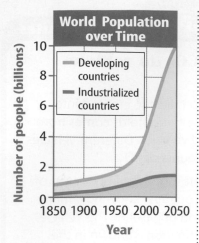

World Population over Time

Number of people (billions) vs. Year (1850–2050)

— Developing countries
— Industrialized countries

▲ **Figure 18** Earth's population is predicted to increase to more than 9 billion people by 2050.

Human Population

In 2000, more than 6 billion people inhabited Earth. As shown in **Figure 18,** Earth's population is expected to increase to 9 billion by the year 2050. What effects will a 50-percent increase in population have on Earth's atmosphere?

It is predicted that by the year 2030, two of every three people on Earth will live in urban areas. Many of these areas will be in developing countries in Africa and Asia. Large areas of forests are already being cleared to make room for expanding cities. Significant amounts of greenhouse gases and other air pollutants will be added to the atmosphere.

 Reading Check How could an increase in human population affect climate change?

Ways to Reduce Greenhouse Gases

People have many options for reducing levels of pollution and greenhouse gases. One way is to develop alternative sources of energy that do not release carbon dioxide into the atmosphere, such as solar energy or wind energy. Automobile emissions can be reduced by as much as 35 percent by using hybrid vehicles. Hybrid vehicles use an electric motor part of the time, which reduces fuel use.

Emissions can be further reduced by green building. Green building is the practice of creating energy-efficient buildings, such as the one shown in **Figure 19.** People can also help remove carbon dioxide from the atmosphere by planting trees in deforested areas.

You can also help control greenhouse gases and pollution by conserving fuel and recycling. Turning off lights and electronic equipment when you are not using them reduces the amount of electricity you use. Recycling metal, paper, plastic, and glass reduces the amount of fuel required to manufacture these materials.

Figure 19 Solar heating, natural lighting, and water recycling are some of the technologies used in green buildings. ▶

Bruce Harber/age fotostock

✓ **Assessment** Online Quiz

? **Inquiry** Virtual Lab

Visual Summary

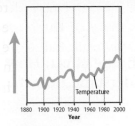

Many scientists suggest that global warming is due to increased levels of greenhouse gases in atmosphere.

Human activities, such as deforestation and burning fossil fuels, can contribute to global warming.

Ways to reduce greenhouse gas emissions include using solar and wind energy, and creating energy-efficient buildings.

FOLDABLES

Use your lesson Foldable to review the lesson. Save your Foldable for the project at the end of the chapter.

What do you think NOW?

You first read the statements below at the beginning of the chapter.

5. Human activities can impact climate.

6. You can help reduce the amount of greenhouse gases released into the atmosphere.

Did you change your mind about whether you agree or disagree with the statements? Rewrite any false statements to make them true.

Use Vocabulary

1 **Define** *global warming* in your own words.

2 A set of complex equations used to predict future climates is called _____.

3 **Use the term** *deforestation* in a sentence.

Understand Key Concepts 🔑

4 Which human activity can have a cooling effect on climate?
- A. release of aerosols
- B. global climate models
- C. greenhouse gas emission
- D. large area deforestation

5 **Describe** how human activities can impact climate.

6 **Identify** the advantages and disadvantages of global climate models.

7 **Describe** two ways deforestation contributes to the greenhouse effect.

Interpret Graphics

8 **Determine Cause and Effect** Draw a graphic organizer like the one below to identify two ways burning fossil fuels impacts climate.

Critical Thinking

9 **Suggest** ways you can reduce greenhouse gas emissions.

10 **Assess** the effects of global warming in the area where you live.

Math Skills ×÷

Review — Math Practice —

11 A 32-inch LCD flat-panel TV uses about 125 watts of electricity. If the screen size is increased to 40 inches, the TV uses 200 watts of electricity. What is the percent reduction of electricity if you use a 32-inch TV instead of a 40-inch TV?

The greenhouse effect is a gas!

Materials

plastic wrap

2 jars with lids

sand

thermometer

desk lamp

stopwatch

rubber band

Safety

Human survival on Earth depends on the greenhouse effect. How can you model the greenhouse effect to help understand how it keeps Earth's temperature in balance?

Ask a Question

How will the temperature in a greenhouse compare to that of an open system when exposed to solar energy?

Make Observations

1 Read and complete a lab safety form.

2 Decide which type of container you think will make a good model of a greenhouse. Make two identical models.

3 Place equal amounts of sand in the bottom of each greenhouse.

4 Place a thermometer in each greenhouse in a position where you can read the temperature. Secure it on the wall of the container so you are not measuring the temperature of the sand.

5 Leave one container open, and close the other container.

6 Place the greenhouses under a light source—the Sun or a lamp. Have the light source the same distance from each greenhouse and at the same angle.

7 Read the starting temperature and then every 5–10 minutes for at least three readings. Record the temperatures in your Science Journal and organize them in a table like the one shown on the next page.

Form a Hypothesis

8 Think about some adjustments you could make to your greenhouses to model other components of the greenhouse effect. For example, translucent tops, or white tops, could represent materials that would reflect more light and thermal energy.

9 Based on your observations, form a hypothesis about what materials would most accurately model the greenhouse effect.

Temperature (°C)			
	Reading 1	Reading 2	Reading 3
Greenhouse 1			
Greenhouse 2			

Test Your Hypothesis

10 Set up both greenhouse models in the same way for the hypothesis you are testing. Determine how many trials are sufficient for a valid conclusion. Graph your data to give a visual for your comparison.

Analyze and Conclude

11 Did thermal energy escape from either model? How does this compare to solar energy that reaches Earth and radiates back into the atmosphere?

12 If the greenhouse gases trap thermal energy and keep Earth's temperature warm enough, what would happen if they were not in the atmosphere?

13 If too much of a greenhouse gas, such as CO_2, entered the atmosphere, would the temperature rise?

14 **The Big Idea** If you could add water vapor or CO_2 to your model greenhouses to create an imbalance of greenhouse gases, would this affect the temperature of either system? Apply this to Earth's greenhouse gases.

Communicate Your Results

Discuss your findings with your group and organize your data. Share your graphs, models, and conclusions with the class. Explain why you chose certain materials and how these related directly to your hypothesis.

 **Extension**

Now that you understand the importance of the function of the greenhouse effect, do further investigating into what happens when the balance of greenhouse gases changes. This could result in global warming, which can have a very negative impact on Earth and the atmosphere. Design an experiment that could show how global warming occurs.

Lab Tips

☑ Focus on one concept in designing your lab so you do not get confused with the complexities of materials and data.

☑ Do not add clouds to your greenhouse as part of your model. Clouds are condensed water; water vapor is a gas.

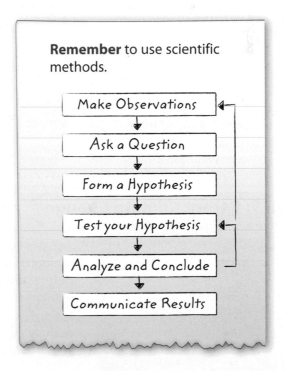

Remember to use scientific methods.

Make Observations → Ask a Question → Form a Hypothesis → Test your Hypothesis → Analyze and Conclude → Communicate Results

Chapter 15 Study Guide

Climate is the long-term average weather conditions that occur in an area. Living things have adaptations to the climate in which they live.

Key Concepts Summary 🔑	Vocabulary

Lesson 1: Climates of Earth

- **Climate** is the long-term average weather conditions that occur in a particular region.
- Climate is affected by factors such as latitude, altitude, **rain shadows** on the downwind slope of mountains, vegetation, and the **specific heat** of water.
- Climate is classified based on precipitation, temperature, and native vegetation.

Vocabulary:
climate
rain shadow
specific heat
microclimate

Lesson 2: Climate Cycles

- Over the past 4.6 billion years, climate on Earth has varied between **ice ages** and warm periods. **Interglacials** mark warm periods on Earth during or between ice ages.
- Earth's axis is tilted. This causes seasons as Earth revolves around the Sun.
- The **El Niño/Southern Oscillation** and **monsoons** are two climate patterns that result from interactions between oceans and the atmosphere.

Vocabulary:
ice age
interglacial
El Niño/Southern Oscillation
monsoon
drought

Lesson 3: Recent Climate Change

- Releasing carbon dioxide and aerosols into the atmosphere through burning fossil fuels and **deforestation** are two ways humans can affect climate change.
- Predictions about future climate change are made using computers and **global climate models.**

Vocabulary:
global warming
greenhouse gas
deforestation
global climate model

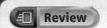
FOLDABLES® Chapter Project

Assemble your lesson Foldables as shown to make a Chapter Project. Use the project to review what you have learned in this chapter.

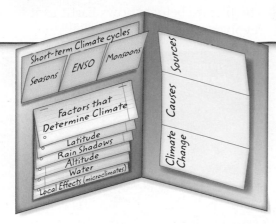

Use Vocabulary

1 A(n) _____ is an area of low rainfall on the downwind slope of a mountain.

2 Forests often have their own _____, with cooler temperatures than the surrounding countryside.

3 The lower _____ of land causes it to warm up faster than water.

4 A wind circulation pattern that changes direction with the seasons is a(n) _____.

5 Upwelling, trade winds, and air pressure patterns across the Pacific Ocean change during a(n) _____.

6 Earth's current _____ is called the Holocene Epoch.

7 A(n) _____ such as carbon dioxide absorbs Earth's infrared radiation and warms the atmosphere.

8 Additional CO_2 is added to the atmosphere when _____ of large land areas occurs.

Link Vocabulary and Key Concepts

《O Concepts in Motion 》 Interactive Concept Map

Copy this concept map, and then use vocabulary terms from the previous page and other terms in this chapter to complete the concept map.

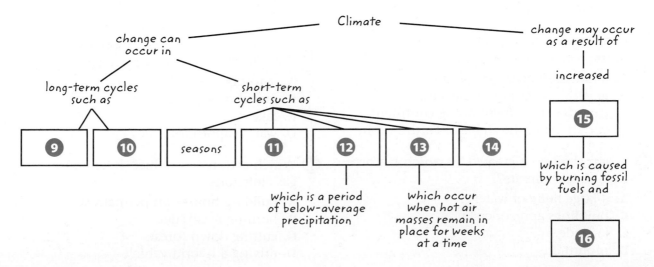

Understand Key Concepts

1 The specific heat of water is _____ than the specific heat of land.

A. higher
B. lower
C. less efficient
D. more efficient

2 The graph below shows average monthly temperature and precipitation of an area over the course of a year.

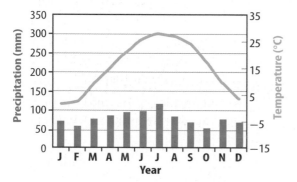

Which is the most likely location of the area?

A. in the middle of a large continent
B. in the middle of the ocean
C. near the North Pole
D. on the coast of a large continent

3 Which are warm periods during or between ice ages?

A. ENSO
B. interglacials
C. monsoons
D. Pacific oscillations

4 Long-term climate cycles are caused by all of the following EXCEPT

A. changes in ocean circulation.
B. Earth's revolution of the Sun.
C. the slow movement of the continents.
D. variations in the shape of Earth's orbit.

5 A rain shadow is created by which factor that affects climate?

A. a large body of water
B. buildings and concrete
C. latitude
D. mountains

6 During which event do trade winds weaken and the usual pattern of pressure across the Pacific Ocean reverses?

A. drought
B. El Niño/Southern Oscillation event
C. North Atlantic Oscillation event
D. volcanic eruption

7 The picture below shows Earth as it revolves around the Sun.

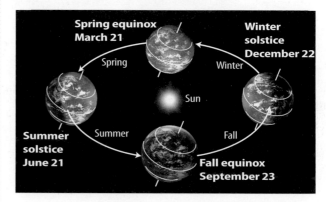

Which season is it in the southern hemisphere in July?

A. fall
B. spring
C. summer
D. winter

8 Which is not a greenhouse gas?

A. carbon dioxide
B. methane
C. oxygen
D. water vapor

9 Which cools the climate by preventing sunlight from reaching Earth's surface?

A. aerosols
B. greenhouse gases
C. lakes
D. water vapor molecules

10 Which action can reduce greenhouse gas emissions?

A. building houses on permafrost
B. burning fossil fuels
C. cutting down forests
D. driving a hybrid vehicle

Critical Thinking

11 **Hypothesize** how the climate of your town would change if North America and Asia moved together and became one enormous continent.

12 **Interpret Graphics** Identify the factor that affects climate, as shown in this graph. How does this factor affect climate?

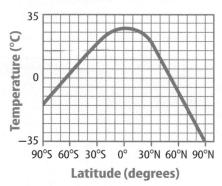

13 **Diagram** Draw a diagram that explains the changes that occur during an El Niño/Southern Oscillation event.

14 **Evaluate** which would cause more problems for your city or town: a drought, a heat wave, or a cold wave. Explain.

15 **Recommend** a life change you could make if the climate in your city were to change.

16 **Formulate** your opinion about the cause of global warming. Use facts to support your opinion.

17 **Predict** the effects of population increase on the climate where you live.

18 **Compare** how moisture affects the climates on either side of a mountain range.

Writing in Science

19 **Write** a short paragraph that describes a microclimate near your school or your home. What is the cause of the microclimate?

REVIEW **THE BIG IDEA**

20 What is climate? Explain what factors affect climate and give three examples of different types of climate.

21 Explain how life on Earth is affected by climate.

Math Skills

Review
Math Practice

Use Percentages

22 Fred switches from a sport-utility vehicle that uses 800 gal of gasoline a year to a compact car that uses 450 gal.

   a. By what percent did Fred reduce the amount of gasoline used?

   b. If each gallon of gasoline released 20 pounds of CO_2, by what percent did Fred reduce the released CO_2?

23 Of the 186 billion tons of CO_2 that enter Earth's atmosphere each year from all sources, 6 billion tons are from human activity. If humans reduced their CO_2 production by half, what percentage decrease would it make in the total CO_2 entering the atmosphere?

Standardized Test Practice

Record your answers on the answer sheet provided by your teacher or on a sheet of paper.

Multiple Choice

1 Which is a drawback of a global climate model?

   A Its accuracy is nearly impossible to evaluate.

   B Its calculations are limited to specific regions.

   C Its predictions are short-term only.

   D Its results are difficult to interpret.

Use the diagram below to answer question 2.

2 What kind of climate would you expect to find at position 4?

   A mild

   B continental

   C tropical

   D dry

3 The difference in air temperature between a city and the surrounding rural area is an example of a(n)

   A inversion.

   B microclimate.

   C seasonal variation.

   D weather system.

4 Which does NOT help explain climate differences?

   A altitude

   B latitude

   C oceans

   D organisms

5 What is the primary cause of seasonal changes on Earth?

   A Earth's distance from the Sun

   B Earth's ocean currents

   C Earth's prevailing winds

   D Earth's tilt on its axis

Use the diagram below to answer question 6.

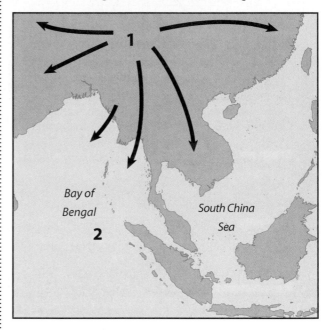

6 In the above diagram of the Asian winter monsoon, what does 1 represent?

   A high pressure

   B increased precipitation

   C low temperatures

   D wind speed

7 Climate is the _____ average weather conditions that occur in a particular region. Which completes the definition of *climate*?

   A global

   B long-term

   C mid-latitude

   D seasonal

Use the diagram below to answer question 8.

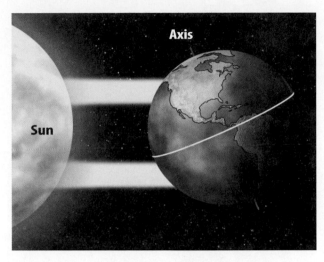

8 In the diagram above, what season is North America experiencing?

A fall

B spring

C summer

D winter

9 Which climate typically has warm summers, cold winters, and moderate precipitation?

A continental

B dry

C polar

D tropical

10 Which characterizes interglacials?

A earthquakes

B monsoons

C precipitation

D warmth

Constructed Response

Use the diagram below to answer question 11.

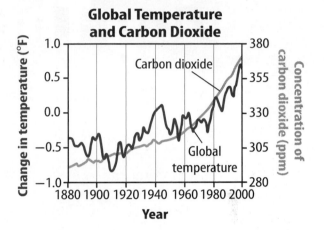

11 Compare the lines in the graph above. What does this graph suggest about the relationship between global temperature and atmospheric carbon dioxide?

Use the table below to answer questions 12 and 13.

Human Sources	Natural Sources

12 List two human and three natural sources of carbon dioxide. How do the listed human activities increase carbon dioxide levels in the atmosphere?

13 Which human activity listed in the table above also produces aerosols? What are two ways aerosols cool Earth?

NEED EXTRA HELP?													
If You Missed Question...	1	2	3	4	5	6	7	8	9	10	11	12	13
Go to Lesson...	3	1	1	1	2	2	1	2	1	2	3	3	3

Chapter 16

AID S2.1a, S2.1b, S2.1d, S3.1a; ICT 5.2;
LE 3.2a, 5.1d, 5.1e, 6.1a, 6.1b, 6.1c,
6.2c, 7.1a, 7.1b, 7.1c, 7.1d, 7.2a, 7.2b

Interactions of Living Things

THE BIG IDEA

How do living things interact with and depend on the other parts of an ecosystem?

inquiry **Good Neighbors?**

These prairie dogs live together in a network of burrows and tunnels. By cooperating with each other, they can survive more easily than each prairie dog can on its own.

- What types of resources do the prairie dogs need in order to survive?
- How might living together help them survive?
- How do these prairie dogs interact with each other and their environment?

©W. Perry Conway/age fotostock

Get Ready to Read

What do you think?

Before you read, decide if you agree or disagree with each of these statements. As you read this chapter, see if you change your mind about any of the statements.

1 An ecosystem contains both living and nonliving things.

2 All changes in an ecosystem occur over a long period of time.

3 Changes that occur in an ecosystem can cause populations to become larger or smaller.

4 Some organisms have relationships with other types of organisms that help them to survive.

5 Most of the energy used by organisms on Earth comes from the Sun.

6 Both nature and humans affect the environment.

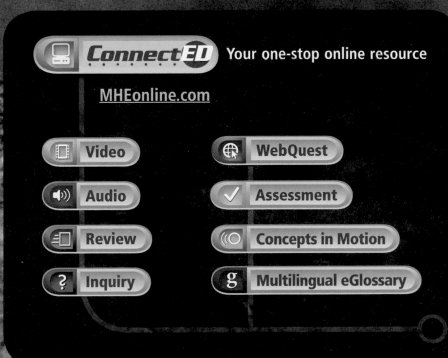

ConnectED Your one-stop online resource

MHEonline.com

Video

Audio

Review

Inquiry

WebQuest

Assessment

Concepts in Motion

Multilingual eGlossary

Lesson 1

Reading Guide

Key Concepts 🔑
ESSENTIAL QUESTIONS

- What are ecosystems?
- What are biomes?
- What happens when environments change?

Vocabulary

ecosystem
abiotic factor
biotic factor
population
community
biome
succession

 Multilingual eGlossary

 Video **BrainPOP®**

 AID S2.1d; LE 7.1a, 7.2a, 7.2b

Ecosystems and Biomes

Inquiry Is anyone home?

This is a photograph of Arctic tundra, a cold region with little rainfall and a short growing season. What kinds of organisms might live here? What might happen if the climate got warmer?

Jon Mullen/E+/Getty Images

How do environments differ?

Have you ever been enjoying a warm sunny day when it suddenly started to rain? Weather is part of your environment. The different environments on Earth can vary greatly. Some organisms are more comfortable in one environment than another.

1 Read and complete a lab safety form.

2 Your teacher will divide the class into three groups. Students in one group will wear **heavy coats**. Students in another group will hold a **bag of ice**. Students in the third group will have no change to their environment.

3 After five minutes, determine how comfortable you are in your environment.

Think About This

1. What types of environments were represented by the three groups?

2. **Key Concept** How did your environment change? What did you do to respond?

What are ecosystems?

How are you similar to a wolf and a pine tree? You, the wolf, and the pine tree are all living things also called organisms. All organisms have some characteristics in common. They all use energy and do certain things to survive. Organisms also interact with their environments. Ecology is the study of how organisms interact with each other and with their environments.

Every organism on Earth lives in an **ecosystem**—*the living and nonliving things in one place.* Different organisms depend on different parts of an ecosystem to survive. For example, the deer in **Figure 1** might eat leaves and drink water from a stream. Although leaves are alive and the water is not, the deer need both to survive. A fish in the stream also needs water to survive, but it interacts differently with water than deer do.

 **Key Concept Check** What is an ecosystem?

Abiotic Factors

Water is just one example of a part of an ecosystem that was never alive. **Abiotic factors** *are the nonliving parts of an ecosystem.* Some important abiotic factors include water, light, temperature, atmosphere, and soil. The types and amounts of these factors available in an ecosystem help determine which organisms can live there.

Figure 1 These deer live in a woodland environment.

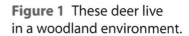 **Visual Check** Which abiotic factors can you identify in this photo?

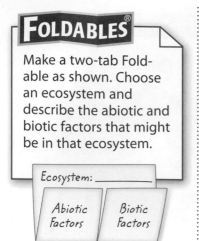
Water

Look at the plants shown in the two environments in **Figure 2.** How do the water requirements of these plants differ? A cactus grows in a desert, where it does not rain often. Ferns and vines live in a rain forest where it is very moist. All organisms need water to live, but some need more water than others do. The type of water in an ecosystem also helps determine which organisms can live there. Some organisms must live in saltwater environments, such as oceans, while others, like humans, must have freshwater to survive.

Light and Temperature

The amount of light available and the temperature of an ecosystem can also determine which organisms can live there. Some organisms, such as plants, require light energy for making food. Temperatures in ecosystems vary, and ecosystems with more sunlight generally have higher temperatures. How are the plants shown in **Figure 2** different? Ferns thrive in a warm rain forest. A cactus survives in a desert environment that can be very hot during the day and very cold at night.

Atmosphere

Very few living things can survive in an ecosystem without oxygen. Earth's **atmosphere** contains oxygen gas as well as other gases, such as water vapor, carbon dioxide, and nitrogen, that organisms need.

Ecosystems 🔑

Figure 2 Deserts and rain forests have different amounts of water. This is one factor that affects which types of plants and animals can live in each environment.

✔ **Visual Check** Which factors determine the types of plants and animals that live in each environment?

Soil

Different ecosystems contain different amounts and types of nutrients, minerals, and rocks in the soil. Soil also can have different textures and hold different amounts of moisture. The depth of soil in an ecosystem can differ as well. All of these factors determine which organisms can live in an ecosystem. How do you think the soils in the environments in **Figure 2** differ?

Biotic Factors

You have read about the nonliving, or abiotic, parts of an ecosystem. These parts are important to the survival of living things. **Biotic factors** *are all of the living or once-living things in an ecosystem.* A parrot is one biotic factor in a rain forest, and so is a fallen tree. Biotic factors can be categorized and studied in several ways.

Populations

Think of the last time you saw a flock of birds. The birds you saw were part of a population. *A* **population** *is made up of all the members of one species that live in an area.* For example, all the gray squirrels living in a neighborhood are a population. Organisms in a population interact and compete for food, shelter, and mates.

Communities

Most ecosystems contain many populations, and these populations form a community. *A* **community** *is all the populations living in an ecosystem at the same time.* For example, populations of trees, worms, insects, and toads are part of a forest community. These populations interact with each other in some way. When trees in a forest ecosystem lose their leaves in the fall, the leaves become food for worms and insects. Toads might use the leaves to hide from predators. Waste from these animals provides nutrients to the trees and insects. You will read more about the types of interactions in communities later in this chapter.

Inquiry MiniLab **20 minutes**

How many living and nonliving things can you find?

Scientists study ecosystems by noting what and how many organisms live in an ecosystem. They also take account of nonliving factors that help make up an ecosystem. You can study a small area of your ecosystem in the same way.

1. Read and complete a lab safety form.

2. In a safe outdoor area, use **string** to section off 1 m² of ground.

3. Inspect your area for 10 minutes with a **magnifying lens.** Create a table like the one below. Record each different living and nonliving thing that you find. Be sure to record if you find the same thing more than once.

Living Things	Nonliving Things	Number of Times Found
	Small rock	5
Beetle		1

Analyze and Conclude

1. **Describe** any trends you see in the numbers and types of organisms that you found.

2. **Predict** how your results might be different if you made your observations during different times of the year.

3. 🔑 **Key Concept** List four factors in the ecosystem you studied that affect the numbers and types of organisms that live there.

WORD ORIGIN

community
from Latin *communitatem,* means "fellowship"

Biomes

The populations and communities that interact in a desert are very different from those that interact in an ocean. Deserts and oceans are different biomes. *A **biome** is a geographic area on Earth that contains ecosystems with similar biotic and abiotic features.* Biomes contain ecosystems, populations, and communities, as well as specific biotic and abiotic factors. As a result, biomes can be very different from each other. Some examples of Earth's major biomes are shown in **Figure 3.**

 Key Concept Check What is a biome?

All biomes are part of the biosphere—the part of Earth that supports life. Earth's biomes can be described as either terrestrial or aquatic. *Terrestrial* means related to land, and *aquatic* means related to water. Terrestrial biomes include forests, deserts, tundra, and grasslands. Aquatic biomes include saltwater areas and freshwater areas. Biomes—like communities—can affect each other. For example, a beach ecosystem is part of both a terrestrial and an aquatic biome. Some organisms from each of these biomes interact in the beach ecosystem.

Earth's Major Biomes 🔑

Figure 3 The Earth's biosphere includes all the different ecosystems.

Desert biome

Forest biome

Tundra biome

Biosphere

Freshwater biome

Grassland biome

Saltwater biome

What happens when environments change?

The photographs in **Figure 4** are of Mount St. Helens, an active volcano in the state of Washington. The top two photos were taken only one day apart—before and after a large volcanic explosion. The ecosystem changed dramatically in a very short period of time because of the volcanic eruption. Over time, Earth's ecosystems, including Mount St. Helens, have undergone countless alterations ranging from tiny to enormous.

Changes in the environment are caused by both natural processes and human actions. Some of these changes can occur abruptly, like the erupting volcano at Mount St. Helens. Other changes, such as the river flow that slowly carved into the land and created the Grand Canyon in Arizona, can take millions of years.

Response to Change

Sometimes changes have positive effects on ecosystems, such as greater rainfall that results in more plants growing. Other changes can have negative effects. A very dry season could cause plants to die, and animals might starve. Usually, a change in an ecosystem results in both positive and negative effects.

Succession

Over long periods of time, communities can change through succession until they are very different. **Succession** *is the gradual change from one community to another community in an area.* When succession occurs, some species are replaced by others as time passes. The bottom picture in **Figure 4** shows how Mount St. Helens looked about 30 years after its devastating eruption. How did succession change Mount St. Helens and the environment around it?

 Key Concept Check Which biotic and abiotic factors changed after the Mount St. Helens eruption?

Figure 4 An unexpected volcanic eruption changed the ecosystem of Mount St. Helens suddenly. Then, over many years, succession occurred and Mount St. Helens changed again.

May 17, 1980

May 18, 1980

July 23, 2010

(t)USGS Photograph by Harry Glicken; (c)Harry Glicken/USGS; (b)©Tom Uhlman/Alamy; (bkgd)InterNetwork Media/Getty Images

Lesson 1 Review

Visual Summary

Biotic factors are the living parts of an ecosystem.

Earth's biosphere contains many different biomes.

Changes in a community can be very slow or very rapid.

FOLDABLES®

Use your lesson Foldable to review the lesson. Save your Foldable for the project at the end of the chapter.

What do you think NOW?

You first read the statements below at the beginning of the chapter.

1. An ecosystem contains both living and nonliving things.

2. All changes in an ecosystem occur over a long period of time.

Did you change your mind about whether you agree or disagree with the statements? Rewrite any false statements to make them true.

Use Vocabulary

1 **Describe** the parts of an ecosystem.

2 **Define** *succession* using your own words.

3 **Distinguish** between biome and biosphere.

Understand Key Concepts

4 **Explain** the difference between biotic and abiotic factors.

5 **Choose** which describes a biotic factor.
   A. community
   B. sunlight
   C. temperature
   D. water

6 **Determine** whether people in your area have changed the local environment. Give some examples.

Interpret Graphics

7 **Compare** two different biomes. Copy the table below and write the name of each biome in the top row. Write the characteristics of each biome in the spaces below its name.

8 **Describe** how the abiotic factors differ between these two communities.

Critical Thinking

9 **Design** your own ecosystem. Tell how the abiotic and biotic factors affect the living things in your ecosystem. Which types of plants and animals live there? How do they interact?

All for One,
One for All

▲ Gordon uses a device called a theodolite to measure locations of ant colonies. She tracks changes in a colony's behavior as it ages and grows.

If you've ever watched ants move single file across a sidewalk, you might have wondered how they know which way to go. This is a question that Dr. Deborah M. Gordon, an ecologist at Stanford University, might ask. She studies the behavior of red harvester ants.

Gordon studies the organization of ant colonies. A colony has one or more reproductive queens and many sterile workers living together. At any given time, ants might be working together on a specific task, such as building new tunnels, protecting the colony, or collecting food. However, no one ant in the colony directs the other ants. Gordon investigates how each ant within a colony takes on different tasks and how they work together as a group.

Ants communicate using chemicals. They release chemicals that other ants smell with their antennae. Each colony has its own unique odor, and only ants from that colony can recognize it. In addition, harvester ants have a chemical "vocabulary." They signal a specific task by communicating with a particular chemical.

To study ant communication, Gordon and her colleagues closely observe red harvester ants in their habitats and conduct experiments. Her team might isolate one of the communication chemicals and then place it in different locations or in the same location at different times of day. Gordon has learned that these ants can change tasks when they meet other ants. When one ant's antennae touch another ant, it can tell by the odor what task the other ant is doing. Gordon is studying how ants use encounters to interact with each other and their environments.

▲ The red harvester ant is one of only 50 ant species that have been well studied. Scientists have discovered about 10,000 ant species in all.

It's Your Turn

FIELD JOURNAL Find two animals to observe in their natural habitats. Record your observations in your Science Journal. How did they interact with the environment or with other animals? Share your results with classmates.

Lesson 2

Reading Guide

Key Concepts 🔑

ESSENTIAL QUESTIONS

- How do individuals and groups of organisms interact?

- What are some examples of symbiotic relationships?

Vocabulary

limiting factor

biotic potential

carrying capacity

habitat

niche

symbiotic relationship

 Multilingual eGlossary

 AID S3.1a, S3.1b; ICT 5.2; LE 3.2a, 7.1a, 7.1b, 7.1c

Populations and Communities

Inquiry Community?

These leafcutter ants work together making homes and getting food. The ants in the population interact with each other as well as with other populations in the community. What other populations might the ants interact with?

Bryan Mullennix/Getty Images

What is the density of your environment?

Imagine you are in a crowded elevator. Everyone jostles and bumps each other. The temperature increases and ordinary noises seem louder. Like people in an elevator, organisms in an area interact. How does the amount of space available to each organism affect its interaction with other organisms in the same area?

1. Use a **meterstick** to measure the length and width of the classroom.

2. Multiply the length by the width to find the area of the room in square meters.

3. Draw a map of your classroom, including the number and position of desks. Count the number of individuals in your class. Divide the area of the classroom by the number of individuals. In your Science Journal, record how much space each person has.

Think About This

1. What would happen if the number of students in your classroom doubled?

2. 🔑 **Key Concept** How might your interactions with your classmates change if each person had less space?

Populations

Have you ever gone fishing at a lake? If so, recall that each individual fish in the lake is a member of a population. You read in Lesson 1 that a population is all the members of one species that live in an area. The area in which a population lives can be very large, such as the population of all fish in an ocean, as shown at the top of **Figure 5.** The area in which a population lives can also be small, like fish in a lake shown at the bottom of **Figure 5.**

Recall that organisms respond to abiotic and biotic factors in their ecosystem. Sunlight, temperature, and water quality are examples of abiotic factors that affect the fish in the lake and in the ocean. Biotic factors, such as the plants they eat and other organisms that hunt them, also affect the fish. If any of these factors change, the fish population can also change.

Figure 5 Populations can live in very large areas, such as an ocean, or small areas, such as a lake.

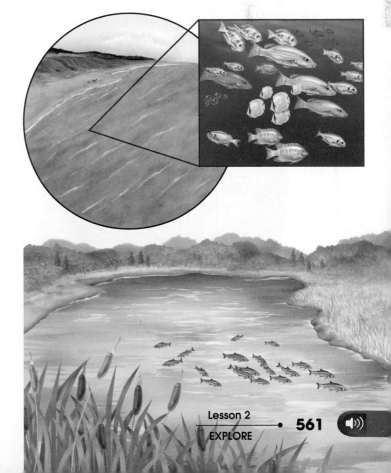

Figure 6 The size of a fish population can change in several different ways.

✔ **Visual Check** How do you think fish hatching affects the other populations in the community?

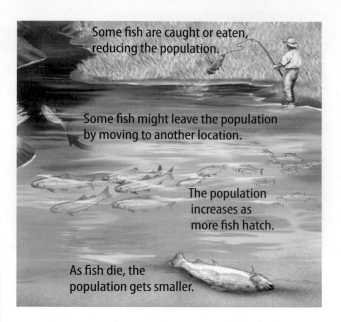

Some fish are caught or eaten, reducing the population.

Some fish might leave the population by moving to another location.

The population increases as more fish hatch.

As fish die, the population gets smaller.

Inquiry MiniLab
20 minutes

How does a fish population change?

Imagine a pond where an alien species of fish has been released accidentally. There are no predators and plenty of food. How could the size of this fish population change?

1 Read and complete a lab safety form.

2 Draw a grid of 16 spaces on a sheet of **construction paper.** Each box represents the minimum amount of space required for one fish. Place a **gummy fish** in each of two boxes on your grid. This is the first generation.

⚠ *Do not eat the gummy fish.*

3 This fish population doubles with each generation. Keeping track of the total number of fish for each generation, place gummy fish in empty boxes until all the boxes are filled.

Analyze and Conclude

1. **Create a graph** to summarize the population growth in this model.

2. 🔑 **Key Concept** Explain what factors might affect the number of individuals the pond can support.

Population Size

Think about the fish in the lake. What might happen to the population if a large number of fish eggs hatched or a hundred people caught fish all at once?

Population size can increase or decrease, as shown in **Figure 6.** Populations can increase when new individuals move into an area or when more individuals are born. Populations can decrease when individuals move away from an area or die. Sometimes the size of a population changes because the ecosystem changes. For example, if there is not much rainfall, a pond might shrink and some fish might die.

Population Density

Are the hallways in your school crowded or is there lots of room? The population density of the hallways reflects how crowded the halls are. Population density describes the number of organisms in the population relative to the amount of space available. A very dense population might have one fish for every few cubic meters of water. If a population is very dense, organisms might have a hard time finding enough resources to survive. They might not grow as large as individuals in less crowded conditions.

Limiting Factors

Populations can increase or decrease in size. What do you think keeps populations from becoming too large? **Limiting factors** *are factors that can limit the growth of a population.* The amounts of available water, space, shelter, and food affect a population's size. With too few resources, some individuals cannot survive. Other factors, like predation, competition, and disease, can also limit how many individuals survive. Some limiting factors in a rabbit population are shown in **Figure 7.**

Biotic Potential Imagine a population of rabbits with an unlimited supply of food, an unlimited amount of land to live on, and no predators. The population would keep growing until it reached its biotic potential. **Biotic potential** *is the potential growth of a population if it could grow in perfect conditions with no limiting factors.* The population's rate of birth is the highest it can be, and its rate of death is the lowest it can be.

Carrying Capacity Almost no population reaches its biotic potential. Instead, it reaches its carrying capacity. **Carrying capacity** *is the largest number of individuals of one species that an ecosystem can support over time.* The limiting factors of an area determine the area's carrying capacity.

Overpopulation Sometimes a population becomes larger than an ecosystem's carrying capacity. Overpopulation is when a population's size grows beyond the ability of the area to support it. This often results in overcrowding, a lack of resources, and an unhealthy environment. For instance, with overcrowding the trout in a lake might not grow very large. Waste from the members of the population might build up faster than it can be broken down, making the population sick.

 Reading Check Why is overpopulation harmful to organisms?

Figure 7 The number of limiting factors in an area limits the growth of a population.

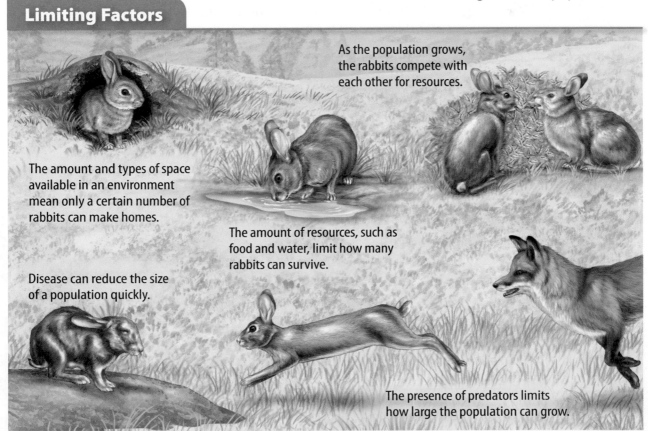

Limiting Factors

As the population grows, the rabbits compete with each other for resources.

The amount and types of space available in an environment mean only a certain number of rabbits can make homes.

The amount of resources, such as food and water, limit how many rabbits can survive.

Disease can reduce the size of a population quickly.

The presence of predators limits how large the population can grow.

FOLDABLES®

Make a three-tab book and label it as shown. Use it to organize your notes on the types of symbiotic relationships that can be in communities.

Mutualism Parasitism Commensalism

Communities

Recall that populations in the same area interact as a community. Think again about the fish in the lake. Many other populations of organisms also live in and around the lake. These include other species of fish, frogs, algae, bacteria, insects, plants, raccoons, and other organisms.

All the populations in a lake community, such as the one shown in **Figure 8,** interact with each other in different ways. For example, the populations might compete with each other for some of the resources available in the lake. The organisms of each population must have a certain amount of the limited space in the lake in which to live. In some cases, the populations might compete directly as they hunt each other for food or hide from predators.

 Key Concept Check How do the different populations in a lake interact with each other?

Symbiotic Relationships

Populations affect their community by the ways in which they interact with each other. Each population has different ways to stay alive and reproduce. All of the populations in a community share a **habitat,** *the physical place where a population or organism lives.* Each organism also has a niche in the community. A **niche** *is the unique ways an organism survives, obtains food and shelter, and avoids danger in its habitat.*

Some organisms develop relationships with other organisms that help them survive. *A* **symbiotic relationship** *is one in which two different species live together and interact closely over a long period of time.* These relationships can be beneficial to both organisms, beneficial to one and harmful to the other, or beneficial to one and neutral to the other.

Figure 8 Communities are made up of many populations.

✔ **Visual Check** How might populations of turtles and ducks interact?

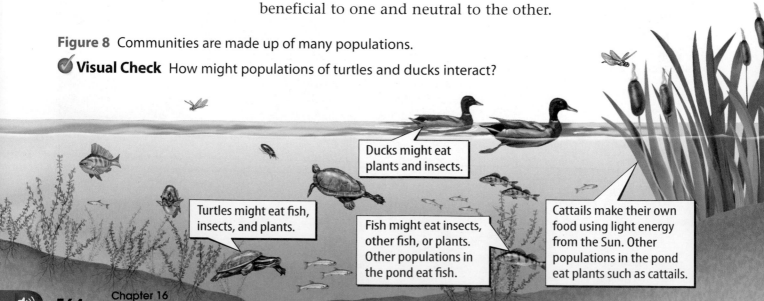

Ducks might eat plants and insects.

Turtles might eat fish, insects, and plants.

Fish might eat insects, other fish, or plants. Other populations in the pond eat fish.

Cattails make their own food using light energy from the Sun. Other populations in the pond eat plants such as cattails.

Mutualism

Recall the leafcutter ants shown at the beginning of this lesson. Leafcutter ants collect plant material and bring it back to their nest. There, they do not eat the leaves, but chew them into small pieces. A fungus grows on the pieces, as shown at the top of **Figure 9.** Some members of the population clean the fungus, removing any molds or other organisms that might harm it. The ants then eat this fungus. The ants provide the fungus with food (the leaves) and in turn use the fungus as a food source. The ants and the fungus have a mutualistic relationship. Mutualism is a symbiotic relationship in which two species in a community benefit from the relationship.

Parasitism

Mistletoe prompts kisses during the holidays—but did you know it is also a parasite? Parasitism is a symbiotic relationship in which one species (the parasite) benefits while another (the host) is harmed. Mistletoe grows in the branches of some trees. It sends its roots into the tissue of its host, the tree. The mistletoe plant takes food and water from the tree. This can weaken the tree. Too many mistletoe plants can eventually kill even strong, old trees like the one shown in the photograph to the right.

Commensalism

Sometimes two organisms can have a symbiotic relationship that affects only one of the organisms. Commensalism is a symbiotic relationship where one species benefits and the other is neither helped nor harmed. Notice the cocklebur attached to the clothing at the bottom of **Figure 9.** Plants produce these cockleburs that will stick to passing animals and humans and spread the plant's seeds around a larger area. The plant benefits from its seeds being spread, while the other organism is not harmed or helped.

Key Concept Check What is one example of a symbiotic relationship?

Figure 9 Many different types of symbiotic relationships exist among different organisms.

▲ Leafcutter ants and fungi have a mutualistic relationship.

▲ Mistletoe weakens its tree host by taking away vital food and water.

▲ This cocklebur contains the seeds of a plant. By sticking onto an animal or person, it can spread seeds over a larger distance.

Visual Check What makes the cocklebur effective?

(t)Gregory G. Dimijian, M.D./Science Source; (c)Raimund Linke/Photodisc/Getty Images; (b)Joe Blossom/Alamy

Lesson 2 Review

Visual Summary

The factors that limit the size a population of organisms can reach are called limiting factors.

A habitat is the physical environment where a population of organisms lives.

A symbiotic relationship exists when two different species of organisms live together in a close relationship over a long period of time.

FOLDABLES®

Use your lesson Foldable to review the lesson. Save your Foldable for the project at the end of the chapter.

What do you think NOW?

You first read the statements below at the beginning of the chapter.

3. Changes that occur in an ecosystem can cause populations to become larger or smaller.

4. Some organisms form relationships with other types of organisms that help them survive.

Did you change your mind about whether you agree or disagree with the statements? Rewrite any false statements to make them true.

Use Vocabulary

1. **Distinguish** between population and community.

2. **Explain** in your own words how limiting factors affect populations.

3. **Contrast** the terms *parasitism* and *mutualism* in a sentence.

Understand Key Concepts

4. **Summarize** some ways that individuals and groups of organisms interact.

5. **Illustrate** two kinds of symbiotic relationships. Indicate whether a species is helped, harmed, or not affected.

6. Which factor does NOT change the size of a population?
   A. aging   C. death
   B. birth   D. leaving

Interpret Graphics

7. **Summarize** Copy and fill in the graphic organizer below to identify symbiotic relationships.

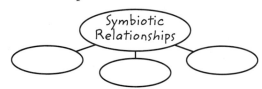

8. **Identify** three populations shown in the community below and explain how they interact with each other.

Critical Thinking

9. **Describe** two problems that occur when a human population grows. Use examples.

10. **Invent** a parasite. You may draw it or write about it. Explain how it uses its host. Tell how it benefits while its host is harmed.

Can you make predictions about a population size?

The table below shows the population size of Soay sheep from the Island of Hirta in Scotland. The data show how the population changed each year between 1986 and 2002. The size of a population can change for many reasons. For example, the population of sheep might increase if the weather is warm, causing more grass to grow for grazing. If there is little rain, grass might not grow as well and fewer sheep will survive. In some populations, cycles occur in which the population grows until resources run out, and the population size begins to decrease. Once resources are available again, the population increases once more.

Learn It

By identifying patterns in the way the sheep population changed, you might be able to guess, or **make a prediction** about, what will happen to the population in the future.

Year	Population Size
1986	700
1987	1,050
1988	1,500
1989	700
1990	900
1991	1,500
1992	950
1993	1,300
1994	1,600
1995	1,200
1996	1,800
1997	1,700
1998	2,000
1999	900
2000	1,500
2001	2,000
2002	900

Try It

1 Using the data in the table, make a graph with population size in the y-axis and time on the x-axis.

2 Examine the graph you have made. Does the population size increase every year? Does it decrease?

3 On the x-axis of your graph, highlight in one color the years that the population decreases. Highlight the years that the population increases in another color.

4 What is the best pattern you could use to describe the data?

Apply It

5 Based on the pattern you identified, would you predict that the population of sheep increased or decreased in 2003? Explain your answer.

6 Were there any years in which the pattern you identified did not occur? Which years were they?

7 🔑 **Key Concept** Using what you read about limiting factors, what interactions between organisms might cause the pattern you identified in the sheep population?

Reading Guide

Key Concepts 🔑
ESSENTIAL QUESTIONS

- How does energy move in ecosystems?
- How is the movement of energy in an ecosystem modeled?
- How does matter move in ecosystems?

Vocabulary

producer
consumer
food chain
food web
energy pyramid

[g] **Multilingual eGlossary**

AID S2.1a, S2.1b, S2.1d;
LE 5.1d, 5.1e, 6.1a, 6.1b, 6.1c, 6.2c, 7.1d

Energy and Matter

Inquiry **Who is Faster?**

This impala hopes to avoid the menacing teeth of a cheetah. A cheetah must constantly find and catch other animals to eat. How does catching and eating prey help a cheetah survive? How are the diets of animals different from each other?

Federico Veronesi/Getty Images

Where do you get energy?

You probably eat many different foods to get the energy you need to do things. Have you ever thought about how energy becomes a part of your food? For example, what do cows eat in order to obtain energy for making milk?

Food Item	Origin	Energy Source
Steak	Cow	Grass
Broccoli	Plant	the Sun

1️⃣ Write down all the foods you ate for dinner last night.

2️⃣ In your Science Journal, create a table that lists the food you ate in one column. Then write the origin of each food in the second column and the energy source for the food item in the last column. Consider that some animals eat a variety of foods. For instance, cows eat mainly grass, but chickens might eat insects as well as grass.

Think About This

1. Based on your table, do you get most of your energy from plants or animals? Where do these organisms get their energy?

2. Where might humans fit into a food chain?

3. 🔑 **Key Concept** Can you extend the energy source column with another link for any of the foods you ate? What do you think is the ultimate source of energy for foods?

Energy Flow

What did you eat for breakfast this morning? The food you take into your body is your energy source—it gives you fuel to walk, play games, read books, sit at a desk, and even to sleep. All life on Earth needs energy for cell processes.

Organisms get energy from food that they make using light or chemical energy or by eating other organisms. When one organism eats another, the energy in the organism that is eaten is transferred to the organism that eats it. In this way, energy travels through organisms, populations, communities, and ecosystems in a flow. When energy moves in a flow, like the one illustrated in **Figure 10,** it does not return to its source, as it does when matter cycles.

Organisms and Energy

Scientists classify organisms by the way they get the energy that they need to survive. Almost all energy on Earth comes from the Sun. Some organisms, such as plants, are able to capture this energy directly and convert it into energy-rich sugars that they use for food. A few organisms are able to capture energy from chemicals in the environment and make food. Other organisms cannot capture energy from sunlight or chemicals. They must obtain their energy by eating food. Organisms that cannot make their own food using the Sun must depend on organisms that can.

ACADEMIC VOCABULARY

source
(*noun*) a point of origin

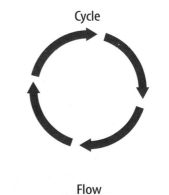

Cycle

Flow

Figure 10 Energy in a flow does not return to its source as it does in a cycle.

Producers

How do some organisms obtain the energy that comes from the Sun? You might recall that energy cannot be created or destroyed, but it can change form. **Producers** *change the energy available in their environment into food energy.* They then use this food energy for living and reproducing. Humans and other organisms can get this energy by eating producers.

Reading Check Why must producers be present in an environment?

Photosynthesis Energy from the Sun always enters a community through producers. Some producers use a chemical process called photosynthesis and transform light energy from the Sun into food energy. Producers that use light energy include most plants, algae, and some microorganisms. **Figure 11** illustrates how the process of photosynthesis converts light energy into food energy.

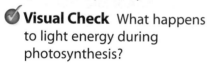

Producer

Figure 11 Light energy is changed into food energy by the process of photosynthesis.

Visual Check What happens to light energy during photosynthesis?

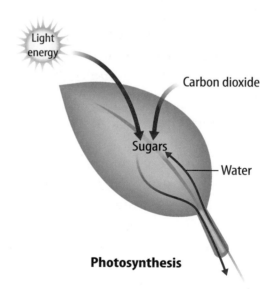

Chemosynthesis In some communities, producers get their energy from sources other than light energy. Chemosynthesis is the chemical process some producers use to change chemical energy into food energy.

One example of chemosynthesis occurs in the deep oceans. Bacteria living near volcano vents in the ocean floor use the chemicals as an energy source for making food energy.

Key Concept Check How does energy move from a producer to other organisms?

Consumers

Recall that energy moves through organisms in an ecosystem. Where does light or chemical energy go after producers like shrubs and other plants **transform** it into food energy? Organisms that cannot use light or chemical energy for making food must get their energy by eating other organisms. These organisms are called consumers. **Consumers** *cannot make their own food and get energy by eating other organisms.* Scientists classify organisms as producers or consumers, but they also classify consumers depending on what they eat. Examples of different types of consumers are shown in **Figure 12.** Consumers are classified as either herbivores, omnivores, carnivores, or detritivores based on their diet.

- Herbivores are animals that eat only producers, such as plants.

- Omnivores, such as human beings, are animals that eat both producers and other consumers.

- Carnivores, such as lions, eat only other consumers.

- Detritivores, including some insects, fungi, worms, and some bacteria and protists, eat dead plant or animal material. A type of detritivore called a decomposer breaks down dead material into simple molecules that can be used by other organisms, such as plants.

 Reading Check What are the four types of consumers?

ACADEMIC VOCABULARY

transform
(verb) to change in composition or structure

🔊 **New York FYI**

Beneficial Bacteria Microorganisms such as bacteria may be small, but they are big helpers! By decomposing dead plants and animals, they return nutrients to the soil. Then new plants can grow, which is essential to the survival of herbivores, omnivores, and carnivores.

Figure 12 Consumers are classified according to the type of food they eat.

Consumers 🔑

Herbivore

Omnivore

Carnivore

Detritivore

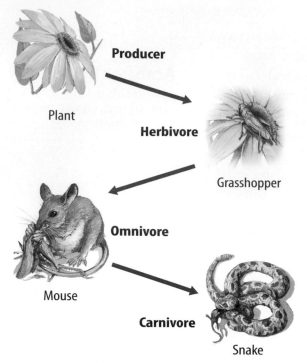

Producer
Plant

Herbivore
Grasshopper

Omnivore
Mouse

Carnivore
Snake

▲ **Figure 13** In this food chain, energy is passed from the plant to the grasshopper, the mouse, and then the snake.

Review   Personal Tutor

Food Web 🔑

▲ **Figure 14** A food web conveys more information than a food chain. Notice the arrows that show the many ways energy travels through an ecosystem.

Modeling Energy Flow

Although you cannot see energy, it is always moving through ecosystems. By noticing what different organisms eat, you can study how energy travels through a community. You can use a model to understand how this happens.

A **food chain** *models how energy flows in an ecosystem through feeding relationships.* A food chain is like a connect-the-dots drawing. Food energy moves from a plant to a grasshopper, then to a mouse, and then to a snake in the food chain shown in **Figure 13.**

Each stage of a food chain has less available food energy than the last one because some food energy is converted to thermal energy, commonly called heat, and moves to the environment. For example, it takes a lot of plant material to feed one grasshopper, and then many grasshoppers to feed one mouse. A mouse uses some of that food energy and the rest is transformed into thermal energy. This means less food energy is available to be passed on to the snake.

Food Webs

Food chains are simple models but they do not show all the energy transfers in an ecosystem. *A* **food web** *is a model that shows several connected food chains.*

Food webs show how energy travels through producers, consumers, and decomposers in different ecosystems. The food web in **Figure 14** models the many ways food energy is transferred throughout a desert ecosystem. Terrestrial and aquatic food webs can interact. For example, raccoons might eat crayfish from streams. Food webs also show that food energy can move through several different pathways. For example, the energy in a mouse might be consumed by a fox or a hawk.

🔑 **Key Concept Check** Compare a food chain with a food web.

Modeling Energy Pyramids

As energy travels through different organisms, the amount of available food energy decreases. One way to model the available food energy in an ecosystem is to use an energy pyramid. *An **energy pyramid** shows the amount of energy available at each step of a food chain.*

Concepts in Motion Animation

Figure 15 This energy pyramid shows how energy flows from producers to consumers.

As shown in the energy pyramid in **Figure 15,** more food energy is available at the "base" of the pyramid where producers are. The food energy from the producers moves into consumers—herbivores, omnivores, and carnivores—at the next level. Recall that some food energy is transformed into thermal energy by organisms. At each level of the pyramid, the amount of usable food energy decreases.

The top level of an energy pyramid usually shows the carnivores in an ecosystem—those animals in the ecosystem that prey only on other animals. What are some carnivores in the ecosystem around you?

Reading Check What happens to the amount of available energy in higher levels of an energy pyramid?

Inquiry MiniLab   **20 minutes**

How is energy transferred in a food chain?

Producers get their energy from the environment. Consumers get their energy by eating producers. However, some of that energy is transformed in transfer.

1. Read and complete a lab safety form.
2. Each student is assigned a role. One student is the Sun. Others might be plants, mice, or an owl. The Sun will give one **cup of dried beans** (to represent energy) to each plant.
3. Each plant should keep 20 of its beans and put the rest into a **box.** This represents energy that the organism does not pass on.
4. Each mouse takes 20 beans (representing usable energy) from the plants in its group. Each mouse can use only 8 beans. Each mouse should keep eight beans and put the rest into the box.
5. The owl should take 8 beans from each mouse. The owl uses only one bean and puts the rest of the beans in the box.

Analyze and Conclude

1. **Describe** any patterns you see in how much energy is transferred.

2. **Key Concept** Explain why there are fewer organisms in the higher levels of an energy pyramid.

Matter Cycles

You need food for energy, but you also eat and drink to replace vitamins, water, and minerals that leave your body. These substances—food, vitamins, minerals, and water—are examples of matter.

Matter is the physical material that makes up the world around you. Your body—like everything else on Earth—consists of matter. Most of the matter in your body is water. Your body also contains matter in other forms such as carbon and nitrogen. Like energy, matter is not created or destroyed. Instead it is transferred through the environment. Unlike energy, though, matter does not flow but moves in a cycle. It is used again and again throughout different parts of an ecosystem. Matter can change forms as it moves through an environment. For example, the liquid form of a type of matter might turn into the gas form. The types of matter found in different environments, as well as the amounts available, determine which organisms can live there.

Water Cycle

Water is important to all life. It moves through every ecosystem on Earth and is in different forms. Its forms include a liquid, a gas (known as water vapor), and a solid (ice). **Figure 16** illustrates how water moves through the environment in the water cycle.

1. Water evaporates from oceans, rivers, and other bodies of water. Plants release water vapor during transpiration and some organisms release water vapor when they breathe out (exhalation).

2. The water vapor then rises into the atmosphere, where it condenses and falls as rain or snow.

3. Water moves across the surface of Earth in lakes, streams and rivers, soaks into the ground, or is taken in by organisms. This water is eventually released again, and the cycle continues.

Key Concept Check What forms does water take in the water cycle?

Water Cycle

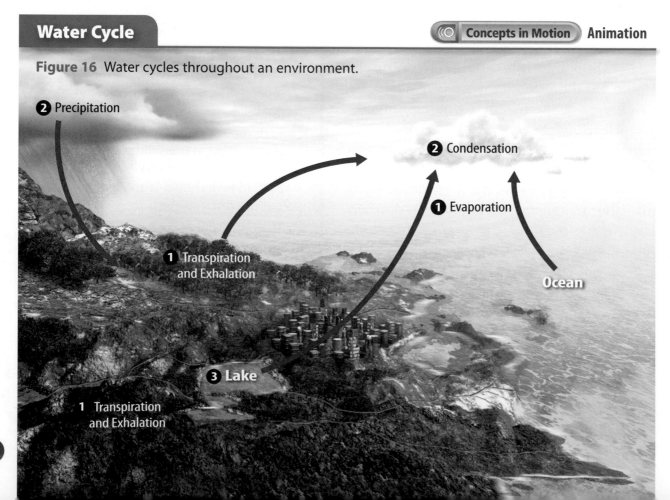

Figure 16 Water cycles throughout an environment.

2 Precipitation

2 Condensation

1 Evaporation

1 Transpiration and Exhalation

Ocean

3 Lake

1 Transpiration and Exhalation

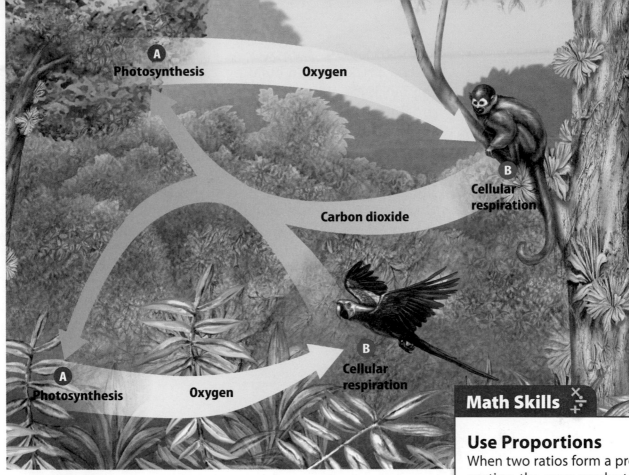

Figure 17 Producers release oxygen gas and consumers take it in.

⊘ **Visual Check** What do the consumers in this image release to the atmosphere?

Oxygen Cycle

Like water, oxygen also cycles through the environment. Oxygen is another example of matter that is important to the survival of many organisms. You take in oxygen when you breathe, and your blood carries the oxygen to all parts of your body. Oxygen is also a part of many molecules that are important to life, such as sugars.

Plants release oxygen as a waste product of photosynthesis. This oxygen enters the atmosphere, and many consumers take it in when they breathe. When these organisms exhale, they release carbon dioxide, which is a by-product of cellular respiration. Carbon dioxide contains oxygen. Some producers take in carbon dioxide, and the cycle continues.

The oxygen cycle in a rain forest is shown in **Figure 17.** There, many plants release large amounts of oxygen. Besides supplying all the rain forest organisms with oxygen, these plants are also an important source of oxygen for other organisms on Earth.

✔ **Reading Check** What organisms are part of the oxygen cycle?

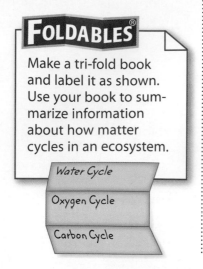

FOLDABLES®

Make a tri-fold book and label it as shown. Use your book to summarize information about how matter cycles in an ecosystem.

Water Cycle

Oxygen Cycle

Carbon Cycle

Carbon Cycle

Like bricks used in building, carbon is a fundamental building block for all living things. It is part of molecules such as proteins, carbohydrates, and fats. It is also almost everywhere on Earth in nonliving things. The carbon cycle diagram in **Figure 18** illustrates how carbon moves throughout Earth's environment. When producers use carbon dioxide during photosynthesis, carbon is removed from the atmosphere. Consumers eat these producers and release carbon back into the environment as a waste product. Human activities such as the burning of fossil fuels also add carbon to the atmosphere. Producers again remove the carbon from the atmosphere as they continue making food, and the cycle continues.

✓ **Reading Check** Where is carbon in living organisms?

Concepts in Motion Animation

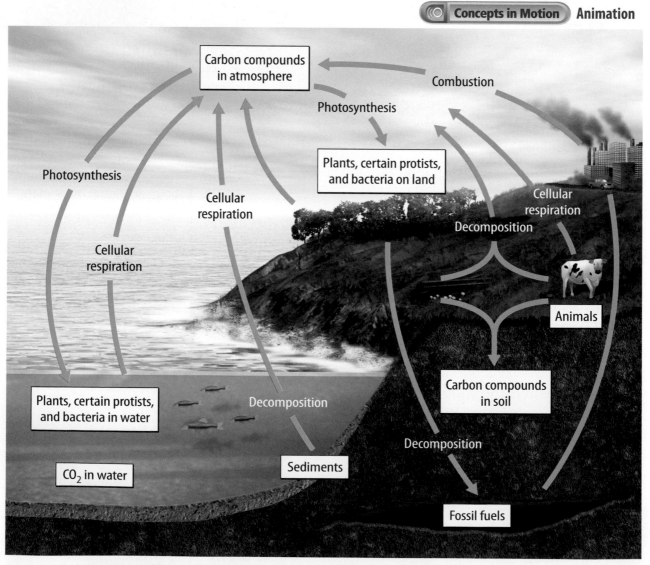

Figure 18 Carbon moves throughout the environment through processes such as photosynthesis.

✓ **Visual Check** What processes add carbon compounds to the atmosphere?

Lesson 3 Review

Visual Summary

A producer changes the energy available in the environment into food energy.

Consumers must use the energy and nutrients stored in other organisms for living and reproducing.

An energy pyramid shows how much food energy is available to organisms at each level of a community.

FOLDABLES®

Use your lesson Foldable to review the lesson. Save your Foldable for the project at the end of the chapter.

What do you think **NOW?**

You first read the statements below at the beginning of the chapter.

5. Most of the energy used by organisms on Earth comes from the Sun.

6. Both nature and humans affect the environment.

Did you change your mind about whether you agree or disagree with the statements? Rewrite any false statements to make them true.

Juanmonino/iStock/360/Getty Images

Use Vocabulary

1 **Describe** the process of chemosynthesis.

2 **Distinguish** between producers and consumers.

3 **Write** a sentence using the word *decomposer*.

Understand Key Concepts

4 **Explain** how energy from the Sun enters an ecosystem.

5 Which does NOT cycle through an environment?
- **A.** nitrogen
- **C.** sunlight
- **B.** oxygen
- **D.** water

6 **State** whether you are an herbivore, an omnivore, or a carnivore. Explain your answer.

Interpret Graphics

7 **Organize Information** Copy and fill in the graphic organizer below for a a food chain of herbivores, carnivores, and producers.

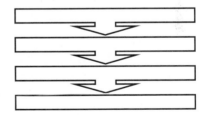

Critical Thinking

8 **Draw** a food web for a local habitat. What are the producers and the consumers? Which are omnivores, carnivores, and herbivores? Draw arrows to connect the organisms and label the different species.

Math Skills $\frac{\times}{+} \frac{\div}{-}$ **Review**
Math Practice

9 One liter of air contains about 0.21 L of oxygen (O_2). When filled, the human lungs hold about 6.0 L of air. How much O_2 is in the lungs when they are filled with air?

Materials

bromthymol blue

powdered calcium carbonate or crushed natural chalk

vinegar

250-mL Erlenmeyer flask

20-mL test tube

balloon

filter paper

Safety

Can you observe part of the carbon cycle?

The carbon cycle includes all of the paths that carbon takes as it is transferred through the environment. During one part of the carbon cycle, tiny ocean organisms called phytoplankton (fi toh PLANK tuhn) take in carbon dioxide gas from the air. The carbon dioxide gas is converted to calcium carbonate, which the phytoplankton use to build their skeletons. When phytoplankton die, many of them sink to the bottom of the ocean, where their skeletons become fossilized. Over time, these fossilized skeletons build up and turn into chalk. When this chalk is weathered by rain and waves, it releases carbon dioxide gas into the air. This gas can then move through the many paths of the carbon cycle.

Question

How can you model part of the carbon cycle?

Procedure

1. Read and complete a lab safety form.

2. Measure 15 g of calcium carbonate powder onto filter paper.

3. Pour the calcium carbonate powder into a 250-mL Erlenmeyer flask.

4. Add 50 mL of vinegar to the flask.

5. Quickly stretch the mouth of the balloon over the opening of the flask. Record your observations in your Science Journal.

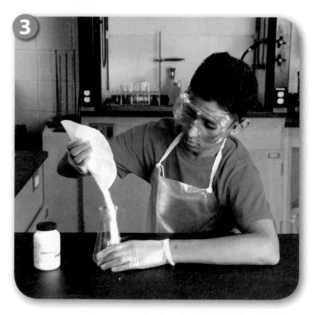

(t to b, 2, 4–5, 7, br)Hutchings Photography/Digital Light Source; (3, 6)Jacques Cornell/McGraw-Hill Education

6 Fill the test tube almost to the top with water. Add 15 drops of bromthymol blue, a chemical indicator that turns yellow when exposed to carbon dioxide. Observe the color of the liquid in the test tube.

7 Pinch the neck of your balloon and remove it from the flask. Place the neck of the balloon over the mouth of the test tube and then release the neck, allowing the gas to enter the test tube. Record your observations in an observation table in your Science Journal.

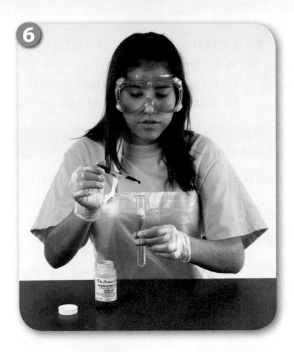

Analyze and Conclude

8 **Interpret Data** What happened to the color of the liquid in the test tube? What did this indicate?

9 **Identify** Where did the gas in the balloon come from?

10 **The Big Idea** Describe the part of the carbon cycle you modeled in this experiment. How do living things affect this part of the carbon cycle? How do nonliving things affect this part of the carbon cycle?

Lab Tips

☑ Carefully swirl the calcium carbonate and vinegar in your flask to get the most gas from your reaction.

Communicate Your Results

Draw the carbon cycle. Highlight the parts of the carbon cycle you modeled in this experiment.

 **Extension**

When you released carbon from the calcium carbonate, you might have released the same molecules that a dinosaur exhaled millions of years ago. Draw a picture showing the flow of carbon through the environment, including how dinosaur breath could have been captured in calcium carbonate.

Remember to use scientific methods.

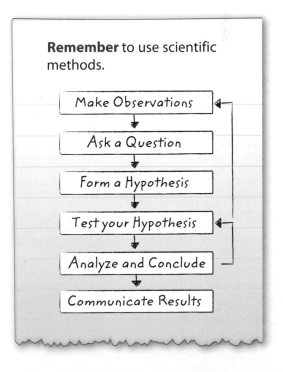

Make Observations
↓
Ask a Question
↓
Form a Hypothesis
↓
Test your Hypothesis
↓
Analyze and Conclude
↓
Communicate Results

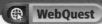
 THE BIG IDEA

Living things interact with each other in a variety of ways that can be either beneficial or harmful. Living things depend on both living and nonliving resources from the ecosystem to survive.

Key Concepts Summary 🔑

Vocabulary

Lesson 1: Ecosystems and Biomes

- An **ecosystem** is made up of all the living and nonliving things in a location.
- **Biomes** are large regions that have specific types of climate, physical characteristics, and organisms.
- One environment changes into another in a process called **succession.**

ecosystem
abiotic factor
biotic factor
population
community
biome
succession

Lesson 2: Populations and Communities

- Organisms must compete with each other to obtain resources, such as food, water, and living space.
- **Symbiotic relationships** include mutualism, parasitism, and commensalism.

limiting factor
biotic potential
carrying capacity
habitat
niche
symbiotic relationship

Lesson 3: Energy and Matter

- Light energy from the Sun is changed into food energy by **producers.** Energy then moves through an ecosystem as organisms eat producers or other **consumers.**
- Energy movement can be modeled simply as a **food chain.** A **food web** models the movement of energy through many food chains in an ecosystem.
- Matter moves through ecosystems in cycles. Examples of matter cycles include the carbon, water, and oxygen cycles.

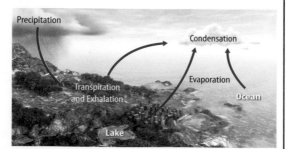

producer
consumer
food chain
food web
energy pyramid

FOLDABLES® Chapter Project

Assemble your lesson Foldables as shown to make a Chapter Project. Use the project to review what you have learned in this chapter.

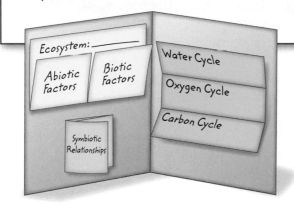

Use Vocabulary

1 A(n) _____ factor is any of the living parts of an ecosystem.

2 The biosphere contains all of Earth's _____.

3 The _____ of a population is the largest number of individuals that can survive in a location over time.

4 Each organism has a(n) _____ that includes the ways it survives, obtains food and shelter, and avoids danger in its habitat.

5 A(n) _____ cannot make food, and must obtain energy from other organisms.

6 A(n) _____ models how much energy is available as it moves through an ecosystem.

Link Vocabulary and Key Concepts

Concepts in Motion Interactive Concept Map

Copy this concept map, and then use vocabulary terms from the previous page to complete the concept map.

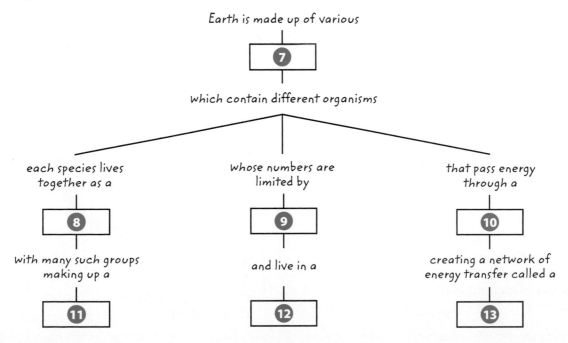

Earth is made up of various

7

which contain different organisms

each species lives together as a	whose numbers are limited by	that pass energy through a
8	**9**	**10**
with many such groups making up a	and live in a	creating a network of energy transfer called a
11	**12**	**13**

Understand Key Concepts 🔑

1 Which is NOT an abiotic factor?
A. atmosphere
B. prey
C. sunlight
D. temperature

2 Which biome is shown below?

A. desert
B. forest
C. grassland
D. tundra

3 Which term describes a slow change in an environment?
A. abiotic
B. biotic
C. regression
D. succession

4 Which is NOT a limiting factor?
A. competition
B. disease
C. amount of resources
D. biotic potential

5 What is a niche?
A. a cycle of matter
B. a source of energy
C. a source of energy
D. where an animal lives

6 Which type of symbiotic relationship is beneficial for both organisms?
A. commensalism
B. competition
C. mutualism
D. parasitism

7 Which includes the process of transpiration?
A. succession
B. condensation
C. oxygen cycle
D. water cycle

8 What is released as a product of photosynthesis?
A. carbon
B. oxygen
C. soil
D. water

9 Which type of consumer gets all the energy it needs from producers?
A. carnivore
B. detritivore
C. herbivore
D. omnivore

10 Which type of process is illustrated by the diagram below?

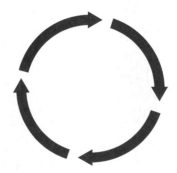

A. a cycle
B. a flow
C. an energy pyramid
D. a food web

Critical Thinking

11 **Contrast** aquatic and terrestrial ecosystems, and explain how they might interact.

12 **List** some of the biotic and abiotic factors you respond to each day. Describe how they impact you.

13 **Consider** the value of the study of ecology. Why is it important or not important?

14 **Differentiate** between a habitat and a niche.

15 **Reflect** on whether human beings have a symbiotic relationship with Earth.

16 **Describe** the symbiotic relationship shown below.

17 **Hypothesize** what might happen to a lake ecosystem if very little rain fell for many years. How would the lake community change? What would happen if the amount of rain greatly increased rather than decreased?

18 **Construct** a food chain that includes you.

Writing in Science

19 **Visualize** succession in your community. What changes have occurred in your community over the last hundred years? What might occur over the next hundred? The next thousand? Write a paragraph describing your predictions.

REVIEW THE BIG IDEA

20 How are the living and nonliving parts of an environment important to an organism? Give an example in which one organism must depend on another organism in order to survive.

21 The photo below shows a population of prairie dogs. How might living together as a population be helpful to the prairie dogs? How might living together be more difficult than living alone?

Math Skills ✕÷

Use Proportion

22 A large tree releases about 0.31 kg of oxygen per day. A typical adult uses 0.84 kg of oxygen per day. How many trees would provide enough oxygen for the adult?

23 In one year, an acre of trees can provide enough oxygen for about 18 people. How many acres of trees would provide enough oxygen for the population of New York City —about 8,300,000?

Standardized Test Practice

Record your answers on the answer sheet provided by your teacher or on a sheet of paper.

Multiple Choice

1 All of the nonliving and living things in one place are

  A a biome.

  B a population.

  C an ecosystem.

  D an organism.

Use the table below to answer question 2.

Organism	Interaction
Cattails	Make food using sunlight energy
Ducks	Eat plants or insects
Fish	Eat plants, insects, or other fish
Turtles	Eat fish, insects, or plants

2 The organisms in the table above live in or around a lake. Together they form a

  A community.

  B habitat.

  C niche.

  D population.

3 What describes the size of a population in ideal conditions?

  A community

  B biotic potential

  C carrying capacity

  D limiting factor

4 A grassland changes to a desert after many years of little rain. This is an example of what?

  A migration

  B overpopulation

  C predation

  D succession

Use the diagram below to answer question 5.

5 Which limiting factor does the diagram illustrate?

  A carrying capacity

  B overpopulation

  C predation

  D competition for resources

6 Which is true of the movement of matter in ecosystems?

  A Matter is used again and again.

  B Matter retains its original form.

  C Matter increases in amount as it moves.

  D Matter moves in a flow.

7 An owl eats mice and other small rodents in a forest. This owl lives in a hole in the side of a dead tree. What do these two statements describe?

  A a biome

  B a community

  C a niche

  D a population

8 Which illustrates organization from smallest to largest?

  A biome → population → community

  B community → biome → population

  C community → population → biome

  D population → community → biome

Use the diagram below to answer question 9.

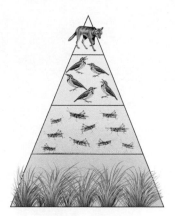

9 Which level has the *least* amount of food energy?

A birds

B grasses

C grasshoppers

D coyote

10 Which is a symbiotic relationship?

A a hawk eating a mouse

B a fish laying eggs in a stream

C a mistletoe plant living on a tree

D a plant using sunlight and making food

11 Consumers are generally classified into one of four categories based on their

A appearance.

B diet.

C habitat.

D size.

Constructed Response

Use the chart below to answer question 12.

Abiotic Factor	Importance

12 List the abiotic factors in your ecosystem. Briefly describe their importance.

Use the diagram below to answer questions 13 and 14.

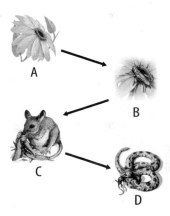

13 Match each letter in the diagram with the word that describes the organism: *carnivore, herbivore, omnivore,* and *producer.* What does the diagram reveal about the movement of energy in an ecosystem?

14 Describe what would happen if (a) mice disappeared from this ecosystem; (b) foxes entered this ecosystem; and (c) drought killed much of the plant life in this ecosystem.

NEED EXTRA HELP?														
If You Missed Question...	1	2	3	4	5	6	7	8	9	10	11	12	13	14
Go to Lesson...	1	1	2	1	2	3	2	1	3	2	3	1	3	3

Chapter 17

AID M1.1a, M2.1a, S1.1b, S2.1d, S3.1a, S3.2b, S3.2f, S3.2h, T1.1a, T1.2a, T1.4a; IS 1.3; ICT 2.1; IPS 1.1, 1.3, 2.1; PS 2.2r

Environmental Impacts

THE BIG IDEA

How do human activities impact the environment?

Inquiry How many people are there?

More than 6 billion people live on Earth. Every day, people all over the world travel, eat, use water, and participate in recreational activities.

- What resources do people need and use?
- What might happen if any resources run out?
- How do human activities impact the environment?

Grant Faint/Getty Images

Get Ready to Read

What do you think?

Before you read, decide if you agree or disagree with each of these statements. As you read this chapter, see if you change your mind about any of the statements.

1 Earth can support an unlimited number of people.

2 Humans can have both positive and negative impacts on the environment.

3 Deforestation does not affect soil quality.

4 Most trash is recycled.

5 Sources of water pollution are always easy to identify.

6 The proper method of disposal for used motor oil is to pour it down the drain.

7 The greenhouse effect is harmful to life on Earth.

8 Air pollution can affect human health.

 **ConnectED** Your one-stop online resource

MHEonline.com

 Video   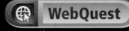 WebQuest

 Audio   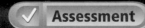 Assessment

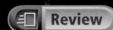 Review   Concepts in Motion

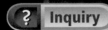 Inquiry   **g** Multilingual eGlossary

People and the Environment

Reading Guide

Key Concepts
ESSENTIAL QUESTIONS

- What is the relationship between resource availability and human population growth?

- How do daily activities impact the environment?

Vocabulary

population

carrying capacity

 Multilingual eGlossary

▢ Video

- **BrainPOP®**
- **Science Video**
- **What's Science Got to do With It?**

 AID S3.2b, S3.2f

Inquiry) What's the impact?

This satellite image shows light coming from Europe and Africa at night. You can see where large cities are located. What do you think the dark areas represent? When you turn on the lights at night, where does the energy to power the lights come from? How might this daily activity impact the environment?

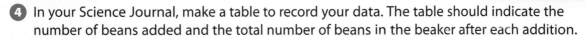
What happens as populations increase in size?

In the year 200, the human population consisted of about a quarter of a billion people. By the year 2000, it had increased to more than 6 billion, and by 2050, it is projected to be more than 9 billion. However, the amount of space available on Earth will remain the same.

1 Read and complete a lab safety form.

2 Place 10 **dried beans** in a **100-mL beaker.**

3 At the start signal, double the number of beans in the beaker. There should now be 20 beans.

4 In your Science Journal, make a table to record your data. The table should indicate the number of beans added and the total number of beans in the beaker after each addition.

5 Double the number of beans each time the start signal sounds. Continue until the stop signal sounds.

Think About This

1. Can you add any more beans to the beaker? Why or why not?

2. How many times did you have to double the beans to fill the beaker?

3. **Key Concept** How might the growth of a population affect the availability of resources, such as space?

Population and Carrying Capacity

Have you ever seen a sign such as the one shown in **Figure 1?** The sign shows the population of a city. In this case, population means how many people live in the city. Scientists use the term *population,* too, but in a slightly different way. For scientists, a **population** *is all the members of a species living in a given area.* You are part of a population of humans. The other species in your area, such as birds or trees, each make up a separate population.

The Human Population

When the first American towns were settled, most had low populations. Today, some of those towns are large cities, crowded with people. In a similar way, Earth was once home to relatively few humans. Today, about 6.7 billion people live on Earth. The greatest increase in human population occurred during the last few centuries.

Figure 1 This sign shows the population of the city. Scientists use the word *population* to describe all the members of a species in an area.

Figure 2 Human population stayed fairly steady for most of history and then "exploded" in the last few hundred years.

Visual Check How does the rate of human population growth from the years 200 to 1800 compare to the rate of growth from 1800 to 2000?

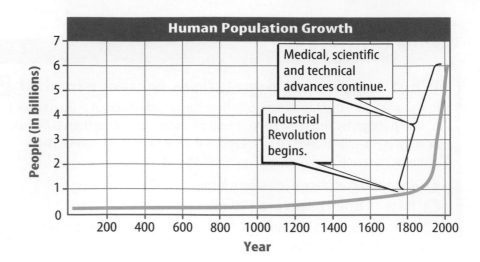

Human Population Growth

Medical, scientific and technical advances continue.

Industrial Revolution begins.

People (in billions): 0–7
Year: 200, 400, 600, 800, 1000, 1200, 1400, 1600, 1800, 2000

WORD ORIGIN · · · · · · · · · ·

population
from Latin *populus*, means "people"

FOLDABLES

Use a sheet of paper to make a small vertical shutterfold. Draw the arrows on each tab and label as illustrated. Use the Foldable to discuss how human population growth is related to resources.

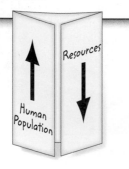

Resources

Human Population

Population Trends

Have you ever heard the phrase *population explosion?* Population explosion describes the sudden rise in human population that has happened in recent history. The graph in **Figure 2** shows how the human population has changed. The population increased at a fairly steady rate for most of human history. In the 1800s, the population began to rise sharply.

What caused this sharp increase? Improved health care, clean water, and other technological advancements mean that more people are living longer and reproducing. In the hour or so it might take you to read this chapter, about 15,000 babies will be born worldwide.

Reading Check What factors contributed to the increase in human population?

Population Limits

Every human being needs certain things, such as food, clean water, and shelter, to survive. People also need clothes, transportation, and other items. All the items used by people come from resources found on Earth. Does Earth have enough resources to support an unlimited number of humans?

Earth has limited resources. It cannot support a population of any species in a given environment beyond its carrying capacity. **Carrying capacity** *is the largest number of individuals of a given species that Earth's resources can support and maintain for a long period of time.* If the human population continues to grow beyond Earth's carrying capacity, eventually Earth will not have enough resources to support humans.

Key Concept Check What is the relationship between the availability of resources and human population growth?

Impact of Daily Actions

Each of the 6.7 billion people on Earth uses **resources** in some way. The use of these resources affects the environment. Consider the impact of one activity—a shower.

Consuming Resources

Like many people, you might take a shower each day. The metal in the water pipes comes from resources mined from the ground. Mining can destroy habitats and pollute soil and water. Your towel might be made of cotton, a resource obtained from plants. Growing plants often involves the use of fertilizers and other chemicals that run off into water and affect its quality.

The water itself also is a resource—one that is scarce in some areas of the world. Most likely, fossil fuels are used to heat the water. Recall that fossil fuels are nonrenewable resources, which means they are used up faster than they can be replaced by natural processes. Burning fossil fuels also releases pollution into the atmosphere.

Now, think about all the activities that you do in one day, such as going to school, eating meals, or playing computer games. All of these activities use resources. Over the course of your lifetime, your potential impact on the environment is great. Multiply this impact by 6.7 billion, and you can understand why it is important to use resources wisely.

 Key Concept Check What are three things you did today that impacted the environment?

Positive and Negative Impacts

As shown in **Figure 3,** not all human activities have a negative impact on the environment. In the following lessons, you will learn how human activities affect soil, water, and air quality. You will also learn things you can do to help reduce the impact of your actions on the environment.

SCIENCE USE v. COMMON USE

resource
Science Use a natural source of supply or support

Common Use a source of information or expertise

Figure 3 Cleaning up streams and picking up litter are ways people can positively impact the environment.

Jeff Greenberg/Alamy

Lesson 1 Review

Visual Summary

Human population has exploded since the 1800s. Every day billions of people use Earth's resources. The human population will eventually reach its carrying capacity.

When humans use resources, they can have both negative and positive impacts on the environment. It is important for humans to use resources wisely.

FOLDABLES®

Use your lesson Foldable to review the lesson. Save your Foldable for the project at the end of the chapter.

What do you think NOW?

You first read the statements below at the beginning of the chapter.

1. Earth can support an unlimited number of people.

2. Humans can have both positive and negative impacts on the environment.

Did you change your mind about whether you agree or disagree with the statements? Rewrite any false statements to make them true.

Use Vocabulary

① **Define** *carrying capacity* in your own words.

② All the members of a certain species living in a given area is a(n) _____.

Understand Key Concepts

③ Approximately how many people live on Earth?
   A. 2.4 billion   C. 7.6 billion
   B. 6.7 billion   D. 12.1 billion

④ **Identify** something you could do to reduce your impact on the environment.

⑤ **Reason** Why do carrying capacities exist for all species on Earth?

Interpret Graphics

⑥ **Take Notes** Copy the graphic organizer below. List two human activities and the effect of each activity on the environment.

Activity	Effect on the Environment

⑦ **Summarize** how human population growth has changed over time, using the graph below.

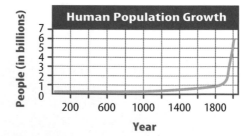

Critical Thinking

⑧ **Predict** What might happen if a species reaches Earth's carrying capacity?

⑨ **Reflect** Technological advances allow farmers to grow more crops. Do you think these advances affect the carrying capacity for humans? Explain.

What amount of Earth's resources do you use in a day?

Many of the practices we engage in today became habits long before we realized the negative effects that they have on the environment. By analyzing your daily resource use, you might identify some different practices that can help protect Earth's resources.

Learn It

In science, **data** are **collected** as accurate numbers and descriptions and organized in specific ways. The meaning of your observations can be determined by **analyzing** the data you collected.

Try It

1 With your group, design a data collection form for recording each group member's resource use for one 24-h period.

2 You should include space to collect data on water use, fossil fuel use (which may include electricity use and transportation), how much meat and dairy products you eat, how much trash you discard, and any other resources you might use in a typical 24-h period. Indicate the units in which you will record the data.

3 Share your form with the other groups, and complete a final draft using the best features from each group's design.

4 Distribute copies of the form to each group member. Record each instance and quantity of resource use during a 24-h period.

5 For each resource, calculate how much you would use in 1 year, based on your usage in the 24-h period.

Apply It

6 Consider whether a single 24-h period is representative of each of the 365 days of your year. Explain your answer.

7 How would you modify your data collection design to reflect a more realistic measure of your resource use over a year?

8 🔑 **Key Concept** Explain how two of the activities that you recorded deplete resources or pollute the soil, the water, or the air. How can you change your activities to reduce your impact or have a positive impact?

Hutchings Photography/Digital Light Source

Lesson 2

Reading Guide

Key Concepts 🔑
ESSENTIAL QUESTIONS

- What are the consequences of using land as a resource?
- How does proper waste management help prevent pollution?
- What actions help protect the land?

Vocabulary

deforestation

desertification

urban sprawl

reforestation

reclamation

g Multilingual eGlossary

▢ Video

- Science Video
- What's Science Got to do With It?

🌀 AID M1.1a, S2.1d

Impacts on the Land

Inquiry **How do people use land?**

Study this photo of an area in England, and list three ways people use land. What other possible land uses are not shown in the photo? What impact do humans have on land resources?

How can items be reused? 🔧 🧴 🧤

As an individual, you can have an effect on the use and the protection of Earth's resources by reducing, reusing, and recycling the materials you use every day.

1. Read and complete a lab safety form.

2. Have one member of your group pull an item from the **item bag.**

3. Discuss the item with your group and take turns describing as many different ways to reuse it as possible.

4. List the different uses in your Science Journal.

5. Repeat steps 2–4.

6. Share your lists with the other groups. What uses did other groups think of that were different from your group's ideas for the same item?

Think About This

1. Describe your group's items and three different ways that you thought to reuse each item.

2. How does reusing these items help to reduce the use of Earth's resources?

3. 🔑 **Key Concept** How do you think the action of reusing items helps to protect the land?

Using Land Resources

What do the metal in staples and the paper in your notebook have in common? Both come from resources found in or on land. People use land for timber production, agriculture, and mining. All of these activities impact the environment.

Forest Resources

Trees are cut down to make wood and paper products, such as your notebook. Trees are also cut for fuel and to clear land for agriculture, grazing, or building houses or highways.

Sometimes forests are cleared, as shown in **Figure 4.** **Deforestation** *is the removal of large areas of forests for human purposes.* Approximately 130,000 km^2 of tropical rain forests are cut down each year, an area equal in size to the state of Louisiana. Tropical rain forests are home to an estimated 50 percent of all the species on Earth. Deforestation destroys habitats, which can lead to species' extinction.

Deforestation also can affect soil quality. Plant roots hold soil in place. Without these natural anchors, soil erodes away. In addition, deforestation affects air quality. Recall that trees remove carbon dioxide from the air when they undergo photosynthesis. When there are fewer trees on Earth, more carbon dioxide remains in the atmosphere. You will learn more about carbon dioxide in Lesson 4.

Figure 4 Deforestation occurs when forests are cleared for agriculture, grazing, or other purposes.

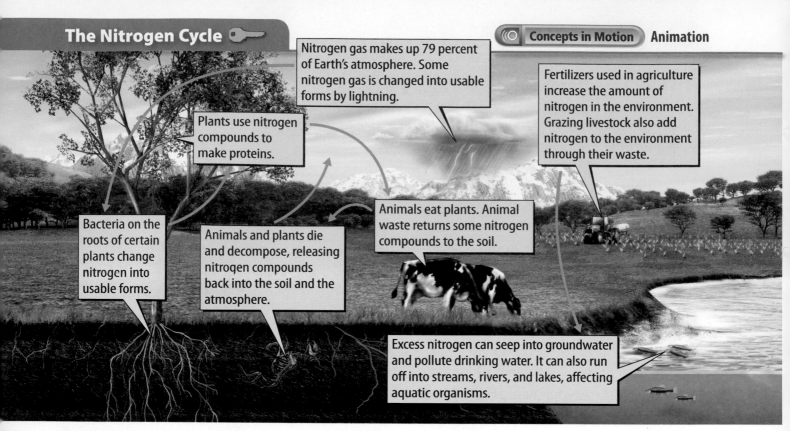

The Nitrogen Cycle 🔑

Nitrogen gas makes up 79 percent of Earth's atmosphere. Some nitrogen gas is changed into usable forms by lightning.

Plants use nitrogen compounds to make proteins.

Fertilizers used in agriculture increase the amount of nitrogen in the environment. Grazing livestock also add nitrogen to the environment through their waste.

Bacteria on the roots of certain plants change nitrogen into usable forms.

Animals and plants die and decompose, releasing nitrogen compounds back into the soil and the atmosphere.

Animals eat plants. Animal waste returns some nitrogen compounds to the soil.

Excess nitrogen can seep into groundwater and pollute drinking water. It can also run off into streams, rivers, and lakes, affecting aquatic organisms.

Figure 5 Agricultural practices can increase the amount of nitrogen that cycles through ecosystems.

✓ **Visual Check** How does the use of fertilizers affect the environment?

Agriculture and the Nitrogen Cycle

It takes a lot of food to feed 6.7 billion people. To meet the food demands of the world's population, farmers often add fertilizers that contain nitrogen to soil to increase crop yields.

As shown in **Figure 5,** nitrogen is an element that naturally cycles through ecosystems. Living things use nitrogen to make proteins. And when these living things die and decompose or produce waste, they release nitrogen into the soil or the atmosphere.

Although nitrogen gas makes up about 79 percent of Earth's atmosphere, most living things cannot use nitrogen in its gaseous form. Nitrogen must be converted into a usable form. Bacteria that live on the roots of certain plants convert atmospheric nitrogen to a form that is usable by plants. Modern agricultural practices include adding fertilizer that contains a usable form of nitrogen to soil.

Scientists estimate that human activities such as manufacturing and applying fertilizers to crops have doubled the amount of nitrogen cycling through ecosystems. Excess nitrogen can kill plants adapted to low nitrogen levels and affect organisms that depend on those plants for food. Fertilizers can seep into groundwater supplies, polluting drinking water. They can also run off into streams and rivers, affecting aquatic organisms.

Other Effects of Agriculture

Agriculture can impact soil quality in other ways, too. Soil erosion can occur when land is overfarmed or overgrazed. High rates of soil erosion can lead to desertification. **Desertification** *is the development of desertlike conditions due to human activities and/or climate change.* A region of land that undergoes desertification is no longer useful for food production.

✓ **Reading Check** What causes desertification?

Figure 6 🔑 Some resources must be mined from the ground.

Mining

Many useful rocks and minerals are removed from the ground by mining. For example, copper is removed from the surface by digging a strip mine, such as the one shown in **Figure 6.** Coal and other in-ground resources also can be removed by digging underground mines.

Mines are essential for obtaining much-needed resources. However, digging mines disturbs habitats and changes the landscape. If proper regulations are not followed, water can be polluted by **runoff** that contains heavy metals from mines.

🔑 **Key Concept Check** What are some consequences of using land as a resource?

REVIEW VOCABULARY

runoff
the portion of precipitation that moves over land and eventually reaches streams, rivers, lakes, and oceans

Construction and Development

You have read about important resources that are found on or in land. But did you know that land itself is a resource? People use land for living space. Your home, your school, your favorite stores, and your neighborhood streets are all built on land.

Inquiry MiniLab   **20 minutes**

What happens when you mine?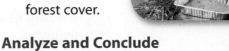

Coal is a fossil fuel that provides energy for many activities. People obtain coal by mining, or digging, into Earth's surface.

1. Read and complete a lab safety form.
2. Research the difference between strip-mining and underground mining.
3. Use **salt dough** and **other materials** to build a model hill that contains coal deposits. Follow the instructions provided on how to build the model.
4. Sketch the profile of the hill. Use a **ruler** to measure the dimensions of the hill.
5. Decide which mining method to use to remove the coal. Mine the coal.

6. Try to restore the hill to its original size, shape, and forest cover.

Analyze and Conclude

1. **Compare** the appearance of your restored hill to the drawing of the original hill.

2. 🔑 **Key Concept** Describe two consequences of the lost forest cover and loose soil on the mined hill.

Figure 7 Urban sprawl can lead to habitat destruction as forests are cut down to make room for housing developments.

Math Skills

Use Percentages

Between 1960 and today, interstate highways increased from a total of 16,000 km to 47,000 km. What percent increase does this represent?

1. Subtract the starting value from the final value.

47,000 km − 16,000 km = 31,000 km

2. Divide the difference by the starting value.

$\frac{31,000 \text{ km}}{16,000 \text{ km}} = 1.94$

3. Multiply by 100 and add a % sign.

1.94 × 100 = 194%

Practice

In 1950, the U.S. population was about 150,000,000. By 2007, it was nearly 300,000,000. What was the percent increase?

 Review

- **Math Practice**
- **Personal Tutor**

Urban Sprawl

In the 1950s, large tracts of rural land in the United States were developed as suburbs, residential areas on the outside edges of a city. When the suburbs became crowded, people moved farther out into the country, as shown in **Figure 7**. More open land was cleared for still more development. *The development of land for houses and other buildings near a city is called* **urban sprawl.** The impacts of urban sprawl include habitat destruction and loss of farmland. Increased runoff also occurs, as large areas are paved for sidewalks and streets. An increase in runoff, especially if it contains sediments or chemical pollutants, can reduce the water quality of streams, rivers, and groundwater.

Roadways

Urban sprawl occurred at the same time as another trend in the United States—increased motor vehicle use. Only a small percentage of Americans owned cars before the 1940s. By 2005, there were 240 million vehicles for 295 million people, greatly increasing the need for roadways. In 1960, the United States had about 16,000 km of interstate highways. Today, the interstate highway system includes 47,000 km of paved roadways. Like urban sprawl, roadways increase runoff and disturb habitats.

 Reading Check What two trends triggered the need for more highways?

Recreation

Not all of the land used by people is paved and developed. People also use land for recreation. They hike, bike, ski, and picnic, among other activities. In urban areas, some of these activities take place in public parks. As you will learn later in this lesson, parks and other green spaces help decrease runoff.

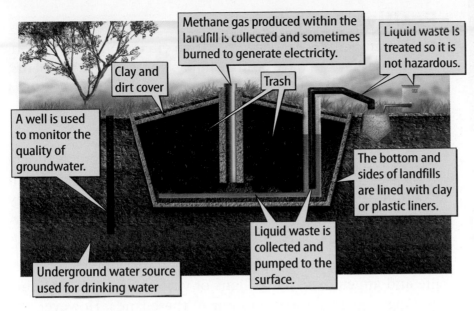

Methane gas produced within the landfill is collected and sometimes burned to generate electricity.

Clay and dirt cover

Trash

Liquid waste is treated so it is not hazardous.

A well is used to monitor the quality of groundwater.

The bottom and sides of landfills are lined with clay or plastic liners.

Underground water source used for drinking water

Liquid waste is collected and pumped to the surface.

Figure 8 About 54 percent of the trash in the United States is disposed of in landfills.

Visual Check How can the methane gas produced within a landfill be used?

Waste Management

On a typical day, each person in the United States generates about 2.1 kg of trash. That adds up to about 230 million metric tons per year! Where does all that trash go?

Landfills

About 31 percent of the trash is recycled and composted. About 14 percent is burned, and the remaining 55 percent is placed in landfills, such as the one shown in **Figure 8.** Landfills are areas where trash is buried. Landfills are another way that people use land.

A landfill is carefully designed to meet government regulations. Trash is covered by soil to keep it from blowing away. Special liners help prevent pollutants from leaking into soil and groundwater supplies.

 Key Concept Check What is done to prevent the trash in landfills from polluting air, soil, and water?

Hazardous Waste

Some trash cannot be placed in landfills because it contains harmful substances that can affect soil, air, and water quality. This trash is called hazardous waste. The substances in hazardous waste also can affect the health of humans and other living things.

Both industries and households generate hazardous waste. For example, hazardous waste from the medical industry includes used needles and bandages. Household hazardous waste includes used motor oil and batteries. The U.S. Environmental Protection Agency (EPA) works with state and local agencies to help people safely **dispose** of hazardous waste.

FOLDABLES

Use a sheet of notebook paper to make a horizontal two-tab concept map. Label and draw arrows as illustrated. Use the Foldable to identify positive and negative factors that have an impact on land.

Impacts on Land

+   −

ACADEMIC VOCABULARY

dispose
(verb) to throw away

Figure 9 Yellowstone Falls are in Yellowstone National Park, which was created in 1872.

WORD ORIGIN · · · · · · · · · · · ·

reclamation
from Latin *reclamare*, means "to call back"

Figure 10 Reforestation involves planting trees to replace ones that have been removed.

Positive Actions

Human actions can have negative effects on the environment, but they can have positive impacts as well. Governments, society, and individuals can work together to reduce the impact of human activities on land resources.

Protecting the Land

The area shown in **Figure 9** is part of Yellowstone National Park, the first national park in the world. The park was an example for the United States and other countries as they began setting aside land for preservation. State and local governments also followed this example.

Protected forests and parks are important habitats for wildlife and are enjoyed by millions of visitors each year. Mining and logging are allowed on some of these lands. However, the removal of resources must meet environmental regulations.

Reforestation and Reclamation

A forest is a complex ecosystem. With careful planning, it can be managed as a renewable resource. For example, trees can be select-cut. That means that only some trees in one area are cut down, rather than the entire forest. In addition, people can practice reforestation. **Reforestation** *involves planting trees to replace trees that have been cut or burned down.* Reforestation, shown in **Figure 10,** can keep a forest healthy or help reestablish a deforested area.

Mined land also can be made environmentally healthy through reclamation. **Reclamation** *is the process of restoring land disturbed by mining.* Mined areas can be reshaped, covered with soil, and then replanted with trees and other vegetation.

 Reading Check How do reforestation and reclamation positively impact land?

(t)Karl Weatherly/Getty Images; (b)George Clerk/Getty Images

Green Spaces

In urban areas, much of the land is covered with parking lots, streets, buildings, and sidewalks. Many cities use green spaces to create natural environments in urban settings. Green spaces are areas that are left undeveloped or lightly developed. They include parks within cities and forests around suburbs. Green spaces, such as the park shown in **Figure 11,** provide recreational opportunities for people and shelter for wildlife. Green spaces also reduce runoff and improve air quality as plants remove excess carbon dioxide from the air.

How can you help?

Individuals can have a big impact on land-use issues by practicing the three Rs—reusing, reducing, and recycling. Reusing is using an item for a new purpose. For example, you might have made a bird feeder from a used plastic milk jug. Reducing is using fewer resources. You can turn off the lights when you leave a room to reduce your use of electricity.

Recycling is making a new product from a used product. Plastic containers can be recycled into new plastic products. Recycled aluminum cans are used to make new aluminum cans. Paper, shown in **Figure 11,** also can be recycled.

Figure 11 shows another way people can lessen their environmental impact on the land. The student in the bottom photo is composting food scraps into a material that is added to soil to increase its fertility. Compost is a mixture of decaying organic matter, such as leaves, food scraps, and grass clippings. It is used to improve soil quality by adding nutrients to soil. Composting and reusing, reducing, and recycling all help reduce the amount of trash that ends up in landfills.

Key Concept Check What can you do to help lessen your impact on the land?

Figure 11 Green spaces, recycling, and composting are three things that can have positive impacts on land resources.

Parks provide recreational opportunities for people and habitats for wildlife, such as birds.

Using recycled paper to make new paper reduces deforestation as well as water use during paper production.

Composting speeds up the rate of decomposition for vegetable scraps, leaving a rich material that can be used as natural fertilizer.

Lesson 2

601

EXPLAIN

(t)Doug Menuez/Photodisc/Getty Images; (c)©moodboard/Corbis; (b)Wave Royalty Free/Alamy

✓ **Assessment** Online Quiz

? **Inquiry** Virtual Lab

Visual Summary

Deforestation, agriculture, and mining for useful rocks and minerals all can affect land resources negatively.

People use land for living space, which can lead to urban sprawl, an increase in roadways, and the need for proper waste disposal.

Creating national parks, preserves and local green spaces, reforestation, and practicing the three Rs are all ways people can positively impact land resources.

FOLDABLES®

Use your lesson Foldable to review the lesson. Save your Foldable for the project at the end of the chapter.

What do you think NOW?

You first read the statements below at the beginning of the chapter.

3. Deforestation does not affect soil quality.

4. Most trash is recycled.

Did you change your mind about whether you agree or disagree with the statements? Rewrite any false statements to make them true.

Use Vocabulary

1 **Distinguish** between deforestation and reforestation.

2 **Use the term** *urban sprawl* in a sentence.

3 **Define** *desertification*.

Understand Key Concepts

4 Which has a positive impact on land?
   A. composting   C. mining
   B. deforestation   D. urban sprawl

5 **Apply** How can the addition of fertilizers to crops affect the nitrogen cycle?

6 **Analyze** Why must waste disposal be carefully managed?

Interpret Graphics

7 **Organize** Copy and fill in the graphic organizer below. In each oval, list one way that people use land.

8 **Describe** the function of the liner in the diagram below.

Liner

Math Skills ×÷+   Review
—— Math Practice ——

9 In 1950, 35.1 million people lived in suburban areas. By 1990, the number had increased to 120 million people. What was the percent increase in suburban population?

Materials

creative construction materials

paper towels

scissors

masking tape

Safety

How will you design an environmentally safe landfill?

Your city is planning to build an environmentally safe landfill and is accepting design proposals. Your task is to develop and test a design to submit to city officials.

Learn It

When you **design an experiment,** you consider the variables you want to test and how you will measure the results.

Try It

1. Read and complete a lab safety form.

2. Read the information provided about landfill requirements as set by the Environmental Protection Agency.

3. Plan and diagram your landfill design.

4. Use the materials to build your landfill model. Add waste materials.

5. Pour 350 mL of water on your landfill to simulate rain. Observe the path the water takes.

6. Collect the leachate and compare its volume with that of the other groups. Leachate is the liquid that seeps out of your landfill.

7. Compare your landfill design to that of other groups.

Apply It

8. Explain how you designed your landfill to meet requirements and function efficiently.

9. How did your landfill design compare to those of other groups? How much leachate did your group collect compared to other groups?

10. What changes would you make to the design of your landfill? What changes would you make to your procedure to test the effectiveness of your landfill?

11. 🔑 **Key Concept** Explain how your landfill helped to prevent the pollution of soil and water.

(t to b)McGraw-Hill Education; (2, 4)Hutchings Photography/Digital Light Source; (3)Jacques Cornell/McGraw-Hill Education; (r)Alain Choisnet/Getty Images

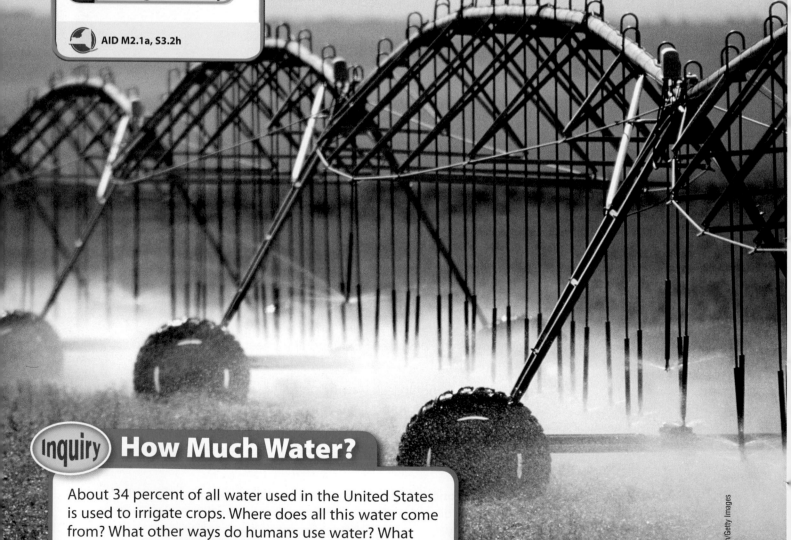

Reading Guide

Key Concepts
ESSENTIAL QUESTIONS

- How do humans use water as a resource?
- How can pollution affect water quality?
- What actions help prevent water pollution?

Vocabulary

point-source pollution

nonpoint-source pollution

g Multilingual eGlossary

AID M2.1a, S3.2h

Impacts on Water

Inquiry How Much Water?

About 34 percent of all water used in the United States is used to irrigate crops. Where does all this water come from? What other ways do humans use water? What happens when water is polluted or runs out?

Noah Clayton/Getty Images

Which water filter is the most effective?

Suppose you have been hired by the Super-Clean Water Treatment Plant to test new water filters. Their old filters do not remove all of the particles from the treated water. Your job is to design an effective water filter.

1 Read and complete a lab safety form.

2 Obtain a **water sample,** a **funnel,** and two **500-mL beakers.**

3 Use **coffee filters, paper towels, cotton,** and **gravel** to make a filter in the funnel. Hold the funnel over the first beaker. Pour half of your water sample into the funnel and collect the water in the beaker. Record your results in your Science Journal.

4 Remove the filter and rinse the funnel. Based on your results, make a second, more efficient filter. Repeat step 3 using the second beaker.

5 Draw a diagram of both filtering methods in your Science Journal.

Think About This

1. Were either of your filters successful in removing the particles from the water? Why or why not?

2. What changes would you make to your filter to make it work more efficiently?

3. **Key Concept** How do water treatment plants make more water available for human use?

Water as a Resource

Most of Earth's surface is covered with water, and living things on Earth are made mostly of water. Neither the largest whale nor the smallest algae can live without this important resource. Like other organisms, humans need water to survive. Humans also use water in ways that other organisms do not. People wash cars, do laundry, and use water for recreation and transportation.

Household activities, however, make up only a small part of human water use. As shown in **Figure 12,** most water in the United States is used by power plants. The water is used to generate electricity and to cool equipment. Like the land uses you learned about earlier, the use of water as a resource also impacts the environment.

Key Concept Check How do humans use water as a resource?

Water Use

Water Use in the United States

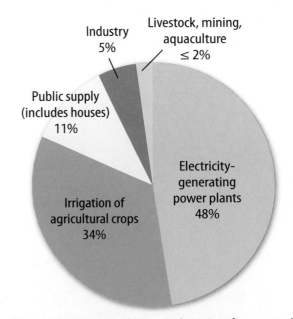

Industry
5%

Livestock, mining, aquaculture
≤ 2%

Public supply (includes houses)
11%

Irrigation of agricultural crops
34%

Electricity-generating power plants
48%

Figure 12 Power plants, industries, farms, and households all use water.

Sources of Water Pollution

Water moves from Earth's surface to the atmosphere and back again in the water cycle. Thermal energy from the Sun causes water at Earth's surface to evaporate into the atmosphere. Water vapor in the air cools as it rises, then condenses and forms clouds. Water returns to Earth's surface as precipitation. Runoff reenters oceans and rivers or it can seep into the ground. Pollution from a variety of sources can impact the quality of water as it moves through the water cycle.

Point-Source Pollution

Point-source pollution *is pollution from a single source that can be identified.* The discharge pipe in **Figure 13** that is releasing industrial waste directly into a river is an example of point-source pollution. Other examples of point-source pollution in **Figure 13** are the oil spilling from the tanker and the runoff from the mining operation.

WORD ORIGIN

pollution
from Latin *polluere,* means "to contaminate"

Sources of Water Pollution 🔑

Review   Personal Tutor

Figure 13 Pollution can affect water quality in several ways.

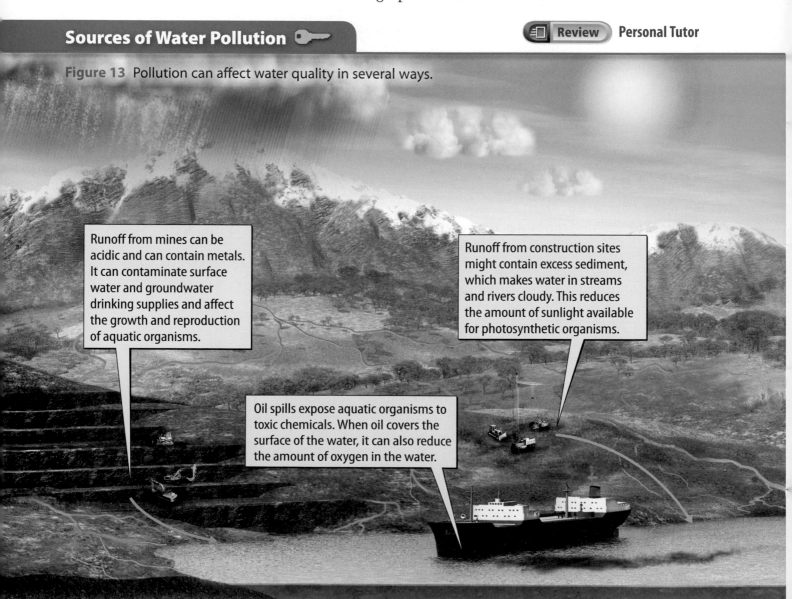

Runoff from mines can be acidic and can contain metals. It can contaminate surface water and groundwater drinking supplies and affect the growth and reproduction of aquatic organisms.

Runoff from construction sites might contain excess sediment, which makes water in streams and rivers cloudy. This reduces the amount of sunlight available for photosynthetic organisms.

Oil spills expose aquatic organisms to toxic chemicals. When oil covers the surface of the water, it can also reduce the amount of oxygen in the water.

Nonpoint-Source Pollution

Pollution from several widespread sources that cannot be traced back to a single location is called **nonpoint-source pollution.** As precipitation runs over Earth's surface, the water picks up materials and substances from farms and urban developments, such as the ones shown in **Figure 13.** These different sources might be several kilometers apart. This makes it difficult to trace the pollution in the water back to one specific source. Runoff from farms and urban developments are examples of nonpoint-source pollution. Runoff from construction sites, which can contain excess amounts of sediment, is another example of nonpoint-source pollution.

Most of the water pollution in the United States comes from nonpoint sources. This kind of pollution is harder to pinpoint and therefore harder to control.

 Key Concept Check How can pollution affect water quality?

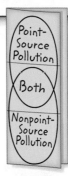

FOLDABLES

Make a vertical three-tab book. Draw a Venn diagram on the front. Cut the folds to form three tabs. Label as illustrated. Use the Foldable to compare and contrast sources of pollution.

Point-Source Pollution

Both

Nonpoint-Source Pollution

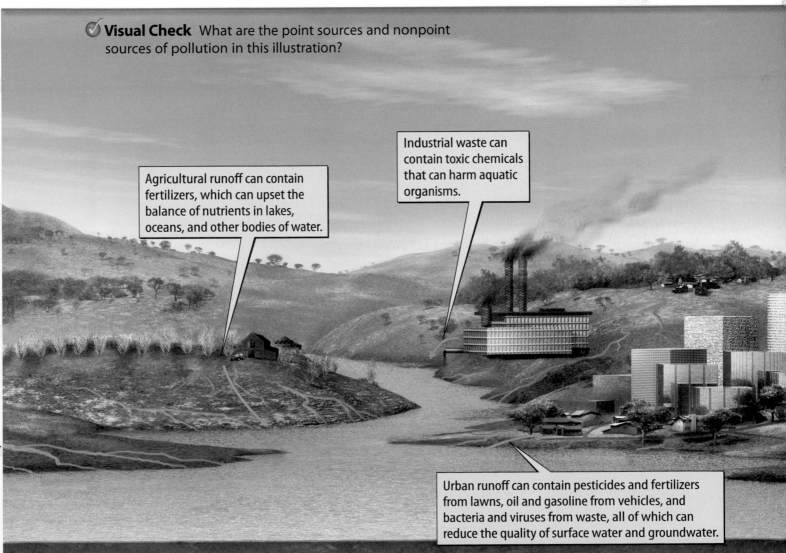

✅ **Visual Check** What are the point sources and nonpoint sources of pollution in this illustration?

Agricultural runoff can contain fertilizers, which can upset the balance of nutrients in lakes, oceans, and other bodies of water.

Industrial waste can contain toxic chemicals that can harm aquatic organisms.

Urban runoff can contain pesticides and fertilizers from lawns, oil and gasoline from vehicles, and bacteria and viruses from waste, all of which can reduce the quality of surface water and groundwater.

Positive Actions

Once pollution enters water, it is difficult to remove. In fact, it can take decades to clean polluted groundwater! That is why most efforts to reduce water pollution focus on preventing it from entering the environment, rather than cleaning it up.

International Cooperation

In the 1960s, Lake Erie, one of the Great Lakes, was heavily polluted by runoff from fertilized fields and industrial wastes. Rivers that flowed into the lake were polluted, too. Litter soaked with chemicals floated on the surface of one of these rivers—the Cuyahoga River. As shown in **Figure 14,** the litter caught fire. The fire spurred Canada and the United States—the two countries that border the Great Lakes—into action.

The countries formed several agreements to clean up the Great Lakes. The goals of the countries are pollution prevention, as well as cleanup and research. Although, the Great Lakes still face challenges from aquatic species that are not native to the lakes and from the impact of excess sediments, pollution from toxic chemicals has decreased.

 Reading Check Why is it important to focus on preventing water pollution before it happens?

Figure 14 In 1969, burning litter and chemical pollution floating on the Cuyahoga River in northeastern Ohio inspired international efforts to clean up the Great Lakes.

Inquiry MiniLab

20 minutes

What's in well water?

The graph shows the level of nitrates in well water in Spanish Springs Valley, Nevada, over a 10-year period. Nitrate is a form of nitrogen that can contaminate groundwater when it leaches out of septic systems.

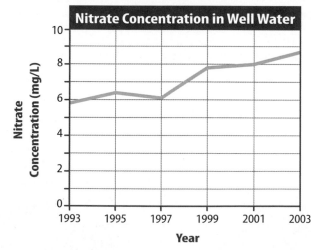

Analyze and Conclude

1. **Describe** what happened to the average level of nitrate in the well water of Spanish Springs Valley between 1993 and 2003.

2. **Analyze** Excess nitrate in drinking water can cause serious illness, especially in infants. The maximum allowable level in public drinking water is 10 mg/L. How close did the highest level of nitrate concentration come to the maximum level allowed?

3. 🔑 **Key Concept** An article in the newspaper described a Spanish Springs Valley project to connect all houses to the sewer system. Predict how this will affect nitrate levels in the well water.

AP Images

National Initiatives

In addition to working with other governments, the United States has laws to help maintain water quality within its borders. The Clean Water Act, for example, regulates sources of water pollution, including sewage systems. The Safe Drinking Water Act protects supplies of drinking water throughout the country.

How can you help?

Laws are effective ways to reduce water pollution. But simple actions taken by individuals can have positive impacts, too.

Reduce Use of Harmful Chemicals Many household products, such as paints and cleaners, contain harmful chemicals. People can use alternative products that do not contain toxins. For example, baking soda and white vinegar are safe, inexpensive cleaning products. In addition, people can reduce their use of artificial fertilizers on gardens and lawns. As you read earlier, compost can enrich soils without harming water quality.

Dispose of Waste Safely Sometimes using products that contain pollutants is necessary. Vehicles, for example, cannot run without motor oil. This motor oil has to be replaced regularly. People should never pour motor oil or other hazardous substances into drains, onto the ground, or directly into streams or lakes. These substances must be disposed of safely. Your local waste management agency has tips for safe disposal of hazardous waste.

Conserve Water Water pollution can be reduced simply by reducing water use. Easy ways to conserve water include taking shorter showers and turning off the water when you brush your teeth. **Figure 15** shows other ways to reduce water use.

 Key Concept Check How can individuals help prevent water pollution?

Figure 15  People can help reduce water pollution by conserving water.

Visual Check How does sweeping a deck help reduce water pollution?

Keeping water in the refrigerator instead of running water from a faucet until the water is cold helps conserve water.

Sweeping leaves and branches from a deck instead of spraying them off using water from a hose helps conserve water.

Lesson 3 Review

Visual Summary

Water is an important resource; all living things need water to survive. Water is used for agriculture, for electricity production, and in homes and businesses every day.

Runoff from mines

Water pollution can come from many sources, including chemicals from agriculture and industry and oil spills.

International cooperation and national laws help prevent water pollution. Individuals can help conserve water by reducing water use and disposing of wastes properly.

FOLDABLES®

Use your lesson Foldable to review the lesson. Save your Foldable for the project at the end of the chapter.

What do you think NOW?

You first read the statements below at the beginning of the chapter.

5. Sources of water pollution are always easy to identify.

6. The proper method of disposal for used motor oil is to pour it down the drain.

Did you change your mind about whether you agree or disagree with the statements? Rewrite any false statements to make them true.

Use Vocabulary

1. **Define** *nonpoint-source pollution* and *point-source pollution* in your own words.

2. **Use the term** *nonpoint-source pollution* in a sentence.

Understand Key Concepts

3. Which uses the most water in the United States?
   - **A.** factories
   - **B.** farms
   - **C.** households
   - **D.** power plants

4. **Survey** three classmates to find out how they conserve water at home.

5. **Diagram** Make a diagram showing how runoff from lawns can impact water quality.

Interpret Graphics

6. **Sequence** Draw a graphic organizer such as the one below to illustrate the cleanup of Lake Erie, beginning with the pollution of the lake.

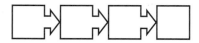

7. **Classify** the pollution source shown below as point-source or nonpoint-source. Explain your reasoning.

Critical Thinking

8. **Visualize** a map of a river that flows through several countries. Explain why international cooperation is needed to reduce water pollution.

9. **Identify** a human activity that impacts water quality negatively. Then describe a positive action that can help reduce the pollution caused by the activity.

Dead Zones

What causes lifeless areas in the ocean?

For thousands of years, people have lived on coasts, making a living by shipping goods or by fishing. Today, fisheries in the Gulf of Mexico provide jobs for thousands of people and food for millions more. Although humans and other organisms depend on the ocean, human activities can harm marine ecosystems. Scientists have been tracking dead zones in the ocean for several decades. They believe that these zones are a result of human activities on land.

A large dead zone in the Gulf of Mexico forms every year when runoff from spring and summer rain in the Midwest drains into the Mississippi River. The runoff contains nitrogen and phosphorous from fertilizer, animal waste, and sewage from farms and cities. This nutrient-rich water flows into the gulf. Algae feed on excess nutrients and multiply rapidly, creating an algal bloom. The results of the algal bloom are shown below.

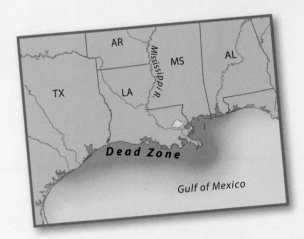

AR
MS
AL
TX
LA
Mississippi R.

Dead Zone

Gulf of Mexico

Some simple changes in human activity can help prevent dead zones. People upstream from the Gulf can decrease the use of fertilizer and apply it at times when it is less likely to be carried away by runoff. Picking up or containing animal waste can help, too. Also, people can modernize and improve septic and sewage systems. How do we know these steps would work? Using them has already restored life to dead zones in the Great Lakes!

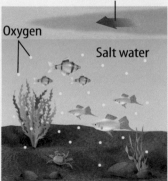

Freshwater runoff

Oxygen

Salt water

❶ River water containing nitrogen and phosphorous flows into the Gulf of Mexico.

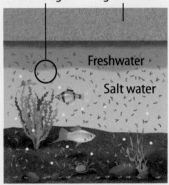

Dead algae   Algal bloom

Freshwater

Salt water

❷ After the algal bloom, dead algae sink to the ocean floor.

Dead fish

Freshwater

Dead zone

❸ Decomposing algae deplete the water's oxygen, killing other organisms.

It's Your Turn

RESEARCH AND REPORT Earth's oceans contain about 150 dead zones. Choose three. Plot them on a map and write a report about what causes each dead zone.

Impacts on the Atmosphere

Reading Guide

Key Concepts
ESSENTIAL QUESTIONS

- What are some types of air pollution?
- How are global warming and the carbon cycle related?
- How does air pollution affect human health?
- What actions help prevent air pollution?

Vocabulary

photochemical smog
acid precipitation
particulate matter
global warming
greenhouse effect
Air Quality Index

g Multilingual eGlossary

▣ Video BrainPOP®

AID S1.1b, S2.1d, S3.1a, S3.2f, S3.2h, T1.1a, T1.2a, T1.4a; IS 1.3; ICT 2.1; IPS 1.1, 1.3, 2.1; PS 2.2r

Inquiry Why wear a mask?

In some areas of the world, people wear masks to help protect themselves against high levels of air pollution. Where does this pollution come from? How do you think air pollution affects human health and the environment?

©Fritz Hoffmann/Corbis

Where's the air?

In 1986, an explosion at a nuclear power plant in Chernobyl, Russia, sent radioactive pollution 6 km into the atmosphere. Within three weeks, the radioactive cloud had reached Italy, Finland, Iceland, and North America.

1. Read and complete a lab safety form.
2. With your group, move to your assigned area of the room.
3. Lay out **sheets of paper** to cover the table.
4. When the **fan** starts blowing, observe whether water droplets appear on the paper. Record your observations in your Science Journal.
5. Lay out another set of paper sheets and record your observations when the fan blows in a different direction.

Think About This

1. Did the water droplets reach your location? Why or why not?

2. How is the movement of air and particles by the fan similar to the movement of the pollution from Chernobyl? How does the movement differ?

3. **Key Concept** How do you think the health of a person in Iceland could be affected by the explosion in Chernobyl?

Importance of Clean Air

Your body, and the bodies of other animals, uses oxygen in air to produce some of the energy it needs. Many organisms can survive for only a few minutes without air. But the air you breathe must be clean or it can harm your body.

Types of Air Pollution

Human activities can produce pollution that enters the air and affects air quality. Types of air pollution include smog, acid precipitation, particulate matter, chlorofluorocarbons (CFCs), and carbon monoxide.

Smog

The brownish haze in the sky in **Figure 16** is photochemical smog. **Photochemical smog** *is caused when nitrogen and carbon compounds in the air react in sunlight.* Nitrogen and carbon compounds are released when fossil fuels are burned to provide energy for vehicles and power plants. These compounds react in sunlight and form other substances. One of these substances is ozone. Ozone high in the atmosphere helps protect living things from the Sun's ultraviolet radiation. However, ozone close to Earth's surface is a major component of smog.

Figure 16 Burning fossil fuels releases compounds that can react in sunlight and form smog.

Acid Precipitation

Another form of pollution that occurs as a result of burning fossil fuels is acid precipitation. **Acid precipitation** *is rain or snow that has a lower pH than that of normal rainwater.* The pH of normal rainwater is about 5.6. Acid precipitation forms when gases containing nitrogen and sulfur react with water, oxygen, and other chemicals in the atmosphere. Acid precipitation falls into lakes and ponds or onto the ground. It makes the water and the soil more acidic. Many living things cannot survive if the pH of water or soil becomes too low. The trees shown in **Figure 17** have been affected by acid precipitation.

Figure 17 Acid precipitation can make the soil acidic and kill trees and other plant life.

 Review

Personal Tutor

WORD ORIGIN · · · · · · · · · · · ·

particulate
from Latin *particula*, means "small part"

FOLDABLES

Make a two-tab book. Label the tabs as illustrated. Use your Foldable to record factors that increase or decrease air pollution.

Factors That Increase Air Pollution | Factors That Decrease Air Pollution

Particulate Matter

The mix of both solid and liquid particles in the air is called **particulate matter.** Solid particles include smoke, dust, and dirt. These particles enter the air from natural processes, such as volcanic eruptions and forest fires. Human activities, such as burning fossil fuels at power plants and in vehicles, also release particulate matter. Inhaling particulate matter can cause coughing, difficulty breathing, and other respiratory problems.

CFCs

Ozone in the upper atmosphere absorbs harmful ultraviolet (UV) rays from the Sun. Using products that contain CFCs, such as air conditioners and refrigerators made before 1996, affects the ozone layer. CFCs react with sunlight and destroy ozone molecules. As a result, the ozone layer thins and more UV rays reach Earth's surface. Increased skin cancer rates have been linked with an increase in UV rays.

Carbon Monoxide

Carbon monoxide is a gas released from vehicles and industrial processes. Forest fires also release carbon monoxide into the air. Wood-burning and gas stoves are sources of carbon monoxide indoors. Breathing carbon monoxide reduces the amount of oxygen that reaches the body's tissues and organs.

 Key Concept Check What are some types of air pollution?

Piotr Zawisza/Getty Images

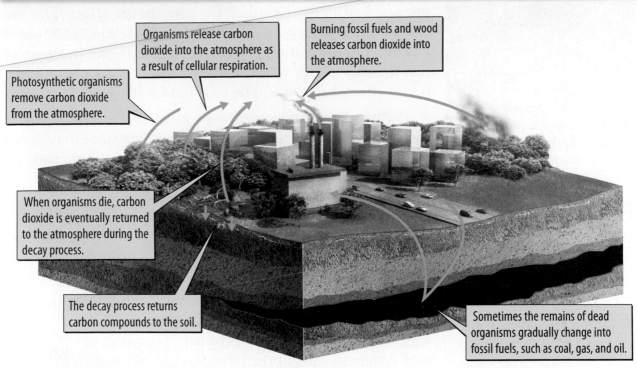

Photosynthetic organisms remove carbon dioxide from the atmosphere.

Organisms release carbon dioxide into the atmosphere as a result of cellular respiration.

Burning fossil fuels and wood releases carbon dioxide into the atmosphere.

When organisms die, carbon dioxide is eventually returned to the atmosphere during the decay process.

The decay process returns carbon compounds to the soil.

Sometimes the remains of dead organisms gradually change into fossil fuels, such as coal, gas, and oil.

Figure 18 Some human activities can increase the amount of carbon dioxide in the atmosphere.

Visual Check Which processes add carbon to the atmosphere?

Global Warming and the Carbon Cycle

Air pollution affects natural cycles on Earth. For example, burning fossil fuels for electricity, heating, and transportation releases substances that cause acid precipitation. Burning fossil fuels also releases carbon dioxide into the atmosphere, as shown in **Figure 18.** An increased concentration of carbon dioxide in the atmosphere can lead to **global warming,** *an increase in Earth's average surface temperature.* Earth's temperature has increased about 0.7°C over the past 100 years. Scientists estimate it will rise an additional 1.8 to 4.0°C over the next 100 years. Even a small increase in Earth's average surface temperature can cause widespread problems.

Effects of Global Warming

Warmer temperatures can cause ice to melt, making sea levels rise. Higher sea levels can cause flooding along coastal areas. In addition, warmer ocean waters might lead to an increase in the intensity and frequency of storms.

Global warming also can affect the kinds of living things found in ecosystems. Some hardwood trees, for example, do not thrive in warm environments. These trees will no longer be found in some areas if temperatures continue to rise.

🔑 **Key Concept Check** How are global warming and the carbon cycle related?

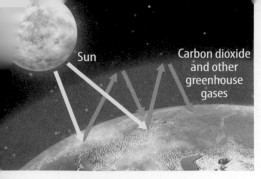

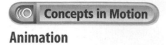

Sun | **Carbon dioxide and other greenhouse gases**

Figure 19 Greenhouse gases absorb and reradiate thermal energy from the Sun and warm Earth's surface.

Concepts in Motion

Animation

The Greenhouse Effect

Why does too much carbon dioxide in the atmosphere increase Earth's temperature? *The greenhouse effect is the natural process that occurs when certain gases in the atmosphere absorb and reradiate thermal energy from the Sun.* As shown in **Figure 19,** this thermal energy warms Earth's surface. Without the greenhouse effect, Earth would be too cold for life as it exists now.

Carbon dioxide is a greenhouse gas. Other greenhouse gases include methane and water vapor. When the amount of greenhouse gases increases, more thermal energy is trapped and Earth's surface temperature rises. Global warming occurs.

Reading Check How are the greenhouse effect and global warming related?

Health Disorders

Air pollution affects the environment and human health as well. Air pollution can cause respiratory problems, including triggering asthma attacks. Asthma is a disorder of the respiratory system in which breathing passageways narrow during an attack, making it hard for a person to breathe. **Figure 20** shows some health disorders caused by pollutants in the air.

Figure 20 Air pollution can harm the environment and your health.

Key Concept Check How can air pollution affect human health?

Health Effects of Air Pollution

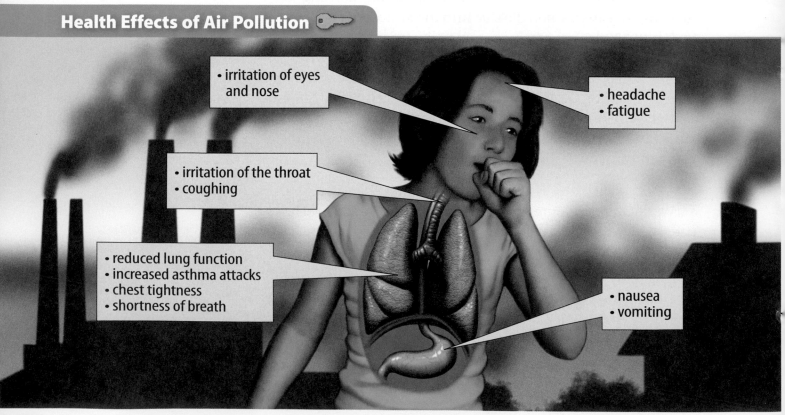

- irritation of eyes and nose
- headache
- fatigue
- irritation of the throat
- coughing
- reduced lung function
- increased asthma attacks
- chest tightness
- shortness of breath
- nausea
- vomiting

Table 1 Air Quality Index

Ozone Concentration (parts per million)	Air Quality Index Values	Air Quality Description	Preventative Actions
0.0 to 0.064	0 to 50	good	No preventative actions needed.
0.065 to 0.084	51 to 100	moderate	Highly sensitive people should limit prolonged outdoor activity.
0.085 to 0.104	101 to 150	unhealthy for sensitive groups	Sensitive people should limit prolonged outdoor activity.
0.105 to 0.124	151 to 200	unhealthy	All groups should limit prolonged outdoor activity.
0.125 to 0.404	201 to 300	very unhealthy	Sensitive people should avoid outdoor activity. All other groups should limit outdoor activity.

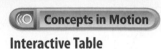

Concepts in Motion

Interactive Table

Measuring Air Quality

Some pollutants, such as smoke from forest fires, are easily seen. Other pollutants, such as carbon monoxide, are invisible. How can people know when levels of air pollution are high?

The EPA works with state and local agencies to measure and report air quality. *The* **Air Quality Index** *(AQI) is a scale that ranks levels of ozone and other air pollutants.* Study the AQI for ozone in **Table 1.** It uses color codes to rank ozone levels on a scale of 0 to 300. Although ozone in the upper atmosphere blocks harmful rays from the Sun, ozone that is close to Earth's surface can cause health problems, including throat irritation, coughing, and chest pain. The EPA cautions that no one should do physical activities outside when AQI values reach 300.

Inquiry MiniLab   **10 minutes**

What's in the air?

Suppose your friend suffers from asthma. People with respiratory problems such as asthma are usually more sensitive to air pollution. *Sensitive* is a term used on the AQI. Use the AQI in **Table 1** to answer the questions below.

Analyze and Conclude

1. **Identify** Today's AQI value is 130. What is the concentration of ozone in the air?

2. **Decide** Is today a good day for you and your friend to go to the park to play basketball for a few hours? Why or why not?

3. **Key Concept** Predict how you and your friend might be affected by the air if you played basketball today.

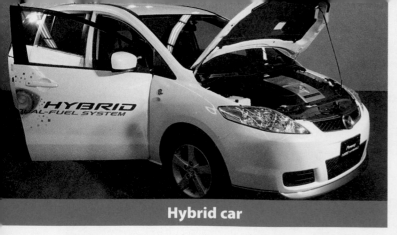

Hybrid car

Solar car

Figure 21 Energy-efficient and renewable-energy vehicles help reduce air pollution.

✓ **Visual Check** How does driving a solar car help reduce air pollution?

Positive Actions

Countries around the world are working together to reduce air pollution. For example, 190 countries, including the United States, have signed the Montreal Protocol to phase out the use of CFCs. Levels of CFCs have since decreased. The Kyoto Protocol aims to reduce emissions of greenhouse gases. Currently, 184 countries have accepted the agreement.

National Initiatives

In the United States, the Clean Air Act sets limits on the amount of certain pollutants that can be released into the air. Since the law was passed in 1970, amounts of carbon monoxide, ozone near Earth's surface, and acid precipitation-producing substances have decreased by more than 50 percent. Toxins from industrial factories have gone down by 90 percent.

Cleaner Energy

Using renewable energy resources such as solar power, wind power, and geothermal energy to heat homes helps reduce air pollution. Recall that renewable resources are resources that can be replaced by natural processes in a relatively short amount of time. People also can invest in more energy-efficient appliances and vehicles. The hybrid car shown in **Figure 21** uses both a battery and fossil fuels for power. It is more energy efficient and emits less pollution than vehicles that are powered by fossil fuels alone. The solar car shown in **Figure 21** uses only the Sun's energy for power.

How can you help?

Reducing energy use means that fewer pollutants are released into the air. You can turn the thermostat down in the winter and up in the summer to save energy. You can walk to the store or use public transportation. Each small step you take to conserve energy helps improve air, water, and soil quality.

✓ **Key Concept Check** How can people help prevent air pollution?

Lesson 4 Review

Visual Summary

Burning fossil fuels releases nitrogen and carbon compounds and particulate matter into the air.

Air pollution can affect human health, causing eye, nose, and throat irritation, increased asthma, and headaches.

Certain laws and international agreements require people to reduce air pollution. Individuals can reduce air pollution by using alternative forms of energy to heat homes and power vehicles.

FOLDABLES

Use your lesson Foldable to review the lesson. Save your Foldable for the project at the end of the chapter.

What do you think NOW?

You first read the statements below at the beginning of the chapter.

7. The greenhouse effect is harmful to life on Earth.

8. Air pollution can affect human health.

Did you change your mind about whether you agree or disagree with the statements? Rewrite any false statements to make them true.

Use Vocabulary

1 **Use the term** *air quality index* in a sentence.

2 The natural heating of Earth's surface that occurs when certain gases absorb and reradiate thermal energy from the Sun is _____.

3 **Define** *global warming* in your own words.

Understand Key Concepts

4 Which is NOT a possible heath effect of exposure to air pollution?
A. chest tightness
B. eye irritation
C. increased lung function
D. shortness of breath

5 **Relate** What happens in the carbon cycle when fossil fuels are burned for energy?

6 **Compare** the goals of the Montreal Protocol and the Kyoto Protocol.

Interpret Graphics

7 **Sequence** Copy and fill in the graphic organizer below to identify types of air pollution.

8 **Describe** air quality when the ozone concentration is 0.112 ppm using the table below.

Ozone Concentration (ppm)	Air Quality Index Values	Air Quality Description
0.105 to 0.124	151 to 200	unhealthy
0.125 to 0.404	201 to 300	very unhealthy

Critical Thinking

9 **Predict** Some carbon is stored in frozen soils in the Arctic. What might happen to Earth's climate if these soils thawed?

Materials

office supplies

magazines

computer with Internet access

Safety

Design a Green City

City planners have asked the architectural firms in town to design an eco-friendly city that will be based on an environmentally responsible use of land, water, and energy. The city should include homes, businesses, schools, green spaces, industry, waste management, and transportation options.

Question

What are the most environmentally friendly materials and practices to use when designing a green city?

Procedure

1 Make a list of the things you will include in your city.

2 Research environmentally responsible structures and practices for the elements of your city. Your research may include using the library or talking with owners, employees, or patrons of businesses to identify existing environmental problems. Use the questions below to help guide your research.

- What materials can you use for building the structures?

- What building practices and designs can you use to minimize environmental impact?

- How will you address energy use by homeowners, businesses, and industry?

- How will you address water use for homes, businesses, and industry?

- How will you address energy use and pollution issues related to public transportation?

- What is the most environmentally friendly system of waste management?

3 Analyze the information you gathered in step 2. Discuss how you will use what you have learned as you design your city.

4 Design your city. Use the colored pencils and markers to draw a map of the city, including all of the elements of the city. Add captions, other graphics, and/or a key to explain any elements or actions and their intended results.

5 Copy and complete the *Required Elements and Actions* chart on the following page. For each element in your city, explain the environmental issue associated with the element and what action you took in your city to address the issue. Does your design include an action for each element?

McGraw-Hill Education

Required Elements and Actions		
Element	Environmental Issue	Action Taken
Waste management	All waste goes into landfills.	designed a curbside recycling program

6 If needed, modify your design to include any other actions you need to take.

Analyze and Conclude

7 Describe one identified environmental issue, the action taken, and the intended outcome in your design plans.

8 Compare your design to the designs of other groups. What did they do differently?

9 **The Big Idea** Predict whether there will be any changes in the quality of your city's water resources after years of use of your design. Explain your answer.

Communicate Your Results

Suppose your classmates are members of the city planning board. Present your design to the board. Explain the structures and practices that are intended to make the city environmentally responsible.

 **Extension**

Make a 3-D model of your city. Try to use recycled or environmentally friendly materials to represent the structures in your city.

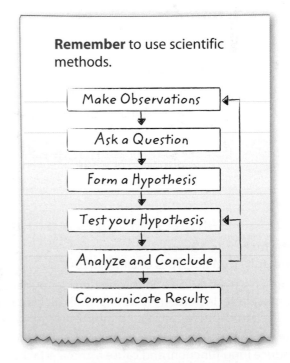

Remember to use scientific methods.

Make Observations
↓
Ask a Question
↓
Form a Hypothesis
↓
Test your Hypothesis
↓
Analyze and Conclude
↓
Communicate Results

Mark Scheuern/Alamy

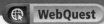
 THE BIG IDEA Human activities can impact the environment negatively, including deforestation, water pollution, and global warming, and positively, such as through reforestation, reclamation, and water conservation.

Key Concepts Summary 🔑	Vocabulary
Lesson 1: People and the Environment • Earth has limited resources and cannot support unlimited human **population** growth. • Daily actions can deplete resources and pollute soil, water, and air. 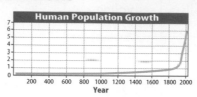	population carrying capacity
Lesson 2: Impacts on the Land • **Deforestation, desertification,** habitat destruction, and increased rates of extinction are associated with using land as a resource. • Landfills are constructed to prevent contamination of soil and water by pollutants from waste. Hazardous waste must be disposed of in a safe manner. • Positive impacts on land include preservation, **reforestation,** and **reclamation.** 	deforestation desertification urban sprawl reforestation reclamation
Lesson 3: Impacts on Water 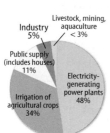 • Humans use water in electricity production, industry, and agriculture, as well as for recreation and transportation. • **Point-source pollution** and **nonpoint-source pollution** can reduce water quality. • International agreements and national laws help prevent water pollution. Other positive actions include disposing of waste safely and conserving water.	point-source pollution nonpoint-source pollution
Lesson 4: Impacts on the Atmosphere • **Photochemical smog,** CFCs, and **acid precipitation** are types of air pollution. • Human activities can add carbon dioxide to the atmosphere. Increased levels of carbon dioxide in the atmosphere can lead to **global warming.**  • Air pollutants such as ozone can irritate the respiratory system, reduce lung function, and cause asthma attacks. • International agreements, laws, and individual actions such as conserving energy help decrease air pollution.	photochemical smog acid precipitation particulate matter global warming greenhouse effect Air Quality Index

FOLDABLES® Chapter Project

Assemble your lesson Foldables as shown to make a Chapter Project. Use the project to review what you have learned in this chapter.

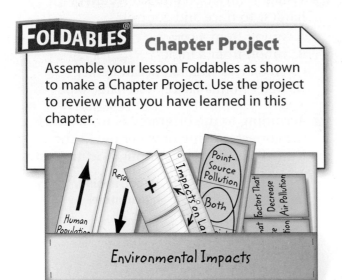

Use Vocabulary

1 Use the term *carrying capacity* in a sentence.

2 Distinguish between desertification and deforestation.

3 Planting trees to replace logged trees is called _____.

4 Distinguish between point-source and nonpoint-source pollution.

5 Define the greenhouse effect in your own words.

6 Solid and liquid particles in the air are called _____.

Link Vocabulary and Key Concepts

Concepts in Motion Interactive Concept Map

Copy this concept map, and then use vocabulary terms from the previous page to complete the concept map.

Impacts on Land

negative
- **7** _____
- **8** _____
- urban sprawl

positive
- **9** _____
- **10** _____

Impacts on Water

negative
- **11** _____
- **12** _____

positive
- proper waste disposal
- conservation

Impacts on the Atmosphere

negative
- **13** _____
- **14** _____
- **15** _____
- global warming

positive
- Montreal Protocol
- Kyoto Protocol
- Clean Air Act
- renewable energy resources

Understand Key Concepts 🗝

1 Which is a population?
- A. all the animals in a zoo
- B. all the living things in a forest
- C. all the people in a park
- D. all the plants in a meadow

2 Which caused the greatest increase of the growth of the human population?
- A. higher death rates
- B. increased marriage rates
- C. medical advances
- D. widespread disease

3 What percentage of species on Earth live in tropical rain forests?
- A. 10 percent
- B. 25 percent
- C. 50 percent
- D. 75 percent

4 What process is illustrated in the diagram below?

Newly planted trees

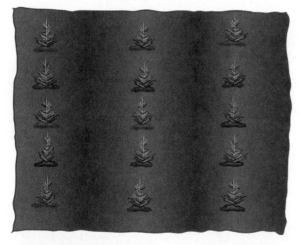

- A. desertification
- B. recycling
- C. reforestation
- D. waste management

5 Which could harm human health?
- A. compost
- B. hazardous waste
- C. nitrogen
- D. reclamation

6 Which source of pollution would be hardest to trace and control?
- A. runoff from a city
- B. runoff from a mine
- C. an oil leak from an ocean tanker
- D. water from a factory discharge pipe

7 According to the diagram below, which is the correct ranking of water use in the United States, in order from most to least?

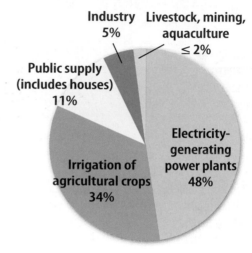

- A. industrial, public supply, irrigation, power plants
- B. irrigation, industrial, public supply, power plants
- C. power plants, irrigation, public supply, industrial
- D. public supply, power plants, industrial, irrigation

8 What is the main purpose of the Safe Drinking Water Act?
- A. to ban point-source pollution
- B. to clean up the Great Lakes
- C. to protect drinking-water supplies
- D. to regulate landfills

9 Why has the use of CFCs been phased out?
- A. They cause acid rain.
- B. They produce smog.
- C. They destroy ozone molecules.
- D. They impact the nitrogen cycle.

Critical Thinking

10 Decide Rates of human population growth are higher in developing countries than in developed countries. Yet, people in developed countries use more resources than those in developing countries. Should international efforts focus on reducing population growth or reducing resource use? Explain.

11 Relate How does the carrying capacity for a species help regulate its population growth?

12 Assess your personal impact on the environment today. Include both positive and negative impacts on soil, water, and air.

13 Infer How does deforestation affect levels of carbon in the atmosphere?

14 Role-Play Suppose you are a soil expert advising a farmer on the use of fertilizers. What would you tell the farmer about the environmental impact of the fertilizers?

15 Create Use the data below to create a circle graph showing waste disposal methods in the United States.

Waste Disposal Methods—United States	
Method	**Percent of Waste Disposed**
Landfill	55%
Recycling/composting	31%
Incineration	14%

Writing in Science

16 Compose a letter to a younger student to help him or her understand air pollution. The letter should identify the different kinds of pollution and explain their causes.

REVIEW THE B**I**G IDEA

17 How do human activities impact the environment? Give one example each of how human activities impact land, water, and air resources.

18 What positive actions can people take to reduce or reverse negative impacts on the environment?

Math Skills

📖 **Review**

— Math Practice —

Use Percentages

19 Between 1960 and 1990, the number of people per square mile in the United States grew from 50.7 people to 70.3 people. What was the percent change?

20 Between 1950 and 1998, the rural population in the United States decreased from 66.2 million to 53.8 million people. What was the percent change in rural population?

21 During the twentieth century, the population of the western states increased from 4.3 million people to 61.2 million people. What was the percent change during the century?

Grant Faint/Getty Images

Standardized Test Practice

Record your answers on the answer sheet provided by your teacher or on a sheet of paper.

Multiple Choice

1 Which action can help restore land that has been disturbed by mining?

   A deforestation

   B desertification

   C preservation

   D reclamation

2 Which is a consequence of deforestation?

   A Animal habitats are destroyed.

   B Carbon in the atmosphere is reduced.

   C Soil erosion is prevented.

   D The rate of extinction is slowed.

Use the graph below to answer question 3.

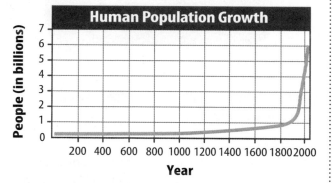

3 During which time span did the human population increase most?

   A 1400–1600

   B 1600–1800

   C 1800–1900

   D 1900–2000

4 Which accounts for the least water use in the United States?

   A electricity-generating power plants

   B irrigation of agricultural crops

   C mines, livestock, and aquaculture

   D public supply, including houses

5 Which is a point source of water pollution?

   A discharge pipes

   B runoff from farms

   C runoff from construction sites

   D runoff from urban areas

6 Which air pollutant contains ozone?

   A acid precipitation

   B carbon monoxide

   C CFCs

   D smog

Use the figure below to answer question 7.

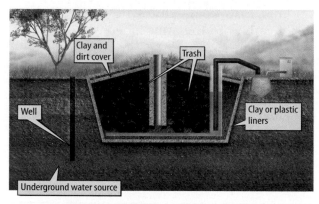

7 What is the function of the well in the figure above?

   A to generate electricity

   B to monitor quality of groundwater

   C to prevent pollution of nearby land

   D to treat hazardous water

8 Which action helps prevent water pollution?

   A pouring motor oil on the ground

   B putting hazardous wastes in the trash

   C using fertilizers when gardening

   D using vinegar when cleaning

9 What effect does ozone near Earth's surface have on the human body?

  A It increases lung function.

  B It increases throat irritation.

  C It reduces breathing problems.

  D It reduces skin cancer.

Use the figure below to answer question 10.

10 Which term describes what is shown in the figure above?

  A acid precipitation

  B global warming

  C greenhouse effect

  D urban sprawl

11 Which results in habitat destruction?

  A reclamation

  B reforestation

  C urban sprawl

  D water conservation

Constructed Response

Use the figure below to answer questions 12 and 13.

12 Which events shown in the figure remove carbon dioxide from the atmosphere?

13 Relate the carbon cycle shown in the figure to global warming and the greenhouse effect.

14 List two actions that help prevent air pollution. Then explain the pros and the cons of taking each action.

15 Explain how taking a hot shower can impact the environment.

16 Create an advertisement for a solar car. Include information about the environmental impacts of the car in your ad.

NEED EXTRA HELP?																
If You Missed Question...	1	2	3	4	5	6	7	8	9	10	11	12	13	14	15	16
Go to Lesson...	2	2	1	3	3	4	2	3	4	2	2	4	4	4	1	4

 **LE 5.1f, 5.1g**

Homeostasis

The human body can sense changes outside and inside itself. It responds to these changes by making changes to body functions. These responses keep the body's inside environment about the same at all times. Scientists call this ability of an organism to keep its internal environment about the same at all times **homeostasis.**

Interdependence of Body Systems

You have probably noticed that your heart rate and breathing are faster after you exercise. These changes are responses to an increased level of activity. During physical activity, your muscle cells use up more and more oxygen and produce lots of carbon dioxide waste. Without you being aware of it, your brain responds to these changes. It directs your heart and lungs to work harder, delivering more oxygen to your muscle cells and carrying away carbon dioxide at a faster rate. This restores homeostasis to your muscles.

Homeostasis is also active when the body overheats, as shown in **Figure 1.** When the brain senses an increased internal temperature, it directs the body to make changes to cool it down. Sweating, for example, is one response to an increased internal temperature. Sweat is mostly water. The evaporation of water from the skin carries away thermal energy and helps cool the body. Another response that cools the body is the opening or dilation of blood vessels in the skin. This means that more blood passes near the surface of the skin, which helps to release excess thermal energy.

Figure 1 The regulation of body temperature is a familiar example of homeostasis.

Clerkenwell/Getty Images

Negative Feedback Most body systems maintain homeostasis by negative feedback. Negative feedback is all of the body's responses that happen to restore a specific normal condition. When you exercise and become overheated, negative feedback responses remove excess thermal energy from your body. Blood pressure also is controlled by negative feedback. The walls of major arteries have cells that sense changes in blood pressure. If blood pressure increases, a message about this change travels from the arteries to the brain. The brain responds by sending a message to the heart to slow down—an action that decreases blood pressure.

Negative feedback also is important for maintaining a normal chemical balance in the body. Glucose is a type of sugar. It is carried in the blood throughout your body.

The glucose level in the blood usually becomes greater than normal after you eat, as shown in **Figure 2.** When the glucose level in the blood is too high, the pancreas releases the hormone insulin. Cells respond to insulin by taking in more glucose. Also, the liver takes in and stores excess glucose as glycogen. Both of these actions help keep a normal level of glucose in the blood.

If the glucose level in the blood is too low, the pancreas releases the hormone glucagon. Glucagon causes the liver to change glycogen back into glucose and to release it into the blood. This restores the normal glucose level in the blood.

Figure 2 Negative-feedback systems control many internal body conditions, such as hormone level, blood sugar level, and body temperature.

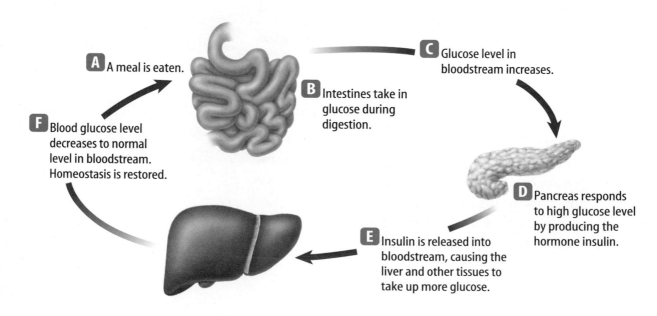

A A meal is eaten.

B Intestines take in glucose during digestion.

C Glucose level in bloodstream increases.

D Pancreas responds to high glucose level by producing the hormone insulin.

E Insulin is released into bloodstream, causing the liver and other tissues to take up more glucose.

F Blood glucose level decreases to normal level in bloodstream. Homeostasis is restored.

Positive Feedback Unlike negative feedback, positive feedback does not restore the body back to a normal level. Instead, the body responds by creating even more change. Positive feedback is rare in the healthy body.

Blood clotting, as shown in **Figure 3,** is an example of positive feedback. A cut or tear to the skin and a blood vessel causes the blood vessel to narrow. This limits the amount of blood that can escape. Next chemicals are released that activate platelets in the blood.

Platelets move to and clump at the damaged area of the vessel. This happens because chemical reactions occur in the platelets that make their surfaces sticky. This stickiness increases the release of chemicals that activate additional platelets. Therefore, more platelets become sticky and stick to one another. The process stops when the opening in the vessel is plugged. The clot becomes hard, white blood cells destroy any bacteria that might be present, and skin cells begin to repair the cut or tear.

Homeostasis in Invertebrates

Invertebrates are animals without backbones. They are the most numerous animals on Earth, accounting for more than 95 percent of animal species. They range in size from tiny rotifers, measuring less than 0.001 mm in length, to giant squid, which can be over 13 m long. Invertebrates thrive in forests, deserts, oceans, and even in the air around us. The ability to maintain homeostasis allows invertebrates to function effectively across a large range of environmental conditions.

Figure 3 When the skin is damaged, a sticky blood clot seals the leaking blood vessel. Eventually a scab forms to protect the wound from further damage and allow it to heal.

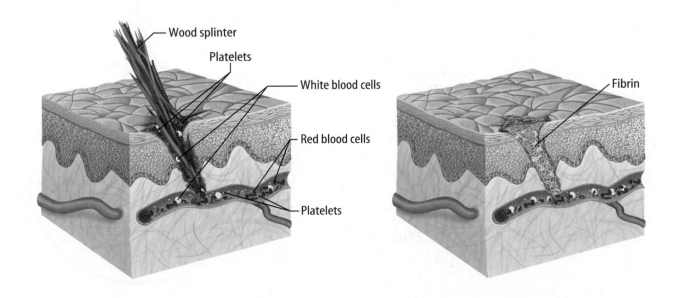

Wood splinter
Platelets
White blood cells
Red blood cells
Platelets
Fibrin

Figure 4 In the two cell-layer body plan of a cnidarian, such as the lion's mane jellyfish, no cell is ever far from the water. In each cell, oxygen from the water is exchanged for carbon dioxide and other cell wastes.

Oxygen/Carbon Dioxide Balance To survive, animals must take in oxygen from the environment and remove waste carbon dioxide. These actions must be balanced to maintain homeostasis. **Cnidarians,** which are simple invertebrates such as jellyfish, sea anemones, and corals, and **annelids,** such as earthworms, accomplish this exchange through direct diffusion. **Direct diffusion** is when oxygen passes from the surrounding environment through cells on the animal's surface and into individual cells inside the organism. As waste carbon dioxide accumulates, it diffuses back across cell surfaces into the surrounding water or air. The lion's mane jellyfish, as shown in **Figure 4,** maintains homeostasis through direct diffusion.

Some invertebrates have specialized body structures for exchanging oxygen and carbon dioxide. Some arachnids, like a spider, have organs called **book lungs,** as shown in **Figure 5.** As air moves over the folded "pages," or plates, making up the book lung, oxygen diffuses into the blood while carbon dioxide diffuses out. Because the book lung is folded, it has a larger surface area over which the exchange of gases can take place.

Many insects have openings, called **spiracles,** along their bodies that allow air to enter and exit. The spiracles connect to a network of tubes, which extends throughout the body. Air moves through successively smaller tubes, eventually reaching specialized cells called tracheoles. The exchange of oxygen and carbon dioxide occurs in **tracheoles.** Many insects have valves that close the spiracles and prevent water loss.

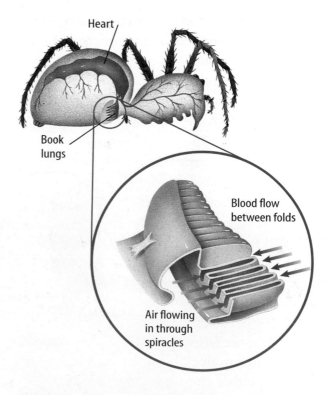

Figure 5 Air circulates between the moist folds of the book lungs, bringing oxygen to the blood.

Purestock/SuperStock

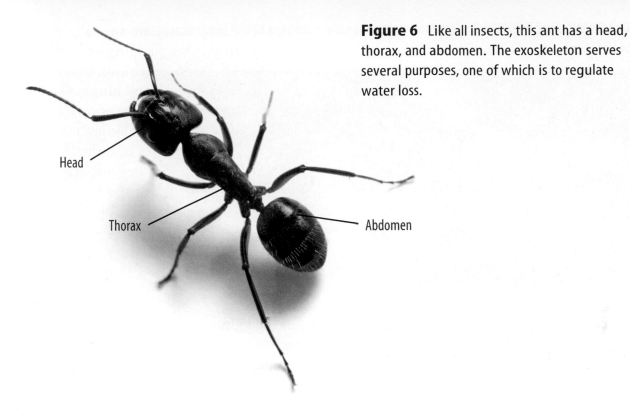

Figure 6 Like all insects, this ant has a head, thorax, and abdomen. The exoskeleton serves several purposes, one of which is to regulate water loss.

Head

Thorax

Abdomen

Antagain/iStock/360/Getty Images

Water Balance Insects are members of phylum **Arthropoda.** Insects have three body regions—a head, thorax, and abdomen, as shown in **Figure 6.** A hard outer covering called an **exoskeleton** provides support and protection for internal organs. The exoskeleton is also important in regulating water loss. Because an insect's body has a large surface area to volume ratio, it can dry out easily. The exoskeleton has a waxy, water-repellent component that forms a seal, slowing water loss from the insect's body.

Cold temperatures can present special water-related issues for insects. Freezing temperatures cause ice crystals to form that can destroy cells and tissues and sometimes cause death. As temperatures approach freezing, some insects undergo a process in which water molecules in the cells are replaced with a chemical called glycerol. Glycerol acts as an antifreeze in insect cells, reducing the temperature at which freezing

will occur. As temperatures increase, the process is reversed: Glycerol is broken down and replaced with water.

Temperature Control Flying insects like bees use specific strategies to maintain homeostasis across temperature extremes. Bumblebees, for example, are covered in a thick layer of furry scales that provide insulation. When the air temperature is cool, a bumblebee may hang from a leaf or flower and warm up in the sunshine. A bee can also increase its body temperature by shivering its flight muscles. Contracting these muscles metabolizes stored energy, releasing heat which is distributed through the bee's body. In honeybee colonies, worker bees huddle together in groups to keep warm during the winter. Bees in the core of the cluster shiver, releasing heat that is shared throughout the colony. Bees near the outside of the cluster insulate the colony against heat loss.

Figure 7 When animals need to replace water, messages are sent to the brain that result in a feeling of thirst.

Homeostasis in Vertebrates

Animals with backbones are called **vertebrates.** Vertebrates include mammals, amphibians, reptiles, birds, and fish. They have skulls that enclose and protect a brain, advanced nervous systems, and muscles. These features allow vertebrates to move efficiently and in complex ways. Vertebrates have tremendous advantages when competing for resources in the natural world. Internal processes and external behaviors help vertebrates maintain homeostasis in a variety of environmental conditions.

Water Balance Why do mammals, like the animals in **Figure 7,** feel thirsty? Thirst is one strategy for maintaining homeostasis in body chemistry. Normal body function can cause cells to lose water, resulting in dehydration. In dehydrated cells, the balance between sodium and water is disrupted. How does the body respond to this imbalance?

When an animal is dehydrated, receptor cells in the brain detect an increase in the amount of sodium compared to water. These cells trigger another part of the brain to send a signal to the pituitary gland. The pituitary gland releases a substance that causes the kidneys to slow the production of urine. At the same time, a thirst drive is created in the brain. Thirst causes the animal to drink fluid, restoring the balance between sodium and water.

Hibernation Many vertebrates live in regions where temperature and food availability vary greatly over time. American red squirrels are ground squirrels that inhabit evergreen forests in North America. They survive the cold winter months by **hibernating.**

Environmental stimuli, including changes in the hours of daylight and a decreasing food supply, trigger specific responses in these squirrels. Before hibernating, a ground squirrel eats more food. It also gathers and stores food in its den. Once the squirrel enters its den for the winter, physical changes occur. Its body temperature lowers until it is slightly above the outside temperature. Breathing and heart rate slow greatly. During hibernation, the squirrel's heart will beat only a few times each minute. Because the amount of energy required to sustain life functions is reduced, the squirrel can maintain homeostasis during extreme environmental conditions.

Estivation A process similar to hibernation, **estivation** occurs in some organisms that live in hot, dry regions. Snakes are **ectotherms,** organisms that regulate body temperature by moving to warmer or cooler places as necessary. During long periods of hot, dry weather, a snake might estivate. A snake may seek shelter under a bush or rock. As the snake's body cools, its breathing and heart rate slow down. With greatly reduced energy requirements, the snake can survive long periods with relatively little food or water.

Thermal Regulation Vertebrates known as **endotherms** maintain a steady body temperature regardless of the surrounding environment. How does this happen? When an endotherm's body temperature changes, specialized receptors alert the brain, which sends the body into action. When an endotherm loses thermal energy, the brain triggers muscle contractions that cause the animal to shiver. Shivering releases thermal energy that increases the organism's body temperature. When an endotherm's body temperature rises above a certain level, responses may include panting or sweating, actions that cool the animal through evaporation.

Metabolic Control What bird beats its wings between 60 and 80 times each second during normal flight? If you guessed the hummingbird, you are right. A hummingbird needs a lot of energy to fly. To maintain an energy balance, the hummingbird must take in at least as many calories in food as it uses through its life functions.

A hummingbird spends much of its life gathering food to meet its energy needs. It may eat up to 50 percent of its weight in sugar each day from nectar and tree sap. Insects eaten by hummingbirds provide the protein needed for muscle growth. But, how does a hummingbird meet its energy needs when the weather is too cold for feeding? It may enter a sleeplike state called **torpor,** during which both body temperature and heart rate decrease. As the hummingbird comes out of torpor, its heart rate and breathing increase, and it begins vibrating its wings. This vibration uses stored energy and releases thermal energy, warming the hummingbird's body.

Homeostasis in Plants

As the basis for most food chains on Earth, **plants** are crucial to the survival of Earth's inhabitants. Plants help regulate climates, stabilize soil, and produce oxygen as a by-product of their life processes. From single-celled phytoplankton floating in the ocean, to moss covering a stony slope in Antarctica, to a giant sequoia towering 100 meters above the forest floor, plants display unique adaptations that allow them to thrive nearly everywhere on Earth.

What characteristics do plants share? Most have roots or rootlike structures that help anchor them to a surface. Many plants contain **chlorophyll,** and most are green due to the presence of this chemical in their cells. Chlorophyll absorbs sunlight and is necessary for **photosynthesis.** Plant cells are bound by a **cell wall,** and though their water requirements vary greatly, all plants need water. Like animals, plants must maintain homeostasis to survive.

Maintaining Water Balance Have you ever been asked to water a plant? If so, you know that a plant can appear quite different before and after watering. Deprived of sufficient amounts of water, a plant will die. Likewise, a plant can also die if it receives more water than it needs. Because survival depends on a healthy water balance, plant adaptations enable the storage of water and release of water to the air.

Activity

Observing Homeostasis in *Elodea*

Procedure

1. Using **forceps,** remove **one leaf** from near the tip of the *Elodea* plant.
2. Prepare a wet mount of this leaf using **tap water, a slide,** and **a coverslip.** If you need help, see page 679.
3. Examine your wet-mount slide under the **microscope** on low and then high power. Draw what you observe on high power in your Science Journal. Label the cell wall, cell membrane, and chloroplasts.
4. Remove the slide from the stage of the microscope. Touch the edge of the coverslip with a **paper towel.** Absorb as much water as possible.
5. Use a **dropper** and place one or two drops of the **salt solution** next to the edge of the coverslip.
6. Wait two minutes, then examine your wet-mount slide under the microscope on low and then high power. Draw what you observe in your Science Journal.
7. Repeat step 4.
8. Place one or two drops of **distilled water** next to the edge of the coverslip.
9. Repeat step 6.

Analysis

1. Compare and contrast the positions of the chloroplasts in step 3 with what you observed in step 5.
2. Describe how the distilled water affected the cells.
3. Explain how a plant cell's semi-permeable cell membrane helps maintain homeostasis.

Vacuoles are cell organelles that store materials needed for plant growth, including salts, minerals, and nutrients. Under optimal conditions, vacuoles are filled with water and exert pressure against the cell wall. This helps the plant to remain rigid. When water is lost, vacuoles shrink. Because vacuoles can no longer assist the cell wall in its support role, the plant begins to wilt.

How does a plant maintain homeostasis during dry conditions? Water escapes from a plant through **stomata,** microscopic openings in plant leaves through which gases travel into and out of plant cells. Two **guard cells** surround each stoma and regulate its size. As water moves into these guard cells, they swell and bend apart. This opens the stoma and allows carbon dioxide, water vapor, and waste gases to move into and out of the plant. When guard cells lose water, they deflate and the stoma closes. This limits the plant's water loss. **Figure 8** shows closed and open stomata.

Figure 8 Stomata act as doorways for raw materials, such as carbon dioxide, water vapor, and waste gases to enter and exit the leaf.

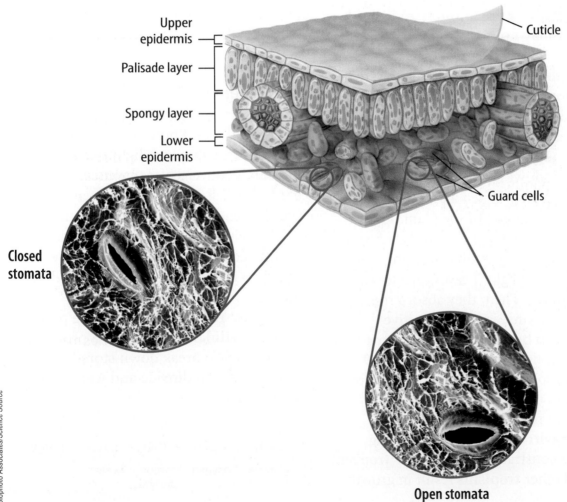

Upper epidermis

Palisade layer

Spongy layer

Lower epidermis

Cuticle

Guard cells

Closed stomata

Open stomata

Figure 9 Tropisms are responses to external stimuli.

This plant is growing toward the light, an example of positive phototropism.

This plant was turned on its side. With the roots visible, you can see that they are showing positive gravitropism.

Responding to Environmental Stimuli

While they may not be able to move in the way animals do, plants can respond to conditions in the environment through movement. Plant movements help them maintain homeostasis related to factors like gravity and the availability of light.

Have you ever seen a plant leaning toward a window? Light is an important stimulus to plants. When a plant responds to light, cells on the side of the plant opposite the light become longer than cells facing the light. This uneven growth causes the plant to bend toward the light. Leaves turn toward the light source. Then, they absorb more light. This response is called **positive phototropism** because the plant's movement is toward the light, as shown in **Figure 9.**

Plants also respond to gravity. The downward growth of plant roots, as shown in **Figure 9,** is a response to gravity called **positive gravitropism.** A stem growing upward demonstrates **negative gravitropism.** These and other **tropisms** result in growth patterns in response to environmental conditions. Plants also respond to temperature and darkness.

Supplying Energy for Seeds Plants make sugars using light energy through **photosynthesis**. Photosynthesis is the process through which light energy from the Sun is converted to chemical energy for use by the cell. In this reaction, autotrophs use light energy, carbon dioxide, and water to form glucose and oxygen. The plant's energy requirements are balanced by its ability to produce, store, and break down these sugars.

A plant releases energy for life processes through **cellular respiration,** a process that uses oxygen to break down stored sugars, produce carbon dioxide and water, and release energy.

$$C_6H_{12}O_6 + 6O_2 \rightarrow 6CO_2 + 6H_2O + energy$$

glucose   oxygen   carbon   water
                                      dioxide

Matt Meadows

Figure 10 Seed germination results in a new plant.

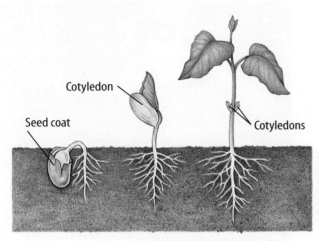

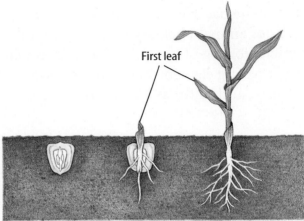

Dormancy What about seeds? While seeds perform a critical function in some plants' life cycles, they cannot transform light energy in the same way the parent plant can. Instead, seeds rely on stored energy reserves to survive. After a seed drops from a plant, it usually enters a resting period called **dormancy.** During dormancy, the seed's chemical activities are low. This means the seed uses stored energy reserves slowly and maintains homeostasis. Because seeds and nuts contain large reserves of food, they can survive long periods of dormancy.

Germination Specific environmental stimuli, including factors such as the breakdown of the seed coat, changes in soil temperature and moisture, and changes in light, trigger seed **germination.** As a seed emerges from dormancy and begins to germinate, its energy needs greatly increase. Cellular respiration increases to meet these needs. As shown in **Figure 10,** seeds emerging from dormancy respire at a much higher rate, using stored food faster to meet the increased energy demand.

Homeostasis in Fungi, Bacteria, and Protists

Unlike plants, **fungi** do not have chlorophyll and cannot produce their own food. What is their energy supply? A fungus releases enzymes into the organic matter in its environment. These enzymes break down the material, which is then absorbed into fungal cells.

Spore Survival Fungi reproduction usually involves the production of **spores,** which are reproductive cells that can grow into a new fungus. Spores can survive in conditions where the parent might not. The spore cells of some fungi are surrounded by thick, tough cell walls. These cells are waterproof and can survive long periods of unfavorable conditions including freezing, lack of food, and dry conditions.

Bacteria Like fungi, **bacteria** are decomposers. **Decomposers** break down chemical elements inside other living or dead organisms. Some bacteria live in the intestinal tracks of animals, helping decompose food particles for digestion. Other bacteria live in soil, recycling elements including carbon, nitrogen, and sulfur as they decompose matter.

Dormancy in Bacteria The environmental conditions that a bacterium requires for growth differs with each species. In response to unfavorable environmental conditions, some bacteria can produce thick-walled structures called **endospores.** An endospore contains the DNA of the original bacterium. While in dormancy, endospores require no food and are resistant to ultraviolet radiation, drying out, and temperature extremes. Endospores can exist for hundreds of years before they begin growing again. When environmental conditions improve, endospores emerge from dormancy. Metabolism resumes, and these structures develop into bacterial cells.

Figure 11 Most slime molds are found on decaying logs or dead leaves in moist, cool, shady environments.

Protists The **protist** kingdom includes both unicellular and multicellular organisms. Protists have one or more **eukaryotic** cells, which contain a nucleus and other membrane-bound organelles. Organisms in this kingdom can be classified based on how they obtain energy.

Some protists, like the slime mold shown in **Figure 11,** are similar to fungi. They produce spores and cannot make their own food. Plantlike protists, like green algae, contain chlorophyll and have the ability to make their own food using light energy.

Paulian Lenting-Smulders/Getty Images

Figure 12 Paramecium are found in many freshwater environments. These rapidly swimming protists consume bacteria.

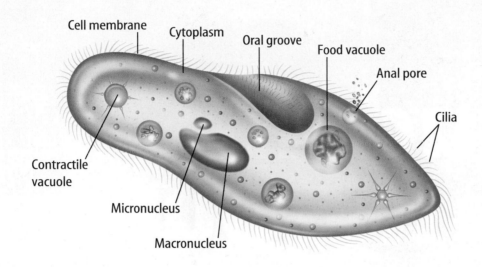

Cell membrane · Cytoplasm · Oral groove · Food vacuole · Anal pore · Cilia · Contractile vacuole · Micronucleus · Macronucleus

Water Regulation in Protists

Surrounded by a watery environment, a protist must maintain a balance of fluid in its cells. Excess water in an organism could cause the cell to burst, resulting in death. An organelle called the **contractile vacuole** helps some protists maintain homeostasis. The contractile vacuole collects and stores extra water in the cell. When the vacuole contracts, excess water is ejected from the cell into the surrounding environment. The vacuole can then fill again. By pumping water out of the organism as needed, fluid pressure inside the organism remains balanced and homeostasis is maintained.

Importance of Homeostasis

The survival of every organism, from the simplest protozoan to the most complex vertebrate, depends on its ability to successfully respond to changes in its environment. If an organism cannot maintain stable, balanced internal conditions, it will suffer damage or death. Organisms monitor internal and external environmental factors constantly and make specific adjustments that allow body processes to remain in equilibrium. This dynamic interaction among body systems makes homeostasis, and survival, possible.

Student Resources

For Students and Parents/Guardians

These resources are designed to help you achieve success in science. You will find useful information on laboratory safety, math skills, and science skills. In addition, science reference materials are found in the Reference Handbook. You'll find the information you need to learn and sharpen your skills in these resources.

Table of Contents

(bkgd)Gallo Images - Neil Overy/Getty Images

Scientific Methods

Scientists use an orderly approach called the scientific method to solve problems. This includes organizing and recording data so others can understand them. Scientists use many variations in this method when they solve problems.

Identify a Question

The first step in a scientific investigation or experiment is to identify a question to be answered or a problem to be solved. For example, you might ask which gasoline is the most efficient.

Gather and Organize Information

After you have identified your question, begin gathering and organizing information. There are many ways to gather information, such as researching in a library, interviewing those knowledgeable about the subject, and testing and working in the laboratory and field. Fieldwork is investigations and observations done outside of a laboratory.

Researching Information Before moving in a new direction, it is important to gather the information that already is known about the subject. Start by asking yourself questions to determine exactly what you need to know. Then you will look for the information in various reference sources, like the student is doing in **Figure 1.** Some sources may include textbooks, encyclopedias, government documents, professional journals, science magazines, and the Internet. Always list the sources of your information.

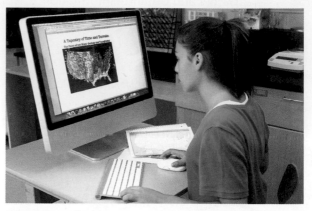

Figure 1 The Internet can be a valuable research tool.

Evaluate Sources of Information Not all sources of information are reliable. You should evaluate all of your sources of information, and use only those you know to be dependable. For example, if you are researching ways to make homes more energy efficient, a site written by the U.S. Department of Energy would be more reliable than a site written by a company that is trying to sell a new type of weatherproofing material. Also, remember that research always is changing. Consult the most current resources available to you. For example, a 1985 resource about saving energy would not reflect the most recent findings.

Sometimes scientists use data that they did not collect themselves, or conclusions drawn by other researchers. This data must be evaluated carefully. Ask questions about how the data were obtained, if the investigation was carried out properly, and if it has been duplicated exactly with the same results. Would you reach the same conclusion from the data? Only when you have confidence in the data can you believe it is true and feel comfortable using it.

SCIENCE SKILL HANDBOOK

MATH SKILL HANDBOOK

FOLDABLES HANDBOOK

REFERENCE HANDBOOK

GLOSSARY/ GLOSARIO

INDEX

Interpret Scientific Illustrations As you research a topic in science, you will see drawings, diagrams, and photographs to help you understand what you read. Some illustrations are included to help you understand an idea that you can't see easily by yourself, like the tiny particles in an atom in **Figure 2.** A drawing helps many people to remember details more easily and provides examples that clarify difficult concepts or give additional information about the topic you are studying. Most illustrations have labels or a caption to identify or to provide more information.

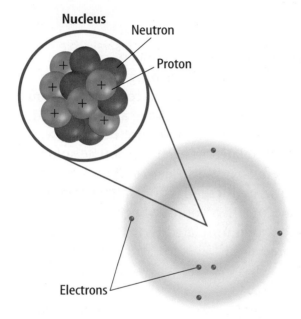

Figure 2 This drawing shows an atom of carbon with its six protons, six neutrons, and six electrons.

Concept Maps One way to organize data is to draw a diagram that shows relationships among ideas (or concepts). A concept map can help make the meanings of ideas and terms more clear, and help you understand and remember what you are studying. Concept maps are useful for breaking large concepts down into smaller parts, making learning easier.

Network Tree A type of concept map that not only shows a relationship, but how the concepts are related is a network tree, shown in **Figure 3.** In a network tree, the words are written in the ovals, while the description of the type of relationship is written across the connecting lines.

When constructing a network tree, write down the topic and all major topics on separate pieces of paper or notecards. Then arrange them in order from general to specific. Branch the related concepts from the major concept and describe the relationship on the connecting line. Continue to more specific concepts until finished.

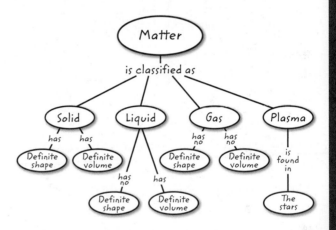

Figure 3 A network tree shows how concepts or objects are related.

Events Chain Another type of concept map is an events chain. Sometimes called a flow chart, it models the order or sequence of items. An events chain can be used to describe a sequence of events, the steps in a procedure, or the stages of a process.

When making an events chain, first find the one event that starts the chain. This event is called the initiating event. Then, find the next event and continue until the outcome is reached, as shown in **Figure 4** on the next page.

SCIENCE SKILL HANDBOOK

MATH SKILL HANDBOOK

FOLDABLES HANDBOOK

REFERENCE HANDBOOK

GLOSSARY/ GLOSARIO

INDEX

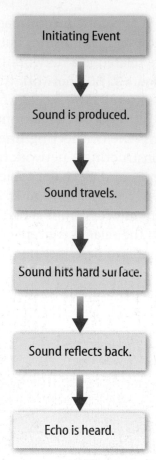

Figure 4 Events-chain concept maps show the order of steps in a process or event. This concept map shows how a sound makes an echo.

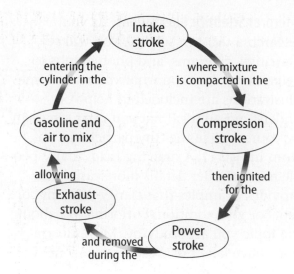

Figure 5 A cycle map shows events that occur in a cycle.

Spider Map A type of concept map that you can use for brainstorming is the spider map. When you have a central idea, you might find that you have a jumble of ideas that relate to it but are not necessarily clearly related to each other. The spider map on sound in **Figure 6** shows that if you write these ideas outside the main concept, then you can begin to separate and group unrelated terms so they become more useful.

Cycle Map A specific type of events chain is a cycle map. It is used when the series of events do not produce a final outcome, but instead relate back to the beginning event, such as in **Figure 5.** Therefore, the cycle repeats itself.

To make a cycle map, first decide what event is the beginning event. This is also called the initiating event. Then list the next events in the order that they occur, with the last event relating back to the initiating event. Words can be written between the events that describe what happens from one event to the next. The number of events in a cycle map can vary, but usually contain three or more events.

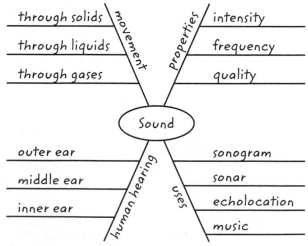

Figure 6 A spider map allows you to list ideas that relate to a central topic but not necessarily to one another.

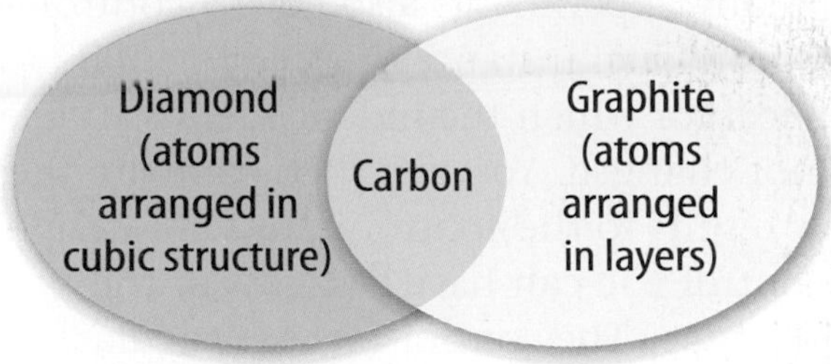

Figure 7 This Venn diagram compares and contrasts two substances made from carbon.

Venn Diagram To illustrate how two subjects compare and contrast you can use a Venn diagram. You can see the characteristics that the subjects have in common and those that they do not, shown in **Figure 7.**

To create a Venn diagram, draw two overlapping ovals that are big enough to write in. List the characteristics unique to one subject in one oval, and the characteristics of the other subject in the other oval. The characteristics in common are listed in the overlapping section.

Make and Use Tables One way to organize information so it is easier to understand is to use a table. Tables can contain numbers, words, or both.

To make a table, list the items to be compared in the first column and the characteristics to be compared in the first row. The title should clearly indicate the content of the table, and the column or row heads should be clear. Notice that in **Table 1** the units are included.

Table 1 Recyclables Collected During Week			
Day of Week	Paper (kg)	Aluminum (kg)	Glass (kg)
Monday	5.0	4.0	12.0
Wednesday	4.0	1.0	10.0
Friday	2.5	2.0	10.0

Make a Model One way to help you better understand the parts of a structure, the way a process works, or to show things too large or small for viewing is to make a model. For example, an atomic model made of a plastic-ball nucleus and chenille stem electron shells can help you visualize how the parts of an atom relate to each other. Other types of models can be devised on a computer or represented by equations.

Form a Hypothesis

A possible explanation based on previous knowledge and observations is called a hypothesis. After researching gasoline types and recalling previous experiences in your family's car you form a hypothesis—our car runs more efficiently because we use premium gasoline. To be valid, a hypothesis has to be something you can test by using an investigation.

Predict When you apply a hypothesis to a specific situation, you predict something about that situation. A prediction makes a statement in advance, based on prior observation, experience, or scientific reasoning. People use predictions to make everyday decisions. Scientists test predictions by performing investigations. Based on previous observations and experiences, you might form a prediction that cars are more efficient with premium gasoline. The prediction can be tested in an investigation.

Design an Experiment A scientist needs to make many decisions before beginning an investigation. Some of these include: how to carry out the investigation, what steps to follow, how to record the data, and how the investigation will answer the question. It also is important to address any safety concerns.

SCIENCE SKILL HANDBOOK

MATH SKILL HANDBOOK

FOLDABLES HANDBOOK

REFERENCE HANDBOOK

GLOSSARY/ GLOSARIO

INDEX

Test the Hypothesis

Now that you have formed your hypothesis, you need to test it. Using an investigation, you will make observations and collect data, or information. This data might either support or not support your hypothesis. Scientists collect and organize data as numbers and descriptions.

Follow a Procedure In order to know what materials to use, as well as how and in what order to use them, you must follow a procedure. **Figure 8** shows a procedure you might follow to test your hypothesis.

Procedure

Step 1	Use regular gasoline for two weeks.
Step 2	Record the number of kilometers between fill-ups and the amount of gasoline used.
Step 3	Switch to premium gasoline for two weeks.
Step 4	Record the number of kilometers between fill-ups and the amount of gasoline used.

Figure 8 A procedure tells you what to do step-by-step.

Identify and Manipulate Variables and Controls

In any experiment, it is important to keep everything the same except for the item you are testing. The one factor you change is called the independent variable. The change that results is the dependent variable. Make sure you have only one independent variable, to assure yourself of the cause of the changes you observe in the dependent variable. For example, in your gasoline experiment the type of fuel is the independent variable. The dependent variable is the efficiency.

Many experiments also have a control—an individual instance or experimental subject for which the independent variable is not changed. You can then compare the test results to the control results. To design a control you can have two cars of the same type. The control car uses regular gasoline for four weeks. After you are done with the test, you can compare the experimental results to the control results.

Collect Data

Whether you are carrying out an investigation or a short observational experiment, you will collect data, as shown in **Figure 9.** Scientists collect data as numbers and descriptions and organize them in specific ways.

Observe Scientists observe items and events, then record what they see. When they use only words to describe an observation, it is called qualitative data. Scientists' observations also can describe how much there is of something. These observations use numbers, as well as words, in the description and are called quantitative data. For example, if a sample of the element gold is described as being "shiny and very dense" the data are qualitative. Quantitative data on this sample of gold might include "a mass of 30 g and a density of 19.3 g/cm^3."

Figure 9 Collecting data is one way to gather information directly.

Michell D. Bridwell/PhotoEdit

Figure 10 Record data neatly and clearly so it is easy to understand.

When you make observations you should examine the entire object or situation first, and then look carefully for details. It is important to record observations accurately and completely. Always record your notes immediately as you make them, so you do not miss details or make a mistake when recording results from memory. Never put unidentified observations on scraps of paper. Instead they should be recorded in a notebook, like the one in **Figure 10.** Write your data neatly so you can easily read it later. At each point in the experiment, record your observations and label them. That way, you will not have to determine what the figures mean when you look at your notes later. Set up any tables that you will need to use ahead of time, so you can record any observations right away. Remember to avoid bias when collecting data by not including personal thoughts when you record observations. Record only what you observe.

Estimate Scientific work also involves estimating. To estimate is to make a judgment about the size or the number of something without measuring or counting. This is important when the number or size of an object or population is too large or too difficult to accurately count or measure.

Sample Scientists may use a sample or a portion of the total number as a type of estimation. To sample is to take a small, representative portion of the objects or organisms of a population for research. By making careful observations or manipulating variables within that portion of the group, information is discovered and conclusions are drawn that might apply to the whole population. A poorly chosen sample can be unrepresentative of the whole. If you were trying to determine the rainfall in an area, it would not be best to take a rainfall sample from under a tree.

Measure You use measurements every day. Scientists also take measurements when collecting data. When taking measurements, it is important to know how to use measuring tools properly. Accuracy also is important.

Length To measure length, the distance between two points, scientists use meters. Smaller measurements might be measured in centimeters or millimeters.

Length is measured using a metric ruler or meterstick. When using a metric ruler, line up the 0-cm mark with the end of the object being measured and read the number of the unit where the object ends. Look at the metric ruler shown in **Figure 11.** The centimeter lines are the long, numbered lines, and the shorter lines are millimeter lines. In this instance, the length would be 4.50 cm.

Figure 11 This metric ruler has centimeter and millimeter divisions.

SCIENCE SKILL HANDBOOK
MATH SKILL HANDBOOK
FOLDABLES HANDBOOK
REFERENCE HANDBOOK
GLOSSARY/ GLOSARIO
INDEX

SCIENCE SKILL HANDBOOK

MATH SKILL HANDBOOK

FOLDABLES HANDBOOK

REFERENCE HANDBOOK

GLOSSARY/ GLOSARIO

INDEX

Mass The SI unit for mass is the kilogram (kg). Scientists can measure mass using units formed by adding metric prefixes to the unit gram (g), such as milligram (mg). To measure mass, you might use a triple-beam balance similar to the one shown in **Figure 12.** The balance has a pan on one side and a set of beams on the other side. Each beam has a rider that slides on the beam.

When using a triple-beam balance, place an object on the pan. Slide the largest rider along its beam until the pointer drops below zero. Then move it back one notch. Repeat the process for each rider proceeding from the larger to smaller until the pointer swings an equal distance above and below the zero point. Sum the masses on each beam to find the mass of the object. Move all riders back to zero when finished.

Instead of putting materials directly on the balance, scientists often take a tare of a container. A tare is the mass of a container into which objects or substances are placed for measuring their masses. To find the mass of objects or substances, find the mass of a clean container. Remove the container from the pan, and place the object or substances in the container. Find the mass of the container with the materials in it. Subtract the mass of the empty container from the mass of the filled container to find the mass of the materials you are using.

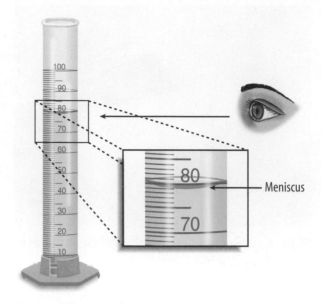

Figure 13 Graduated cylinders measure liquid volume.

Liquid Volume To measure liquids, the unit used is the liter. When a smaller unit is needed, scientists might use a milliliter. Because a milliliter takes up the volume of a cube measuring 1 cm on each side it also can be called a cubic centimeter ($cm^3 = cm \times cm \times cm$).

You can use beakers and graduated cylinders to measure liquid volume. A graduated cylinder, shown in **Figure 13,** is marked from bottom to top in milliliters. In lab, you might use a 10-mL graduated cylinder or a 100-mL graduated cylinder. When measuring liquids, notice that the liquid has a curved surface. Look at the surface at eye level, and measure the bottom of the curve. This is called the meniscus. The graduated cylinder in **Figure 13** contains 79.0 mL, or 79.0 cm^3, of a liquid.

Temperature Scientists often measure temperature using the Celsius scale. Pure water has a freezing point of 0°C and boiling point of 100°C. The unit of measurement is degrees Celsius. Two other scales often used are the Fahrenheit and Kelvin scales.

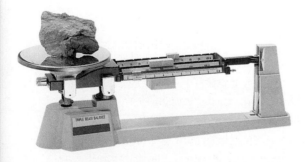

Figure 12 A triple-beam balance is used to determine the mass of an object.

StudiOhio

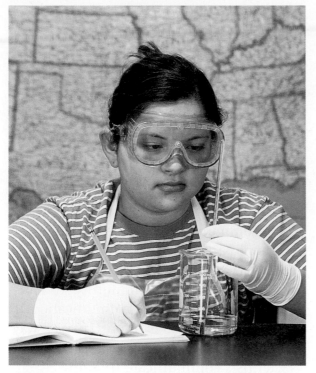

Figure 14 A thermometer measures the temperature of an object.

Scientists use a thermometer to measure temperature. Most thermometers in a laboratory are glass tubes with a bulb at the bottom end containing a liquid such as colored alcohol. The liquid rises or falls with a change in temperature. To read a glass thermometer like the thermometer in **Figure 14,** rotate it slowly until a red line appears. Read the temperature where the red line ends.

Form Operational Definitions An operational definition defines an object by how it functions, works, or behaves. For example, when you are playing hide and seek and a tree is home base, you have created an operational definition for a tree.

Objects can have more than one operational definition. For example, a ruler can be defined as a tool that measures the length of an object (how it is used). It can also be a tool with a series of marks used as a standard when measuring (how it works).

Analyze the Data

To determine the meaning of your observations and investigation results, you will need to look for patterns in the data. Then you must think critically to determine what the data mean. Scientists use several approaches when they analyze the data they have collected and recorded. Each approach is useful for identifying specific patterns.

Interpret Data The word *interpret* means "to explain the meaning of something." When analyzing data from an experiment, try to find out what the data show. Identify the control group and the test group to see whether changes in the independent variable have had an effect. Look for differences in the dependent variable between the control and test groups.

Classify Sorting objects or events into groups based on common features is called classifying. When classifying, first observe the objects or events to be classified. Then select one feature that is shared by some members in the group, but not by all. Place those members that share that feature in a subgroup. You can classify members into smaller and smaller subgroups based on characteristics. Remember that when you classify, you are grouping objects or events for a purpose. Keep your purpose in mind as you select the features to form groups and subgroups.

Compare and Contrast Observations can be analyzed by noting the similarities and differences between two or more objects or events that you observe. When you look at objects or events to see how they are similar, you are comparing them. Contrasting is looking for differences in objects or events.

SCIENCE SKILL HANDBOOK

MATH SKILL HANDBOOK

FOLDABLES HANDBOOK

REFERENCE HANDBOOK

GLOSSARY/ GLOSARIO

INDEX

SCIENCE SKILL HANDBOOK

MATH SKILL HANDBOOK

FOLDABLES HANDBOOK

REFERENCE HANDBOOK

GLOSSARY/ GLOSARIO

INDEX

Recognize Cause and Effect A cause is a reason for an action or condition. The effect is that action or condition. When two events happen together, it is not necessarily true that one event caused the other. Scientists must design a controlled investigation to recognize the exact cause and effect.

Draw Conclusions

When scientists have analyzed the data they collected, they proceed to draw conclusions about the data. These conclusions are sometimes stated in words similar to the hypothesis that you formed earlier. They may confirm a hypothesis, or lead you to a new hypothesis.

Infer Scientists often make inferences based on their observations. An inference is an attempt to explain observations or to indicate a cause. An inference is not a fact, but a logical conclusion that needs further investigation. For example, you may infer that a fire has caused smoke. Until you investigate, however, you do not know for sure.

Apply When you draw a conclusion, you must apply those conclusions to determine whether the data supports the hypothesis. If your data do not support your hypothesis, it does not mean that the hypothesis is wrong. It means only that the result of the investigation did not support the hypothesis. Maybe the experiment needs to be redesigned, or some of the initial observations on which the hypothesis was based were incomplete or biased. Perhaps more observation or research is needed to refine your hypothesis. A successful investigation does not always come out the way you originally predicted.

Avoid Bias Sometimes a scientific investigation involves making judgments. When you make a judgment, you form an opinion. It is important to be honest and not to allow any expectations of results to bias your judgments. This is important throughout the entire investigation, from researching to collecting data to drawing conclusions.

Communicate

The communication of ideas is an important part of the work of scientists. A discovery that is not reported will not advance the scientific community's understanding or knowledge. Communication among scientists also is important as a way of improving their investigations.

Scientists communicate in many ways, from writing articles in journals and magazines that explain their investigations and experiments, to announcing important discoveries on television and radio. Scientists also share ideas with colleagues on the Internet or present them as lectures, like the student is doing in **Figure 15.**

Figure 15 A student communicates to his peers about his investigation.

These safety symbols are used in laboratory and field investigations in this book to indicate possible hazards. Learn the meaning of each symbol and refer to this page often. *Remember to wash your hands thoroughly after completing lab procedures.*

PROTECTIVE EQUIPMENT
Do not begin any lab without the proper protection equipment.

 GOGGLES Proper eye protection must be worn when performing or observing science activities that involve items or conditions as listed below.

 APRON Wear an approved apron when using substances that could stain, wet, or destroy cloth.

 SOAP Wash hands with soap and water before removing goggles and after all lab activities.

 GLOVES Wear gloves when working with biological materials, chemicals, animals, or materials that can stain or irritate hands.

LABORATORY HAZARDS

Symbols	Potential Hazards	Precaution	Response
DISPOSAL	contamination of classroom or environment due to improper disposal of materials such as chemicals and live specimens	• DO NOT dispose of hazardous materials in the sink or trash can. • Dispose of wastes as directed by your teacher.	• If hazardous materials are disposed of improperly, notify your teacher immediately.
EXTREME TEMPERATURE	skin burns due to extremely hot or cold materials such as hot glass, liquids, or metals; liquid nitrogen; dry ice	• Use proper protective equipment, such as hot mitts and/or tongs, when handling objects with extreme temperatures.	• If injury occurs, notify your teacher immediately.
SHARP OBJECTS	punctures or cuts from sharp objects such as razor blades, pins, scalpels, and broken glass	• Handle glassware carefully to avoid breakage. • Walk with sharp objects pointed downward, away from you and others.	• If broken glass or injury occurs, notify your teacher immediately.
ELECTRICAL	electric shock or skin burn due to improper grounding, short circuits, liquid spills, or exposed wires	• Check condition of wires and apparatus for fraying or uninsulated wires, and broken or cracked equipment. • Use only GFCI-protected outlets	• DO NOT attempt to fix electrical problems. Notify your teacher immediately.
CHEMICAL	skin irritation or burns, breathing difficulty, and/or poisoning due to touching, swallowing, or inhalation of chemicals such as acids, bases, bleach, metal compounds, iodine, poinsettias, pollen, ammonia, acetone, nail polish remover, heated chemicals, mothballs, and any other chemicals labeled or known to be dangerous	• Wear proper protective equipment such as goggles, apron, and gloves when using chemicals. • Ensure proper room ventilation or use a fume hood when using materials that produce fumes. • NEVER smell fumes directly. • NEVER taste or eat any material in the laboratory.	• If contact occurs, immediately flush affected area with water and notify your teacher. • If a spill occurs, leave the area immediately and notify your teacher.
FLAMMABLE	unexpected fire due to liquids or gases that ignite easily such as rubbing alcohol	• Avoid open flames, sparks, or heat when flammable liquids are present.	• If a fire occurs, leave the area immediately and notify your teacher.
OPEN FLAME	burns or fire due to open flame from matches, Bunsen burners, or burning materials	• Tie back loose hair and clothing. • Keep flame away from all materials. • Follow teacher instructions when lighting and extinguishing flames. • Use proper protection, such as hot mitts or tongs, when handling hot objects.	• If a fire occurs, leave the area immediately and notify your teacher.
ANIMAL SAFETY	injury to or from laboratory animals	• Wear proper protective equipment such as gloves, apron, and goggles when working with animals. • Wash hands after handling animals.	• If injury occurs, notify your teacher immediately.
BIOLOGICAL	infection or adverse reaction due to contact with organisms such as bacteria, fungi, and biological materials such as blood, animal or plant materials	• Wear proper protective equipment such as gloves, goggles, and apron when working with biological materials. • Avoid skin contact with an organism or any part of the organism. • Wash hands after handling organisms.	• If contact occurs, wash the affected area and notify your teacher immediately.
FUME	breathing difficulties from inhalation of fumes from substances such as ammonia, acetone, nail polish remover, heated chemicals, and mothballs	• Wear goggles, apron, and gloves. • Ensure proper room ventilation or use a fume hood when using substances that produce fumes. • NEVER smell fumes directly.	• If a spill occurs, leave area and notify your teacher immediately.
IRRITANT	irritation of skin, mucous membranes, or respiratory tract due to materials such as acids, bases, bleach, pollen, mothballs, steel wool, and potassium permanganate	• Wear goggles, apron, and gloves. • Wear a dust mask to protect against fine particles.	• If skin contact occurs, immediately flush the affected area with water and notify your teacher.
RADIOACTIVE	excessive exposure from alpha, beta, and gamma particles	• Remove gloves and wash hands with soap and water before removing remainder of protective equipment.	• If cracks or holes are found in the container, notify your teacher immediately.

SCIENCE SKILL HANDBOOK

MATH SKILL HANDBOOK

FOLDABLES HANDBOOK

REFERENCE HANDBOOK

GLOSSARY/GLOSARIO

INDEX

Safety in the Science Laboratory

Introduction to Science Safety

The science laboratory is a safe place to work if you follow standard safety procedures. Being responsible for your own safety helps to make the entire laboratory a safer place for everyone. When performing any lab, read and apply the caution statements and safety symbol listed at the beginning of the lab.

General Safety Rules

1. Complete the *Lab Safety Form* or other safety contract BEFORE starting any science lab.

2. Study the procedure. Ask your teacher any questions. Be sure you understand safety symbols shown on the page.

3. Notify your teacher about allergies or other health conditions that can affect your participation in a lab.

4. Learn and follow use and safety procedures for your equipment. If unsure, ask your teacher.

5. Never eat, drink, chew gum, apply cosmetics, or do any personal grooming in the lab. Never use lab glassware as food or drink containers. Keep your hands away from your face and mouth.

6. Know the location and proper use of the safety shower, eye wash, fire blanket, and fire alarm.

Prevent Accidents

1. Use the safety equipment provided to you. Goggles and a safety apron should be worn during investigations.

2. Do NOT use hair spray, mousse, or other flammable hair products. Tie back long hair and tie down loose clothing.

3. Do NOT wear sandals or other open-toed shoes in the lab.

4. Remove jewelry on hands and wrists. Loose jewelry, such as chains and long necklaces, should be removed to prevent them from getting caught in equipment.

5. Do not taste any substances or draw any material into a tube with your mouth.

6. Proper behavior is expected in the lab. Practical jokes and fooling around can lead to accidents and injury.

7. Keep your work area uncluttered.

Laboratory Work

1. Collect and carry all equipment and materials to your work area before beginning a lab.

2. Remain in your own work area unless given permission by your teacher to leave it.

SCIENCE SKILL HANDBOOK

MATH SKILL HANDBOOK

FOLDABLES HANDBOOK

REFERENCE HANDBOOK

GLOSSARY/ GLOSARIO

INDEX

3. Always slant test tubes away from yourself and others when heating them, adding substances to them, or rinsing them.

4. If instructed to smell a substance in a container, hold the container a short distance away and fan vapors toward your nose.

5. Do NOT substitute other chemicals/substances for those in the materials list unless instructed to do so by your teacher.

6. Do NOT take any materials or chemicals outside of the laboratory.

7. Stay out of storage areas unless instructed to be there and supervised by your teacher.

Laboratory Cleanup

1. Turn off all burners, water, and gas, and disconnect all electrical devices.

2. Clean all pieces of equipment and return all materials to their proper places.

3. Dispose of chemicals and other materials as directed by your teacher. Place broken glass and solid substances in the proper containers. Never discard materials in the sink.

4. Clean your work area.

5. Wash your hands with soap and water thoroughly BEFORE removing your goggles.

Emergencies

1. Report any fire, electrical shock, glassware breakage, spill, or injury, no matter how small, to your teacher immediately. Follow his or her instructions.

2. If your clothing should catch fire, STOP, DROP, and ROLL. If possible, smother it with the fire blanket or get under a safety shower. NEVER RUN.

3. If a fire should occur, turn off all gas and leave the room according to established procedures.

4. In most instances, your teacher will clean up spills. Do NOT attempt to clean up spills unless you are given permission and instructions to do so.

5. If chemicals come into contact with your eyes or skin, notify your teacher immediately. Use the eyewash, or flush your skin or eyes with large quantities of water.

6. The fire extinguisher and first-aid kit should only be used by your teacher unless it is an extreme emergency and you have been given permission.

7. If someone is injured or becomes ill, only a professional medical provider or someone certified in first aid should perform first-aid procedures.

Matt Meadows

SCIENCE SKILL HANDBOOK

MATH SKILL HANDBOOK

FOLDABLES HANDBOOK

REFERENCE HANDBOOK

GLOSSARY/ GLOSARIO

INDEX

Use Fractions

A fraction compares a part to a whole. In the fraction $\frac{2}{3}$, the 2 represents the part and is the numerator. The 3 represents the whole and is the denominator.

Reduce Fractions To reduce a fraction, you must find the largest factor that is common to both the numerator and the denominator, the greatest common factor (GCF). Divide both numbers by the GCF. The fraction has then been reduced, or it is in its simplest form.

Example

Twelve of the 20 chemicals in the science lab are in powder form. What fraction of the chemicals used in the lab are in powder form?

Step 1 Write the fraction.

$$\frac{part}{whole} = \frac{12}{20}$$

Step 2 To find the GCF of the numerator and denominator, list all of the factors of each number.

Factors of 12: 1, 2, 3, 4, 6, 12
(the numbers that divide evenly into 12)

Factors of 20: 1, 2, 4, 5, 10, 20
(the numbers that divide evenly into 20)

Step 3 List the common factors.

1, 2, 4

Step 4 Choose the greatest factor in the list. The GCF of 12 and 20 is 4.

Step 5 Divide the numerator and denominator by the GCF.

$$\frac{12 \div 4}{20 \div 4} = \frac{3}{5}$$

In the lab, $\frac{3}{5}$ of the chemicals are in powder form.

Practice Problem At an amusement park, 66 of 90 rides have a height restriction. What fraction of the rides, in its simplest form, has a height restriction?

Add and Subtract Fractions with Like Denominators To add or subtract fractions with the same denominator, add or subtract the numerators and write the sum or difference over the denominator. After finding the sum or difference, find the simplest form for your fraction.

Example 1

In the forest outside your house, $\frac{1}{8}$ of the animals are rabbits, $\frac{3}{8}$ are squirrels, and the remainder are birds and insects. How many are mammals?

Step 1 Add the numerators.

$$\frac{1}{8} + \frac{3}{8} = \frac{(1 + 3)}{8} = \frac{4}{8}$$

Step 2 Find the GCF.

$$\frac{4}{8} \text{ (GCF, 4)}$$

Step 3 Divide the numerator and denominator by the GCF.

$$\frac{4 \div 4}{8 \div 4} = \frac{1}{2}$$

$\frac{1}{2}$ of the animals are mammals.

Example 2

If $\frac{7}{16}$ of the Earth is covered by freshwater, and $\frac{1}{16}$ of that is in glaciers, how much freshwater is not frozen?

Step 1 Subtract the numerators.

$$\frac{7}{16} - \frac{1}{16} = \frac{(7 - 1)}{16} = \frac{6}{16}$$

Step 2 Find the GCF.

$$\frac{6}{16} \text{ (GCF, 2)}$$

Step 3 Divide the numerator and denominator by the GCF.

$$\frac{6 \div 2}{16 \div 2} = \frac{3}{8}$$

$\frac{3}{8}$ of the freshwater is not frozen.

Practice Problem A bicycle rider is riding at a rate of 15 km/h for $\frac{4}{9}$ of his ride, 10 km/h for $\frac{2}{9}$ of his ride, and 8 km/h for the remainder of the ride. How much of his ride is he riding at a rate greater than 8 km/h?

Add and Subtract Fractions with Unlike Denominators To add or subtract fractions with unlike denominators, first find the least common denominator (LCD). This is the smallest number that is a common multiple of both denominators. Rename each fraction with the LCD, and then add or subtract. Find the simplest form if necessary.

Example 1

A chemist makes a paste that is $\frac{1}{2}$ table salt (NaCl), $\frac{1}{3}$ sugar ($C_6H_{12}O_6$), and the remainder is water (H_2O). How much of the paste is a solid?

Step 1 Find the LCD of the fractions.

$$\frac{1}{2} + \frac{1}{3} \text{ (LCD, 6)}$$

Step 2 Rename each numerator and each denominator with the LCD.

Step 3 Add the numerators.

$$\frac{3}{6} + \frac{2}{6} = \frac{(3+2)}{6} = \frac{5}{6}$$

$\frac{5}{6}$ of the paste is a solid.

Example 2

The average precipitation in Grand Junction, CO, is $\frac{7}{10}$ inch in November, and $\frac{3}{5}$ inch in December. What is the total average precipitation?

Step 1 Find the LCD of the fractions.

$$\frac{7}{10} + \frac{3}{5} \text{ (LCD, 10)}$$

Step 2 Rename each numerator and each denominator with the LCD.

Step 3 Add the numerators.

$$\frac{7}{10} + \frac{6}{10} = \frac{(7+6)}{10} = \frac{13}{10}$$

$\frac{13}{10}$ inches total precipitation, or $1\frac{3}{10}$ inches.

Practice Problem On an electric bill, about $\frac{1}{8}$ of the energy is from solar energy and about $\frac{1}{10}$ is from wind power. How much of the total bill is from solar energy and wind power combined?

Example 3

In your body, $\frac{7}{10}$ of your muscle contractions are involuntary (cardiac and smooth muscle tissue). Smooth muscle makes $\frac{3}{15}$ of your muscle contractions. How many of your muscle contractions are made by cardiac muscle?

Step 1 Find the LCD of the fractions.

$$\frac{7}{10} - \frac{3}{15} \text{ (LCD, 30)}$$

Step 2 Rename each numerator and each denominator with the LCD.

$$\frac{7 \times 3}{10 \times 3} = \frac{21}{30}$$

$$\frac{3 \times 2}{15 \times 2} = \frac{6}{30}$$

Step 3 Subtract the numerators.

$$\frac{21}{30} - \frac{6}{30} = \frac{(21-6)}{30} = \frac{15}{30}$$

Step 4 Find the GCF.

$$\frac{15}{30} \text{ (GCF, 15)}$$

$$\frac{1}{2}$$

$\frac{1}{2}$ of all muscle contractions are cardiac muscle.

Example 4

Tony wants to make cookies that call for $\frac{3}{4}$ of a cup of flour, but he only has $\frac{1}{3}$ of a cup. How much more flour does he need?

Step 1 Find the LCD of the fractions.

$$\frac{3}{4} - \frac{1}{3} \text{ (LCD, 12)}$$

Step 2 Rename each numerator and each denominator with the LCD.

$$\frac{3 \times 3}{4 \times 3} = \frac{9}{12}$$

$$\frac{1 \times 4}{3 \times 4} = \frac{4}{12}$$

Step 3 Subtract the numerators.

$$\frac{9}{12} - \frac{4}{12} = \frac{(9-4)}{12} = \frac{5}{12}$$

$\frac{5}{12}$ of a cup of flour

Practice Problem Using the information provided to you in Example 3 above, determine how many muscle contractions are voluntary (skeletal muscle).

SCIENCE SKILL HANDBOOK

MATH SKILL HANDBOOK

FOLDABLES HANDBOOK

REFERENCE HANDBOOK

GLOSSARY/ GLOSARIO

INDEX

SCIENCE SKILL HANDBOOK

MATH SKILL HANDBOOK

FOLDABLES HANDBOOK

REFERENCE HANDBOOK

GLOSSARY/ GLOSARIO

INDEX

Multiply Fractions To multiply with fractions, multiply the numerators and multiply the denominators. Find the simplest form if necessary.

Example

Multiply $\frac{3}{5}$ by $\frac{1}{3}$.

Step 1 Multiply the numerators and denominators.

$$\frac{3}{5} \times \frac{1}{3} = \frac{(3 \times 1)}{(5 \times 3)} \frac{3}{15}$$

Step 2 Find the GCF.

$$\frac{3}{15} \text{ (GCF, 3)}$$

Step 3 Divide the numerator and denominator by the GCF.

$$\frac{3 \div 3}{15 \div 3} = \frac{1}{5}$$

$\frac{3}{5}$ multiplied by $\frac{1}{3}$ is $\frac{1}{5}$.

Practice Problem Multiply $\frac{3}{14}$ by $\frac{5}{16}$.

Find a Reciprocal Two numbers whose product is 1 are called multiplicative inverses, or reciprocals.

Example

Find the reciprocal of $\frac{3}{8}$.

Step 1 Inverse the fraction by putting the denominator on top and the numerator on the bottom.

$$\frac{8}{3}$$

The reciprocal of $\frac{3}{8}$ is $\frac{8}{3}$.

Practice Problem Find the reciprocal of $\frac{4}{9}$.

Divide Fractions To divide one fraction by another fraction, multiply the dividend by the reciprocal of the divisor. Find the simplest form if necessary.

Example 1

Divide $\frac{1}{9}$ by $\frac{1}{3}$.

Step 1 Find the reciprocal of the divisor.

The reciprocal of $\frac{1}{3}$ is $\frac{3}{1}$.

Step 2 Multiply the dividend by the reciprocal of the divisor.

$$\frac{\frac{1}{9}}{\frac{1}{3}} = \frac{1}{9} \times \frac{3}{1} = \frac{(1 \times 3)}{(9 \times 1)} = \frac{3}{9}$$

Step 3 Find the GCF.

$$\frac{3}{9} \text{ (GCF, 3)}$$

Step 4 Divide the numerator and denominator by the GCF.

$$\frac{3 \div 3}{9 \div 3} = \frac{1}{3}$$

$\frac{1}{9}$ divided by $\frac{1}{3}$ is $\frac{1}{3}$.

Example 2

Divide $\frac{3}{5}$ by $\frac{1}{4}$.

Step 1 Find the reciprocal of the divisor.

The reciprocal of $\frac{1}{4}$ is $\frac{4}{1}$.

Step 2 Multiply the dividend by the reciprocal of the divisor.

$$\frac{\frac{3}{5}}{\frac{1}{4}} = \frac{3}{5} \times \frac{4}{1} = \frac{(3 \times 4)}{(5 \times 1)} = \frac{12}{5}$$

$\frac{3}{5}$ divided by $\frac{1}{4}$ is $\frac{12}{5}$ or $2\frac{2}{5}$.

Practice Problem Divide $\frac{3}{11}$ by $\frac{7}{10}$.

Use Ratios

When you compare two numbers by division, you are using a ratio. Ratios can be written 3 to 5, 3:5, or $\frac{3}{5}$. Ratios, like fractions, also can be written in simplest form.

Ratios can represent one type of probability, called odds. This is a ratio that compares the number of ways a certain outcome occurs to the number of possible outcomes. For example, if you flip a coin 100 times, what are the odds that it will come up heads? There are two possible outcomes, heads or tails, so the odds of coming up heads are 50:100. Another way to say this is that 50 out of 100 times the coin will come up heads. In its simplest form, the ratio is 1:2.

Example 1

A chemical solution contains 40 g of salt and 64 g of baking soda. What is the ratio of salt to baking soda as a fraction in simplest form?

Step 1   Write the ratio as a fraction.

$$\frac{salt}{baking\ soda} = \frac{40}{64}$$

Step 2   Express the fraction in simplest form. The GCF of 40 and 64 is 8.

$$\frac{40}{64} = \frac{40 \div 8}{64 \div 8} = \frac{5}{8}$$

The ratio of salt to baking soda in the sample is 5:8.

Example 2

Sean rolls a 6-sided die 6 times. What are the odds that the side with a 3 will show?

Step 1   Write the ratio as a fraction.

$$\frac{number\ of\ sides\ with\ a\ 3}{number\ of\ possible\ sides} = \frac{1}{6}$$

Step 2   Multiply by the number of attempts.

$$\frac{1}{6} \times 6\ attempts = \frac{6}{6}\ attempts = 1\ attempt$$

1 attempt out of 6 will show a 3.

Practice Problem   Two metal rods measure 100 cm and 144 cm in length. What is the ratio of their lengths in simplest form?

Use Decimals

A fraction with a denominator that is a power of ten can be written as a decimal. For example, 0.27 means $\frac{27}{100}$. The decimal point separates the ones place from the tenths place.

Any fraction can be written as a decimal using division. For example, the fraction $\frac{5}{8}$ can be written as a decimal by dividing 5 by 8. Written as a decimal, it is 0.625.

Add or Subtract Decimals   When adding and subtracting decimals, line up the decimal points before carrying out the operation.

Example 1

Find the sum of 47.68 and 7.80.

Step 1   Line up the decimal places when you write the numbers.

$$
\begin{array}{r}
47.68 \\
+\ 7.80 \\
\end{array}
$$

Step 2   Add the decimals.

$$
\begin{array}{r}
{\scriptstyle 1\ 1} \\
47.68 \\
+\ 7.80 \\
\hline
55.48 \\
\end{array}
$$

The sum of 47.68 and 7.80 is 55.48.

Example 2

Find the difference of 42.17 and 15.85.

Step 1   Line up the decimal places when you write the number.

$$
\begin{array}{r}
42.17 \\
-15.85 \\
\end{array}
$$

Step 2   Subtract the decimals.

$$
\begin{array}{r}
{\scriptstyle 3\ 11} \\
42.17 \\
-15.85 \\
\hline
26.32 \\
\end{array}
$$

The difference of 42.17 and 15.85 is 26.32.

Practice Problem   Find the sum of 1.245 and 3.842.

SCIENCE SKILL HANDBOOK

MATH SKILL HANDBOOK

FOLDABLES HANDBOOK

REFERENCE HANDBOOK

GLOSSARY/ GLOSARIO

INDEX

SCIENCE SKILL HANDBOOK

MATH SKILL HANDBOOK

FOLDABLES HANDBOOK

REFERENCE HANDBOOK

GLOSSARY/ GLOSARIO

INDEX

Multiply Decimals To multiply decimals, multiply the numbers like numbers without decimal points. Count the decimal places in each factor. The product will have the same number of decimal places as the sum of the decimal places in the factors.

Example

Multiply 2.4 by 5.9.

Step 1 Multiply the factors like two whole numbers.

$24 \times 59 = 1416$

Step 2 Find the sum of the number of decimal places in the factors. Each factor has one decimal place, for a sum of two decimal places.

Step 3 The product will have two decimal places.

14.16

The product of 2.4 and 5.9 is 14.16.

Practice Problem Multiply 4.6 by 2.2.

Divide Decimals When dividing decimals, change the divisor to a whole number. To do this, multiply both the divisor and the dividend by the same power of ten. Then place the decimal point in the quotient directly above the decimal point in the dividend. Then divide as you do with whole numbers.

Example

Divide 8.84 by 3.4.

Step 1 Multiply both factors by 10.

$3.4 \times 10 = 34$, $8.84 \times 10 = 88.4$

Step 2 Divide 88.4 by 34.

```
       2.6
   34)88.4
      −68
      204
     −204
        0
```

8.84 divided by 3.4 is 2.6.

Practice Problem Divide 75.6 by 3.6.

Use Proportions

An equation that shows that two ratios are equivalent is a proportion. The ratios $\frac{2}{4}$ and $\frac{5}{10}$ are equivalent, so they can be written as $\frac{2}{4} = \frac{5}{10}$. This equation is a proportion.

When two ratios form a proportion, the cross products are equal. To find the cross products in the proportion $\frac{2}{4} = \frac{5}{10}$, multiply the 2 and the 10, and the 4 and the 5. Therefore $2 \times 10 = 4 \times 5$, or $20 = 20$.

Because you know that both ratios are equal, you can use cross products to find a missing term in a proportion. This is known as solving the proportion.

Example

The heights of a tree and a pole are proportional to the lengths of their shadows. The tree casts a shadow of 24 m when a 6-m pole casts a shadow of 4 m. What is the height of the tree?

Step 1 Write a proportion.

$$\frac{\text{height of tree}}{\text{height of pole}} = \frac{\text{length of tree's shadow}}{\text{length of pole's shadow}}$$

Step 2 Substitute the known values into the proportion. Let h represent the unknown value, the height of the tree.

$$\frac{h}{6} \times \frac{24}{4}$$

Step 3 Find the cross products.

$$h \times 4 = 6 \times 24$$

Step 4 Simplify the equation.

$$4h \times 144$$

Step 5 Divide each side by 4.

$$\frac{4h}{4} \times \frac{144}{4}$$

$$h = 36$$

The height of the tree is 36 m.

Practice Problem The ratios of the weights of two objects on the Moon and on Earth are in proportion. A rock weighing 3 N on the Moon weighs 18 N on Earth. How much would a rock that weighs 5 N on the Moon weigh on Earth?

Use Percentages

The word *percent* means "out of one hundred." It is a ratio that compares a number to 100. Suppose you read that 77 percent of Earth's surface is covered by water. That is the same as reading that the fraction of Earth's surface covered by water is $\frac{77}{100}$. To express a fraction as a percent, first find the equivalent decimal for the fraction. Then, multiply the decimal by 100 and add the percent symbol.

Example 1

Express $\frac{13}{20}$ as a percent.

Step 1 Find the equivalent decimal for the fraction.

$$
\begin{array}{r}
0.65 \\
20)\overline{13.00} \\
\underline{12\ 0} \\
1\ 00 \\
\underline{1\ 00} \\
0
\end{array}
$$

Step 2 Rewrite the fraction $\frac{13}{20}$ as 0.65.

Step 3 Multiply 0.65 by 100 and add the % symbol.

$$0.65 \times 100 = 65 = 65\%$$

So, $\frac{13}{20} = 65\%$.

This also can be solved as a proportion.

Example 2

Express $\frac{13}{20}$ as a percent.

Step 1 Write a proportion.

$$\frac{13}{20} = \frac{x}{100}$$

Step 2 Find the cross products.

$$1300 = 20x$$

Step 3 Divide each side by 20.

$$\frac{1300}{20} = \frac{20x}{20}$$

$$65\% = x$$

Practice Problem In one year, 73 of 365 days were rainy in one city. What percent of the days in that city were rainy?

Solve One-Step Equations

A statement that two expressions are equal is an equation. For example, $A = B$ is an equation that states that A is equal to B.

An equation is solved when a variable is replaced with a value that makes both sides of the equation equal. To make both sides equal the inverse operation is used. Addition and subtraction are inverses, and multiplication and division are inverses.

Example 1

Solve the equation $x - 10 = 35$.

Step 1 Find the solution by adding 10 to each side of the equation.

$$x - 10 = 35$$
$$x - 10 + 10 = 35 - 10$$
$$x = 45$$

Step 2 Check the solution.

$$x - 10 = 35$$
$$45 - 10 = 35$$
$$35 = 35$$

Both sides of the equation are equal, so $x = 45$.

Example 2

In the formula $a = bc$, find the value of c if $a = 20$ and $b = 2$.

Step 1 Rearrange the formula so the unknown value is by itself on one side of the equation by dividing both sides by b.

$$a = bc$$
$$\frac{a}{b} = \frac{bc}{b}$$
$$\frac{a}{b} = c$$

Step 2 Replace the variables a and b with the values that are given.

$$\frac{a}{b} = c$$
$$\frac{20}{2} = c$$
$$10 = c$$

Step 3 Check the solution.

$$a = bc$$
$$20 = 2 \times 10$$
$$20 = 20$$

Both sides of the equation are equal, so $c = 10$ is the solution when $a = 20$ and $b = 2$.

Practice Problem In the formula $h = gd$, find the value of d if $g = 12.3$ and $h = 17.4$.

SCIENCE SKILL HANDBOOK

MATH SKILL HANDBOOK

FOLDABLES HANDBOOK

REFERENCE HANDBOOK

GLOSSARY/ GLOSARIO

INDEX

SCIENCE SKILL HANDBOOK

MATH SKILL HANDBOOK

FOLDABLES HANDBOOK

REFERENCE HANDBOOK

GLOSSARY/ GLOSARIO

INDEX

Use Statistics

The branch of mathematics that deals with collecting, analyzing, and presenting data is statistics. In statistics, there are three common ways to summarize data with a single number—the mean, the median, and the mode.

The **mean** of a set of data is the arithmetic average. It is found by adding the numbers in the data set and dividing by the number of items in the set.

The **median** is the middle number in a set of data when the data are arranged in numerical order. If there were an even number of data points, the median would be the mean of the two middle numbers.

The **mode** of a set of data is the number or item that appears most often.

Another number that often is used to describe a set of data is the range. The **range** is the difference between the largest number and the smallest number in a set of data.

Example

The speeds (in m/s) for a race car during five different time trials are 39, 37, 44, 36, and 44.

To find the mean:

Step 1 Find the sum of the numbers.

$$39 + 37 + 44 + 36 + 44 = 200$$

Step 2 Divide the sum by the number of items, which is 5.

$$200 \div 5 = 40$$

The mean is 40 m/s.

To find the median:

Step 1 Arrange the measures from least to greatest.

36, 37, 39, 44, 44

Step 2 Determine the middle measure.

36, 37, <u>39</u>, 44, 44

The median is 39 m/s.

To find the mode:

Step 1 Group the numbers that are the same together.

44, 44, 36, 37, 39

Step 2 Determine the number that occurs most in the set.

<u>44, 44</u>, 36, 37, 39

The mode is 44 m/s.

To find the range:

Step 1 Arrange the measures from greatest to least.

44, 44, 39, 37, 36

Step 2 Determine the greatest and least measures in the set.

<u>44</u>, 44, 39, 37, <u>36</u>

Step 3 Find the difference between the greatest and least measures.

$$44 - 36 = 8$$

The range is 8 m/s.

Practice Problem Find the mean, median, mode, and range for the data set 8, 4, 12, 8, 11, 14, 16.

A **frequency table** shows how many times each piece of data occurs, usually in a survey. **Table 1** below shows the results of a student survey on favorite color.

Table 1 Student Color Choice		
Color	**Tally**	**Frequency**
red	IIII	4
blue	ⅣL	5
black	II	2
green	III	3
purple	ⅣL II	7
yellow	ⅣL I	6

Based on the frequency table data, which color is the favorite?

Use Geometry

The branch of mathematics that deals with the measurement, properties, and relationships of points, lines, angles, surfaces, and solids is called geometry.

Perimeter The **perimeter** (P) is the distance around a geometric figure. To find the perimeter of a rectangle, add the length and width and multiply that sum by two, or $2(l + w)$. To find perimeters of irregular figures, add the length of the sides.

Example 1

Find the perimeter of a rectangle that is 3 m long and 5 m wide.

Step 1 You know that the perimeter is 2 times the sum of the width and length.

$P = 2(3\text{ m} + 5\text{ m})$

Step 2 Find the sum of the width and length.

$P = 2(8\text{ m})$

Step 3 Multiply by 2.

$P = 16\text{ m}$

The perimeter is 16 m.

Example 2

Find the perimeter of a shape with sides measuring 2 cm, 5 cm, 6 cm, 3 cm.

Step 1 You know that the perimeter is the sum of all the sides.

$P = 2 + 5 + 6 + 3$

Step 2 Find the sum of the sides.

$P = 2 + 5 + 6 + 3$

$P = 16$

The perimeter is 16 cm.

Practice Problem Find the perimeter of a rectangle with a length of 18 m and a width of 7 m.

Practice Problem Find the perimeter of a triangle measuring 1.6 cm by 2.4 cm by 2.4 cm.

Area of a Rectangle The **area** (A) is the number of square units needed to cover a surface. To find the area of a rectangle, multiply the length times the width, or $l \times w$. When finding area, the units also are multiplied. Area is given in square units.

Example

Find the area of a rectangle with a length of 1 cm and a width of 10 cm.

Step 1 You know that the area is the length multiplied by the width.

$A = (1\text{ cm} \times 10\text{ cm})$

Step 2 Multiply the length by the width. Also multiply the units.

$A = 10\text{ cm}^2$

The area is 10 cm².

Practice Problem Find the area of a square whose sides measure 4 m.

Area of a Triangle To find the area of a triangle, use the formula:

$A = \frac{1}{2}(\text{base} \times \text{height})$

The base of a triangle can be any of its sides. The height is the perpendicular distance from a base to the opposite endpoint, or vertex.

Example

Find the area of a triangle with a base of 18 m and a height of 7 m.

Step 1 You know that the area is $\frac{1}{2}$ the base times the height.

$A = \frac{1}{2}(18\text{ m} \times 7\text{ m})$

Step 2 Multiply $\frac{1}{2}$ by the product of 18×7. Multiply the units.

$A = \frac{1}{2}(126\text{ m}^2)$

$A = 63\text{ m}^2$

The area is 63 m².

Practice Problem Find the area of a triangle with a base of 27 cm and a height of 17 cm.

SCIENCE SKILL HANDBOOK

MATH SKILL HANDBOOK

FOLDABLES HANDBOOK

REFERENCE HANDBOOK

GLOSSARY/ GLOSARIO

INDEX

SCIENCE SKILL HANDBOOK

MATH SKILL HANDBOOK

FOLDABLES HANDBOOK

REFERENCE HANDBOOK

GLOSSARY/ GLOSARIO

INDEX

Circumference of a Circle The **diameter** (d) of a circle is the distance across the circle through its center, and the **radius** (r) is the distance from the center to any point on the circle. The radius is half of the diameter. The distance around the circle is called the **circumference** (C). The formula for finding the circumference is:

$C = 2\pi r$ or $C = \pi d$

The circumference divided by the diameter is always equal to 3.1415926… This nonterminating and nonrepeating number is represented by the Greek letter π (pi). An approximation often used for π is 3.14.

Example 1

Find the circumference of a circle with a radius of 3 m.

Step 1 You know the formula for the circumference is 2 times the radius times π.

$C = 2\pi(3)$

Step 2 Multiply 2 times the radius.

$C = 6\pi$

Step 3 Multiply by π.

$C \approx 19$ m

The circumference is about 19 m.

Example 2

Find the circumference of a circle with a diameter of 24.0 cm.

Step 1 You know the formula for the circumference is the diameter times π.

$C = \pi(24.0)$

Step 2 Multiply the diameter by π.

$C \approx 75.4$ cm

The circumference is about 75.4 cm.

Practice Problem Find the circumference of a circle with a radius of 19 cm.

Area of a Circle The formula for the area of a circle is: $A = \pi r^2$

Example 1

Find the area of a circle with a radius of 4.0 cm.

Step 1 $A = \pi(4.0)^2$

Step 2 Find the square of the radius.

$A = 16\pi$

Step 3 Multiply the square of the radius by π.

$A \approx 50$ cm^2

The area of the circle is about 50 cm^2.

Example 2

Find the area of a circle with a radius of 225 m.

Step 1 $A = \pi(225)^2$

Step 2 Find the square of the radius.

$A = 50625\pi$

Step 3 Multiply the square of the radius by π.

$A \approx 159043.1$

The area of the circle is about 159043.1 m^2.

Example 3

Find the area of a circle whose diameter is 20.0 mm.

Step 1 Remember that the radius is half of the diameter.

$A = \pi\left(\dfrac{20.0}{2}\right)^2$

Step 2 Find the radius.

$A = \pi(10.0)^2$

Step 3 Find the square of the radius.

$A = 100\pi$

Step 4 Multiply the square of the radius by π.

$A \approx 314$ mm^2

The area of the circle is about 314 mm^2.

Practice Problem Find the area of a circle with a radius of 16 m.

Volume The measure of space occupied by a solid is the **volume** (V). To find the volume of a rectangular solid multiply the length times width times height, or $V = l \times w \times h$. It is measured in cubic units, such as cubic centimeters (cm^3).

Example

Find the volume of a rectangular solid with a length of 2.0 m, a width of 4.0 m, and a height of 3.0 m.

Step 1 You know the formula for volume is the length times the width times the height.

$$V = 2.0 \text{ m} \times 4.0 \text{ m} \times 3.0 \text{ m}$$

Step 2 Multiply the length times the width times the height.

$$V = 24 \text{ m}^3$$

The volume is 24 m^3.

Practice Problem Find the volume of a rectangular solid that is 8 m long, 4 m wide, and 4 m high.

To find the volume of other solids, multiply the area of the base times the height.

Example 1

Find the volume of a solid that has a triangular base with a length of 8.0 m and a height of 7.0 m. The height of the entire solid is 15.0 m.

Step 1 You know that the base is a triangle, and the area of a triangle is $\frac{1}{2}$ the base times the height, and the volume is the area of the base times the height.

$$V = \left[\frac{1}{2}(b \times h)\right] \times 15$$

Step 2 Find the area of the base.

$$V = \left[\frac{1}{2}(8 \times 7)\right] \times 15$$
$$V = \left(\frac{1}{2} \times 56\right) \times 15$$

Step 3 Multiply the area of the base by the height of the solid.

$$V = 28 \times 15$$
$$V = 420 \text{ m}^3$$

The volume is 420 m^3.

Example 2

Find the volume of a cylinder that has a base with a radius of 12.0 cm, and a height of 21.0 cm.

Step 1 You know that the base is a circle, and the area of a circle is the square of the radius times π, and the volume is the area of the base times the height.

$$V = (\pi r^2) \times 21$$
$$V = (\pi 12^2) \times 21$$

Step 2 Find the area of the base.

$$V = 144\pi \times 21$$
$$V = 452 \times 21$$

Step 3 Multiply the area of the base by the height of the solid.

$$V \approx 9{,}500 \text{ cm}^3$$

The volume is about 9,500 cm^3.

Example 3

Find the volume of a cylinder that has a diameter of 15 mm and a height of 4.8 mm.

Step 1 You know that the base is a circle with an area equal to the square of the radius times π. The radius is one-half the diameter. The volume is the area of the base times the height.

$$V = (\pi r^2) \times 4.8$$
$$V = \left[\pi\left(\frac{1}{2} \times 15\right)^2\right] \times 4.8$$
$$V = (\pi 7.5^2) \times 4.8$$

Step 2 Find the area of the base.

$$V = 56.25\pi \times 4.8$$
$$V \approx 176.71 \times 4.8$$

Step 3 Multiply the area of the base by the height of the solid.

$$V \approx 848.2$$

The volume is about 848.2 mm^3.

Practice Problem Find the volume of a cylinder with a diameter of 7 cm in the base and a height of 16 cm.

SCIENCE SKILL HANDBOOK

MATH SKILL HANDBOOK

FOLDABLES HANDBOOK

REFERENCE HANDBOOK

GLOSSARY/ GLOSARIO

INDEX

Science Applications

SCIENCE SKILL HANDBOOK

MATH SKILL HANDBOOK

FOLDABLES HANDBOOK

REFERENCE HANDBOOK

GLOSSARY/ GLOSARIO

INDEX

Measure in SI

The metric system of measurement was developed in 1795. A modern form of the metric system, called the International System (SI), was adopted in 1960 and provides the standard measurements that all scientists around the world can understand.

The SI system is convenient because unit sizes vary by powers of 10. Prefixes are used to name units. Look at **Table 2** for some common SI prefixes and their meanings.

Table 2 Common SI Prefixes

Prefix	Symbol	Meaning	
kilo–	k	1,000	thousandth
hecto–	h	100	hundred
deka–	da	10	ten
deci–	d	0.1	tenth
centi–	c	0.01	hundreth
milli–	m	0.001	thousandth

Example

How many grams equal one kilogram?

Step 1 Find the prefix *kilo–* in **Table 2.**

Step 2 Using **Table 2,** determine the meaning of *kilo–*. According to the table, it means 1,000. When the prefix *kilo–* is added to a unit, it means that there are 1,000 of the units in a "kilounit."

Step 3 Apply the prefix to the units in the question. The units in the question are grams. There are 1,000 grams in a kilogram.

Practice Problem Is a milligram larger or smaller than a gram? How many of the smaller units equal one larger unit? What fraction of the larger unit does one smaller unit represent?

Dimensional Analysis

Convert SI Units In science, quantities such as length, mass, and time sometimes are measured using different units. A process called dimensional analysis can be used to change one unit of measure to another. This process involves multiplying your starting quantity and units by one or more conversion factors. A conversion factor is a ratio equal to one and can be made from any two equal quantities with different units. If 1,000 mL equal 1 L then two ratios can be made.

$$\frac{1{,}000 \text{ mL}}{1 \text{ L}} = \frac{1 \text{ L}}{1{,}000 \text{ mL}} = 1$$

One can convert between units in the SI system by using the equivalents in **Table 2** to make conversion factors.

Example

How many cm are in 4 m?

Step 1 Write conversion factors for the units given. From **Table 2,** you know that 100 cm = 1 m. The conversion factors are

$$\frac{100 \text{ cm}}{1 \text{ m}} \text{ and } \frac{1 \text{ m}}{100 \text{ cm}}$$

Step 2 Decide which conversion factor to use. Select the factor that has the units you are converting from (m) in the denominator and the units you are converting to (cm) in the numerator.

$$\frac{100 \text{ cm}}{1 \text{ m}}$$

Step 3 Multiply the starting quantity and units by the conversion factor. Cancel the starting units with the units in the denominator. There are 400 cm in 4 m.

$$4 \text{ m} = \frac{100 \text{ cm}}{1 \text{ m}} = 400 \text{ cm}$$

Practice Problem How many milligrams are in one kilogram? (Hint: You will need to use two conversion factors from **Table 2.**)

Table 3 Unit System Equivalents

Type of Measurement	Equivalent
Length	1 in = 2.54 cm 1 yd = 0.91 m 1 mi = 1.61 km
Mass and weight*	1 oz = 28.35 g 1 lb = 0.45 kg 1 ton (short) = 0.91 tonnes (metric tons) 1 lb = 4.45 N
Volume	$1\ in^3 = 16.39\ cm^3$ 1 qt = 0.95 L 1 gal = 3.78 L
Area	$1\ in^2 = 6.45\ cm^2$ $1\ yd^2 = 0.83\ m^2$ $1\ mi^2 = 2.59\ km^2$ 1 acre = 0.40 hectares
Temperature	$°C = \frac{(°F - 32)}{1.8}$ $K = °C + 273$

*Weight is measured in standard Earth gravity.

Convert Between Unit Systems **Table 3** gives a list of equivalents that can be used to convert between English and SI units.

Example

If a meterstick has a length of 100 cm, how long is the meterstick in inches?

Step 1 Write the conversion factors for the units given. From **Table 3,** 1 in = 2.54 cm.

$$\frac{1\ in}{2.54\ cm}\ and\ \frac{2.54\ cm}{1\ in}$$

Step 2 Determine which conversion factor to use. You are converting from cm to in. Use the conversion factor with cm on the bottom.

$$\frac{1\ in}{2.54\ cm}$$

Step 3 Multiply the starting quantity and units by the conversion factor. Cancel the starting units with the units in the denominator. Round your answer to the nearest tenth.

$$100\ \cancel{cm} \times \frac{1\ in}{2.54\ \cancel{cm}} = 39.37\ in$$

The meterstick is about 39.4 in long.

Practice Problem 1 A book has a mass of 5 lb. What is the mass of the book in kg?

Practice Problem 2 Use the equivalent for in and cm (1 in = 2.54 cm) to show how $1\ in^3 \approx 16.39\ cm^3$.

SCIENCE SKILL HANDBOOK

MATH SKILL HANDBOOK

FOLDABLES HANDBOOK

REFERENCE HANDBOOK

GLOSSARY/ GLOSARIO

INDEX

Precision and Significant Digits

When you make a measurement, the value you record depends on the precision of the measuring instrument. This precision is represented by the number of significant digits recorded in the measurement. When counting the number of significant digits, all digits are counted except zeros at the end of a number with no decimal point such as 2,050, and zeros at the beginning of a decimal such as 0.03020. When adding or subtracting numbers with different precision, round the answer to the smallest number of decimal places of any number in the sum or difference. When multiplying or dividing, the answer is rounded to the smallest number of significant digits of any number being multiplied or divided.

Example

The lengths 5.28 and 5.2 are measured in meters. Find the sum of these lengths and record your answer using the correct number of significant digits.

Step 1   Find the sum.

  5.28 m   2 digits after the decimal

+ 5.2 m   1 digit after the decimal

  10.48 m

Step 2   Round to one digit after the decimal because the least number of digits after the decimal of the numbers being added is 1.

The sum is 10.5 m.

Practice Problem 1 How many significant digits are in the measurement 7,071,301 m? How many significant digits are in the measurement 0.003010 g?

Practice Problem 2 Multiply 5.28 and 5.2 using the rule for multiplying and dividing. Record the answer using the correct number of significant digits.

Scientific Notation

Many times numbers used in science are very small or very large. Because these numbers are difficult to work with scientists use scientific notation. To write numbers in scientific notation, move the decimal point until only one non-zero digit remains on the left. Then count the number of places you moved the decimal point and use that number as a power of ten. For example, the average distance from the Sun to Mars is 227,800,000,000 m. In scientific notation, this distance is 2.278×10^{11} m. Because you moved the decimal point to the left, the number is a positive power of ten.

The mass of an electron is about 0.000 000 000 000 000 000 000 000 000 000 911 kg. Expressed in scientific notation, this mass is 9.11×10^{-31} kg. Because the decimal point was moved to the right, the number is a negative power of ten.

Example

Earth is 149,600,000 km from the Sun. Express this in scientific notation.

Step 1   Move the decimal point until one non-zero digit remains on the left.

  1.496 000 00

Step 2   Count the number of decimal places you have moved. In this case, eight.

Step 2   Show that number as a power of ten, 10^8.

Earth is 1.496×10^8 km from the Sun.

Practice Problem 1 How many significant digits are in 149,600,000 km? How many significant digits are in 1.496×10^8 km?

Practice Problem 2 Parts used in a high performance car must be measured to 7×10^{-6} m. Express this number as a decimal.

Practice Problem 3 A CD is spinning at 539 revolutions per minute. Express this number in scientific notation.

Make and Use Graphs

Data in tables can be displayed in a graph—a visual representation of data. Common graph types include line graphs, bar graphs, and circle graphs.

Line Graph A line graph shows a relationship between two variables that change continuously. The independent variable is changed and is plotted on the x-axis. The dependent variable is observed, and is plotted on the y-axis.

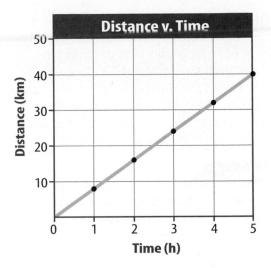

Figure 8 This line graph shows the relationship between distance and time during a bicycle ride.

Practice Problem A puppy's shoulder height is measured during the first year of her life. The following measurements were collected: (3 mo, 52 cm), (6 mo, 72 cm), (9 mo, 83 cm), (12 mo, 86 cm). Graph this data.

Find a Slope The slope of a straight line is the ratio of the vertical change, rise, to the horizontal change, run.

$$\text{Slope} = \frac{\text{vertical change (rise)}}{\text{horizontal change (run)}} = \frac{\text{change in } y}{\text{change in } x}$$

Example

Draw a line graph of the data below from a cyclist in a long-distance race.

Table 4 Bicycle Race Data

Time (h)	Distance (km)
0	0
1	8
2	16
3	24
4	32
5	40

Step 1 Determine the x-axis and y-axis variables. Time varies independently of distance and is plotted on the x-axis. Distance is dependent on time and is plotted on the y-axis.

Step 2 Determine the scale of each axis. The x-axis data ranges from 0 to 5. The y-axis data ranges from 0 to 50.

Step 3 Using graph paper, draw and label the axes. Include units in the labels.

Step 4 Draw a point at the intersection of the time value on the x-axis and corresponding distance value on the y-axis. Connect the points and label the graph with a title, as shown in **Figure 8**.

Example

Find the slope of the graph in **Figure 8**.

Step 1 You know that the slope is the change in y divided by the change in x.

$$\text{Slope} = \frac{\text{change in } y}{\text{change in } x}$$

Step 2 Determine the data points you will be using. For a straight line, choose the two sets of points that are the farthest apart.

$$\text{Slope} = \frac{(40 - 0) \text{ km}}{(5 - 0) \text{ h}}$$

Step 3 Find the change in y and x.

$$\text{Slope} = \frac{40 \text{ km}}{5 \text{ h}}$$

Step 4 Divide the change in y by the change in x.

$$\text{Slope} = \frac{8 \text{ km}}{\text{h}}$$

The slope of the graph is 8 km/h.

SCIENCE SKILL HANDBOOK

MATH SKILL HANDBOOK

FOLDABLES HANDBOOK

REFERENCE HANDBOOK

GLOSSARY/ GLOSARIO

INDEX

SCIENCE SKILL HANDBOOK

MATH SKILL HANDBOOK

FOLDABLES HANDBOOK

REFERENCE HANDBOOK

GLOSSARY/ GLOSARIO

INDEX

Bar Graph To compare data that does not change continuously you might choose a bar graph. A bar graph uses bars to show the relationships between variables. The *x*-axis variable is divided into parts. The parts can be numbers such as years, or a category such as a type of animal. The *y*-axis is a number and increases continuously along the axis.

Example

A recycling center collects 4.0 kg of aluminum on Monday, 1.0 kg on Wednesday, and 2.0 kg on Friday. Create a bar graph of this data.

Step 1 Select the *x*-axis and *y*-axis variables. The measured numbers (the masses of aluminum) should be placed on the *y*-axis. The variable divided into parts (collection days) is placed on the *x*-axis.

Step 2 Create a graph grid like you would for a line graph. Include labels and units.

Step 3 For each measured number, draw a vertical bar above the *x*-axis value up to the *y*-axis value. For the first data point, draw a vertical bar above Monday up to 4.0 kg.

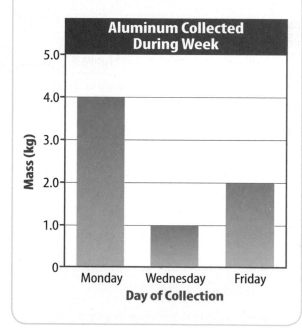

Practice Problem Draw a bar graph of the gases in air: 78% nitrogen, 21% oxygen, 1% other gases.

Circle Graph To display data as parts of a whole, you might use a circle graph. A circle graph is a circle divided into sections that represent the relative size of each piece of data. The entire circle represents 100%, half represents 50%, and so on.

Example

Air is made up of 78% nitrogen, 21% oxygen, and 1% other gases. Display the composition of air in a circle graph.

Step 1 Multiply each percent by 360° and divide by 100 to find the angle of each section in the circle.

$$78\% \times \frac{360°}{100} = 280.8°$$

$$21\% \times \frac{360°}{100} = 75.6°$$

$$1\% \times \frac{360°}{100} = 3.6°$$

Step 2 Use a compass to draw a circle and to mark the center of the circle. Draw a straight line from the center to the edge of the circle.

Step 3 Use a protractor and the angles you calculated to divide the circle into parts. Place the center of the protractor over the center of the circle and line the base of the protractor over the straight line.

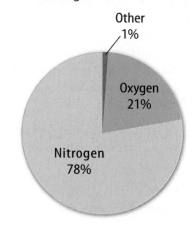

Practice Problem Draw a circle graph to represent the amount of aluminum collected during the week shown in the bar graph to the left.

Student Study Guides & Instructions
By Dinah Zike

1. You will find suggestions for Study Guides, also known as Foldables or books, in each chapter lesson and as a final project. Look at the end of the chapter to determine the project format and glue the Foldables in place as you progress through the chapter lessons.

2. Creating the Foldables or books is simple and easy to do by using copy paper, art paper, and internet printouts. Photocopies of maps, diagrams, or your own illustrations may also be used for some of the Foldables. Notebook paper is the most common source of material for study guides and 83% of all Foldables are created from it. When folded to make books, notebook paper Foldables easily fit into 11″ × 17″ or 12″ × 18″ chapter projects with space left over. Foldables made using photocopy paper are slightly larger and they fit into Projects, but snugly. Use the least amount of glue, tape, and staples needed to assemble the Foldables.

3. Seven of the Foldables can be made using either small or large paper. When 11″ × 17″ or 12″ × 18″ paper is used, these become projects for housing smaller Foldables. Project format boxes are located within the instructions to remind you of this option.

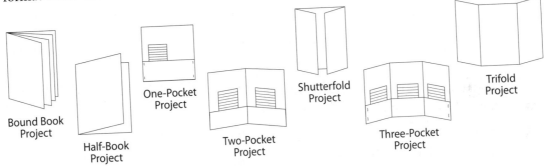

Bound Book Project

Half-Book Project

One-Pocket Project

Two-Pocket Project

Shutterfold Project

Three-Pocket Project

Trifold Project

4. Use one-gallon self-locking plastic bags to store your projects. Place strips of two-inch clear tape along the left, long side of the bag and punch holes through the taped edge. Cut the bottom corners off the bag so it will not hold air. Store this Project Portfolio inside a three-hole binder. To store a large collection of project bags, use a giant laundry-soap box. Holes can be punched in some of the Foldable Projects so they can be stored in a three-hole binder without using a plastic bag. Punch holes in the pocket books before gluing or stapling the pocket.

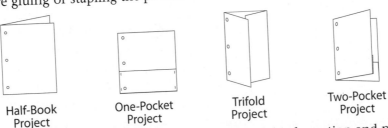

Half-Book Project

One-Pocket Project

Trifold Project

Two-Pocket Project

5. Maximize the use of the projects by collecting additional information and placing it on the back of the project and other unused spaces of the large Foldables.

SCIENCE SKILL HANDBOOK

MATH SKILL HANDBOOK

FOLDABLES HANDBOOK

REFERENCE HANDBOOK

GLOSSARY/ GLOSARIO

INDEX

Half-Book Foldable® By Dinah Zike

Step 1 Fold a sheet of notebook or copy paper in half.

Label the exterior tab and use the inside space to write information.

PROJECT FORMAT
Use 11″ × 17″ or 12″ × 18″ paper on the horizontal axis to make a large project book.

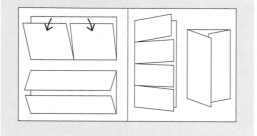

Variations

Paper can be folded horizontally, like a *hamburger* or vertically, like a *hot dog*.

C Half-books can be folded so that one side is ½ inch longer than the other side. A title or question can be written on the extended tab.

- -

Worksheet Foldable or Folded Book® By Dinah Zike

Step 1 Make a half-book (see above) using work sheets, internet print-outs, diagrams, or maps.

Step 2 Fold it in half again.

Variations

A This folded sheet as a small book with two pages can be used for comparing and contrasting, cause and effect, or other skills.

B When the sheet of paper is open, the four sections can be used separately or used collectively to show sequences or steps.

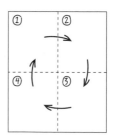

SCIENCE SKILL HANDBOOK

MATH SKILL HANDBOOK

FOLDABLES HANDBOOK

REFERENCE HANDBOOK

GLOSSARY/ GLOSARIO

INDEX

Two-Tab and Concept-Map Foldable® By Dinah Zike

Step 1 Fold a sheet of notebook or copy paper in half vertically or horizontally.

Step 2 Fold it in half again, as shown.

Step 3 Unfold once and cut along the fold line or valley of the top flap to make two flaps.

Variations

A Concept maps can be made by leaving a ½ inch tab at the top when folding the paper in half. Use arrows and labels to relate topics to the primary concept.

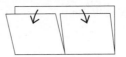

B Use two sheets of paper to make multiple page tab books. Glue or staple books together at the top fold.

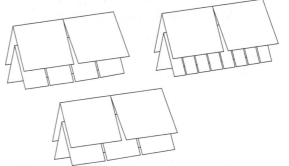

Three-Quarter Foldable® By Dinah Zike

Step 1 Make a two-tab book (see above) and cut the left tab off at the top of the fold line.

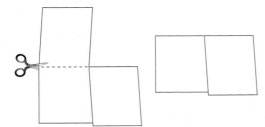

Variations

A Use this book to draw a diagram or a map on the exposed left tab. Write questions about the illustration on the top right tab and provide complete answers on the space under the tab.

B Compose a self-test using multiple choice answers for your questions. Include the correct answer with three wrong responses. The correct answers can be written on the back of the book or upside down on the bottom of the inside page.

SCIENCE SKILL HANDBOOK

MATH SKILL HANDBOOK

FOLDABLES HANDBOOK

REFERENCE HANDBOOK

GLOSSARY/ GLOSARIO

INDEX

Three-Tab Foldable® By Dinah Zike

Step 1 Fold a sheet of paper in half horizontally.

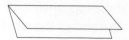

Step 2 Fold into thirds.

Step 3 Unfold and cut along the folds of the top flap to make three sections.

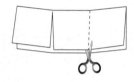

Variations

A Before cutting the three tabs draw a Venn diagram across the front of the book.

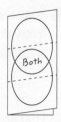

B Make a space to use for titles or concept maps by leaving a ½ inch tab at the top when folding the paper in half.

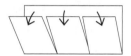

Four-Tab Foldable® By Dinah Zike

Step 1 Fold a sheet of paper in half horizontally.

Step 2 Fold in half and then fold each half as shown below.

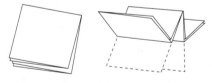

Step 3 Unfold and cut along the fold lines of the top flap to make four tabs.

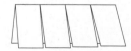

Variations

A Make a space to use for titles or concept maps by leaving a ½ inch tab at the top when folding the paper in half.

B Use the book on the vertical axis, with or without an extended tab.

SCIENCE SKILL HANDBOOK

MATH SKILL HANDBOOK

FOLDABLES HANDBOOK

REFERENCE HANDBOOK

GLOSSARY/ GLOSARIO

INDEX

Folding Fifths for a Foldable® By Dinah Zike

Step 1 Fold a sheet of paper in half horizontally.

Step 2 Fold again so one-third of the paper is exposed and two-thirds are covered.

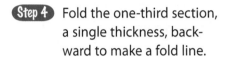

Step 3 Fold the two-thirds section in half.

Step 4 Fold the one-third section, a single thickness, backward to make a fold line.

Variations

A Unfold and cut along the fold lines to make five tabs.

B Make a five-tab book with a ½ inch tab at the top (see two-tab instructions).

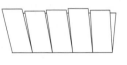

C Use 11″ × 17″ or 12″ × 18″ paper and fold into fifths for a five-column and/or row table or chart.

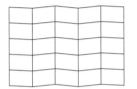

- -

Folded Table or Chart, and Trifold Foldable® By Dinah Zike

Step 1 Fold a sheet of paper in the required number of vertical columns for the table or chart.

Step 2 Fold the horizontal rows needed for the table or chart.

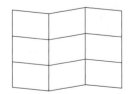

PROJECT FORMAT
Use 11″ × 17″ or 12″ × 18″ paper and fold it to make a large trifold project book or larger tables and charts.

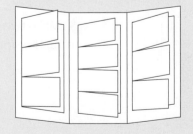

Variations

A Make a trifold by folding the paper into thirds vertically or horizontally.

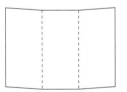

B Make a trifold book. Unfold it and draw a Venn diagram on the inside.

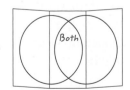

SCIENCE SKILL HANDBOOK

MATH SKILL HANDBOOK

FOLDABLES HANDBOOK

REFERENCE HANDBOOK

GLOSSARY/ GLOSARIO

INDEX

Science Skill Handbook

Math Skill Handbook

Foldables Handbook

Reference Handbook

Glossary/ Glosario

Index

Two or Three-Pockets Foldable® By Dinah Zike

Step 1 Fold up the long side of a horizontal sheet of paper about 5 cm.

Step 2 Fold the paper in half.

Step 3 Open the paper and glue or staple the outer edges to make two compartments.

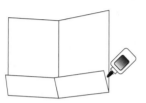

Variations

A Make a multi-page booklet by gluing several pocket books together.

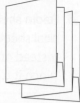

B Make a three-pocket book by using a trifold (see previous instructions).

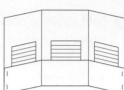

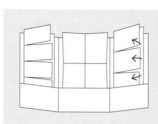

PROJECT FORMAT
Use 11″ × 17″ or 12″ × 18″ paper and fold it horizontally to make a large multi-pocket project.

Matchbook Foldable® By Dinah Zike

Step 1 Fold a sheet of paper almost in half and make the back edge about 1–2 cm longer than the front edge.

Step 2 Find the midpoint of the shorter flap.

Step 3 Open the paper and cut the short side along the midpoint making two tabs.

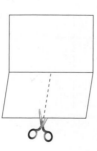

Step 4 Close the book and fold the tab over the short side.

Variations

A Make a single-tab matchbook by skipping Steps 2 and 3.

B Make two smaller matchbooks by cutting the single-tab matchbook in half.

Shutterfold Foldable® By Dinah Zike

Step 1 Begin as if you were folding a vertical sheet of paper in half, but instead of creasing the paper, pinch it to show the midpoint.

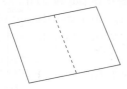

Step 2 Fold the top and bottom to the middle and crease the folds.

Variations

A Use the shutterfold on the horizontal axis.

B Create a center tab by leaving .5–2 cm between the flaps in Step 2.

PROJECT FORMAT
Use 11" × 17" or 12" × 18" paper and fold it to make a large shutterfold project.

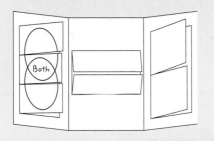

Four-Door Foldable® By Dinah Zike

Step 1 Make a shutterfold (see above).

Step 2 Fold the sheet of paper in half.

Step 3 Open the last fold and cut along the inside fold lines to make four tabs.

Variations

A Use the four-door book on the opposite axis.

B Create a center tab by leaving .5–2 cm between the flaps in Step 1.

SCIENCE SKILL HANDBOOK

MATH SKILL HANDBOOK

FOLDABLES HANDBOOK

REFERENCE HANDBOOK

GLOSSARY/ GLOSARIO

INDEX

Bound Book Foldable® By Dinah Zike

Step 1 Fold three sheets of paper in half. Place the papers in a stack, leaving about .5 cm between each top fold. Mark all three sheets about 3 cm from the outer edges.

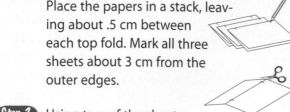

Step 2 Using two of the sheets, cut from the outer edges to the marked spots on each side. On the other sheet, cut between the marked spots.

Step 3 Take the two sheets from Step 1 and slide them through the cut in the third sheet to make a 12-page book.

Step 4 Fold the bound pages in half to form a book.

Variation

A Use two sheets of paper to make an eight-page book, or increase the number of pages by using more than three sheets.

PROJECT FORMAT
Use two or more sheets of 11" × 17" or 12" × 18" paper and fold it to make a large bound book project.

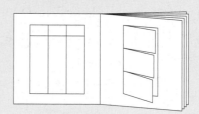

Accordian Foldable® By Dinah Zike

Step 1 Fold the selected paper in half vertically, like a *hamburger*.

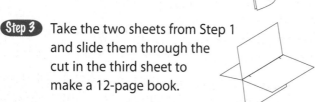

Step 2 Cut each sheet of folded paper in half along the fold lines.

Step 3 Fold each half-sheet almost in half, leaving a 2 cm tab at the top.

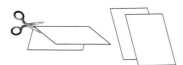

Step 4 Fold the top tab over the short side, then fold it in the opposite direction.

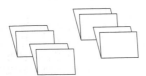

Variations

A Glue the straight edge of one paper inside the tab of another sheet. Leave a tab at the end of the book to add more pages.

B Tape the straight edge of one paper to the tab of another sheet, or just tape the straight edges of nonfolded paper end to end to make an accordian.

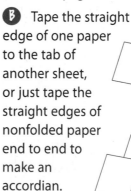

C Use whole sheets of paper to make a large accordian.

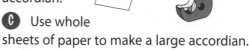

SCIENCE SKILL HANDBOOK
MATH SKILL HANDBOOK
FOLDABLES HANDBOOK
REFERENCE HANDBOOK
GLOSSARY/GLOSARIO
INDEX

Layered Foldable® By Dinah Zike

Step 1 Stack two sheets of paper about 1–2 cm apart. Keep the right and left edges even.

Step 2 Fold up the bottom edges to form four tabs. Crease the fold to hold the tabs in place.

Step 3 Staple along the folded edge, or open and glue the papers together at the fold line.

Variations

A Rotate the book so the fold is at the top or to the side.

B Extend the book by using more than two sheets of paper.

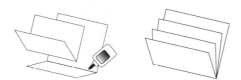

- -

Envelope Foldable® By Dinah Zike

Step 1 Fold a sheet of paper into a *taco*. Cut off the tab at the top.

Step 2 Open the *taco* and fold it the opposite way making another *taco* and an X-fold pattern on the sheet of paper.

Step 3 Cut a map, illustration, or diagram to fit the inside of the envelope.

Step 4 Use the outside tabs for labels and inside tabs for writing information.

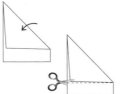

Variations

A Use 11″ × 17″ or 12″ × 18″ paper to make a large envelope.

B Cut off the points of the four tabs to make a window in the middle of the book.

SCIENCE SKILL HANDBOOK

MATH SKILL HANDBOOK

FOLDABLES HANDBOOK

REFERENCE HANDBOOK

GLOSSARY/ GLOSARIO

INDEX

Sentence Strip Foldable® By Dinah Zike

Step 1 Fold two sheets of paper in half vertically, like a *hamburger*.

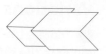

Step 2 Unfold and cut along fold lines making four half sheets.

Step 3 Fold each half sheet in half horizontally, like a *hot dog*.

Step 4 Stack folded horizontal sheets evenly and staple together on the left side.

Step 5 Open the top flap of the first sentence strip and make a cut about 2 cm from the stapled edge to the fold line. This forms a flap that can be raisied and lowered. Repeat this step for each sentence strip.

Variations

A Expand this book by using more than two sheets of paper.

B Use whole sheets of paper to make large books.

Pyramid Foldable® By Dinah Zike

Step 1 Fold a sheet of paper into a *taco*. Crease the fold line, but do not cut it off.

Step 2 Open the folded sheet and refold it like a *taco* in the opposite direction to create an X-fold pattern.

Step 3 Cut one fold line as shown, stopping at the center of the X-fold to make a flap.

Step 4 Outline the fold lines of the X-fold. Label the three front sections and use the inside spaces for notes. Use the tab for the title.

Step 5 Glue the tab into a project book or notebook. Use the space under the pyramid for other information.

Title:

Step 6 To display the pyramid, fold the flap under and secure with a paper clip, if needed.

Title:

SCIENCE SKILL HANDBOOK

MATH SKILL HANDBOOK

FOLDABLES HANDBOOK

REFERENCE HANDBOOK

GLOSSARY/ GLOSARIO

INDEX

Single-Pocket or One-Pocket Foldable® By Dinah Zike

Step 1 Using a large piece of paper on a vertical axis, fold the bottom edge of the paper upwards, about 5 cm.

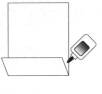

Step 2 Glue or staple the outer edges to make a large pocket.

PROJECT FORMAT
Use 11″ × 17″ or 12″ × 18″ paper and fold it vertically or horizontally to make a large pocket project.

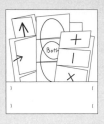

Variations

A Make the one-pocket project using the paper on the horizontal axis.

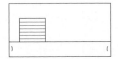

B To store materials securely inside, fold the top of the paper almost to the center, leaving about 2–4 cm between the paper edges. Slip the Foldables through the opening and under the top and bottom pockets.

· ·

Multi-Tab Foldable® By Dinah Zike

Step 1 Fold a sheet of notebook paper in half like a *hot dog*.

Step 2 Open the paper and on one side cut every third line. This makes ten tabs on wide ruled notebook paper and twelve tabs on college ruled.

Step 3 Label the tabs on the front side and use the inside space for definitions or other information.

Variation

A Make a tab for a title by folding the paper so the holes remain uncovered. This allows the notebook Foldable to be stored in a three-hole binder.

SCIENCE SKILL HANDBOOK

MATH SKILL HANDBOOK

FOLDABLES HANDBOOK

REFERENCE HANDBOOK

GLOSSARY/ GLOSARIO

INDEX

PERIODIC TABLE OF THE ELEMENTS

Element — Hydrogen
Atomic number — 1
Symbol — **H**
Atomic mass — 1.01
State of matter

Gas
Liquid
Solid
⊙ Synthetic

A column in the periodic table is called a **group.**

A row in the periodic table is called a **period.**

	1	2	3	4	5	6	7	8	9
1	Hydrogen 1 **H** 1.01								
2	Lithium 3 **Li** 6.94	Beryllium 4 **Be** 9.01							
3	Sodium 11 **Na** 22.99	Magnesium 12 **Mg** 24.31							
4	Potassium 19 **K** 39.10	Calcium 20 **Ca** 40.08	Scandium 21 **Sc** 44.96	Titanium 22 **Ti** 47.87	Vanadium 23 **V** 50.94	Chromium 24 **Cr** 52.00	Manganese 25 **Mn** 54.94	Iron 26 **Fe** 55.85	Cobalt 27 **Co** 58.93
5	Rubidium 37 **Rb** 85.47	Strontium 38 **Sr** 87.62	Yttrium 39 **Y** 88.91	Zirconium 40 **Zr** 91.22	Niobium 41 **Nb** 92.91	Molybdenum 42 **Mo** 95.96	Technetium 43 ⊙ **Tc** (98)	Ruthenium 44 **Ru** 101.07	Rhodium 45 **Rh** 102.91
6	Cesium 55 **Cs** 132.91	Barium 56 **Ba** 137.33	Lanthanum 57 **La** 138.91	Hafnium 72 **Hf** 178.49	Tantalum 73 **Ta** 180.95	Tungsten 74 **W** 183.84	Rhenium 75 **Re** 186.21	Osmium 76 **Os** 190.23	Iridium 77 **Ir** 192.22
7	Francium 87 **Fr** (223)	Radium 88 **Ra** (226)	Actinium 89 **Ac** (227)	Rutherfordium 104 ⊙ **Rf** (267)	Dubnium 105 ⊙ **Db** (268)	Seaborgium 106 ⊙ **Sg** (271)	Bohrium 107 ⊙ **Bh** (272)	Hassium 108 ⊙ **Hs** (270)	Meitnerium 109 ⊙ **Mt** (276)

The number in parentheses is the mass number of the longest lived isotope for that element.

Lanthanide series	Cerium 58 **Ce** 140.12	Praseodymium 59 **Pr** 140.91	Neodymium 60 **Nd** 144.24	Promethium 61 ⊙ **Pm** (145)	Samarium 62 **Sm** 150.36	Europium 63 **Eu** 151.96
Actinide series	Thorium 90 **Th** 232.04	Protactinium 91 **Pa** 231.04	Uranium 92 **U** 238.03	Neptunium 93 ⊙ **Np** (237)	Plutonium 94 ⊙ **Pu** (244)	Americium 95 ⊙ **Am** (243)

Science Skill Handbook
Math Skill Handbook
Foldables Handbook
Reference Handbook
Glossary/Glosario
Index

Metal
Metalloid
Nonmetal
Recently discovered

18

13   **14**   **15**   **16**   **17**

Helium
2
He
4.00

Boron
5
B
10.81

Carbon
6
C
12.01

Nitrogen
7
N
14.01

Oxygen
8
O
16.00

Fluorine
9
F
19.00

Neon
10
Ne
20.18

Aluminum
13
Al
26.98

Silicon
14
Si
28.09

Phosphorus
15
P
30.97

Sulfur
16
S
32.07

Chlorine
17
Cl
35.45

Argon
18
Ar
39.95

10   **11**   **12**

Nickel
28
Ni
58.69

Copper
29
Cu
63.55

Zinc
30
Zn
65.38

Gallium
31
Ga
69.72

Germanium
32
Ge
72.64

Arsenic
33
As
74.92

Selenium
34
Se
78.96

Bromine
35
Br
79.90

Krypton
36
Kr
83.80

Palladium
46
Pd
106.42

Silver
47
Ag
107.87

Cadmium
48
Cd
112.41

Indium
49
In
114.82

Tin
50
Sn
118.71

Antimony
51
Sb
121.76

Tellurium
52
Te
127.60

Iodine
53
I
126.90

Xenon
54
Xe
131.29

Platinum
78
Pt
195.08

Gold
79
Au
196.97

Mercury
80
Hg
200.59

Thallium
81
Tl
204.38

Lead
82
Pb
207.20

Bismuth
83
Bi
208.98

Polonium
84
Po
(209)

Astatine
85
At
(210)

Radon
86
Rn
(222)

Darmstadtium
110
Ds
(281)

Roentgenium
111
Rg
(280)

Copernicium
112
Cn
(285)

* Ununtrium
113
Uut
(284)

Flerovium
114
Fl
(289)

* Ununpentium
115
Uup
(288)

Livermorium
116
Lv
(293)

* Ununoctium
118
Uuo
(294)

*The names and symbols for elements 113, 115 and 118 are temporary. Final names will be selected when the elements' discoveries are verified.

Gadolinium
64
Gd
157.25

Terbium
65
Tb
158.93

Dysprosium
66
Dy
162.50

Holmium
67
Ho
164.93

Erbium
68
Er
167.26

Thulium
69
Tm
168.93

Ytterbium
70
Yb
173.05

Lutetium
71
Lu
174.97

Curium
96
Cm
(247)

Berkelium
97
Bk
(247)

Californium
98
Cf
(251)

Einsteinium
99
Es
(252)

Fermium
100
Fm
(257)

Mendelevium
101
Md
(258)

Nobelium
102
No
(259)

Lawrencium
103
Lr
(262)

SCIENCE SKILL HANDBOOK

MATH SKILL HANDBOOK

FOLDABLES HANDBOOK

REFERENCE HANDBOOK

GLOSSARY/ GLOSARIO

INDEX

Topographic Map Symbols

▬▬▬▬ Primary highway, hard surface	⌁ Index contour
▬●▬●▬ Secondary highway, hard surface	⋯⋯⋯ Supplementary contour
═══════ Light-duty road, hard or improved surface	⌁ Intermediate contour
========= Unimproved road	⌁ Depression contours
⊢─┼──┼─⊣ Railroad: single track	
⊢╪──╪──╪⊣ Railroad: multiple track	▬ ▬ ▬ Boundaries: national
⊢╪╪╪╪╪⊣ Railroads in juxtaposition	▬▬ ▬ ▬ State
	▬ ▬ ▬· County, parish, municipal
▪▮▬▦ Buildings	▬ ▬ ▬ Civil township, precinct, town, barrio
⚐ ⊞ cem Schools, church, and cemetery	▬··▬··▬· Incorporated city, village, town, hamlet
▫▭ ▨▨ Buildings (barn, warehouse, etc.)	·▬·▬· Reservation, national or state
○ ○ Wells other than water (labeled as to type)	────── Small park, cemetery, airport, etc.
●●● ⊘ Tanks: oil, water, etc. (labeled only if water)	▬··▬··· Land grant
⊙ ⚇ Located or landmark object; windmill	──────── Township or range line, U.S. land survey
⚒ × Open pit, mine, or quarry; prospect	──────── Township or range line, approximate location
Marsh (swamp)	
Wooded marsh	
Woods or brushwood	≈≈≈ Perennial streams
Vineyard	→─── ← Elevated aqueduct
Land subject to controlled inundation	○ ⌁ Water well and spring
Submerged marsh	⌁ Small rapids
Mangrove	⌁ Large rapids
Orchard	⌁ Intermittent lake
Scrub	⌁ Intermittent stream
Urban area	→═════← Aqueduct tunnel
	⌁ Glacier
	⌁ Small falls
x7369 Spot elevation	⌁ Large falls
670 Water elevation	⌁ Dry lake bed

SCIENCE SKILL HANDBOOK

MATH SKILL HANDBOOK

FOLDABLES HANDBOOK

REFERENCE HANDBOOK

GLOSSARY/ GLOSARIO

INDEX

Rocks

Rocks

Rock Type	Rock Name	Characteristics
Igneous (intrusive)	Granite	Large mineral grains of quartz, feldspar, hornblende, and mica. Usually light in color.
	Diorite	Large mineral grains of feldspar, hornblende, and mica. Less quartz than granite. Intermediate in color.
	Gabbro	Large mineral grains of feldspar, augite, and olivine. No quartz. Dark in color.
Igneous (extrusive)	Rhyolite	Small mineral grains of quartz, feldspar, hornblende, and mica, or no visible grains. Light in color.
	Andesite	Small mineral grains of feldspar, hornblende, and mica or no visible grains. Intermediate in color.
	Basalt	Small mineral grains of feldspar, augite, and possibly olivine or no visible grains. No quartz. Dark in color.
	Obsidian	Glassy texture. No visible grains. Volcanic glass. Fracture looks like broken glass.
	Pumice	Frothy texture. Floats in water. Usually light in color.
Sedimentary (detrital)	Conglomerate	Coarse grained. Gravel or pebble-size grains.
	Sandstone	Sand-sized grains 1/16 to 2 mm.
	Siltstone	Grains are smaller than sand but larger than clay.
	Shale	Smallest grains. Often dark in color. Usually platy.
Sedimentary (chemical or organic)	Limestone	Major mineral is calcite. Usually forms in oceans and lakes. Often contains fossils.
	Coal	Forms in swampy areas. Compacted layers of organic material, mainly plant remains.
Sedimentary (chemical)	Rock Salt	Commonly forms by the evaporation of seawater.
Metamorphic (foliated)	Gneiss	Banding due to alternate layers of different minerals, of different colors. Parent rock often is granite.
	Schist	Parallel arrangement of sheetlike minerals, mainly micas. Forms from different parent rocks.
	Phyllite	Shiny or silky appearance. May look wrinkled. Common parent rocks are shale and slate.
	Slate	Harder, denser, and shinier than shale. Common parent rock is shale.
Metamorphic (nonfoliated)	Marble	Calcite or dolomite. Common parent rock is limestone.
	Soapstone	Mainly of talc. Soft with greasy feel.
	Quartzite	Hard with interlocking quartz crystals. Common parent rock is sandstone.

SCIENCE SKILL HANDBOOK

MATH SKILL HANDBOOK

FOLDABLES HANDBOOK

REFERENCE HANDBOOK

GLOSSARY/ GLOSARIO

INDEX

Minerals

SCIENCE SKILL HANDBOOK

MATH SKILL HANDBOOK

FOLDABLES HANDBOOK

REFERENCE HANDBOOK

GLOSSARY/ GLOSARIO

INDEX

Minerals

Mineral (formula)	Color	Streak	Hardness Pattern	Breakage Properties	Uses and Other
Graphite (C)	black to gray	black to gray	1–1.5	basal cleavage (scales)	pencil lead, lubricants for locks, rods to control some small nuclear reactions, battery poles
Galena (PbS)	gray	gray to black	2.5	cubic cleavage perfect	source of lead, used for pipes, shields for X rays, fishing equipment sinkers
Hematite (Fe_2O_3)	black or reddish-brown	reddish-brown	5.5–6.5	irregular fracture	source of iron; converted to pig iron, made into steel
Magnetite (Fe_3O_4)	black	black	6	conchoidal fracture	source of iron, attracts a magnet
Pyrite (FeS_2)	light, brassy, yellow	greenish-black	6–6.5	uneven fracture	fool's gold
Talc ($Mg_3 Si_4O_{10}$ $(OH)_2$)	white, greenish	white	1	cleavage in one direction	used for talcum powder, sculptures, paper, and tabletops
Gypsum ($CaSO_4 \cdot 2H_2O$)	colorless, gray, white, brown	white	2	basal cleavage	used in plaster of paris and dry wall for building construction
Sphalerite (ZnS)	brown, reddish-brown, greenish	light to dark brown	3.5–4	cleavage in six directions	main ore of zinc; used in paints, dyes, and medicine
Muscovite (KAl_3Si_3 $O_{10}(OH)_2$)	white, light gray, yellow, rose, green	colorless	2–2.5	basal cleavage	occurs in large, flexible plates; used as an insulator in electrical equipment, lubricant
Biotite ($K(Mg,Fe)_3$ $(AlSi_3O_{10})$ $(OH)_2$)	black to dark brown	colorless	2.5–3	basal cleavage	occurs in large, flexible plates
Halite (NaCl)	colorless, red, white, blue	colorless	2.5	cubic cleavage	salt; soluble in water; a preservative

Minerals

Minerals

Mineral (formula)	Color	Streak	Hardness	Breakage Pattern	Uses and Other Properties
Calcite ($CaCO_3$)	colorless, white, pale blue	colorless, white	3	cleavage in three directions	fizzes when HCl is added; used in cements and other building materials
Dolomite ($CaMg(CO_3)_2$)	colorless, white, pink, green, gray, black	white	3.5–4	cleavage in three directions	concrete and cement; used as an ornamental building stone
Fluorite (CaF_2)	colorless, white, blue, green, red, yellow, purple	colorless	4	cleavage in four directions	used in the manufacture of optical equipment; glows under ultraviolet light
Hornblende ($(CaNa)_{2-3}(Mg,Al,Fe)_5-(Al,Si)_2Si_6O_{22}(OH)_2$)	green to black	gray to white	5–6	cleavage in two directions	will transmit light on thin edges; 6-sided cross section
Feldspar ($KAlSi_3O_8$) ($NaAlSi_3O_8$), ($CaAl_2Si_2O_8$)	colorless, white to gray, green	colorless	6	two cleavage planes meet at 90° angle	used in the manufacture of ceramics
Augite ($(Ca,Na)(Mg,Fe,Al)(Al,Si)_2O_6$)	black	colorless	6	cleavage in two directions	square or 8-sided cross section
Olivine ($(Mg,Fe)_2SiO_4$)	olive, green	none	6.5–7	conchoidal fracture	gemstones, refractory sand
Quartz (SiO_2)	colorless, various colors	none	7	conchoidal fracture	used in glass manufacture, electronic equipment, radios, computers, watches, gemstones

SCIENCE SKILL HANDBOOK

MATH SKILL HANDBOOK

FOLDABLES HANDBOOK

REFERENCE HANDBOOK

GLOSSARY/ GLOSARIO

INDEX

Weather Map Symbols

Sample Station Model

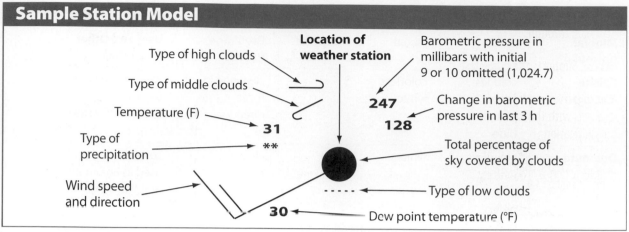

Type of high clouds

Type of middle clouds

Temperature (F)

Type of precipitation

Wind speed and direction

Location of weather station

Barometric pressure in millibars with initial 9 or 10 omitted (1,024.7)

247

128

Change in barometric pressure in last 3 h

31

**

30

Total percentage of sky covered by clouds

Type of low clouds

Dew point temperature (°F)

Sample Plotted Report at Each Station

Precipitation	Wind Speed and Direction	Sky Coverage	Some Types of High Clouds
☰ Fog	○ 0 calm	○ No cover	Scattered cirrus
★ Snow	1–2 knots	◐ 1/10 or less	Dense cirrus in patches
● Rain	3–7 knots	◕ 2/10 to 3/10	Veil of cirrus covering entire sky
Thunderstorm	8–12 knots	◑ 4/10	Cirrus not covering entire sky
' Drizzle	13–17 knots	◖ –	
▽ Showers	18–22 knots	◒ 6/10	
	23–27 knots	◕ 7/10	
	48–52 knots	◍ Overcast with openings	
	1 knot = 1.852 km/h	● Completely overcast	

Some Types of Middle Clouds	Some Types of Low Clouds	Fronts and Pressure Systems
Thin altostratus layer	⌒ Cumulus of fair weather	(H) or High (L) or Low — Center of high- or low-pressure system
Thick altostratus layer	⌣ Stratocumulus	▲▲▲▲ Cold front
Thin altostratus in patches	----- Fractocumulus of bad weather	●●●● Warm front
Thin altostratus in bands	— Stratus of fair weather	▲●▲● Occluded front
		●▲●▲ Stationary front

SCIENCE SKILL HANDBOOK

MATH SKILL HANDBOOK

FOLDABLES HANDBOOK

REFERENCE HANDBOOK

GLOSSARY/ GLOSARIO

INDEX

Use and Care of a Microscope

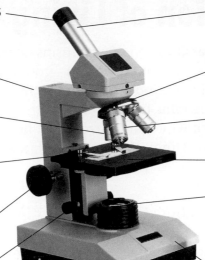

Eyepiece Contains magnifying lenses you look through.

Arm Supports the body tube.

Low-power objective Contains the lens with the lowest power magnification.

Stage clips Hold the microscope slide in place.

Coarse adjustment Focuses the image under low power.

Fine adjustment Sharpens the image under high magnification.

Body tube Connects the eyepiece to the revolving nosepiece.

Revolving nosepiece Holds and turns the objectives into viewing position.

High-power objective Contains the lens with the highest magnification.

Stage Supports the microscope slide.

Light source Provides light that passes upward through the diaphragm, the specimen, and the lenses.

Base Provides support for the microscope.

Caring for a Microscope

1. Always carry the microscope holding the arm with one hand and supporting the base with the other hand.
2. Don't touch the lenses with your fingers.
3. The coarse adjustment knob is used only when looking through the lowest-power objective lens. The fine adjustment knob is used when the high-power objective is in place.
4. Cover the microscope when you store it.

Using a Microscope

1. Place the microscope on a flat surface that is clear of objects. The arm should be toward you.
2. Look through the eyepiece. Adjust the diaphragm so light comes through the opening in the stage.
3. Place a slide on the stage so the specimen is in the field of view. Hold it firmly in place by using the stage clips.

4. Always focus with the coarse adjustment and the low-power objective lens first. After the object is in focus on low power, turn the nosepiece until the high-power objective is in place. Use ONLY the fine adjustment to focus with the high-power objective lens.

Making a Wet-Mount Slide

1. Carefully place the item you want to look at in the center of a clean, glass slide. Make sure the sample is thin enough for light to pass through.
2. Use a dropper to place one or two drops of water on the sample.
3. Hold a clean coverslip by the edges and place it at one edge of the water. Slowly lower the coverslip onto the water until it lies flat.
4. If you have too much water or a lot of air bubbles, touch the edge of a paper towel to the edge of the coverslip to draw off extra water and draw out unwanted air.

SCIENCE SKILL HANDBOOK

MATH SKILL HANDBOOK

FOLDABLES HANDBOOK

REFERENCE HANDBOOK

GLOSSARY/ GLOSARIO

INDEX

SCIENCE SKILL HANDBOOK

MATH SKILL HANDBOOK

FOLDABLES HANDBOOK

REFERENCE HANDBOOK

GLOSSARY/ GLOSARIO

INDEX

Diversity of Life: Classification of Living Organisms

A six-kingdom system of classification of organisms is used today. Two kingdoms—Kingdom Archaebacteria and Kingdom Eubacteria—contain organisms that do not have a nucleus and that lack membrane-bound structures in the cytoplasm of their cells. The members of the other four kingdoms have a cell or cells that contain a nucleus and structures in the cytoplasm, some of which are surrounded by membranes. These kingdoms are Kingdom Protista, Kingdom Fungi, Kingdom Plantae, and Kingdom Animalia.

Kingdom Archaebacteria

one-celled; some absorb food from their surroundings; some are photosynthetic; some are chemosynthetic; many are found in extremely harsh environments including salt ponds, hot springs, swamps, and deep-sea hydrothermal vents

Kingdom Eubacteria

one-celled; most absorb food from their surroundings; some are photosynthetic; some are chemosynthetic; many are parasites; many are round, spiral, or rod-shaped; some form colonies

Kingdom Protista

Phylum Euglenophyta one-celled; photosynthetic or take in food; most have one flagellum; euglenoids

Kingdom Eubacteria
Bacillus anthracis

Phylum Bacillariophyta one-celled; photosynthetic; have unique double shells made of silica; diatoms

Phylum Dinoflagellata one-celled; photosynthetic; contain red pigments; have two flagella; dinoflagellates

Phylum Chlorophyta one-celled, many-celled, or colonies; photosynthetic; contain chlorophyll; live on land, in freshwater, or salt water; green algae

Phylum Rhodophyta most are many-celled; photosynthetic; contain red pigments; most live in deep, saltwater environments; red algae

Phylum Phaeophyta most are many-celled; photosynthetic; contain brown pigments; most live in saltwater environments; brown algae

Phylum Rhizopoda one-celled; take in food; are free-living or parasitic; move by means of pseudopods; amoebas

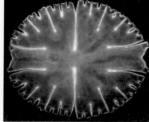

Phylum Chlorophyta
Desmids

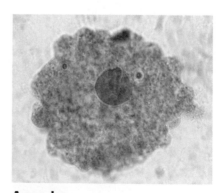

Amoeba

Phylum Zoomastigina one-celled; take in food; free-living or parasitic; have one or more flagella; zoomastigotes

Phylum Ciliophora one-celled; take in food; have large numbers of cilia; ciliates

Phylum Sporozoa one-celled; take in food; have no means of movement; are parasites in animals; sporozoans

Phylum Myxomycota
Slime mold

Phylum Oomycota
Phytophthora infestans

Phyla Myxomycota and Acrasiomycota one- or many-celled; absorb food; change form during life cycle; cellular and plasmodial slime molds

Phylum Oomycota many-celled; are either parasites or decomposers; live in freshwater or salt water; water molds, rusts and downy mildews

Kingdom Fungi

Phylum Zygomycota many-celled; absorb food; spores are produced in sporangia; zygote fungi; bread mold

Phylum Ascomycota one- and many-celled; absorb food; spores produced in asci; sac fungi; yeast

Phylum Basidiomycota many-celled; absorb food; spores produced in basidia; club fungi; mushrooms

Phylum Deuteromycota members with unknown reproductive structures; imperfect fungi; *Penicillium*

Phylum Mycophycota organisms formed by symbiotic relationship between an ascomycote or a basidiomycote and green alga or cyanobacterium; lichens

Lichens

SCIENCE SKILL HANDBOOK

MATH SKILL HANDBOOK

FOLDABLES HANDBOOK

REFERENCE HANDBOOK

GLOSSARY/ GLOSARIO

INDEX

Science Skill Handbook

Math Skill Handbook

Foldables Handbook

Reference Handbook

Glossary/Glosario

Index

Kingdom Plantae

Divisions Bryophyta (mosses), **Anthocerophyta** (hornworts), **Hepaticophyta** (liverworts), **Psilophyta** (whisk ferns) many-celled non-vascular plants; reproduce by spores produced in capsules; green; grow in moist, land environments

Division Lycophyta many-celled vascular plants; spores are produced in conelike structures; live on land; are photosynthetic; club mosses

Division Arthrophyta vascular plants; ribbed and jointed stems; scalelike leaves; spores produced in conelike structures; horsetails

Division Pterophyta vascular plants; leaves called fronds; spores produced in clusters of sporangia called sori; live on land or in water; ferns

Division Ginkgophyta deciduous trees; only one living species; have fan-shaped leaves with branching veins and fleshy cones with seeds; ginkgoes

Division Cycadophyta palmlike plants; have large, featherlike leaves; produces seeds in cones; cycads

Division Coniferophyta deciduous or evergreen; trees or shrubs; have needlelike or scalelike leaves; seeds produced in cones; conifers

Division Anthophyta
Tomato plant

Division Gnetophyta shrubs or woody vines; seeds are produced in cones; division contains only three genera; gnetum

Division Anthophyta dominant group of plants; flowering plants; have fruits with seeds

Kingdom Animalia

Phylum Porifera aquatic organisms that lack true tissues and organs; are asymmetrical and sessile; sponges

Phylum Cnidaria radially symmetrical organisms; have a digestive cavity with one opening; most have tentacles armed with stinging cells; live in aquatic environments singly or in colonies; includes jellyfish, corals, hydra, and sea anemones

Phylum Platyhelminthes bilaterally symmetrical worms; have flattened bodies; digestive system has one opening; parasitic and free-living species; flatworms

Division Bryophyta
Liverwort

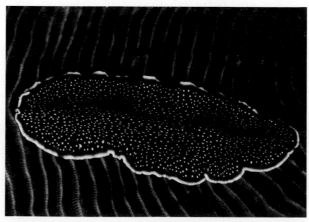

Phylum Platyhelminthes
Flatworm

(l)Lynn Keddie/Photolibrary/Getty Images; (tr)©Steven P. Lynch; (br)R. Aaron Raymond/Radius Images/Getty Images

Phylum Chordata

Phylum Nematoda round, bilaterally symmetrical body; have digestive system with two openings; free-living forms and parasitic forms; roundworms

Phylum Mollusca soft-bodied animals, many with a hard shell and soft foot or footlike appendage; a mantle covers the soft body; aquatic and terrestrial species; includes clams, snails, squid, and octopuses

Phylum Annelida bilaterally symmetrical worms; have round, segmented bodies; terrestrial and aquatic species; includes earthworms, leeches, and marine polychaetes

Phylum Arthropoda largest animal group; have hard exoskeletons, segmented bodies, and pairs of jointed appendages; land and aquatic species; includes insects, crustaceans, and spiders

Phylum Echinodermata marine organisms; have spiny or leathery skin and a water-vascular system with tube feet; are radially symmetrical; includes sea stars, sand dollars, and sea urchins

Phylum Chordata organisms with internal skeletons and specialized body systems; most have paired appendages; all at some time have a notochord, nerve cord, gill slits, and a post-anal tail; include fish, amphibians, reptiles, birds, and mammals

SCIENCE SKILL HANDBOOK

MATH SKILL HANDBOOK

FOLDABLES HANDBOOK

REFERENCE HANDBOOK

GLOSSARY/ GLOSARIO

INDEX

Glossary/Glosario

A science multilingual glossary is available on ConnectEd. The glossary includes the following languages:

Arabic
Bengali
Chinese
English
Haitian Creole

Hmong
Korean
Portuguese
Russian
Spanish

Tagalog
Urdu
Vietnamese

Cómo usar el glosario en español:
1. Busca el término en inglés que desees encontrar.
2. El término en español, junto con la definición, se encuentran en la columna de la derecha.

Pronunciation Key

Use the following key to help you sound out words in the glossary:

a	back (BAK)	ew	food (FEWD)
ay	day (DAY)	yoo	pure (PYOOR)
ah	father (FAH thur)	yew	few (FYEW)
ow	flower (FLOW ur)	uh	comma (CAH muh)
ar	car (CAR)	u (+ con)	rub (RUB)
e	less (LES)	sh	shelf (SHELF)
ee	leaf (LEEF)	ch	nature (NAY chur)
ih	trip (TRIHP)	g	gift (GIHFT)
i (i + con + e) .	idea (i DEE uh)	j	gem (JEM)
oh	go (GOH)	ing	sing (SING)
aw	soft (SAWFT)	zh	vision (VIH zhun)
or	orbit (OR buht)	k	cake (KAYK)
oy	coin (COYN)	s	seed, cent (SEED, SENT)
oo	foot (FOOT)	z	zone, raise (ZOHN, RAYZ)

English — A — Español

abiotic factor/adaptation

abiotic factor (ay bi AH tihk • FAK tuhr): a nonliving thing in an ecosystem. (p. 553)

absorption: the process in which nutrients from digested food are taken into the body. (p. 499)

acceleration: a measure of the change in velocity during a period of time. (p. 12)

acid precipitation: precipitation that has a lower pH than that of normal rainwater (pH 5.6). (pp. 285, 614)

adaptation: an inherited trait that increases an organism's chance of surviving and reproducing in a particular environment. (p. 408)

factor abiótico/adaptación

factor abiótico: componente no vivo de un ecosistema. (pág. 553)

absorción: proceso en el cual los nutrientes del alimento digerido son alojados dentro del cuerpo. (pág. 499)

aceleración: medida del cambio de velocidad durante un período de tiempo. (pág. 12)

precipitación ácida: precipitación que tiene un pH más bajo que el del agua de la lluvia normal. (pH 5.6) (págs. 285, 614)

adaptación: rasgo heredado que aumenta la oportunidad de un organismo de sobrevivir y reproducirse en un medioambiente. (pág. 408)

SCIENCE SKILL HANDBOOK
MATH SKILL HANDBOOK
FOLDABLES HANDBOOK
REFERENCE HANDBOOK
GLOSSARY/ GLOSARIO
INDEX

air mass: a large area of air that has uniform temperature, humidity, and pressure. (p. 310)

air pollution: the contamination of air by harmful substances including gases and smoke. (p. 284)

air pressure: the force that a column of air applies on the air or a surface below it. (p. 302)

Air Quality Index (AQI): a scale that ranks levels of ozone and other air pollutants. (p. 617)

amnion: a protective membrane that surrounds an embryo. (p. 426)

amplitude: the maximum distance a wave varies from its rest position. (p. 192)

angiosperm: a plant that produces flowers and develops fruit. (p. 375)

asymmetry: a body plan in which an organism cannot be divided into any two parts that are nearly mirror images. (p. 406)

atmosphere (AT muh sfihr): a thin layer of gases surrounding Earth. (p. 259)

atmosphere: a thin layer of gases surrounding Earth. (p. 229)

atom: a small particle that is the building block of matter. (p. 143)

autotroph (AW tuh trohf): an organism that converts light energy to usable energy. (p. 344)

masa de aire: amplia zona de aire que tiene uniforme de temperatura, humedad y presión. (pág. 310)

polución del aire: contaminación del aire por sustancias dañinas, como gases y humo. (pág. 284)

presión del aire: presión que una columna de aire ejerce sobre el aire o sobre la superficie debajo de ella. (pág. 302)

Índice de calidad del aire (ICA): escala que clasifica los niveles de ozono y de otros contaminantes del aire. (pág. 617)

saco amniótico: membrana que rodea y protege al embrión. (pág. 426)

amplitud: distancia máxima que varía una onda desde su posición de reposo. (pág. 192)

angiosperma: planta que produce flores y desarrolla frutos. (pág. 375)

asimetría: plano corporal en el cual un organismo no se puede dividir en dos partes que sean casi imágenes al espejo una de otra. (pág. 406)

atmósfera: capa delgada de gases que rodean la Tierra. (pág. 259)

atmósfera: capa delgada de gases que rodean la Tierra. (pág. 229)

átomo: partícula pequeña que es el componente básico de la materia. (pág. 143)

autotrófo: organismo que convierte la energía lumínica en energía útil. (pág. 344)

B

balanced forces: forces acting on an object that combine and form a net force of zero. (p. 23)

B cell: a type of whibalanced forces: forces acting on an object that combine and form a net force of zero. (p. 23)

bilateral symmetry: a body plan in which an organism can be divided into two parts that are nearly mirror images of each other. (p. 406)

binomial nomenclature (bi NOH mee ul • NOH mun klay chur): a naming system that gives each organism a two-word scientific name. (p. 346)

fuerzas en equilibrio: fuerzas que actúan sobre un objeto, se combinan y forman una fuerza neta de cero. (pág. 23)

fuerzas en equilibrio: fuerzas que actúan sobre un objeto, se combinan y forman una fuerza neta de cero. (pág. 23)

simetría bilateral: plano corporal en el cual un organismo se puede dividir en dos partes que sean casi imágenes al espejo una de otra. (pág. 406)

nomenclatura binomial: sistema de nombrar que le da a cada organismo un nombre científico de dos palabras. (pág. 346)

biome: a geographic area on Earth that contains ecosystems with similar biotic and abiotic features. (p. 556)

biosphere: the Earth system that contains all living things. (p. 228)

biotic factor (bi AH tihk • FAK tuhr): a living or once-living thing in an ecosystem. (p. 555)

biotic potential: the potential growth of a population if it could grow in perfect conditions with no limiting factors. (p. 563)

bladder: a muscular sac that holds urine until the urine is excreted. (p. 463)

blizzard: a violent winter storm characterized by freezing temperatures, strong winds, and blowing snow. (p. 317)

Boyle's Law: the law that pressure of a gas increases if the volume decreases and pressure of a gas decreases if the volume increases, when temperature is constant. (p. 138)

bioma: área geográfica en la Tierra que contiene ecosistemas con características bióticas y abióticas similares. (pág. 556)

biosfera: el sistema de la Tierra que contiene todo que está viviendo. (pág. 228)

factor biótico: ser vivo o que una vez estuvo vivo en un ecosistema. (pág. 555)

potencial biótico: crecimiento potencial de una población si puede crecer en condiciones perfectas sin factores limitantes. (pág. 563)

vejiga: bolsa muscular que contiene la orina hasta que se excreta. (pág. 463)

ventisca: tormenta violenta de invierno caracterizada por temperaturas heladas, vientos fuertes, y nieve que sopla. (pág. 317)

Ley de Boyle: ley que afirma que la presión de un gas aumenta si el volumen disminuye y que la presión de un gas disminuye si el volumen aumenta, cuando la temperatura es constante. (pág. 138)

C

Calorie: the amount of energy it takes to raise the temperature of 1 kg of water by 1°C. (p. 441)

carbohydrate (kar boh HI drayt): a macromolecule made up of one or more sugar molecules, which are composed of carbon, hydrogen, and oxygen; usually the body's major source of energy. (p. 442)

carrying capacity: the largest number of individuals of one species that an ecosystem can support over time. (p. 563)

carrying capacity: the largest number of individuals of one species that an ecosystem can support over time. (p. 590)

Charles's Law: the law that volume of a gas increases with increasing temperature, if the pressure is constant. (p. 139)

chemical change: a change in matter in which the substances that make up the matter change into other substances with different chemical and physical properties. (p. 100)

caloría: cantidad de energía necesaria para aumentar la temperatura de 1 kg de agua a 1°C. (pág. 441)

carbohidrato: macromolécula constituida de una o más moléculas de azúcar, las cuales están compuestas de carbono, hidrógeno y oxígeno; usualmente es la mayor fuente de energía del cuerpo. (pág. 442)

capacidad de carga: número mayor de individuos de una especie que un medioambiente puede mantener con el tiempo. (pág. 563)

capacidad de carga: número mayor de individuos de una especie que un medioambiente puede mantener. (pág. 590)

Ley de Charles: ley que afirma que el volumen de un gas aumenta cuando la temperatura aumenta, si la presión es constante. (pág. 139)

cambio químico: cambio de la materia en el cual las sustancias que componen la materia se transforman en otras sustancias con propiedades químicas y físicas diferentes. (pág. 100)

SCIENCE SKILL HANDBOOK

MATH SKILL HANDBOOK

FOLDABLES HANDBOOK

REFERENCE HANDBOOK

GLOSSARY/ GLOSARIO

INDEX

chemical digestion: a process in which chemical reactions break down pieces of food into small molecules. (p. 450)

chemical energy: energy that is stored in and released from the bonds between atoms. (p. 48)

chemical property: the ability or inability of a substance to combine with or change into one or more new substances. (p. 91)

chyme (KIME): a thin, watery liquid made of broken down food molecules and gastric juice. (p. 453)

climate: the long-term average weather conditions that occur in a particular region. (pp. 243, 517)

closed circulatory system: a system that transports materials through blood using vessels. (p. 491)

coelom (SEE lum): a fluid-filled cavity in the body of an animal. (p. 478)

community: all the populations living in an ecosystem at the same time. (p. 555)

complex machine: two or more simple machines working together. (p. 65)

compression: region of a longitudinal wave where the particles of the medium are closest together. (p. 211)

computer model: detailed computer programs that solve a set of complex mathematical formulas. (p. 324)

condensation: the change of state from a gas to a liquid. (p. 130)

condensation: the process by which a gas changes to a liquid. (p. 241)

conduction: the transfer of thermal energy due to collisions between particles. (p. 162)

conduction: the transfer of thermal energy due to collisions between particles. (p. 271)

consumer: an organism that cannot make its own food and gets energy by eating other organisms. (p. 571)

contact force: a push or a pull on one object by another object that is touching it. (p. 20)

digestión química: proceso por el cual las reacciones químicas descomponen partes del alimento en moléculas pequeñas. (pág. 450)

energía química: energía almacenada en y liberada por los enlaces entre los átomos. (pág. 48)

propiedad química: capacidad o incapacidad de una sustancia para combinarse con una o más sustancias o transformarse en una o más sustancias. (pág. 91)

quimo: líquido diluido y acuoso constituido de moléculas de alimento descompuestas y jugos gástricos. (pág. 453)

clima: promedio a largo plazo de las condiciones del tiempo atmosférico de una región en particular. (pág. 243, 517)

sistema circulatorio cerrado: sistema que transporta materiales a través de la sangre usando vasos. (pág. 491)

celoma: cavidad llena de fluido en el cuerpo de un animal. (pág. 478)

comunidad: todas las poblaciones que viven en un ecosistema al mismo tiempo. (pág. 555)

máquina compleja: dos o más máquinas simples que trabajan juntas. (pág. 65)

compresión: región de una onda longitudinal donde las partículas del medio están más cerca. (pág. 211)

modelo de computadora: programas de computadora que resuelven un conjunto de fórmulas matemáticas complejas. (pág. 324)

condensación: cambio de estado gaseoso a líquido. (pág. 130)

condensación: proceso mediante el cual un gas cambia a líquido. (pág. 241)

conducción: transferencia de energía térmica debido a colisiones entre partículas. (pág. 162)

conducción: transferencia de energía térmica mediante la colisión de partículas. (pág. 271)

consumidor: organismo que no elabora su propio alimento y obtiene energía comiendo otros organismos. (pág. 571)

fuerza de contacto: empuje o arrastre ejercido sobre un objeto por otro que lo está tocando. (pág. 20)

SCIENCE SKILL HANDBOOK

MATH SKILL HANDBOOK

FOLDABLES HANDBOOK

REFERENCE HANDBOOK

GLOSSARY/ GLOSARIO

INDEX

convection current: the movement of fluids in a cycle because of convection. (p. 167)

convection: the circulation of particles within a material caused by differences in thermal energy and density. (p. 271)

convection: the transfer of thermal energy by the movement of particles from one part of a material to another. (p. 166)

critical thinking: comparing what you already know about something to new information and deciding whether or not you agree with the new information. (p. NOS 10)

crop: a specialized structure in the digestive system where ingested material is stored. (p. 498)

cytoplasm: the liquid part of a cell inside the cell membrane; contains salts and other molecules. (p. 354)

corriente de convección: movimiento de fluidos en un ciclo debido a la convección. (pág. 167)

convección: circulación de partículas dentro de un material causado por diferencias en la energía térmica y densidad. (pág. 271)

convección: transferencia de energía térmica por el movimiento de partículas de una parte de la materia a otra. (pág. 166)

pensamiento crítico: el comparar de lo que ya se sabe de un asunto con información nueva y el decidir si está de acuerdo con la información nueva. (pág. NOS 10)

buche: estructura especializada en el sistema digestivo donde el material ingerido se almacena. (pág. 498)

citoplasma: fluido en el interior de una célula que contiene sales y otras moléculas. (pág. 354)

D

decibel: the unit used to measure sound intensity or loudness. (p. 213)

deforestation: the removal of large areas of forests for human purposes. (p. 595)

deforestation: the removal of large areas of forests for human purposes. (p. 537)

density: the mass per unit volume of a substance. (p. 89)

dependent variable: the factor a scientist observes or measures during an experiment. (p. NOS 27)

deposition: the process of changing directly from a gas to a solid. (p. 130)

description: a spoken or written summary of an observation. (p. NOS 18)

desertification: the development of desertlike conditions due to human activities and/or climate change. (p. 596)

dew point: temperature at which air is saturated and condensation can occur. (p. 303)

diffusion: the movement of substances from an area of higher concentration to an area of lower concentration. (p. 488)

digestion: the mechanical and chemical

decibel: unidad usada para medir la intensidad o el volumen del sonido. (pág. 213)

deforestación: eliminación de grandes áreas de bosques con propósitos humanos. (pág. 595)

deforestación: eliminación de grandes áreas de bosques con propósitos humanos. (pág. 537)

densidad: cantidad de masa por unidad de volumen de una sustancia. (pág. 89)

variable dependiente: factor que el científico observa o mide durante un experimento. (pág. NOS 27)

deposición: proceso de cambiar directamente de gas a sólido. (pág. 130)

descripción: resumen oral o escrito de una observación de. (pág. NOS 18)

desertificación: desarrollo de condiciones parecidas a las del desierto debido a actividades humanas y/o al cambio en el clima. (pág. 596)

punto de rocío: temperatura en la cual el aire está saturado y occure la condensación. (pág. 303)

difusión: movimiento de sustancias de un área de mayor concentración a un área de menor concentración. (pág. 488)

digestión: descomposición mecánica y química

breakdown of food into small particles and molecules that your body can absorb and use. (p. 449)

displacement: the difference between the initial, or starting, position and the final position of an object that has moved. (p. 10)

distance: the total length of your path. (p. 10)

Doppler radar: a specialized type of radar that can detect precipitation as well as the movement of small particles, which can be used to approximate wind speed. (p. 322)

dormancy: a period of no growth. (p. 381)

drought: a period of below-average precipitation. (p. 531)

del alimento en partículas y moléculas pequeñas que el cuerpo absorbe y usa. (pág. 449)

desplazamiento: diferencia entre la posición inicial, o salida, y la final de un objeto que se ha movido. (pág. 10)

distancia: longitud total de un trayecto. (pág. 10)

radar Doppler: tipo de radar especializado que detecta tanto la precipitación como el movimiento de partículas pequeñas, que se pueden usar para determinar la velocidad aproximada del viento. (pág. 322)

latencia: período sin crecimiento. (pág. 381)

sequía: período de bajo promedio de precipitación. (pág. 531)

ecosystem: all the living things and nonliving things in a given area. (p. 553)

ectotherm: an animal that heats its body from heat in its environment. (p. 426)

efficiency: the ratio of output work to input work. (p. 67)

El Niño/Southern Oscillation: the combined ocean and atmospheric cycle that results in weakened trade winds across the Pacific Ocean. (p. 530)

electric energy: energy carried by an electric current. (p. 46)

electromagnetic wave: a transverse wave that can travel through empty space and through matter. (p. 188)

endoskeleton: the internal rigid framework that supports humans and other animals. (p. 408)

endotherm: an animal that generates its body heat from the inside. (p. 427)

energy pyramid: a model that shows the amount of energy available in each link of a food chain. (p. 573)

energy transformation: the conversion of one form of energy to another. (p. 55)

energy: the ability to cause change. (p. 45)

ecosistema: todos los seres vivos y los componentes no vivos de un área dada. (pág. 553)

ectotérmico: animal que calienta el cuerpo con el calor del medioambiente. (pág. 426)

eficiencia: relación entre energía invertida y energía útil. (pág. 67)

El Niño/Oscilación meridional: ciclo atmosférico y oceánico combinado que produce el debilitamiento de los vientos alisios en el Océano Pacífico. (pág. 530)

energía eléctrica: energía transportada por una corriente eléctrica. (pág. 46)

onda electromagnética: onda transversal que puede viajar a través del espacio vacío y de la materia. (pág. 188)

endoesqueleto: armazón interno y rígido que soporta a los seres humanos y a otros animales. (pág. 408)

endotérmico: animal que genera calor corporal de su interior. (pág. 427)

pirámide energética: modelo que explica la cantidad de energía disponible en cada vínculo de una cadena alimentaria. (pág. 573)

transformación de energía: conversión de una forma de energía a otra. (pág. 55)

energía: capacidad de ocasionar cambio. (pág. 45)

SCIENCE SKILL HANDBOOK

MATH SKILL HANDBOOK

FOLDABLES HANDBOOK

REFERENCE HANDBOOK

GLOSSARY/ GLOSARIO

INDEX

enzyme (EN zime): a protein that helps break down larger molecules into smaller molecules and speeds up, or catalyzes, the rate of chemical reactions. (p. 450)

esophagus (ih SAH fuh gus): a muscular tube that connects the mouth to the stomach. (p. 452)

eukaryotic (yew ker ee AH tihk) cell: a cell that has a nucleus and other membrane-bound organelles. (p. 352)

evaporation: the process of a liquid changing to a gas at the surface of the liquid. (p. 240)

evaporation: the process of a liquid changing to a gas at the surface of the liquid. (p. 366)

excretory system: the system that collects and eliminates wastes from the body and regulates the level of fluid in the body. (p. 459)

exoskeleton: a thick, hard outer covering; protects and supports an animal's body. (p. 408)

explanation: an interpretation of observations. (p. NOS 18)

enzima: proteína que descompone moléculas más grandes en moléculas más pequeñas y acelera, o cataliza, la velocidad de las reacciones químicas. (pág. 450)

esófago: tubo muscular que conecta la boca al estómago. (pág. 452)

célula eucariótica: célula que tiene un núcleo y otros organelos limitados por una membrana. (pág. 352)

evaporación: proceso por el cual un líquido cambia a gas en la superficie de dicho líquido. (pág. 240)

evaporación: proceso mediante el cual un líquido cambia a gas en la superficie del líquido. (pág. 366)

sistema excretor: sistema que recolecta y elimina los desperdicios del cuerpo y regula el nivel de fluidos en el cuerpo. (pág. 459)

exoesqueleto: cubierta externa, gruesa y dura, que protege y soporta el cuerpo de un animal. (pág. 408)

explicación: interpretación de las observaciones. (pág. NOS 18)

F

fat: also called a lipid, a substance in the body that provides energy and helps your body absorb vitamins. (p. 443)

food chain: a model that shows how energy flows in an ecosystem through feeding relationships. (p. 572)

food web: a model of energy transfer that can show how the food chains in a community are interconnected. (p. 572)

force pair: the forces two objects apply to each other. (p. 31)

force: a push or a pull on an object. (p. 19)

frequency: the number of wavelengths that pass by a point each second. (p. 191)

friction: a contact force that resists the sliding motion of two surfaces that are touching. (p. 21)

front: a boundary between two air masses. (p. 312)

grasa: también llamada lípido, sustancia en el cuerpo que proporciona energía y ayuda al cuerpo a absorber vitaminas. (pág. 443)

cadena alimentaria: modelo que explica cómo la energía fluye en un ecosistema a través de relaciones alimentarias. (pág. 572)

red alimentaria: modelo de transferencia de energía que explica cómo las cadenas alimentarias están interconectadas en una comunidad. (pág. 572)

par de fuerzas: fuerzas que dos objetos se aplican entre sí. (pág. 31)

fuerza: empuje o arrastre ejercido sobre un objeto. (pág. 19)

frecuencia: número de longitudes de onda que pasan por un punto cada segundo. (pág. 191)

fricción: fuerza de contacto que resiste el movimiento de dos superficies que están en contacto. (pág. 21)

frente: límite entre dos masas de aire. (pág. 312)

G

gas: matter that has no definite volume and no definite shape. (pp. 86,122)

geosphere: the solid part of Earth. (p. 233)

gill: an organ that exchanges carbon dioxide for oxygen in the water. (p. 424)

gill: an organ that exchanges carbon dioxide for oxygen in water. (p. 489)

gizzard: a muscular pouch similar to a stomach that is used to grind food. (p. 498)

global climate model: a set of complex equations used to predict future climates. (p. 539)

global warming: an increase in the average temperature of Earth's surface. (pp.536, 615)

gravity: an attractive force that exists between all objects that have mass. (p. 21)

greenhouse effect: the natural process that occurs when certain gases in the atmosphere absorb and reradiate thermal energy from the Sun. (p. 616)

greenhouse gas: a gas in the atmosphere that absorbs Earth's outgoing infrared radiation. (p. 536)

groundwater: water that is stored in cracks and pores beneath Earth's surface. (p. 232)

gymnosperm: a plant that produces seeds that are not part of a flower. (p. 374)

gas: materia que no tiene volumen ni forma definidos. (pág. 86,122)

geosfera: parte sólida de la Tierra. (pág. 233)

branquia: órgano que intercambia dióxido de carbono por oxígeno en el agua. (pág. 424)

Branquia: órgano que intercambia dióxido de carbono por oxígeno en el agua. (pág. 489)

molleja: bolsa muscular similar al estómago que sirve para triturar el alimento. (pág. 498)

modelo de clima global: conjunto de ecuaciones complejas para predecir climas futuros. (pág. 539)

calentamiento global: incremento en la temperatura promedio de la superficie de la Tierra. (pág. 536, 615)

gravedad: fuerza de atracción que existe entre todos los objetos que tienen masa. (pág. 21)

efecto invernadero: proceso natural que ocurre cuando ciertos gases en la atmósfera absorben y vuelven a irradiar la energía térmica del Sol. (pág. 536,616)

gas de invernadero: gas en la atmósfera que absorbe la salida de radiación infrarroja de la Tierra. (pág. 536)

agua subterránea: agua almacenada en grietas y poros debajo de la superficie de la Tierra. (pág. 232)

gimnosperma: planta que produce semillas que no son parte de una flor. (pág. 374)

H

habitat: the place within an ecosystem where an organism lives; provides the biotic and abiotic factors an organism needs to survive and reproduce. (p. 564)

habitat: the place within an ecosystem where an organism lives; provides the biotic and abiotic factors an organism needs to survive and reproduce. (p. 345)

heat engine: a machine that converts thermal energy into mechanical energy. (p. 174)

heat: the movement of thermal energy from a region of higher temperature to a region of lower temperature. (p. 157)

hábitat: lugar en un ecosistema donde vive un organismo; proporciona los factores bióticos y abióticos que un organismo necesita para vivir y reproducirse. (pág. 564)

hábitat: lugar en un ecosistema donde vive un organismo; proporciona los factores bióticos y abióticos de un organismo necesita para sobrevivir y reproducirse. (pág. 345)

motor térmico: máquina que convierte energía térmica en energía mecánica. (pág. 174)

calor: movimiento de energía térmica de una región de alta temperatura a una región de baja temperatura. (pág. 157)

SCIENCE SKILL HANDBOOK

MATH SKILL HANDBOOK

FOLDABLES HANDBOOK

REFERENCE HANDBOOK

GLOSSARY/ GLOSARIO

INDEX

heating appliance: a device that converts electric energy into thermal energy. (p. 171)

heterotroph (HE tuh roh trohf): an organism that obtains energy from other organisms. (p. 344)

high-pressure system: a large body of circulating air with high pressure at its center and lower pressure outside of the system. (p. 309)

humidity (hyew MIH duh tee): the amount of water vapor in the air. (p. 302)

hurricane: an intense tropical storm with winds exceeding 119 km/h. (p. 316)

hydrosphere: the system containing all Earth's water. (p. 231)

hydrostatic skeleton: a fluid-filled internal cavity surrounded by muscle tissue. (p. 408)

hydrostatic skeleton: a fluid-filled internal cavity surrounded by muscle tissue. (p. 478)

hypothesis: a possible explanation for an observation that can be tested by scientific investigations. (p. NOS 6)

calentador: aparato que convierte energía eléctrica en energía térmica. (pág. 171)

heterótrofo: organismo que obtiene energía de otros organismos. (pág. 344)

sistema de alta presión: gran cuerpo de aire circulante con presión alta en el centro y presión más baja fuera del sistema. (pág. 309)

humedad: cantidad de vapor de agua en el aire. (pág. 302)

huracán: tormenta tropical intensa con vientos que exceden los 119 km/h. (pág. 316)

hidrosfera: sistema que contiene toda el agua de la Tierra. (pág. 231)

esqueleto hidrostático: cavidad interna llena de fluido y rodeada de tejido muscular. (pág. 408)

hidroesqueleto: cavidad interna llena de fluido rodeada por tejido muscular. (pág. 478)

hipótesis: explicación posible de una observación que se puede probar por medio de investigaciones científicas. (pág. NOS 6)

I

ice age: a period of time when a large portion of Earth's surface is covered by glaciers. (p. 526)

inclined plane: a simple machine that consists of a ramp, or a flat, sloped surface. (p. 64)

independent variable: the factor that is changed by the investigator to observe how it affects a dependent variable. (p. NOS 27)

inertia (ihn UR shuh): the tendency of an object to resist a change in motion. (p. 27)

inference: a logical explanation of an observation that is drawn from prior knowledge or experience. (p. NOS 6)

infrared wave: an electromagnetic wave that has a wavelength shorter than a microwave but longer than visible light. (p. 200)

intensity: the amount of energy that passes through a square meter of space in one second. (p. 204)

era del hielo: período de tiempo cuando los glaciares cubren una gran porción de la superficie de la Tierra. (pág. 526)

plano inclinado: máquina simple que consiste en una rampa, o superficie plana inclinada. (pág. 64)

variable independiente: factor que el investigador cambia para observar cómo afecta la variable dependiente. (pág. NOS 27)

inercia: tendencia de un objeto a resistir un cambio en el movimiento. (pág. 27)

inferencia: explicación lógica de una observación que se extrae de un conocimiento previo o experiencia. (pág. NOS 6)

onda infrarroja: onda electromagnética que tiene una longitud de onda más corta que la de una microonda, pero más larga que la de la luz visible. (pág. 200)

intensidad: cantidad de energía que atraviesa un metro cuadrado de espacio en un segundo. (pág. 204)

SCIENCE SKILL HANDBOOK

MATH SKILL HANDBOOK

FOLDABLES HANDBOOK

REFERENCE HANDBOOK

GLOSSARY/ GLOSARIO

INDEX

interglacial: a warm period that occurs during an ice age or between ice ages. (p. 526)

International System of Units (SI): the internationally accepted system of measurement. (p. NOS 18)

ionosphere: a region within the mesosphere and thermosphere containing ions. (p. 263)

isobar: lines that connect all places on a map where pressure has the same value. (p. 323)

interglacial: período tibio que ocurre durante una era del hielo o entre las eras del hielo. (pág. 526)

Sistema Internacional de Unidades (SI): sistema de medidas aceptado internacionalmente. (pág. NOS 18)

ionosfera: región entre la mesosfera y la termosfera que contiene iones. (pág. 263)

isobara: línea que conectan todos los lugares en un mapa donde la presión tiene el mismo valor. (pág. 323)

jet stream: a narrow band of high winds located near the top of the troposphere. (p. 279)

corriente de chorro: banda angosta de vientos fuertes cerca de la parte superior de la troposfera. (pág. 279)

kidney: a bean-shaped organ that filters, or removes, wastes from blood. (p. 461)

kinetic (kuh NEH tik) energy: energy due to motion. (pp. 46,126)

kinetic molecular theory: an explanation of how particles in matter behave. (p. 136)

riñón: órgano con forma de frijol que filtra, o extrae, los desechos de la sangre. (pág. 461)

energía cinética: energía debida al movimiento. (pág. 46,126)

teoría cinética molecular: explicación de cómo se comportan las partículas en la materia. (pág. 136)

land breeze: a wind that blows from the land to the sea due to local temperature and pressure differences. (p. 280)

law of conservation of energy: law that states that energy can be transformed from one form to another, but it cannot be created or destroyed. (p. 55)

law of conservation of mass: law that states that the total mass of the reactants before a chemical reaction is the same as the total mass of the products after the chemical reaction. (p. 103)

lens: a transparent object with at least one curved side that causes light to change direction.

lever: a simple machine that consists of a bar that pivots, or rotates, around a fixed point. (p. 64)

brisa terrestre: viento que sopla desde la tierra hacia el mar debido a diferencias en la temperatura local y la presión. (pág. 280)

ley de la conservación de la energía: ley que plantea que la energía puede transformarse de una forma a otra, pero no puede crearse ni destruirse. (pág. 55)

ley de la conservación de la masa: ley que plantea que la masa total de los reactivos antes de una reacción química es la misma que la masa total de los productos después de la reacción química. (pág. 103)

lente: un objeto transparente con al menos un lado curvo que hace que la luz para cambiar de dirección.

palanca: máquina simple que consiste en una barra que gira, o rota, alrededor de un punto fijo. (pág. 64)

SCIENCE SKILL HANDBOOK

MATH SKILL HANDBOOK

FOLDABLES HANDBOOK

REFERENCE HANDBOOK

GLOSSARY/ GLOSARIO

INDEX

limiting factor: a factor that can limit the growth of a population. (p. 563)

liquid: matter with a definite volume but no definite shape. (pp. 86,122)

longitudinal (lahn juh TEWD nul) wave: a wave in which the disturbance is parallel to the direction the wave travels. (p. 189)

low-pressure system: a large body of circulating air with low pressure at its center and higher pressure outside of the system. (p. 309)

factor limitante: factor que limita el crecimiento de una población. (pág. 563)

líquido: materia con volumen definido y forma indefinida. (pág. 86,122)

onda longitudinal: onda en la que la perturbación es paralela a la dirección en que viaja la onda. (pág. 189)

sistema baja presión: gran cuerpo de aire circulante con presión baja en el centro y presión más alta fuera del sistema. (pág. 309)

M

mammary gland: special tissue that produces milk for young mammals. (p. 428)

mantle: a thin layer of tissue that covers a mollusk's internal organs. (p. 416)

mass: the amount of matter in an object. (p. 88)

mechanical digestion: a process in which food is physically broken into smaller pieces. (p. 450)

mechanical energy: sum of the potential energy and the kinetic energy in a system. (p. 49)

mechanical wave: a wave that can travel only through matter. (p. 188)

metamorphosis (me tuh MOR fuh sihs): a developmental process in which the body form of an animal changes as it grows from an egg to an adult. (p. 417)

microclimate: a localized climate that is different from the climate of the larger area surrounding it. (p. 521)

mineral: a solid that is naturally occurring, inorganic, and has a crystal structure and definite chemical composition. (p. 233)

mineral: any of several inorganic nutrients that help the body regulate many chemical reactions. (p. 443)

mitochondrion (mi tuh KAHN dree ahn): an organelle that breaks down food and releases energy. (p. 355)

molting: a process in which an outer covering, such as an exoskeleton, is shed and replaced. (p. 416)

glándula mamaria: tejido especial que produce leche para los mamíferos jóvenes. (pág. 428)

manto: capa delgada de tejido que cubre los órganos internos del molusco. (pág. 416)

masa: cantidad de materia en un objeto. (pág. 88)

digestión mecánica: proceso por el cual el alimento se descompone físicamente en pedazos más pequeños. (pág. 450)

energía mecánica: suma de la energía potencial y de la energía cinética en un sistema. (pág. 49)

onda mecánica: onda que puede viajar sólo a través de la materia. (pág. 188)

metamorfosis: proceso de desarrollo en el cual la forma del cuerpo de un animal cambia a medida que crece de huevo a adulto. (pág. 417)

microclima: clima localizado que es diferente del clima de área más extensa que lo rodea. (pág. 521)

mineral: sólido inorganico que se encuentra en la naturaleza, tiene una estructura cristalina y una composición química definida. (pág. 233)

mineral: cualquiera de los varios nutrientes inorgánicos que ayudan al cuerpo a regular muchas reacciones químicas. (pág. 443)

mitocondria: organelo que descompone el alimento y libera energía. (pág. 355)

muda: proceso en el cual una cubierta externa, como un exoesqueleto, se muda y reemplaza. (pág. 416)

monsoon: a wind circulation pattern that changes direction with the seasons. (p. 531)

motion: the process of changing position. (p. 9)

monsón: patrón de viento circulante que cambia de dirección con las estaciones. (pág. 531)

movimiento: proceso de cambiar de posición. (pág. 9)

nephron (NEH frahn): a network of capillaries and small tubes, or tubules, where filtration of blood occurs. (p. 461)

nerve net: a netlike control system that sends signals to and from all parts of the body. (p. 480)

Newton's first law of motion: law that states that if the net force acting on an object is zero, the motion of the object does not change. (p. 27)

Newton's second law of motion: law that states that the acceleration of an object is equal to the net force exerted on the object divided by the object's mass. (p. 30)

Newton's third law of motion: law that states that for every action there is an equal and opposite reaction. (p. 31)

niche (NICH): the way a species interacts with abiotic and biotic factors to obtain food, find shelter, and fulfill other needs. (p. 564)

noncontact force: a force that one object applies to another object without touching it. (p. 20)

nonpoint-source pollution: pollution from several widespread sources that cannot be traced back to a single location. (p. 607)

nonvascular plant: a plant that lacks specialized tissues for transporting water and nutrients. (p. 372)

notochord: a flexible, rod-shaped structure that supports the body of a developing chordate. (p. 422)

nuclear energy: energy stored in and released from the nucleus of an atom. (p. 48)

nefrona: red de capilares y tubos pequeños, o túbulos, donde ocurre la filtración de la sangre. (pág. 461)

red nerviosa: sistema de control parecido a una red que envía señales hacia y desde todas las partes del cuerpo. (pág. 480)

primera ley del movimiento de Newton: ley que establece que si la fuerza neta ejercida sobre un objeto es cero, el movimiento de dicho objeto no cambia. (pág. 27)

segunda ley del movimiento de Newton: ley que establece que la aceleración de un objeto es igual a la fuerza neta que actúa sobre él divida por su masa. (pág. 30)

tercera ley del movimiento de Newton: ley que establece que para cada acción hay una reacción igual en dirección opuesta. (pág. 31)

nicho: forma como una especie interactúa con los factores abióticos y bióticos para obtener alimento, encontrar refugio y satisfacer otras necesidades. (pág. 564)

fuerza de no contacto: fuerza que un objeto puede aplicar sobre otro sin tocarlo. (pág. 20)

contaminación de fuente no puntual: contaminación de varias fuentes apartadas que no se pueden rastrear hasta una sola ubicación. (pág. 607)

planta no vascular: planta que carece de tejidos especializados para transportar agua y nutrientes. (pág. 372)

notocordio: estructura flexible con forma de varilla que soporta el cuerpo de un cordado en desarrollo. (pág. 422)

energía nuclear: energía almacenada en y liberada por el núcleo de un átomo. (pág. 48)

SCIENCE SKILL HANDBOOK

MATH SKILL HANDBOOK

FOLDABLES HANDBOOK

REFERENCE HANDBOOK

GLOSSARY/GLOSARIO

INDEX

SCIENCE SKILL HANDBOOK

MATH SKILL HANDBOOK

FOLDABLES HANDBOOK

REFERENCE HANDBOOK

GLOSSARY/ GLOSARIO

INDEX

O

observation: the act of using one or more of your senses to gather information and take note of what occurs. (p. NOS 6)

opaque: a material through which light does not pass. (p. 202)

open circulatory system: a system that transports blood and other fluids into open spaces that surround organs in the body. (p. 490)

ozone layer: the area of the stratosphere with a high concentration of ozone. (p. 262)

observación: acción de mirar algo y tomar nota de lo que ocurre. (pág. NOS 6)

opaco: material por el que no pasa la luz. (pág. 202)

sistema circulatorio abierto: sistema que transporta sangre y otros fluidos hacia espacios abiertos que rodean a los órgaNOSen el cuerpo. (pág. 490)

capa de ozono: área de la estratosfera con gran concentración de ozono. (pág. 262)

P

parasite: an animal that survives by living inside or on another organism, gets food from the organism, and does not help in the organism's survival. (p. 413)

particulate (par TIH kyuh lut) matter: the mix of both solid and liquid particles in the air. (p. 286)

particulate matter: the mix of both solid and liquid particles in the air. (p. 614)

peristalsis (per uh STAHL sus): waves of muscle contractions that move food through the digestive tract. (p. 452)

pharyngeal (fuh run JEE uhl) pouches: grooves along the side of a developing chordate. (p. 422)

photochemical smog: air pollution that forms from the interaction between chemicals in the air and sunlight. (pp. 285, 613)

physical change: a change in the size, shape, form, or state of matter that does not change the matter's identity. (p. 98)

physical property: a characteristic of matter that you can observe or measure without changing the identity of the matter. (p. 88)

pistil: female reproductive organ of a flower. (p. 382)

pitch: the perception of how high or low a sound is; related to the frequency of a sound wave. (p. 211)

point-source pollution: pollution from a single source that can be identified. (p. 606)

parásito: animal que vive en el interior o encima de otro organismo, y obtiene alimento del organismo sin ayuda a que el organismo sobreviva. (pág. 413)

partículas en suspensión: mezcla de partículas tanto sólidas como líquidas en el aire. (pág. 286)

partículas en suspensión: mezcla de partículas sólidas y líquidas en el aire. (pág. 614)

peristalsis: ondas de contracciones musculares que mueven el alimento por el tracto digestivo. (pág. 452)

hendiduras faríngeas: surcos a lo largo del lado de un cordado en desarrollo. (pág. 422)

smog fotoquímico: polución del aire que se forma de la interacción entre los químicos en el aire y la luz solar. (pág. 285, 613)

cambio físico: cambio en el tamaño, la forma o estado de la materia en el que no cambia la identidad de la materia. (pág. 98)

propiedad física: característica de la materia que puede observarse o medirse sin cambiar la identidad de la materia. (pág. 88)

pistilo: órgano reproductor femenino de una flor. (pág. 382)

tono: percepción de qué tan alto o bajo es el sonido; relacionado con la frecuencia de la onda sonora. (pág. 211)

contaminación de fuente puntual: contaminación de una sola fuente que se puede identificar. (pág. 606)

polar easterlies: cold winds that blow from the east to the west near the North Pole and South Pole. (p. 279)

pollination (pah luh NAY shun): the process that occurs when pollen grains land on a female reproductive structure of a plant that is the same species as the pollen grains. (p. 381)

population: all the organisms of the same species that live in the same area at the same time. (pp. 555, 589)

potential (puh TEN chul) energy: stored energy due to the interactions between objects or particles. (p. 47)

precipitation: water, in liquid or solid form, that falls from the atmosphere. (p. 305)

precipitation: water, in liquid or solid form, that falls from the atmosphere. (p. 367)

prediction: a statement of what will happen next in a sequence of events. (p. NOS 6)

pressure: the amount of force per unit area applied to an object's surface. (p. 137)

producer: an organism that uses an outside energy source, such as the Sun, and produces its own food. (p. 570)

profile view: a drawing showing a vertical "slice" through the ground. (p. 245)

prokaryotic (pro kayr ee AH tihk) cell: a cell that does not have a nucleus or other membrane-bound organelles. (p. 352)

protein: a long chain of amino acid molecules; contains carbon, hydrogen, oxygen, nitrogen, and sometimes sulfur (p. 442)

pulley: a simple machine that consists of a grooved wheel with a rope or cable wrapped around it. (p. 65)

brisas polares: vientos fríos que soplan del este al oeste cerca del Polo Norte y del Polo Sur. (pág. 279)

polinización: proceso que ocurre cuando los granos de polen posan en una estructura reproductora femenina de una planta que es de la misma especie que los granos de polen. (pág. 381)

población: todos los organismos de la misma especie que viven en la misma área al mismo tiempo. (pág. 555, 589)

energía potencial: energía almacenada debido a las interacciones entre objetos o partículas. (pág. 47)

precipitación: agua, de forma líquida o sólida, que cae de la atmósfera. (pág. 305)

precipitación: agua, en forma líquida o sólida, que cae de la atmósfera. (pág. 367)

predicción: afirmación de lo que ocurrirá a continuación en una secuencia de eventos. (pág. NOS 6)

presión: cantidad de fuerza por unidad de área aplicada a la superficie de un objeto. (pág. 137)

productor: organismo que usa una fuente de energía externa, como el Sol, para elaborar su propio alimento. (pág. 570)

vista de perfil: dibujo que muestra un "corte" vertical a través de la tierra. (pág. 245)

célula procariota: célula que no tiene núcleo ni otros organelos limitados por una membrana. (pág. 352)

proteína: larga cadena de aminoácidos; contiene carbono, hidrógeno, oxígeno, nitrógeno y, algunas veces, sulfuro. (pág. 442)

polea: máquina simple que consiste en una rueda acanalada rodeada por una cuerda o cable. (pág. 65)

R

radial symmetry: a body plan in which an organism can be divided into two parts that are nearly mirror images of each other anywhere through its central axis. (p. 406)

radiant energy: energy carried by an electromagnetic wave. (p. 51)

simetría radial: plano corporal en el cual un organismo se puede dividir en dos partes que sean casi imágenes al espejo una de la otra, en cualquier parte de su eje axial. (pág. 406)

energía radiante: energía que transporta una onda electromagnética. (pág. 51)

SCIENCE SKILL HANDBOOK

MATH SKILL HANDBOOK

FOLDABLES HANDBOOK

REFERENCE HANDBOOK

GLOSSARY/ GLOSARIO

INDEX

radiation: energy carried by an electromagnetic wave. (p. 268)

radiation: the transfer of thermal energy by electromagnetic waves. (p. 161)

radio wave: a low-frequency, low-energy electromagnetic wave that has a wavelength longer than about 30 cm. (p. 199)

rain shadow: an area of low rainfall on the downwind slope of a mountain. (p. 519)

rarefaction (rayr uh FAK shun): region of a longitudinal wave where the particles of the medium are farthest apart. (p. 211)

reclamation: a process in which mined land must be recovered with soil and replanted with vegetation. (p. 600)

reference point: the starting point you use to describe the motion or the position of an object. (p. 9)

reforestation: process of planting trees to replace trees that have been cut or burned down. (p. 600)

refraction: the change in direction of a wave as it changes speed in moving from one medium to another. (p. 194)

refrigerator: a device that uses electric energy to pump thermal energy from a cooler location to a warmer location. (p. 172)

relative humidity: the amount of water vapor present in the air compared to the maximum amount of water vapor the air could contain at that temperature. (p. 303)

rhizoid: a structure that anchors a nonvascular plant to a surface. (p. 370)

rock cycle: the series of processes that change one type of rock into another type of rock. (p. 244)

rock: a naturally occurring solid composed of minerals, rock fragments, and sometimes other materials such as organic matter. (p. 234)

radiación: transferencia de energía mediante ondas electromagnéticas. (pág. 268)

radiación: transferencia de energía térmica por ondas electromagnéticas. (pág. 161)

onda de radio: onda electromagnética de baja frecuencia y baja energía que tiene una longitud de onda mayor de más o menos 30 cm. (pág. 199)

sombra de lluvia: área de baja precipitación en la ladera de sotavento de una montaña. (pág. 519)

rarefacción: region de una onda longitudinal donde las partículas del medio están más alejadas. (pág. 211)

recuperación: proceso por el cual las tierras explotadas se deben recubrir con suelo y se deben replantar con vegetación. (pág. 600)

punto de referencia: punto que se escoge para describir el movimiento o posición de un objeto. (pág. 9)

reforestación: proceso de siembra de árboles para reemplazar los árboles que se han cortado o quemado. (pág. 600)

refracción: cambio en la dirección de una onda a medida que cambia de rapidez al moverse de un medio a otro. (pág. 194)

refrigerador: aparato que usa energía eléctrica para bombear energía térmica desde un lugar más frío hacia uno más caliente. (pág. 172)

humedad relativa: cantidad de vapor de agua presente en el aire comparada con la cantidad máxima de vapor de agua que el aire podría contener en esa temperatura. (pág. 303)

rizoide: estructura que sujeta una planta no vascular a una superficie. (pág. 370)

ciclo geológico: series de procesos que cambian un tipo de roca en otro tipo de roca. (pág. 244)

roca: sólido de origen natural compuesto de minerales, acumulación de fragmentos y algunas veces de otros materiales como materia orgánica. (pág. 234)

(S)

science: the investigation and exploration of natural events and of the new information that results from those investigations. (p. NOS 4)

scientific law: a rule that describes a pattern in nature. (p. NOS 9)

scientific theory: an explanation of observations or events that is based on knowledge gained from many observations and investigations. (p. NOS9)

screw: a simple machine that consists of an inclined plane wrapped around a cylinder. (p. 64)

sea breeze: a wind that blows from the sea to the land due to local temperature and pressure differences. (p. 280)

seismic energy: the energy transferred by waves moving through the ground. (p. 50)

significant digits: the number of digits in a measurement that that are known with a certain degree of reliability. (p. NOS 20)

simple machine: a machine that does work using one movement. (p. 63)

solid: matter that has a definite shape and a definite volume. (pp. 86, 119)

solubility (sahl yuh BIH luh tee): the maximum amount of solute that can dissolve in a given amount of solvent at a given temperature and pressure. (p. 90)

sound energy: energy carried by sound waves. (p. 50)

specific heat: the amount of thermal energy (joules) needed to raise the temperature of 1 kg of material 1°C. (p. 519)

specific heat: the amount of thermal energy it takes to increase the temperature of 1 kg of a material by 1°C. (p. 163)

speed: the distance an object moves divided by the time it takes to move that distance. (p. 10)

spiracle: a tiny hole on the surface of an organism where oxygen enters the body and carbon dioxide leaves the body. (p. 488)

ciencia: la investigación y exploración de los eventos naturales y de la información nueva que es el resultado de estas investigaciones. (pág. NOS 4)

ley científica: regla que describe un patrón dado en la naturaleza. (pág. NOS 9)

teoría científica: explicación de observaciones o eventos con base en conocimiento obtenido de muchas observaciones e investigaciones. (pág. NOS9)

tornillo: máquina simple que consiste en un plano inclinado incrustado alrededor de un cilindro. (pág. 64)

brisa marina: viento que sopla del mar hacia la tierra debido a diferencias en la temperatura local y la presión. (pág. 280)

energía sísmica: energía transferida por ondas que se mueven a través del suelo. (pág. 50)

cifras significativas: número de dígitos que se conoce con cierto grado de fiabilidad en una medida. (pág. NOS 20)

máquina simple: máquina que hace trabajo con un movimiento. (pág. 63)

sólido: materia con forma y volumen definidos. (pág. 86, 119)

solubilidad: cantidad máxima de soluto que puede disolverse en una cantidad dada de solvente a temperatura y presión dadas. (pág. 90)

energía sonora: energía que transportan las ondas sonoras. (pág. 50)

calor específico: cantidad de energía (julios) térmica requerida para subir la temperatura de 1 kg de materia a 1°C. (pág. 519)

calor específico: cantidad de energía térmica necesaria para aumentar la temperatura de 1 Kg de un material en 1°C. (pág. 163)

rapidez: distancia que un objeto recorre dividida por el tiempo que éste tarda en recorrer dicha distancia. (pág. 10)

espiráculo: hueco diminuto en la superficie de un organismo por donde entra oxígeno al cuerpo y sale dióxido de carbono. (pág. 488)

stability: whether circulating air motions will be strong or weak. (p. 272)

stamen: the male reproductive organ of a flower. (p. 382)

stimulus (STIHM yuh lus): a change in an organism's environment that causes a response. (p. 391)

stoma (STOH muh): a small opening in the epidermis, or surface layer, of a leaf. (p. 371)

stratosphere (STRA tuh sfihr): the atmospheric layer directly above the troposphere. (p. 262)

sublimation: the process of changing directly from a solid to a gas. (p. 130)

succession: the gradual change from one community to another community in an area. (p. 557)

surface report: a description of a set of weather measurements made on Earth's surface. (p. 321)

surface tension: the uneven forces acting on the particles on the surface of a liquid. (p. 121)

symbiosis: a close, long-term relationship between two species that usually involves an exchange of food or energy. (p. 564)

estabilidad: condición en la que los movimientos del aire circulante pueden ser fuertes o débiles. (pág. 272)

estambre: órgano reproductor masculino de una flor. (pág. 382)

estímulo: cambio en el medioambiente de un organismo que causa una respuesta. (pág. 391)

estoma: abertura pequena en la epidermis, capa superficial, de una hoja. (pág. 371)

estratosfera: capa atmosférica justo arriba de la troposfera. (pág. 262)

sublimación: proceso de cambiar directamente de sólido a gas. (pág. 130)

sucesión: cambio gradual de una comunidad a otra comunidad en un área. (pág. 557)

informe de superficie: descripción de un conjunto de mediciones del tiempo realizadas en la superficie de la Tierra. (pág. 321)

tensión superficial: fuerzas desiguales que actúan sobre las partículas en la superficie de un líquido. (pág. 121)

simbiosis: relación estrecha a largo plazo entre dos especies que generalmente involucra intercambio de alimento o energía. (pág. 564)

(T)

taxon: a group of organisms. (p. 347)

technology: the practical use of scientific knowledge, especially for industrial or commercial use. (p. NOS 8)

temperature inversion: a temperature increase as altitude increases in the troposphere. (p. 273)

temperature: the measure of the average kinetic energy of the particles in a material. (pp. 126, 155)

thermal conductor: a material through which thermal energy flows quickly. (p. 162)

thermal contraction: a decrease in a material's volume when the temperature is decreased. (p. 164)

taxón: grupo de organismos. (pág. 347)

tecnología: uso práctico del conocimiento científico, especialmente para uso industrial o comercial. (pág. NOS 8)

inversión de temperatura: aumento de la temperatura en la troposfera a medida que aumenta la altitud. (pág. 273)

temperatura: medida de la energía cinética promedio de las partículas de un material. (págs. 126, 155)

conductor térmico: material mediante el cual la energía térmica se mueve con rapidez. (pág. 162)

contracción térmica: disminución del volumen de un material cuando disminuye la temperatura. (pág. 164)

thermal energy: the sum of the kinetic energy and the potential energy of the particles that make up an object. (pp. 154, 127)

thermal energy: the sum of the kinetic energy and the potential energy of the particles that make up an object. (p. 49)

thermal expansion: an increase in a material's volume when the temperature is increased. (p. 164)

thermal insulator: a material through which thermal energy flows slowly. (p. 162)

thermostat: a device that regulates the temperature of a system. (p. 172)

tornado: a violent, whirling column of air in contact with the ground. (p. 315)

trade winds: steady winds that flow from east to west between 30°N latitude and 30°S latitude. (p. 279)

translucent: a material that allows most of the light that strikes it to pass through, but through which objects appear blurry. (p. 202)

transparent: a material that allows almost all of the light striking it to pass through, and through which objects can be seen clearly. (p. 202)

transpiration: the process by which plants release water vapor through their leaves. (pp. 240, 390)

transverse wave: a wave in which the disturbance is perpendicular to the direction the wave travels. (p. 189)

tropism (TROH pih zum): plant growth toward or away from an external stimulus. (p. 392)

troposphere (TRO puh sfihr): the atmospheric layer closest to Earth's surface. (p. 262)

energía térmica: suma de la energía cinética y potencial de las partículas que forman un objeto (pág. 154, 127)

energía térmica: suma de la energía cinética y potencial de las partículas que componen un objeto. (pág. 49)

expansión térmica: aumento en el volumen de un material cuando aumenta la temperatura. (pág. 164)

aislante térmico: material en el cual la energía térmica se mueve con lentitud. (pág. 162)

termostato: aparato que regula la temperatura de un sistema. (pág. 172)

tornado: columna de aire violenta y rotativa en contacto con el suelo. (pág. 315)

vientos alisios: vientos constantes que soplan del este al oeste entre 30°N de latitud y 30°S de latitud. (pág. 279)

translúcido: material que permite el paso de la mayor cantidad de luz que lo toca, pero a través del cual los objetos se ven borrosos. (pág. 202)

transparente: material que permite el paso de la mayor cantidad de luz que lo toca, y a través del cual los objetos pueden verse con nitidez. (pág. 202)

transpiración: proceso por el cual las plantas liberan vapor de agua por medio de las hojas. (págs. 240, 390)

onda transversal: onda en la que la perturbación es perpendicular a la dirección en que viaja la onda. (pág. 189)

tropismo: crecimiento de una planta hacia o alejado de un estímulo externo. (pág. 392)

troposfera: capa atmosférica más cercana a la Tierra. (pág. 262)

U

ultraviolet wave: an electromagnetic wave that has a slightly shorter wavelength and higher frequency than visible light. (p. 200)

unbalanced forces: forces acting on an object that combine and form a net force that is not zero. (p. 23)

onda ultravioleta: onda electromagnética que tiene una longitud de onda ligeramente menor y mayor frecuencia que la luz visible. (pág. 200)

fuerzas no balanceadas: fuerzas que actúan sobre un objeto, se combinan y forman una fuerza neta diferente de cero. (pág. 23)

undulation (un juh LAY shun): the wavelike motion of some animals. (p. 482)

uplift: the process that moves large bodies of Earth materials to higher elevations. (p. 244)

upper-air report: a description of wind, temperature, and humidity conditions above Earth's surface. (p. 321)

urban sprawl: the development of land for houses and other buildings near a city. (p. 598)

ureter (YOO ruh tur): a tube through which urine leaves each kidney. (p. 463)

urethra (yoo REE thruh): a tube through which urine leaves the bladder. (p. 463)

urine: the fluid produced when blood is filtered by the kidneys. (p. 461)

ondulación: movimiento de alguNOSanimales parecido a una ola. (pág. 482)

levantamiento: proceso por el cual se mueven grandes cuerpos de materiales de la Tierra hacia elevaciones mayores. (pág. 244)

informe del aire superior: descripción de las condiciones del viento, de la temperatura y de la humedad por encima de la superficie de la Tierra. (pág. 321)

expansión urbana: urbanización de tierra para viviendas y otras construcciones cerca de la ciudad. (pág. 598)

uréter: tubo por el cual la orina sale de cada riñón. (pág. 463)

uretra: tubo por el cual la orina sale de la vejiga. (pág. 463)

orina: fluido que se produce cuando los riñones filtran la sangre. (pág. 461)

vapor: the gas state of a substance that is normally a solid or a liquid at room temperature. (p. 122)

vaporization: the change in state from a liquid to a gas. (p. 129)

variable: any factor that can have more than one value. (p. NOS 27)

vascular plant: a plant that has specialized tissues, called vascular tissues, that transport water and nutrients throughout the plant. (p. 373)

velocity: the speed and the direction of a moving object. (p. 11)

villus (VIH luhs): a fingerlike projection, many of which cover the folds of the small intestine. (p. 454)

viscosity (vihs KAW sih tee): a measurement of a liquid's resistance to flow. (p. 120)

vitamin: any of several nutrients that are needed in small amounts for growth, regulation of body functions, and prevention of some diseases. (p. 443)

volume: the amount of space a sample of matter occupies. (p. 86)

vapor: estado gaseoso de una sustancia que normalmente es sólida o líquida a temperatura ambiente. (pág. 122)

vaporización: cambio de estado líquido a gaseoso. (pág. 129)

variable: cualquier factor que tenga más de un valor. (pág. NOS 27)

planta vascular: planta que tiene tejidos especializados, llamados tejidos vasculares, que transportan agua y nutrientes por la planta. (pág. 373)

velocidad: rapidez y dirección de un objeto en movimiento. (pág. 11)

vellosidad: proyección parecida a un dedo, muchas de las cuales cubren los pliegues del intestino delgado. (pág. 454)

viscosidad: medida de la resistencia de un líquido a fluir. (pág. 120)

vitamina: cualquiera de los varios nutrientes que se necesitan en cantidades pequeñas para el crecimiento, para regulación de las funciones del cuerpo y para prevención de algunas enfermedades. (pág. 443)

volumen: cantidad de espacio que ocupa la materia. (pág. 86)

Science Skill Handbook

Math Skill Handbook

Foldables Handbook

Reference Handbook

Glossary/ Glosario

Index

W

water cycle: the series of natural processes by which water continually moves throughout the hydrosphere. (p. 239)

water cycle: the series of natural processes by which water continually moves throughout the hydrosphere. (p. 305)

water vapor: water in its gaseous form. (p. 260)

weather: the atmospheric conditions, along with short-term changes, of a certain place at a certain time. (pp.242, 368)

wedge: a simple machine that consists of an inclined plane with one or two sloping sides; it is used to split or separate an object. (p. 64)

westerlies: steady winds that flow from west to east between latitudes 30°N and 60°N, and 30°S and 60°S. (p. 279)

wheel and axle: a simple machine that consists of an axle attached to the center of a larger wheel, so that the shaft and wheel rotate together. (p. 64)

wind: the movement of air from areas of high pressure to areas of low pressure. (p. 277)

work: the amount of energy used as a force moves an object over a distance. (p. 57)

ciclo del agua: serie de procesos naturales por los que el cual el agua se mueve continuamente en toda la hidrosfera. (pág. 239)

ciclo del agua: serie de procesos naturales mediante la cual el agua se mueve continuamente en toda la hidrosfera. (pág. 305)

vapor de agua: agua en forma gaseosa. (pág. 260)

tiempo atmosférico: condiciones atmosféricas, junto con cambios a corto plazo, de un lugar determinado a una hora determinada. (pág. 242, 368)

cuña: máquina simple que consiste en un plano inclinado con uno o dos lados inclinados; se usa para partir o separar un objeto. (pág. 64)

vientos del oeste: vientos constantes que soplan de oeste a este entre latitudes 30°N y 60°N, y 30°S y 60°S. (pág. 279)

rueda y eje: máquina simple que consiste en un eje insertado en el centro de una rueda grande, de manera que el eje y la rueda rotan juntos. (pág. 64)

viento: movimiento del aire desde áreas de alta presión hasta áreas de baja presión. (pág. 277)

trabajo: cantidad de energía usada como fuerza que mueve un objeto a cierta distancia. (pág. 57)

SCIENCE SKILL HANDBOOK

MATH SKILL HANDBOOK

FOLDABLES HANDBOOK

REFERENCE HANDBOOK

GLOSSARY/ GLOSARIO

INDEX

Abiotic factors

Italic numbers = illustration/photo   **Bold numbers** = vocabulary term
lab = indicates entry is used in a lab on this page

Auroras

Index

A

Abiotic factors
  atmosphere as, 554
  explanation of, **553**, 561
  light and temperature as, 554
  soil as, 555
  water as, 554, *554*
Absorption, 269, *449*, **199**
  of energy, 193, *193*
  explanation of, **202**
  in plants, 390
Academic Vocabulary, NOS 11, 102,
  198, 245, 268, 314, 342, 371, 414,
  464, 490, 530, 569, 571
Accelerate, 29
Acceleration
  calculation of, 13, 30
  explanation of, **12**
  negative, 13
  Newton's second law and, 30
  positive, 13
Acid, 453
Acid precipitation, 48, **614,** 618
  effects of, 285
  explanation of, **285**
  formation of, 284 *lab*
Acid rain
  formation of, 284 *lab*
Action forces, 31
Adaptations
  behavioral, 409
  in birds, 427, *427*
  explanation of, **207, 408,** 411,
    430–431 *lab*
  functional, 409, *409*
  natural selection and, *207*
  selective breeding and, *208*
  structural, 408, *408*
  types of, *208, 209, 210*
Adenosine triphosphate (ATP),
  388, 389
Aerosols, 537
Agriculture
  environmental impact of, 596
  nitrogen cycle and, 596, *596*
Air. *See also* **Atmosphere**
  on Earth, 227, *227*
  movement of, 277 *lab*
  stable, 273
  unstable, 273
Air circulation
  explanation of, 272
  global wind belts and, 278, *278*
  three-cell model of, 278, *278*, 282 *lab*
Air currents
  global winds and, *277*, 277–279
  local winds and, 280, *280*

Air masses
  Antarctic air masses, 310
  Arctic air masses, 310, 311
  classification of, *310*, 310–311
  explanation of, **310**
Air pollution. *See also* **Pollution**
  acid precipitation as, 285, 284 *lab*
  actions to reduce, 618, *618*
  explanation of, **284,** 612
  health effects of, 616, *616*
  indoor, 288
  monitoring of, 287
  movement of, 286, *286*
  particulate matter as, 286
  smog as, 285, *285*
  sources of, 284
  temperature inversion and, 273
  types of, *613*, 613–614, *614*
Air pressure, 242
  altitude and, 264, *264*
  explanation of, *302*, **302**
  observation of, 311 *lab*
Air quality
  monitoring of, 287
  standards for, 287
  trends in, 288, *288*
Air Quality Index (AQI), 617, *617*
Air temperature
  explanation of, 302
  pressure and, 309, 309 *lab*
  water vapor and, 303, *303*
Albedo, 524
Algae, 611, *611*
Algal blooms, 611, *611*
Alligators, 426
Altitude
  air pressure and, 264, *264*
  temperature and, 264, *264*, 517,
    518, *518*
**American Medical Association
  (AMA),** 208
Amino acids
  explanation of, 442
Amnion, 426
Amoebas, 342
Amphibians, 425
  hearts in, 491
Amplitude, 192, *192,* 212
Anemometer, NOS 18, *NOS 18,*
  302, *302*
Anemones, 413, *414*
Angiosperm, 375, 382
Animal cells, 405, 407
Animals
  adaptations of, *408,* 408–409, *409,*
    430–431 *lab*
  adaptations to climate by, 522
  adapted for unique environments,
    502–503 *lab*

  characteristics of, 405, 477, 493,
    405 *lab*
  circulation in, 487, *490*, 490–491, *491*
  classification of, *406*, 406–407, *407*
  control structures in, *480*, 480–481,
    481
  gas exchange in, 487–489, *489*
  ranges of hearing in, 210, *210*
  reproduction in, 405, 409, 426
  types of movement in, *482*, 482–483,
    483, 485
Annuals, 383
Anopheles **mosquitoes,** 377
Antarctica
  hole in ozone layer above, 266
  temperature in, 517
Ants, communication among, 559
Anvil, 214, *214*
Appendages, 417
Aquatic, 556
Area, 464
Argon, 261
Artemisia annua, 377
Artemisinin, 377
Arthropoda, 417
Arthropods, *417,* 417–418
Asexual reproduction
  explanation of, 343
  in plants, 379, *379,* 380
Ash. *See also* **Volcanic ash**
  in atmosphere, 261, *261*
Asthenosphere
  explanation of, *374*
Astronauts
  function of, 22
Asymmetry, *406,* **406**
Atmosphere. *See also* ; *also* **Air**
  air pressure and, 264, *264*
  changes in, 242–243
  composition of, 261
  explanation of, **229,** *246,* **259,** 554
  gases in, 229, *229*
  importance of, 259
  interactions in, 246
  layers of, 230, *262,* 262–263
  origins of, 260
  oxygen in, 554
  solid particles in, 261, 260 *lab*
  stable, 273
  temperature and, 264
  three-cell model of circulation in,
    278, *278,* 282 *lab*
  unstable, 273
Atoms
  explanation of, 46
ATP (adenosine triphosphate), 355
Attach, 414
Auroras, 263, *263*

Science Skill Handbook
Math Skill Handbook
Foldables Handbook
Reference Handbook
Glossary/ Glosario
Index

SCIENCE SKILL HANDBOOK

MATH SKILL HANDBOOK

FOLDABLES HANDBOOK

REFERENCE HANDBOOK

GLOSSARY/ GLOSARIO

INDEX

SCIENCE SKILL HANDBOOK

MATH SKILL HANDBOOK

FOLDABLES HANDBOOK

REFERENCE HANDBOOK

GLOSSARY/ GLOSARIO

INDEX

SCIENCE SKILL HANDBOOK
MATH SKILL HANDBOOK
FOLDABLES HANDBOOK
REFERENCE HANDBOOK
GLOSSARY/GLOSARIO
INDEX

SCIENCE SKILL HANDBOOK

MATH SKILL HANDBOOK

FOLDABLES HANDBOOK

REFERENCE HANDBOOK

GLOSSARY/ GLOSARIO

INDEX